T3-ALT-692

METHODS in
MICROBIOLOGY

METHODS in
MICROBIOLOGY

Edited by

J. R. NORRIS, John Robert
Borden Microbiological Laboratory,
Shell Research Limited,
Sittingbourne, Kent, England

D. W. RIBBONS
Department of Biochemistry,
University of Miami School of Medicine,
and Howard Hughes Medical Institute,
Miami, Florida, U.S.A.

Volume 6A

 1971

ACADEMIC PRESS
London and New York

ACADEMIC PRESS INC. (LONDON) LTD
24–28 Oval Road,
London NW1 7DX

U.S. Edition published by
ACADEMIC PRESS INC.
111 Fifth Avenue
New York, New York 10003

Library of Congress Catalog Card Number: 68–57745
ISBN: 0–12–521506–1

PRINTED IN GREAT BRITAIN BY
ADLARD AND SON LIMITED
DORKING, SURREY

LIST OF CONTRIBUTORS

S. J. AJL, *Research Laboratories, Albert Einstein Medical Center, Philadelphia, Pennsylvania, U.S.A.*

P. J. CHAPMAN, *Department of Biochemistry, University of Minnesota, St. Paul, U.S.A.*

PATRICIA H. CLARKE, *Department of Biochemistry, University College, London, England*

J. G. COLLEE, *Department of Bacteriology, University of Edinburgh, Edinburgh, Scotland*

S. DAGLEY, *Department of Biochemistry, University of Minnesota, St. Paul, U.S.A.*

E. A. DAWES, *Department of Biochemistry, University of Hull, Kingston-upon-Hull, England*

J. DE LEY, *Laboratory for Microbiology, Faculty of Sciences, State University, Gent, Belgium*

D. T. GIBSON, *Department of Microbiology, The University of Texas at Austin, Texas, U.S.A.*

G. W. GOULD, *Unilever Research Laboratory, Colworth Welwyn, Shabrook, Bedford, England*

W. HEINEN, *Department of Exobiology, Microbiology Branch, University of Nijmegen, Nijmegen, Netherlands*

K. KERSTERS, *Laboratory for Microbiology, Faculty of Sciences, State University, Gent, Belgium*

D. J. MCGILL, *Department of Biochemistry, University of Hull, Kingston-upon-Hull, England*

M. MIDGLEY, *Department of Biochemistry, University of Hull, Kingston-upon-Hull, England*

R. RABIN, *Interdisciplinary Research, N.S.F., Washington, D.C., U.S.A.*

H. C. REEVES, *Department of Microbiology, Arizona State University, Tempe, Arizona, U.S.A.*

M. C. SCRUTTON, *Department of Biochemistry, Rutgers Medical School, New Brunswick, New Jersey, U.S.A.*

W. S. WEGENER, *Department of Microbiology, University of Indiana Medical School, Indianapolis, Indiana, U.S.A.*

ELIZABETH WORK, *Department of Biochemistry, Imperial College of Science and Technology, London, England*

v

ACKNOWLEDGMENTS

For permission to reproduce, in whole or in part, certain figures and diagrams we are grateful to the following—

Elsevier Publishing Co., Amsterdam; Munksgaard, Copenhagen, Denmark; National Research Council of Canada, Ottawa, Ontario, Canada.

Detailed acknowledgments are given in the legends to figures.

PREFACE

The main theme in Volume 6 of "Methods in Microbiology" is the application of biochemical techniques to the study of micro-organisms. The topics covered include the use of biochemical and enzymic tests to characterize microbial types, the quantitative separation and analysis of fermentation products produced by micro-organisms, a critical appraisal of methods available to elucidate metabolic pathways and the control of enzyme synthesis, the assay of selected enzymes in crude extracts of cells as indicators of metabolic pathways, the use of antimetabolites to study biosynthesis and electron transport. The applications of radiotracer techniques are described in detail in five chapters: respiratory measurements with dyes and with electrodes for oxygen and carbon dioxide are included while manometric methods, which are so well described elsewhere (Umbreit, Burris and Stauffer, 1964) have been excluded from this series; articles on nitrogen fixation, calorimetry, electrochemical measurements and methods for studying sporulation and germination are also provided.

The detailed choice of the contents of the various contributions has been left largely to the individual authors. We have, as in the past, edited only to conserve consistency, bridge the gaps and avoid, where possible, overlaps between the articles.

Volume 6, like Volumes 3 and 5, has been divided into two parts. The division of the contributions, although somewhat arbitrary, was made by grouping the more chemical and enzymological topics into Volume 6A and allocating the more physical techniques of isotopes, electrodes, electrometry and calorimetry to Volume 6B.

We are grateful for the pleasant way in which our contributors have co-operated with us during the last three or four years. We must particularly thank those authors who have had the patience to wait for this publication. Some completed manuscripts were received three years ago, and many were subsequently revised by their authors.

J. R. NORRIS

D. W. RIBBONS

September, 1971

CONTENTS

CONTENTS OF PUBLISHED VOLUMES

CHAPTER I

Routine Biochemical Tests

A. J. Holding and J. G. Collee

Departments of Microbiology and Bacteriology, University of Edinburgh

I. GENERAL PRINCIPLES

The selection of a reasonable range of biochemical tests to be performed as a routine for bacterial identification and characterization is dependent upon the source of the material, the diversity of the bacteria likely to be encountered and the aim of the investigation. In general, details of less common tests applicable to special groups of bacteria are listed elsewhere in these volumes, but special tests in common use are also included in this chapter.

Before initiating any detailed examination of a bacterial isolate, the purity of the culture must be confirmed; this is particularly important if colonies have been picked from selective media. Serial subculture on a non-selective medium may be necessary to remove persistent contaminating organisms. The Gram staining procedure, which is usually done at an early stage in the investigation, allows observations on size, shape, and arrangement of cells, and gives provisional information on spore formation. Microscopic examination of a wet preparation from a broth culture may yield information on motility. However, morphology, staining reactions and motility are affected by various factors such as the age of the culture and the composition of the medium.

The reproducibility of a biochemical test is of fundamental importance if the test is to be a reliable step in an identification procedure. Ideally, all the details of test culture media and growth conditions should be defined and strictly observed. The absolute responses sought in classifying bacteria are frequently contrived by adjusting methods and it is increasingly important that methods should be internationally standardized and performed with care. Controls including known positive and negative tests should always be included with routine tests.

Frequently, the only quantitative measurements recorded are the time and temperature at which changes occur. Little attention appears to be paid to such important points as the size of the inoculum, the volume of the test medium, or the type of container to be used. In many tests a standard inoculum pipetted from a liquid culture or a homogeneous suspension of the test organism will prove more reliable than a loopful of growth from an agar slope or plate culture. In general, a small inoculum, e.g. a drop of a slightly turbid homogeneous suspension of an actively growing culture of the organism in saline, is recommended. The stage of growth of the test inoculum may influence the result. In tests that depend upon the detection of end-products of bacterial decomposition of a substrate incorporated in the test culture medium, the ability of the organism to grow in the test medium without the added substrate should normally first be confirmed before a negative result is recorded. Development of turbidity is usually accepted as evidence of growth, but some media develop floccular precipitates after autoclaving or during incubation and this may be misleading. The aseptic addition of separately sterilized salts can often avoid this complication. If precipitation is suspected after incubation, it is necessary to confirm microscopically that growth has occurred.

The development of acidity or alkalinity is frequently demonstrated by a colour change produced by a pH indicator incorporated in the test medium. The disadvantages of the use of pH indicators in this way merit consideration:

(i) Bacterial growth produces changes in redox potential as well as changes in pH. Many indicators are bleached or rendered colourless under the relatively anaerobic conditions that can develop in an actively growing culture. In some cases the change is not readily reversible and it may misleadingly suggest that a pH change has occurred.

(ii) Some indicator solutions are antibacterial and may inhibit or diminish growth.

(iii) Indicator solutions should not be incorporated in culture media that are already strongly coloured by the ingredients, or in cultures that may develop colour as a result of bacterial pigment production.

It therefore follows that pH indicators should be carefully chosen. There is often much to commend the practice of growing the test organism in broth containing the test substrate and of spot-testing the broth culture on a porcelain tile with an indicator that is not incorporated in the medium.

Many media can be sterilized in the autoclave by exposure to wet heat at 121°C (pure steam at 15 lb/in^2 above normal atmospheric pressure) for 15 min. Except where otherwise stated in the chapter, this procedure is recommended.

II. THE DECOMPOSITION OF SIMPLE CARBOHYDRATES, ORGANIC ACIDS AND SOME OTHER COMPOUNDS

The biochemical tests discussed in this section demonstrate one or more of the following:

(a) the ability of the organism to utilize the test compound as a sole source of carbon and energy;

(b) whether oxygen is required for utilization to take place, i.e. whether the organism is oxidizing or fermenting the substrate or is capable of carrying out both processes; and

(c) the detection of an end-product of the metabolism of a compound that is not necessarily serving as an energy source.

A. Demonstration of a sole source of carbon and energy for growth

Large numbers of compounds can readily be tested by using methods similar to those described by Stanier, Palleroni, and Doudoroff (1966) for aerobic pseudomonads. The mineral basal medium contains per litre:

$(Na_2HPO_4 + KH_2PO_4)$ buffer (1M; pH 6·8)	40 ml
$(NH_4)_2SO_4$	1·0 g
Hutner's vitamin-free mineral salts solution	20 ml

The Hutner mineral salts solution (see Cohen-Bazire et al., 1957) which can be replaced by alternative solutions contains the following ingredients per litre:

nitrilotriacetic acid	10 g
$MgSO_4$	14·45 g
$CaCl_2.2H_2O$	3·335 g
$(NH_4)_6Mo_7O_{24}.4H_2O$	9·25 mg
$FeSO_4.7H_2O$	99 mg
stock salts solution	50 ml

The nitrilotriacetic acid is dissolved and neutralized with about 7·3 g KOH. After adding the remaining ingredients the pH is adjusted to 6·8. The stock salts solution contains per litre:

ethylenediamine tetra-acetic acid	2·5 g
$ZnSO_4.7H_2O$	10·95 g
$FeSO_4.7H_2O$	5 g
$MnSO_4.H_2O$	1·54 g
$CuSO_4.5H_2O$	0·392 g
$Co(NO_3)_2.6H_2O$	0·248 g
$Na_2B_4O_7.10H_2O$	0·177 g

A few drops of H_2SO_4 are added to reduce precipitation. The organisms are spot-inoculated onto surface-dried agar plates of yeast extract agar which is made by adding per litre: 5·0 g yeast extract and 20 g agar to the basal mineral medium. After good growth is obtained on the yeast extract agar, inocula from the colonies are transferred by a replica-plating procedure onto plates of the test medium which contains per litre: the basal mineral medium constituents, 10 g Ionagar No. 2 (Oxoid) or some other purified agar, and 1 g of the carbon compound. A lower concentration of certain potentially toxic compounds is required. After incubation, the utilization shown by increased growth is compared with that on the control test medium lacking the carbon source.

This principle can be applied to tests of more fastidious organisms such as lactic acid bacteria if the yeast extract agar is replaced by a more complex medium (see Whittenbury, 1963) and if minimal requirements of growth factors and nitrogenous compounds are added to the test medium. If necessary, the test may be performed with anaerobic cultures.

The utilization of organic acids may be detected more readily by incorporating an appropriate pH indicator (e.g. phenol red, bromothymol blue) into a suitable medium. The breakdown of the acidic substrate brings about an easily detectable rise in the pH of the medium.

Liquid media may facilitate a more sensitive test, since agar, especially less highly purified brands, may provide alternative carbon sources that can promote the utilization of the organic acid. False positive results attributable to carry-over of traces of complex media in the inoculum are also less likely to arise in a liquid test medium than in an agar plate that allows localization of the spot-inoculum.

Tests that demonstrate the utilization of citrate and malonate are of use in the differentiation of certain members of the *Enterobacteriaceae*: In the test for citrate utilization the organisms are inoculated into Koser's liquid citrate medium (Koser, 1923) which contains Na citrate and supplies nitrogen in the inorganic form. Simmons (1926) added agar and an indicator to the medium and the composition, per litre, of a generally useful modification is:

sodium citrate	2 g
$MgSO_4.7H_2O$	0·2 g
NaCl	5 g
$NH_4H_2PO_4$	1 g
K_2HPO_4	1 g
1·5% alcoholic solution of bromothymol blue	10 ml
washed agar	20 g

The medium (pH 6·8) is made with distilled water and distributed as slopes after autoclaving. The cultures are lightly inoculated and should be incubated for 4–5 days at 37°C. A positive result is indicated by the development of turbidity in Koser's medium or by a blue colour on the medium of Simmons. A subculture from a positive test to a second test medium provides a check on false positives attributable to the carry-over of compounds in the initial inoculum.

An organism that produces negative results in Koser's or Simmons's media may or may not produce a positive result in a modified citrate medium of Christensen (1949) that affords a reliable test for citrate utilization in the presence of organic nitrogen. The medium contains per litre:

sodium citrate	3 g
glucose	0·2 g
yeast extract	0·5 g
cysteine monohydrochloride	0.1 g
KH_2PO_4	1 g
NaCl	5 g
phenol red	0·012 g
agar in distilled water	15 g

The pH is not adjusted. The autoclaved medium is dispensed in tubes as short thick slopes and is inoculated by a straight wire. The butt of the slope is stabbed and the wire is then drawn once up the slope. Tests are read after incubation for up to 7 days. A positive result is indicated by the development of a magenta colour; in negative tests, the medium remains yellow. An organism that produces a positive result in Koser's or Simmons's test media will also be positive in Christensen's test medium.

Malonate utilization is tested in a medium that contains per litre:

sodium malonate	3 g
NaCl	2 g
yeast extract	1 g
$(NH_4)_2SO_4$	2 g
K_2HPO_4	0·6 g
KH_2PO_4	0·4 g
bromothymol blue in distilled water	0·025 g

The pH is 7·4. The test organism is cultured in this fluid medium at 37°C for 2 days. If the acidic malonate is utilized, the indicator changes from green to blue, but it should be noted that in this test the sodium malonate is not the sole carbon source. The addition of 2 g DL-phenylalanine or 1 g L-phenylalanine to this malonate broth allows a combined test for malonate utilization and phenylalanine deaminase production (Shaw and Clarke, 1955). When the malonate test has been read, the medium is acidified with 0·1N NCl until it just turns yellow and about 2·2 ml of a 10% aqueous solution of $FeCl_3$ is then added. The mixture is shaken; the development of a dark green colour, which quickly fades, indicates that deamination has occurred.

Fermentation of tartrate, citrate and mucate are reactions of special use in classifying salmonellae. The tests require considerable attention to detail; they are described well by Edwards and Ewing (1962, p. 250) and Cruickshank (1965, p. 820). It should be noted that the lead acetate reagent used in the final stages of the tests for tartrate or citrate fermentation is prepared from the compound known as "neutral lead acetate"; if attempts are made to adjust the pH of the solution to neutrality, much of the salt is precipitated.

B. The oxygen requirement for the utilization of the compound

This characteristic is usually determined by inoculating the organisms into deep agar media in test-tubes. The incorporation of a pH indicator into the medium enables changes in pH value resulting from the decomposition process to be observed in addition to visible signs of growth in different parts of the medium. Cultures are either stab-inoculated with a needle after solidification or shaken cultures are prepared prior to solidification of the agar. The composition of the basal medium is adjusted for the group of organisms under examination and should enable good growth to be obtained when the substrate is being utilized. The method is most extensively used for showing the decomposition of simple carbohydrates. An acidic change at or near the surface indicates that the substrate is being oxidized by aerobic bacteria, whereas the development of uniform acidity throughout the tube shows that facultatively anaerobic organisms are both oxidizing and fermenting the substrate. Anaerobic bacteria that only ferment the substrate usually produce the acidic reaction in the lower part of the tube initially, but acidic materials may diffuse upwards to give an appearance of acid production throughout the tube. The placing of a layer of sterile liquid paraffin or water agar above the medium in a duplicate tube will show a fermentative action more clearly by minimizing any oxidative activity. The usefulness of the oxidation versus fermentation (O/F) reaction was brought into prominence by Hugh and Leifson (1953) in studies on glucose utilization with pseudomonads, coliform organisms and related bacteria. Their medium has the following composition per litre:

peptone (or tryptone)	2 g
NaCl	5 g
K_2HPO_4	0·2 g
agar	3 g
1% aqueous solution of bromothymol blue	3 ml

The pH should be 7·1. One per cent of a filter-sterilized aqueous solution of glucose or other carbon compound is added to the sterile molten medium before use. In peptone-containing media, some organisms that oxidize glucose fail to produce an acidic reaction. A modification suggested by Board and Holding (1960) is devoid of peptone and was used successfully for studies with aerobic Gram-negative bacteria; it permits the growth of organisms requiring growth factors and shows a good correlation between

the development of an acidic reaction and glucose utilization. The medium
has the following composition per litre:

$NH_4H_2PO_4$	0·5 g
K_2HPO_4	0·5 g
yeast extract	0·5 g
agar	5 g

Bromothymol blue and a trace element mineral supplement B are added:
the pH is 7·2. The sugar (0·5%) is added to the molten medium as a filter-
sterilized aqueous solution. A control tube without the added carbon source
should also be inoculated.

The value of a soft-agar medium for this type of work has been demonstrated by Whittenbury (1963) in studies with lactic acid bacteria. A slower
transition from aerobic to anaerobic conditions permits examination of the
response of the test organism to small differences in the gaseous environment, and allows observation of the growth of mutants. The medium
suggested by Whittenbury for the lactic acid bacteria is:

meat extract (Lab-Lemco)	5 g
peptone (Evans)	5 g
yeast extract (Difco)	5 g
Tween 80	0·5 ml
agar	1·5 g
1·6% ethanolic solution of bromocresol purple	1·4 ml

The fermentation of carbohydrates can also be demonstrated by the
production of acid or acid and gas (CO_2 and/or H_2) in liquid media in test-
tubes. Acid production is readily observed by incorporating into the medium
an appropriate pH indicator, e.g. bromocresol purple, bromothymol blue,
phenol red or Andrade's indicator (0·5 g acid fuchsin, 15–18 ml N NaOH
in 100 ml H_2O). Gas production is observed by placing an inverted small
glass (Durham) fermentation tube in each test-tube during the medium
preparation. The composition of the basal medium depends on the group of
organisms under investigation. A medium frequently used for tests of the
Enterobacteriaceae has the following composition per litre:

peptone	10 g
meat extract (Lab-Lemco)	3 g
NaCl	5 g

A filter-sterilized solution of the test carbohydrate is added aseptically to the
medium to give a final concentration of 0·5–1·0%.

A commonly used selective medium (MacConkey broth) in which coliform organisms produce acid and gas has the following composition per
litre:

peptone	20 g
NaCl	5 g
sodium taurocholate	5 g
lactose	10 g
1·6% alcoholic solution of bromocresol purple	2·5 ml

The pH is 7·2.

C. The detection of certain metabolic processes or products

1. *Methyl red and Voges-Proskauer tests*

These tests are normally carried out with cultures grown in glucose phosphate peptone broth which has the following composition per litre:

glucose	5 g
K_2HPO_4	5 g
peptone	5 g

With some organisms, e.g. *Bacillus* spp., more reliable reactions are obtained if the K_2HPO_4 is omitted.

The medium is usually dispensed in 5 ml amounts in $\frac{5}{8}$ in. (55 mm) diam. tubes and the inoculated medium incubated for 2–7 days until good growth is obtained. Duplicate tubes can be inoculated if both tests are being carried out.

(a) *Methyl red test*. This test determines whether the production of acid from the glucose has lowered and held the pH at about 4·2 or below. A few drops of methyl red indicator are added to the culture and a resultant definite red colour is considered positive. Shades intermediate between yellow and red should be considered as doubtful positive results. The indicator is prepared by dissolving 0·1 g methyl red in 300 ml 95% ethyl alcohol, which is then diluted to 500 ml with distilled water.

(b) *Voges-Proskauer test*. Some organisms, after producing acids from the glucose, are capable of converting the acids to acetylmethylcarbinol or 2, 3 butanediol which are neutral substances. Aeration in the presence of alkali then converts the product to diacetyl which in turn reacts with peptone constituents to produce a pink colouration. Two modifications of the test are in use and both enhance the development of the colour.

(i) *O'Meara's modification*. A small quantity, usually a knife-point, of solid creatine and 5 ml of 40% KOH solution are added to the incubated culture (O'Meara, 1931).

(ii) *Barritt's modification*. To 1 ml of the culture is added 0·5 ml 6% alcoholic solution of α-naphthol and 0·5 ml 16% KOH solution (Barritt, 1936).

With both modifications a pale pink colouration will normally appear within about 5 min, but may not reach maximum red colour intensity for about 1 h. Negative cultures should be examined after a longer period. The tubes should be held in an almost horizontal position and vigorous shaking should be carried out intermittently.

2. 3-Ketolactose production

The test was originally developed by Bernearts and DeLey (1963) to show the oxidation of lactose to 3-ketolactose by strains of *Agrobacterium tumefaciens*. The test is carried out by growing the organism initially on a nutrient agar slope of the following composition per litre:

yeast extract	10 g
glucose	20 g
$CaCO_3$	20 g
agar	20 g

Two or more loopfuls of the subsequent growth are transferred to agar plates of a second medium, the growth being heaped up at one point on the plate. The second medium has the following composition per litre:

lactose	10 g
yeast extract	1 g
agar	20 g

The agar plates are incubated for 2 days and are then flooded with Benedict's qualitative reagent. The flooded plates should be held at room temperature for 1 h. If 3-ketolactose has been produced, a yellowish-brown zone of Cu_2O develops around the colony.

3. 2-Ketogluconate production

The oxidation of potassium gluconate to potassium 2-ketogluconate is a characteristic used for the identification of pseudomonads and members of the *Enterobacteriaceae*. Potassium 2-ketogluconate is a reducing substance that can be detected in a liquid medium by the development of a brown, orange or yellow precipitate of Cu_2O with Benedict's reagent.

The medium suggested by Haynes (1951) contains per litre:

tryptone	$1 \cdot 5$ g
yeast extract	1 g
K_2HPO_4	1 g
potassium gluconate	40 g
pH, $7 \cdot 0$	

After the development of good growth, $1 \cdot 0$ ml of Benedict's qualitative reagent is added to 1 ml of the liquid culture in a 15 mm tube. The tube is then heated in boiling water for 10 min and cooled rapidly. The colour change and development of a precipitate is recorded after a few minutes.

More conveniently, "Clinitest" reagent tablets (Ames Co., Nuffield House, London, W.1) may be used for the detection of reducing compounds.

4. β-Galactosidase (ONPG test)

With late-lactose-fermenting paracolon organisms, the power to ferment lactose can be predicted by the demonstration of β-galactosidase activity (Lowe, 1962); this is of use in differentiating these organisms from non-lactose-fermenting bacteria which include *Salmonella* and *Proteus* spp.

β-Galactosidase releases o-nitrophenol from o-nitrophenyl-β-D-galacto-pyranoside (ONPG). This can be demonstrated by growing the test organism in ONPG broth which is made by adding 250 ml of ONPG solution to 750 ml of peptone water and should not be stored for more than 4 weeks at 4°C before use. The ONPG solution contains 0·6% ONPG in 0·01M Na_2HPO_4 buffer at pH 7·5 and is stable. The medium is tubed in 2 ml amounts and should be inoculated heavily with a loopful of the test bacterial culture grown on peptone agar. The release of yellow o-nitrophenol indicates β-galactosidase activity. The colour change may occur within 3 h of incubation at 37°C. Tubes showing no colour change in 24 h may be discarded.

5. Aesculin hydrolysis

The ability of an organism to hydrolyse this glycoside to aesculetin and glucose can be investigated by incorporating 0·1% aesculin into a suitable liquid or agar nutrient medium that supports good growth of the organism. Ferric citrate is added to the medium at a concentration of 0·05%. A positive reaction is shown by the development of a brownish-black colour that is produced by the aesculetin in combination with the iron.

A method used by Gemmell and Hodgkiss (1964) for tests with lacto-bacilli incorporates 1% aesculin into the nutrient agar medium. The hydrolysis is detected by the appearance of coral-like crystals, which are assumed to be aesculetin, and by a simultaneous loss of the characteristic fluorescence of aesculin in ultraviolet light.

The production of acid or acid and gas from the glucose moiety in aesculin can also be used as an index of aesculin decomposition.

6. Hippurate hydrolysis

The hydrolysis of hippurate (benzyl glycine) to benzoate and glycine can be detected by adding acidic $FeCl_3$ to a broth culture grown in the presence of hippurate. Benzoate is less soluble than hippurate in the final test system.

The test is carried out by adding 1% sodium hippurate to a liquid nutrient medium. Small (0·1 ml) aliquots of the acidic $FeCl_3$ reagent (12%

$FeCl_3.6H_2O$ and 2·5% conc. HCl in distilled water) are added to 1 ml of the uninoculated medium until the precipitated hippurate just re-dissolves. The same volume of the reagent is then added to 1 ml of the clear centri-fuged supernatant of an incubated culture. The development of a precipi-tate in the test indicates that the less soluble benzoate has been produced.

The development of an alkaline reaction in a phenol red-containing chemically defined medium in which 0·3% sodium hippurate is the sole carbon-energy source has been used by Thirst (1957) to detect the hydrolysis.

7. Aromatic ring cleavage mechanisms

Organisms that are capable of obtaining energy by metabolizing aromatic compounds may cleave the benzene ring; the cleavage usually occurs at either the meta or ortho positions, but sometimes both mechanisms appear to be involved. Colorimetric tests are available to detect the different inter-mediate metabolic compounds that result from these cleavages.

Fresh growth of the organisms is subcultured onto an agar plate of the test medium (see page 4) to which has been added per litre: 1 g sodium p-hydroxybenzoate. After good growth has been obtained, the organisms are suspended in 2 ml of 0·02 M-tris buffer (pH 8·0) before adding 0·5 ml toluene and 20 μmoles of a solution of sodium protocatechuate. The tubes are shaken and the development of a bright yellow colouration within a few minutes indicates that meta cleavage of the substrate has taken place. If the result is negative, the tube is shaken periodically for 1 h at 30°C before carrying out the Rothera reaction. About 1 g of $(NH_4)_2SO_4$ crystals are added followed by one drop of 1% sodium nitro-prusside solution and then by about 0·5 ml 0·880 sp. gr. ammonia. After mixing, the development of a deep violet colouration due to the presence of β-ketoadipate indicates the ortho cleavage of the substrate. The setests, which have been used to differentiate pseudomonads by Stanier et al. (1966), may also be of value for differentiation within other groups of organisms.

A spot test for catechol 2,3-oxygenase has been described by Pankhurst (1965). A thick suspension of growth from an ordinary nutrient agar medium is mixed with 1–3 drops catechol on a white tile. A positive result is shown by the development of a yellow colouration before the mixture dries. The reasons for the development of a purple-brown colouration are not known.

III. THE UTILIZATION OF NITROGENOUS COMPOUNDS

A. Requirements for growth

Microbial growth requirements for nitrogen compounds vary from the most simple, when only gaseous nitrogen is required, to a complex requirement for a large number of amino-acids and growth factors. The range of nitrogen requirements can be simply divided into four groups: (a) gaseous nitrogen, (b) inorganic nitrogen compounds, (c) one or more amino-acids, and (d) more complex nitrogen compounds and growth factors.

Media used to indicate a requirement for one of these four groups are based on a liquid basal medium (BM) that should provide all the essential nitrogen-free inorganic ions (e.g. Hutner's base) and a utilizable energy source. The different group requirements can then be respectively demonstrated by test cultures in (a) basal medium (BM); (b) BM + 1 g KNO_3 (per litre) and/or 1 g $(NH_4)_2SO_4$; (c) BM + 5 g vitamin-free Casamino acids (Difco); and (d) BM + 1 g yeast extract, or 1 g meat extract, or a component of the normal habitat of the organism, e.g. soil extract, rumen liquor.

Holding (1960) included in each litre of the basal medium: 5 g glucose, 1 g sodium citrate, 1 g sodium acetate, 1 g sodium succinate and 1 g calcium gluconate as energy sources for the study of Gram-negative soil bacteria, whereas Stanier *et al.* (1966) provided only 1 g sodium lactate for a study of pseudomonads.

B. The reduction of nitrate and nitrite

These reduction processes may involve (a) assimilation in which the nitrate is reduced to nitrite and ammonia, which is then converted to amino acids and other nitrogenous organic cell compounds; (b) dissimilation (or respiration) in which nitrate or nitrite replaces oxygen as the terminal hydrogen acceptor, under conditions of low free oxygen availability. In a nitrate-containing medium, the nitrate may be reduced to nitrite only, or to nitrite and ammonium ions, or the nitrate may be completely assimilated. All of these processes are generally referred to as nitrate reduction. When a nitrite-containing medium is used, the reduction of the nitrite to ammonium ions or the complete assimilation is known as nitrite reduction. If either the nitrate or nitrite is dissimilated to a gaseous end-product such as nitrogen or nitrous oxide, the process is referred to as denitrification. The reduced intermediates detected in the biochemical tests are assumed to be released mainly by dissimilatory processes.

Tests for the reduction of nitrate and nitrite are carried out by inoculating organisms into a suitable nutrient broth containing 0·1% KNO_3. The cultures are incubated until good growth is obtained during which time a sample is examined periodically to detect whether reduction of nitrate or nitrite has occurred and to determine the stage of growth at which it takes place. The presence of nitrite can be determined by adding to 5 ml of the culture 0·5 ml 1·0% sulphanilic acid in 5N acetic acid followed by 0·5 ml of 0·6% dimethyl-α-naphthylamine in 5N acetic acid. The development of a red colour indicates a positive result. If the nitrite test is negative, the presence of residual nitrate can be shown by adding approximately 1 mg of zinc dust per ml of culture. The development of a red colour indicates that all of the nitrate has not been broken down.

The nitrite test is very sensitive and an examination of uninoculated media free from added nitrite should be included in the study. Attention is drawn to the carcinogenic properties of α-naphthylamine.

The reduction of nitrite can be demonstrated by replacing the nitrate in the medium with $0 \cdot 01\%$ KNO_2. A positive result is shown by a negative test for nitrite after incubation of the culture. With some organisms the denitrification process appears to take place more readily if either $0 \cdot 5\%$ glycerol or $0 \cdot 5\%$ sodium succinate is included in the medium. Denitrification from nitrite may also be shown more readily by the addition of $0 \cdot 1\%$ KNO_2. The production of nitrogen gas can be detected either by incorporating Durham fermentation tubes into liquid media or by observing the formation of gas bubbles in agar media, both in test-tubes. At present there appears to be no easily applied routine method for determining the production of the oxides of nitrogen. Ammonia production can be detected by using Nessler's reagent (see Herbert, Phipps, and Strange, this Series Volume 5B).

C. Decomposition of amino-acids and other nitrogenous compounds

1. *Indole production*

As a positive result in this test is held to indicate the production of indole by bacterial decomposition of tryptophan, it follows that the peptone for the nutrient broth test medium must contain adequate amounts of tryptophan (e.g. 1%) or the broth should be enriched accordingly. A known positive control organism and a negative control should be included in each batch of tests, since some modifications of the test employ reagents that can introduce false positive results. Bacteria produce indole at varying rates; some organisms actively decompose the indole as soon as it is formed. A 2–3 day nutrient broth culture of the test organism is usually used, but samples should be tested daily for up to a week. Various temperatures of incubation may be employed. The medium should not contain added glucose.

The presence of indole is indicated by the development of a red colour in the reagent, usually Ehrlich's rosindole reagent (q.v.), when it is layered on to a sample of the liquid culture. The reagent is made by dissolving 1 g *p*-dimethyl aminobenzaldehyde in 95 ml absolute ethanol and then adding 20 ml conc. HCl; the solution should be protected from light.

Various modifications of the indole test involve the prior extraction of the indole into an organic phase by shaking the test sample first with 1–2 ml of ether, petroleum ether or xylol before adding the reagent gently down the side of the tube on to the solvent layer.

In a further modification, the test sample is shaken with Kovacs' reagent

(5 g p-dimethylaminobenzaldehyde, 75 g amyl alcohol, 25 ml conc. HCl) and this combines the two steps in one operation.

Alternatively, the volatile indole produced from the culture at 37°C is detected by an impregnated paper strip retained at the top of the tube. The dried paper strip may be impregnated with either a hot saturated aqueous solution of oxalic acid or a solution of 5 g p-dimethylaminobenzaldehyde, 10 ml of pure phosphoric acid, and 50 ml of methanol; with both reagents the strip turns pink or red in the presence of indole.

2. *Hydrogen sulphide production*

Many bacteria produce hydrogen sulphide from organic sulphur compounds in culture media. There are numerous tests for the detection of H_2S production and these vary widely in sensitivity (see Cowan and Steel, 1965, p. 29). The relatively insensitive tests differentiate the strong H_2S producers from the others. The test organism may be grown in a medium containing a source of sulphur (e.g. peptone) and an indicator of sulphide production (0·05% lead acetate, or 0·025% ferric ammonium citrate, or 0·015% ferrous acetate); the medium then turns black if H_2S is produced. A suitable medium is ferric chloride gelatin which contains per litre:

meat extract	7·5 g
peptone	25 g
NaCl	5 g
gelatin	120 g

A 5 ml sterile 10% aqueous solution of $FeCl_3$ is added prior to solidification.

A convenient and sensitive method involves growth in a tube of nutrient broth or on a liver extract agar slope or a serum glucose agar slope. H_2S is detected by blackening of a dried paper impregnated with saturated lead acetate solution and retained at the top of the tube. The culture should be incubated for 7 days. The paper may be changed daily if the time of maximal H_2S production is to be determined.

Growth at 22°C or 30°C instead of 37°C may enhance H_2S production by some bacteria.

3. *Urease*

Most media used for the determination of urease activity incorporate urea and a pH indicator. A positive result is shown by a rise in pH value resulting from the hydrolysis of the urea to ammonia. In general, media with low buffering capacity should be used, but organisms with strong urease activity, e.g. *Proteus* spp., also give a positive result in more highly buffered media.

A medium devised by Christensen (1946) has the following composition per litre:

peptone	1 g
NaCl	5 g
glucose	1 g
KH_2PO_4	2 g
phenol red ($0\cdot2\%$ solution)	6 ml
agar	20 g
pH, $6\cdot9$	

Yeast extract ($0\cdot1\%$) can also be added for organisms requiring growth factors. The medium is prepared in bottles, sterilized and cooled to about 55°C. A 20% solution of urea previously sterilized by filtration, is then added to give a final concentration of 2% urea in the molten medium. The completed medium is dispensed in tubes as agar slopes. Urease activity causes the yellow indicator to change to red.

Stewart (1965) has shown that with some pseudomonads, the presence of free ammonia suppresses urease activity. He obtained more reliable results by incorporating the sterile urea into a medium after appreciable growth of the organism had occurred. A mixed pH indicator to replace the phenol red was also recommended.

4. *Phenylalanine deaminase*

Bacterial deamination of phenylalanine produces phenylpyruvic acid; the keto acid turns a $FeCl_3$ indicator solution green. The reaction is typically associated with organisms of the *Proteus* and *Providence* groups (see Cowan and Steel, 1965, p. 34).

Phenylalanine agar slopes are made with the following ingredients per litre:

DL phenylalamine (or 1 g of the L form)	2 g
yeast extract	3 g
Na_2HPO_4	1 g
NaCl	5 g
agar	20 g

A slope is heavily inoculated with the test organism and incubated overnight. The area of growth is then flooded with $0\cdot2$ ml of a 10% aqueous solution of $FeCl_3$ which turns green if deamination has occurred.

5. *Amino-acid decarboxylases*

Tests that demonstrate bacterial decarboxylation of lysine, arginine, ornithine and glutamic acid are of particular use in identifying members of the *Enterobacteriaceae* (see Møller, 1955).

One per cent of the L-amino acid (L(+)-lysine dihydrochloride, L(+)-arginine monohydrochloride, L(+)-ornithine dihydrochloride, or L(+)-glutamic acid), or 2% of the DL form, is incorporated in a medium containing per litre of distilled water:

peptone	5 g
meat extract	5 g
"pyridoxal"	5 mg
(pyridoxal-5'-phosphoric acid, B.D.H.)	
glucose	0·5 g
0·2% solution of bromothymol blue	5 ml
0·2% solution of cresol red	2·5 ml

and the pH is adjusted to 6·0.

An alternative basal medium includes, per litre:

peptone	5 g
yeast extract	3 g
glucose	1 g
0·2% solution of bromocresol purple	10 ml

The complete medium is dispensed in small narrow tubes and is overlaid with sterile liquid paraffin. Møller specified 1·1 ml of medium in a column of about 2 cm with a 5 mm layer of paraffin.

An inoculum from a culture of the test organism on a solid medium is introduced with a straight wire through the paraffin layer. The various controls should include a control tube containing only the basal medium which is also inoculated and the tests are incubated and examined daily for up to 4 days. As a result of bacterial fermentation of the glucose in the medium, the indicator becomes yellow. The control tube, devoid of amino-acid, will then remain yellow; but a subsequent change to violet or purple in the tests indicates that alkaline degradation products have been produced in the course of decarboxylation of the particular amino-acid. With arginine, the mechanism of breakdown may involve either the decarboxylase or the dihydrolase system (q.v.) or both of these systems. The test with glutamic acid is complicated by various factors and the original paper should be consulted for details of the procedure in this case.

6. *Arginine dihydrolase*

The ability of certain organisms to produce an alkaline reaction in arginine-containing media under relatively anaerobic conditions has been used by Thornley (1960) to differentiate certain types of Gram-negative aerobic bacteria, especially *Pseudomonas* spp. The alkaline reaction is thought to be a result of the production of ornithine, CO_2 and NH_3 from the arginine.

Thornley's medium has the following composition per litre:

peptone	1 g
NaCl	5 g
K_2HPO_4	0·3 g
agar	3 g
phenol red	0·01 g
L(+)-arginine HCl	10 g
pH, 7·2	

About 3 ml of the medium are dispensed in $\frac{1}{4}$-oz screw-capped vials. The organism is stab-inoculated into the medium, which is then sealed off with sterile melted Vaseline and the cap screwed on tightly. Colour changes are recorded after incubation for up to 7 days, the change from yellowish-orange to red being positive.

IV. DECOMPOSITION OF LARGE MOLECULES

A. Phospholipases (lecithinases)

Bacterial phospholipases (lecithinases) decompose phospholipid complexes that occur as emulsifying agents in serum and egg yolk. The enzymic activity breaks the emulsion and liberates free fat so that a turbidity is produced. The phospholipase-C enzymes of *Clostridium welchii* (*Cl. perfringens*) and *Cl. oedematiens* (*Cl. novyi*) are well known phosphatidyl-choline choline phosphohydrolases. Convenient substrates for the reaction are (i) 20% egg yolk (v/v) in saline, or (ii) commercially available egg yolk suspension (Oxoid Ltd., Southwark Bridge Road, London, S.E.1), or preferably (iii) "lecithovitellin solution" which is made by adding 1 egg yolk to 225 ml of saline buffered with 0·1M Na borate buffer at pH 7·2–7·4 with 0·005M $CaCl^2$; 10 g of a filtration aid such as Hyflo Supercel (Johns Manville Co., London) is added and the mixture shaken for 1 h before filtering twice through Whatman No. 1 papers and finally Seitz-filtering with negative pressure. In the simple plate test, 4% of undiluted egg yolk is used.

Plate test: The test organism is cultured directly on a suitable nutrient agar medium preferably incorporating a digest base, with 4% of sterile fresh egg yolk added at 55°C just before the plates are poured. If phospholipase is produced, a zone of turbidity develops in the medium surrounding each colony. In the case of *Clostridium perfringens*, the effect can be specifically inhibited in part of the plate by spreading specific antitoxin on that area of the medium before it is inoculated; this is of use for the preliminary identification of the organism.

Tube test: Serial doubling dilutions of a suitable broth culture supernatant or culture filtrate are made in calcium-gelatin-saline ("Cagsal" see p. 29), and an equal volume of egg yolk suspension or lecithovitellin (see above) is added to each tube. The mixtures are shaken and then incubated at 37°C for 1 h in a waterbath. At this point the first readings are made, and final readings are made after the tubes have been held overnight at 4°C. In strongly positive tests, a layer or curd of fat develops on the surface of the reaction mixture. At higher dilutions, a generalized turbidity is seen. The end-point of the test is judged by visual comparison with a graded positive control series and a phospholipase-negative control.

Note: Phospholipase effects are sometimes confused with other lipolytic effects produced in culture media (see below).

B. Lipases

In general, bacterial lipases are at present poorly characterized, but the demonstration of lipolytic activity is sometimes of practical use. For example, the production of a "pearly layer" on media containing milk or egg yolk is characteristic of certain clostridia and staphylococci; this effect is caused by the breakdown of complex lipids in the culture medium and the liberation of free fatty acids. The affected areas in an agar medium are stained green if they are flooded with a saturated solution of $CuSO_4$. More specific substrates may be incorporated in media designed for the study of lipolytic effects (see, for example, Willis and Turner, 1962), and glyceryl tributyrate (tributyrin) is now commonly used.

On "tributyrin agar" medium containing per litre:

peptone	5 g
yeast extract	3 g
glyceryl tributyrate	10 g

zones of clearing develop around colonies of lipolytic organisms.

An apparently more sensitive method is described by Oterholm and Ordal (1966). Bacterial cell suspensions are placed in wells in thin layers of agar containing 0.3% tributyrin; after incubation for 24 h at 37°C, even weakly lipolytic organisms produce a clear zone at the edge of the well.

In another method, which may involve other enzymes, zones of opacity develop around colonies of "lipolytic" organisms grown in the presence of Tweens. Tweens are thermostable water-soluble long-chain fatty acid esters of a polyoxyalkylene derivative of sorbitan. A suitable medium is supplemented with 0.01% $CaCl_2$ and 1% of the Tween preparation; Tweens 80, 60 and 40 are esters of oleic acid, stearic acid and palmitic acid respectively (see Sierra, 1957). The zones of opacity that develop are composed of crystals of the calcium soaps.

C. Proteinases

Some bacteria appear to be non-proteolytic whilst others are strongly proteolytic and actively decompose the complex protein constituents of media. For example, as a result of proteolytic decomposition, the particles of meat in cooked meat broth become blackened and reduced in volume, foul-smelling products being released. A strongly proteolytic culture incubated on a Loeffler's serum slope will eventually liquefy the medium.

Proteolytic colonies on milk agar produce zones of clearing around each colony as a result of decomposition of the milk protein. This effect may also be seen when egg yolk agar is used. Some of the latter effects are evident after overnight incubation, but there is much variation and prolonged incubation for days or weeks may be necessary before complex protein substrates are broken down. Combined proteolytic and saccharolytic effects may be seen when organisms are cultured for example in litmus milk medium (see p. 26). Nutrient gelatin is commonly used for the detection of proteolytic activity (gelatinase, see below), but a distinction should be made between gelatinase activity and the capacity to decompose other protein substrates.

1. *Tests for gelatinase activity*

(a) *Gelatin liquefaction.* Proteolytic bacteria decompose gelatin (denatured collagen) so that it loses its gelling properties. Simple tests based on this principle involve the incorporation of 15% of high grade gelatin into a nutrient broth medium at pH 8·4 to make nutrient gelatin. Gelatin loses its gelling properties if it is overheated. The preparation of nutrient gelatin is detailed by Cruickshank (1965, p. 822). The medium is dispensed in tubes and inoculated heavily with the test organism by stab-inoculation. Gelatinase activity is indicated by "liquefaction" of the gelatin but, as normal preparations of gelatin are liquid at temperatures above 25°C, test media incubated at above 25°C should be chilled until the control solidifies before observations on liquefaction are made. It may be necessary to incubate such tests for several days before gelatinase activity is evident.

(b) *Plate test for gelatinase.* When a proteolytic organism is grown on a plate of nutrient agar in which gelatin (0·4%) is incorporated, zones of gelatinase activity around the colonies may be demonstrated: if the plate is flooded with aqueous tannic acid (1%), the medium becomes opaque, but zones of gelatinase activity are more opaque. If a solution of 15% $HgCl_2$ and 20% conc. HCl in water is used instead of the tannic acid, the zones appear more transparent than the background medium (Barer, 1946).

(c) *Kohn's test.* When gelatin has been treated with formaldehyde, it remains in the gel state at incubator temperatures at least up to 37°C. Thus, if carbon granules are incorporated into molten gelatin which is then cooled, cut into small cubes and treated with formaldehyde, the treated cubes of gelatin will not liberate their carbon granules when subsequently held in liquid culture media at incubator temperatures above 25°C, unless the gelatin is decomposed by bacterial action during incubation. This is the basis of Kohn's useful test for gelatinase (Kohn, 1953). Suitable charcoal-gelatin disks are commercially available from Oxoid Ltd., Southwark Bridge Road, London, S.E.1.

D. Other enzymes

1. *Amylase*

The test medium is prepared by adding 0·2% soluble starch to an agar medium that will support good growth of the organism. The medium can be added directly to empty Petri dishes or used as a thin layer poured onto the surface of a solidified starch-free nutrient agar. Surface-dried plates of the medium are prepared and up to 10 test strains per plate are spot-inoculated. After incubation has produced good growth, the plate is flooded with a dilute iodine solution. A clear zone of variable diameter around the colony indicates that the starch has been hydrolysed (amylase activity). In the remainder of the plate where the starch is not hydrolysed, a deep blue colouration develops with the iodine.

2. *Other depolymerases*

(a) *Cellulase, chitinase and pectinase.* The ability of organisms to hydrolyse naturally occurring insoluble polymers such as cellulose, chitin and pectin can be investigated routinely. In the methods used for the demonstration of cellulase (see Skinner, 1960) and chitinase (see Lingappa and Lockwood, 1961), the polymer is prepared in a finely divided form and either incorporated into a nutrient agar medium or poured as a thin layer in water agar onto the surface of a solidified nutrient agar plate. The hydrolysis is shown by the development of a clear zone around the colonies. Growth in a liquid medium in which the polymer is the only carbon and energy source can also be used to indicate the utilization of the compound.

Pectinolytic activity can be demonstrated by the method of Wieringa (1947). A pectate gel is prepared by layering a solution of pectin (pH 9·4) over a layer of mineral salts agar with added $CaCl_2$ at pH 5·0 in a Petri dish. Actively pectinolytic organisms produce a liquefaction of the gel. An alternative method that enables a stock pectin solution to be kept in liquid form prior to incorporation into the final medium has been described by Paton (1959).

(b) *Hyaluronidase.* This enzyme catalyses the hydrolysis of hyaluronic acid and is best demonstrated by a modification of the ACRA test (see Oakley and Warrack, 1951; Gadalla and Collee, 1968). A 1 ml volume of test culture supernatant is serially diluted in 1 ml volumes of 0·85% NaCl buffered with 0·1M sodium borate buffer at pH 8·0 and a further 0·5 ml of the borate-buffered saline (BBS) is added to each tube. A 0·5 ml volume of a suitable dilution of bovine synovial fluid in BBS is added to each tube and the mixtures are incubated for 1 h at 37°C in a waterbath. Thereafter, the tubes are chilled for 5 min and 0·4 ml of a 5% aqueous solution of Congo red is added to each tube and mixed by inversion. After 5 min, a drop of each mixture is allowed to fall from a capillary pipette under standard conditions into a solution of 1% HCl in 70% absolute alcohol in a Petri dish. It is important to include controls in this test. In the absence of hyaluronidase activity, the drop of synovial fluid produces a discrete blob in the acid alcohol. If the substrate has been decomposed by hyaluronidase, the drop produces a spreading pattern.

(c) *Deoxyribonuclease*. There are various tests for bacterial deoxyribonuclease (see Cruickshank, 1965). In the slide test of Warrack, Bidwell and Oakley (1951) the deoxyribonuclease activity of a bacterial culture filtrate is demonstrated by its action on rabbit leucocytes; the enzyme alters the affinity of the cell nuclei for Romanowsky stains. A plate test for the demonstration of bacterial decomposition of nucleic acids is described by Jeffries, Holtman and Guse (1957). DNA is readily soluble in water. RNA is solubilized by carefully adding 1N NaOH, the reaction of the solution not exceeding pH 5·0. The fresh solution of the nucleic acid substrate (0·2%) is added to a suitable liquid nutrient agar medium before sterilization and Petri plates of the medium are poured as soon as the autoclaved medium has cooled to 50°C. The test organism is heavily seeded to produce a strip of confluent growth on the surface of the plate. After incubation for 1–2 days at a suitable temperature, the plate is flooded with 1N HCl. Deoxyribonuclease or ribonuclease activity results in clear zones surrounded by a turbidity produced by the precipitation of the unaffected substrate.

In addition to the pH of the medium, the temperature of incubation is an important factor, since maximal enzyme activity might not occur at the temperature of optimal growth.

3. *Neuraminidase (Sialidase)*

Bacterial neuraminidases are detected and assayed by measuring their ability to liberate free neuraminic acid (sialic acid) from a substrate that contains protein-bound neuraminic acid. The glycoprotein fraction of human plasma is a reliable substrate (see Collee and Barr, 1968). Sialyl lactose is more elegant and preferable, but it is expensive.

A sample of a suitable culture of the test organism is incubated with the substrate under conditions that should be determined for individual species; some bacterial neuraminidases are calcium-dependent (e.g. neuraminidase of *Vibrio cholerae*), and the pH optima vary. A 0·2 ml sample of a broth culture with 0·3 ml of suitable buffer is mixed with 0·5 ml of substrate solution and incubated at 37°C for 30 min or 1 h.

The liberated neuraminic acid is detected by the thiobarbituric acid procedure of Warren (1959) or Aminoff's modification of this procedure (see Cassidy, Jourdian, and Roseman, 1966). The procedure used successfully by one of the present writers is as follows: (i) 0·5 ml of the reaction mixture is mixed with 0·25 ml of a 0·025M solution of periodic acid in 0·125N H_2SO_4 and held at 37°C in a water bath for 30 min; (ii) 0·2 ml of a solution containing 2% $NaAsO_2$ in 0·5N HCl is added with shaking until a yellow-brown colour disappears; (iii) 2 ml of a 0·1M solution of 2-thiobarbituric acid, adjusted to pH 9·0 with 0·1N NaOH, is then added; the mixture is shaken thoroughly, heated in vigorously boiling water for 7·5 min and thereafter cooled in tap-water for 5 min. The colour is extracted by shaking with 4·0 ml of n-butanol containing 5% (v/v) 12N HCl and the absorbance of the centrifuged clear organic phase is determined at 549 nm in a 1 cm glass cell rinsed between samples with absolute alcohol or acid butanol. A 0·5 ml sample of water submitted to the above procedure provides a blank control. The positive control may be derived from a solution of N-acetyl neuraminic acid or from egg-white or human serum hydrolysed to release neuraminic acid by heating at 80°C for 2 h with an equal volume of 0·1N H_2SO_4 (see Collee, 1965).

V. MISCELLANEOUS TESTS

A. Use of inhibitors

1. Optochin

Pneumococci (*Streptococcus pneumoniae*) are more sensitive to optochin (ethyl hydrocuprein hydrochloride) than are the other streptococci. Sensitivity is tested by applying tablets containing 0·05 mg optochin or sterilized absorbent paper disks of 6–8 mm diameter moistened in a sterile 0·05% aqueous solution of optochin onto a blood agar plate that has been sown with the test organism. The recommended concentration of optochin is in the range 0·025 to 0·05%. The plate is incubated and the subsequent development of a zone of inhibition of growth of 5 mm diameter or more indicates a degree of sensitivity normally associated with *Streptococcus pneumoniae* (see Bowers and Jeffries, 1955). Some workers consider that any zone of inhibition indicates significant sensitivity.

2. Potassium cyanide

The ability of an organism to grow in the presence of cyanide is tested in KCN broth which contains per litre:

peptone	3 g
NaCl	5 g
KH_2PO_4	0·25 g
$Na_2HPO_4 . 2H_2O$	5·64 g

(see Rogers and Taylor, 1961). The clear basal medium is autoclaved and cooled to 4°C before the addition of 15 ml of a 0·5% sterile aqueous solution of KCN.

The medium can be stored for up to 1 month if held in tightly sealed small screw-capped bottles at 4°C. The medium is inoculated from a 24-h nutrient broth culture of the test organism and the bottle is then sealed with the screw-cap and incubated. Growth indicates the test organism's tolerance of cyanide and a positive result is recorded. After use, a crystal of $FeSO_4$ and about 0·1 ml of 40% KOH should be added to the medium so that cyanide fumes are not released during heat-sterilization.

B. Terminal respiratory enzymes

1. *Catalases*

The principle of this test is that when organisms containing catalase are mixed with hydrogen peroxide (H_2O_2), gaseous oxygen is released.

The test organism is grown on a slope of nutrient agar or some other suitable medium. The medium must not incorporate blood or haematin since red blood cells contain catalase and some organisms normally catalase negative are able to produce the enzyme if haem complexes are included in the medium. About 1 ml of H_2O_2 (3%, 10 vol.) is poured over the culture which should be examined immediately, and if necessary again at 5 min, for the evolution of gas bubbles.

An alternative procedure involves taking a small amount of the test culture on a clean sterile thin glass rod, heat-sealed capillary pipette or platinum wire and holding this below the surface of some of the H_2O_2 reagent in a small tube that has been thoroughly cleaned. If the test organism produces catalase, gas is evolved promptly. Recent evidence indicates that some organisms produce a non-haem catalase, "pseudocatalase", which also gives a positive reaction in tests with hydrogen peroxide (see Whittenbury, 1964). Pseudocatalase is produced by some lactic-acid bacteria grown in media containing a low concentration of glucose or in glucose-free media, but positive reactions due to pseudocatalase are not encountered if these organisms are grown on a nutrient medium containing 1% (w/v) glucose.

2. *Cytochrome oxidase*

The detection of cytochrome oxidase activity is used as a differential test mainly for the aerobic and facultatively anaerobic groups of Gram-negative bacteria. In the organisms studied by Stanier *et al.* (1966) the activity was correlated with the occurrence of a cytochrome of the *c* type. Sugar-free media should be used whenever possible.

In the method recommended by Kovacs (1956) the organisms are freshly grown on nutrient agar. A platinum loop is then used to pick a colony and make a compact smear on filter paper moistened with 2–3 drops of 1% solution of tetramethyl-p-phenylenediamine dihydrochloride. A positive result is recorded if the smear turns violet within 10 sec. Note: the use of a *platinum* loop for the test is important since loops made of other materials can lead to false positive reactions. The activity can also be determined by adding reagents to the growth on a nutrient agar slope or in broth (Gaby and Hadley, 1957). 0·2 ml of Solution A (1% α-naphthol in 95% ethyl alcohol) followed by 0·3 ml of Solution B (1% aqueous solution of p-amino dimethylaniline dihydrochloride or oxalate) are allowed to flow over the agar slope or are added to the broth culture. The development of a purplish blue colour within 30 sec is considered positive. It is recommended that the reagents should be kept in a refrigerator and used within 2 weeks of preparation.

Organisms with less active cytochrome oxidase activity can produce the colour change after longer periods than those stated above. "Late-positive" results can be useful in differentiating these organisms from others such as many coliforms and some types of plant pathogenic pseudomonads that give a colour change no greater than that attributable to the auto-oxidation of the reagents.

C. Other tests

1. *Coagulases*

Pathogenic staphylococci produce coagulase, an enzyme that coagulates plasma. Coagulase may be detected by a test performed on a glass slide or in a tube; the two tests depend upon different mechanisms, but the distinction is not generally made in routine work. The substrate is human or rabbit blood plasma that has been citrated, oxalated or heparinized to prevent natural clotting.

(1) *The slide test*. A portion of the test culture grown on solid medium is taken with a loop and emulsified in each of two drops of physiological saline separately placed on a microscope slide. If the organism is auto-agglutinable and resists emulsification, the slide test cannot be performed; a fairly dense homogeneous suspension of the organism is essential. A drop of the undiluted plasma preparation at room temperature is then placed near one of the suspensions and mixed in. The slide is then rocked. A positive result is indicated by clumping of the organisms in the test suspension within about 30 sec; a drop of saline may be added to the control suspension which should remain homogeneous in the absence of plasma. Equivocal results should be checked with the tube test (but see above).

(2) *The tube test.* This relatively unstandardized test gives useful and fairly reproducible results (see Elek, 1959, p. 209).

The substrate is sterile citrated human or rabbit plasma. A supply of a batch that gives good results should be stored undiluted at 4°C. Human plasma with added glucose is not satisfactory. For the test, the plasma is freshly diluted about 1 in 10 (v/v) with physiological saline; the optimal degree of dilution varies with different samples.

About 5–10 drops (0·1 ml) of an overnight broth culture or an equivalent saline suspension of the test organism are added to about 1 ml of the plasma. The mixture is incubated at 37°C and observed periodically for up to 6 h. A positive reaction, shown by the mixture gelling, usually develops within this period. Control mixtures with known coagulase-negative and coagulase-positive strains should be incubated in parallel. In some equivocal cases, it is necessary to prolong the incubation period or to leave the test mixture at room temperature overnight after initial incubation in order to get a definite result; results obtained in this way are less satisfactory, as complicating factors may operate.

2. *Litmus milk*

The medium is prepared by adding a saturated alcoholic solution of litmus to fresh skimmed milk, or reconstituted powder, until a pale lavender colour is obtained.

The medium is usually distributed in test-tubes and sterilized by steaming for 1 h on 3 successive days. The medium is held at between 22° and 37°C between steamings. After the final steaming the medium should be kept at a similar temperature for at least 3 days to check for sterility. Cultures are usually incubated for up to 6 weeks, with changes recorded at weekly intervals. The litmus solution may be prepared by grinding in a mortar, 8 g granulated litmus in 30 ml 40% ethyl alcohol. After the sediment has settled, the supernatant liquid is poured off and the grinding process repeated twice with the sediment. The total volume is made up to 100 ml with 40% alcohol and boiled for 1 min. The supernatant is again decanted off and the total volume made up to 100 ml with 40% alcohol. If necessary, 1N HCl is added dropwise until a purple colour is obtained.

The changes in the medium brought about by the organisms are mainly due to their action on the lactose and casein. The main types of changes observed are detailed below but intermediate reactions may occur. In addition, the inability of an organism to produce any change can be a useful diagnostic characteristic.

(1) *Acid formation.* The litmus turns pink due mainly to the production of acids from the lactose.

(2) *Acid formation with clotting of the casein.* The litmus turns pink and sufficient acid is produced to bring about clotting of the casein; this normally takes place around pH 4·7. After clotting has taken place, any gas produced by the lactose fermentation can be seen by a cleaving of the clot; the fermentation may be brisk as in the case of the "stormy clot" reaction with *Clostridium welchii.*

(3) *Curdling of the casein by rennet-like enzymes.* With this type of reaction, little or no acid is produced and the clot formed normally shrinks with separation of the whey.

(4) *Casein decomposition.* Proteolytic activity is shown by a clearing of the medium. Frequently, this action occurs initially at the top of the medium. There may be an associated development of alkalinity.

(5) *Reduction of litmus.* The litmus becomes colourless. Some organisms will only bring about the reduction of the litmus after an acidic curd has formed. Bromocresol purple indicator which may be used as an alternative to litmus is not so readily reduced to a colourless compound.

(6) *Alkaline reaction.* The development of alkalinity without any indication of the proteolytic activity is thought to be due to the utilization of the citrate in milk.

3. *Bile solubility*

Pneumococci (*Streptococcus pneumoniae*) are generally soluble in bile or a bile salt solution whereas streptococci of the viridans group and faecal streptococci are usually not soluble.

1·0 ml of a sterile 10% solution of sodium taurocholate in physiological saline is added to 10 ml of an 18-h broth culture of the test organism at a pH between 6·8 and 7·6. If the organism is bile-soluble, clearing occurs in the mixture after incubation for 15–30 min at 37°C.

A recommended modification of this test includes the use of sodium deoxycholate (1·0 ml of a 10% solution) in place of the taurocholate (see Downie, Stent and White, 1931). The limiting final dilution of sodium deoxycholate for lysis was found by these workers to be 1 in 3200.

The test organism should not be grown and tested in broth containing glucose because acid produced in the medium interferes with the autolytic reaction. The use of a centrifuged bacterial deposit resuspended in saline overcomes this problem if a glucose-containing broth has been used as the culture medium; saline-harvested blood agar cultures may also be used. The volumes of test suspension and added reagent may then be reduced ten-fold.

4. *Nicotinic acid (niacin) production*

This test demonstrates the production of nicotinic acid (niacin) and it is of use in the differentiation of mycobacteria.

Reagent 1 is a 10% aqueous solution of cyanogen bromide which produces toxic fumes and must be prepared in a fume cupboard and stored at 4°C. It is necessary to prepare a fresh solution every 2 weeks.

Reagent 2 is a 4% solution of aniline in 95% ethanol. This is stable at 4°C for about 4 weeks. The test is performed by adding 1 ml of Reagent 1 to a well-grown slope culture of the test organism (see Cruickshank, 1965, p. 833). 1 ml of Reagent 2 is added after 5 min. The development of a yellow colour in the added solutions indicates a positive reaction. An alternative procedure is detailed by Collins (1967, p. 281).

A more reliable test devised by the late Dr. N. Kovacs is recommended by Dr. A. T. Wallace, City Hospital, Edinburgh (personal communication). Reagent A is the same as Reagent 1 above. Reagent B is 3% benzidine in a mixture of equal parts of propylene glycol and ethanol. A fresh well-grown culture of the test organism on a Lowenstein–Jensen slope is laid so that the water of condensation floods the surface for 20 min. The water is then pipetted into a small bijou bottle and 3 drops each of Reagents A and B are added. A pink colour develops within 2–3 min in the test material derived from *M. tuberculosis* of the human type.

Caution: All of the above procedures should be performed in a fume cupboard. Ten per cent ammonia (NH_4OH) must be added to the test mixtures to neutralize the cyanogen before sterilization in the autoclave. Benzidine, and other reagents that may be used as alternatives in this test, are potentially carcinogenic.

5. *Haemolysins*

The clearly defined zones of complete haemolysis that develop around colonies of some bacteria grown on blood agar media are referred to as zones of β-haemolysis. This effect is classically associated with β-haemolytic streptococci grown on horse blood agar, but β-haemolysis is also produced by other species if they are cultured on a suitable blood agar medium under suitable conditions.

The term "α-haemolysis" denotes a greenish discolouration of blood agar medium around a colony and this is typically produced by streptococci of the viridans group. In α-haemolysis, the red cells are incompletely lysed and the edge of the zone of discoloration is not clearly defined.

An intermediate and rather indeterminate haemolytic effect in which there is an ill-defined zone of alteration of the blood agar, without discolouration, is term α' (alpha prime) haemolysis. In areas of α' haemolysis, residual apparently unaltered red cells may be seen with the microscope.

The misleading term "γ-haemolysis" is sometimes used to describe the absence of effect around non-haemolytic colonies on blood agar.

Haemolytic effects produced by bacteria grown on blood agar culture media are not invariably caused by a soluble haemolysin. Soluble haemolysins are best demonstrated in tube tests in which serial dilutions of the product derived from a suitable fluid culture are mixed with volumes of a suspension of red cells. The choice of diluent, the species of red cell and the nature of the red cell suspending liquid greatly influence the result of the test.

The diluent is usually physiological saline or a suitably buffered isotonic solution supplemented with any factors that may be critical for the test system. For example, some haemolysins are oxygen labile and it is essential to perform the tests under reducing conditions. In these circumstances a phosphate buffer incorporating thioglycollic acid is recommended (see Report, 1959).

It should be noted that some haemolysins are calcium-dependent and will be inhibited in the presence of a buffer containing phosphate or citrate. The selected diluent may also incorporate plasma albumen or gelatin as a protective agent. A simple diluent for general use is a solution containing $CaCl_2$ and gelatin in physiological saline ("Cagsal": Brooks, Sterne and Warrack, 1957); this contains per litre: 45·5 ml of 1% $CaCl_2$, 9 g NaCl, 40 ml of 5% gelatin, and 1 g phenol.

The red cell suspension. Red cells of different species differ widely in their relative sensitivities to bacterial haemolysins. Test suspensions of a susceptible species of red cell are usually made by repeatedly washing the red cells derived from citrated, oxalated or heparinized whole blood with isotonic saline. The red cells are resuspended in saline or buffer to a concentration that may vary from 1–5% (v/v) and are stored at 4°C for a period that should not exceed 1 week. Suspensions that show traces of lysis should not be used.

The test. Serial dilutions of the culture product are made in a diluent that is suitable for the particular test system and equal volumes of the red cell suspension are added. The mixtures are shaken and incubated for 1 h in a waterbath at 37°C when preliminary readings may be taken. The tests are then chilled overnight at 4°C before final observations of the degree of haemolysis are made (complete, almost complete, definite, doubtful or negative) in comparison with a negative control. More critical readings may be made by preparing control suspensions with graded degrees of haemolysis and these may be compared with the test series by naked-eye examination or by spectrophotometric or colorimetric procedures. Some haemo-lysins exhibit a so-called "hot-cold" phenomenon whereby the lytic activity observed after the incubation period at 37°C is greatly increased when the tests have been chilled.

6. *Phosphatase*

The test is carried out by adding 1 ml of 1·0% filter-sterilized solution of the sodium salt of phenolphthalein diphosphate to 100 ml of an appropriate nutrient agar at 45°C immediately prior to pouring into Petri plates. After incubation of the surface inoculated plates, one drop of 0·880 sp. gr. ammonia is placed in the lid of the inverted plate. Colonies liberating free phenolphthalein by phosphatase activity turn pink when exposed to the ammonia.

VI. COMBINED TESTS AND COMPOSITE TEST MEDIA

Although some of the test systems described above, such as the "stormy clot" reaction in litmus milk, depend upon and demonstrate linked bio-chemical reactions, combined test media may be deliberately contrived to demonstrate multiple reactions. Thus, the same test medium may well be used for the demonstration of gelatin liquefaction and H_2S production. Shaw and Clarke (1955) developed a test medium for the combined detec-tion of malonate utilization and phenylalanine deamination (see p. 6). The composite media developed by Gillies (1956) for the preliminary identifica-tion of enterobacteria provide good illustrations of this approach success-fully applied to routine testing. Willis and Hobbs (1959) similarly developed complex media for the identification of clostridia (see Willis, this series, Volume 3B). It should be borne in mind that the interpretation of fairly variable reactions involving several biological substrates may be less straightforward if the substrates are combined in one medium. For this reason, bacteriologists often prefer to use the simpler test systems that are available. While this view is reasonable if ill-defined substrates such as egg-yolk or milk are necessarily used, the development of useful complex test media with defined substrates will greatly facilitate routine test procedures.

ACKNOWLEDGMENT

The authors acknowledge with thanks the helpful observations and advice afforded by many colleagues during the preparation of this chapter.

REFERENCES

Barer, Gwendoline (1946). *Mon. Bull. Minist. Hlth. Lab. Serv.*, **5**, 28–29.
Barritt, M. M. (1936). *J. Path. Bact.*, **42**, 441–454.
Bernearts, M. J., and De Ley, J. (1963). *Nature, Lond.*, **197**, 406–407.

Board, R. G., and Holding, A. J. (1960). *J. Appl. Bact.*, **23**, xi.

Bowers, E. F., and Jeffries, L. R. (1955). *J. Clin. Path.*, **8**, 58–60.

Brooks, Elizabeth M., Sterne, M., and Warrack, G. Harriet (1957). *J. Path Bact.*, **74**, 185–195.

Cassidy, J. T., Jourdian, G. W., and Roseman, S. (1966). *In* "Methods in Enzymology", Vol. 8, Complex carbohydrates, Ed. by Elizabeth F. Neufeld and V. Ginsburg. (Editors in Chief: S. P. Colowick and N. O. Kaplan). Academic Press, New York and London, p. 680–685.

Christensen, W. B. (1946). *J. Bact.*, **52**, 461–466.

Christensen, W. B. (1949). Res. Bull. No. 1, Lab. Div., Weld County Hlth. Dept., Greeley, Colorado, U.S.A., p. 1–14.

Cohen-Bazire, G., Sistrom, W. R., and Stanier, R. Y. (1957). *J. Cell. Comp. Physiol.*, **49**, 25–68.

Collee, J. G. (1965). *J. Path. Bact.*, **90**, 13–30.

Collee, J. G., and Barr, W. A. (1968). *J. Path. Bact.*, **96**, 184–185.

Collins, C. H. (1967). "Microbiological Methods", 2nd ed. p. 137. Butterworths, London.

Cowan, S. T., and Steel, K. J. (1965). Manual for the identification of medical bacteria. Cambridge University Press.

Cruickshank, R. (1965). "Medical Microbiology", 11th ed. E. & S. Livingstone, Edinburgh and London.

Downie, A. W., Stent, Lois, and White, S. M. (1931). *Br. J. Exp. Path.*, **12**, 1–9.

Edwards, P. R., and Ewing, W. H. (1962). Identification of Enterobacteriaceae, 2nd ed. Burgess Publishing Co., Minneapolis.

Elek, S. D. (1959). "*Staphylococcus pyogenes* and its relation to disease", p. 209. E. & S. Livingstone, Edinburgh and London.

Gaby, W. L., and Hadley, C. (1957). *J. Bact.*, **74**, 356–358.

Gadalla, M. S. A., and Collee, J. G. (1968). *J. Path. Bact.*, **96**, 169–185.

Gemmell, Margaret, and Hodgkiss, W. (1964). *J. Gen. Microbiol.*, **35**, 519–526.

Gillies, R. R. (1956). *J. Clin. Path.*, **9**, 368–371.

Haynes, W. C. (1951). *J. Gen. Microbiol.*, **5**, 939–950.

Holding, A. J. (1960). *J. Appl. Bact.*, **23**, 515–525.

Hugh, R., and Leifson, E. (1953). *J. Bact.*, **66**, 24–26.

Jeffries, C. D., Holtman, D. F., and Guse, D. G. (1957). *J. Bact.*, **73**, 590–591.

Kohn, J. (1953). *J. Clin. Path.*, **6**, 249.

Koser, S. A. (1923). *J. Bact.*, **8**, 493–520.

Kovacs, N. (1956). *Nature, Lond.*, **178**, 703.

Lautrop, H. (1956). *Acta Path. Microbiol. Scand.*, **39**, 357–369.

Lingappa, Y., and Lockwood, J. L. (1961). *Nature, Lond.*, **189**, 158–159.

Lowe, G. H. (1962). *J. Med. Lab. Tech.*, **19**, 21–25.

Møller, V. (1955). *Acta Path. Microbiol. Scand.*, **36**, 158–172.

Oakley, C. L., and Warrack, G. Harriet (1951). *J. Path. Bact.*, **63**, 45–55.

O'Meara, R. A. Q. (1931). *J. Path. Bact.*, **34**, 401–406.

Oterholm, A., and Ordal, Z. J. (1966). *J. Dairy Sci.*, **49**, 1281–1284.

Pankhurst, Eileen S. (1965). *J. Appl. Bact.*, **28**, 309–315.

Paton, A. M. (1959). *Nature, Lond.*, **183**, 1812–1813.

Report (1959). Assoc. Clin. Path. Broadsheet No. 25 New Series, December.

Rogers, K. B., and Taylor, Joan (1961). *Bull. World Hlth. Org.*, **24**, 59–71.

Shaw, Constance, and Clarke, Patricia H. (1955). *J. Gen. Microbiol.*, **13**, 155–161.

Sierra, G. (1957). *Antonie van Leeuwenhoek J. Microbiol. Serol.*, **23**, 15–22.

Simmons, J. S. (1926). *J. Infect. Dis.*, **39**, 209–214.
Skinner, F. E. (1960). *J. Gen. Microbiol.*, **22**, 539–554.
Stanier, R. Y., Palleroni, N. J., and Doudoroff, M. (1966). *J. Gen. Microbiol.*, **43**, 159–271.
Stewart, D. J. (1965). *J. Gen. Microbiol.*, **41**, 169–174.
Thirst, M. L. (1957). *J. Gen. Microbiol.*, **17**, 390–395.
Thornley, M. J. (1960). *J. Appl. Bact.*, **23**, 37–52.
Warrack, G. Harriet, Bidwell, Ethel, and Oakley, C. L. (1951). *J. Path. Bact.*, **63**, 293–302.
Warren, L. (1959). *J. Biol. Chem.*, **234**, 1971–1975.
Whittenbury, R. (1963). *J. Gen. Microbiol.*, **32**, 375–384.
Whittenbury, R. (1964). *J. Gen. Microbiol.*, **35**, 13–26.
Wieringa, K. T. (1947). *Congr. Int. Microbiol.*, *Copenhagen*, **4**, 482–483.
Willis, A. T., and Hobbs, G. (1959). *J. Path. Bact.*, **77**, 511–521.
Willis, A. T., and Turner, G. C. (1962). *J. Path. Bact.*, **84**, 337–347.

CHAPTER II

Enzymic Tests With Resting Cells and Cell-free Extracts

K. Kersters and J. De Ley

Laboratory for Microbiology, Faculty of Sciences, State University, Gent, Belgium

I. INTRODUCTION

Bacterial taxonomy is going through a phase of upheaval and renewal by the application of two main new concepts, one genotypic (DNA base composition and hybridization), and one phenotypic (numerical analysis). In the latter method, a vast number of phenotypic features of many strains are compared. It represents a considerable improvement over the orthodox methods, in which only a few tests are employed. One of the weaknesses of numerical analysis is that most of the physiological and biochemical tests give no information on the underlying enzymic mechanisms. In many classical tests, the bacteria are grown or incubated for several days in complex media. The resulting alterations are often due to a series of enzymes acting on several substrates. Likewise, a positive reaction in a test given by different organisms does not necessarily imply that the same enzymes are involved,

3

and, in fact, different enzymic pathways are quite often followed. Neverthe-less, these tests are scored with equal weight for numerical analysis. The first part of our article describes several simple biochemical tests, performed with resting cells, giving a reasonable certainty that only one enzyme is involved. They are often modifications of classical biochemical tests, meeting the following requirements—

1. Using pure substrates, they should permit the detection of a single enzyme.
2. The tests should be completed within a few hours.
3. The procedure should be simple enough to apply to a large number of enzymes and cultures.

Owing to the large number of enzymes in the cell, their complex inter-actions, permeability factors, etc., resting cells can be used only in a limited number of cases for the reliable identification of single enzymes. In most cases, it is necessary to disrupt the cell structure, to work with cell-free extracts and to impose conditions such that only a selected enzyme system will be detected. This is really nothing more than ordinary enzymological work. In principle, a section on enzyme tests with cell-free bacterial extracts is redundant, because the information and recipes are available, e.g., in *Methods in Enzymology* (Ed. S. P. Colowick and N. O. Kaplan, Academic Press, 10 volumes) and in Bergmeyer (1962). The taxonomist, interested in determining many features of many strains, wants quick, easy, reliable and specific reactions. Unfortunately, several enzyme reactions are complex, time consuming or require expensive or unusual equipment. They are intended more for the enzymologist than for the practicing taxonomist. A whole area is still open for the inventive biochemist and bacteriologist to adapt the existing recipes as simple, rapid techniques. Some of these have been developed in our laboratory; they concern the detection of particulate and of soluble, coenzyme-linked dehydrogenases, as well as the enzyme systems of the Entner–Doudoroff pathway. They are presented here as examples of the many services that can still be rendered to bacterial taxonomy.

II. TESTS WITH INTACT CELLS

A. Oxidase

The oxidase test is particularly valuable for differentiating pseudomonads from certain other Gram-negative rods. It is also useful in distinguishing *Aeromonas* and *Aeromonas*-like cultures from members of the family of Enterobacteriaceae (Ewing and Johnson, 1960; Steel, 1961). The oxidase test is probably based on the presence of the cytochrome c-cytochrome oxidase system.

Two modifications of the oxidase test are currently employed.

1. *Oxidase test according to Kovacs* (1956)

(a) *Principle.* Tetramethyl-*p*-phenylenediamine is oxidized by the cyto-chrome *c*–cytochrome oxidase system to a purple compound, probably Würster's blue, according to the following reaction—

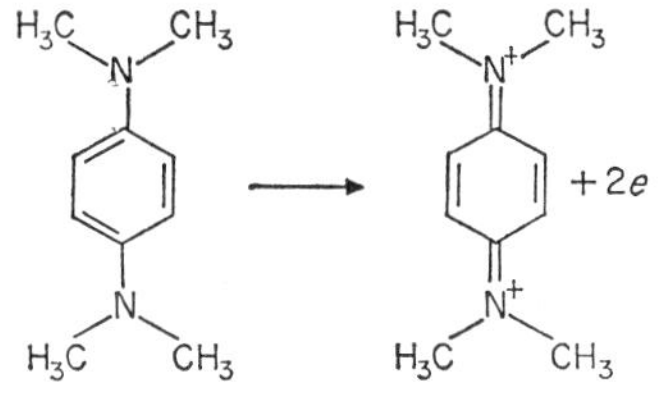

Tetramethyl-*p*-phenylenediamine   Würster's blue

(b) *Test reagent.* This is 1% (w/w) aqueous solution of tetramethyl-*p*-phenylenediamine. The solution may be kept in a dark bottle up to 2 weeks in the refrigerator.

(c) *Procedure.* Soak a strip of filter paper with 2–3 drops of the reagent. Smear a loopful of bacteria from a young slope culture on the moist area. It is important to use a platinum loop, since traces of iron interfere in this reaction. A deep purple colour is produced within 5–10 sec by oxidase positive cultures. Any purple colour development after 60 sec is disregarded. From the enzymological point of view, this decision can be misleading: a "negative" result to the test implies that the enzyme system is absent, which is not always true; the enzyme may be weakly or very weakly active. It is also possible to pour the reagent over the surface of a culture grown on agar in a Petri dish. Oxidase-positive colonies will develop a pink colour, which becomes successively dark red, purple and black in 10–30 min.

2. *The cytochrome oxidase test of Gaby and Hadley* (1957) *modified by Ewing and Johnson* (1960)

(a) *Principle.* The appearance of a blue colour (indophenol blue) on addition of aqueous dimethyl-*p*-phenylenediamine oxalate and ethanolic α-naphthol solutions indicates the presence of cytochrome oxidase.

(b) *Test reagents.* These are 1% (w/w) aqueous dimethyl-*p*-phenylenedi-amine oxalate and 1% (w/w) ethomoric α-paphthol. The micro-organisms are grown on nutrient agar slants for approximately 20 h.

(c) *Procedure.* After incubation, introduce 2–3 drops of each reagent in the slant culture. Tilt the tube so that the reagents are mixed and flow over the growth on the slants. Positive results are indicated by the development of an intense blue colour within 30 sec. Any doubtful or very weak reaction that occurs after 2 min is disregarded.

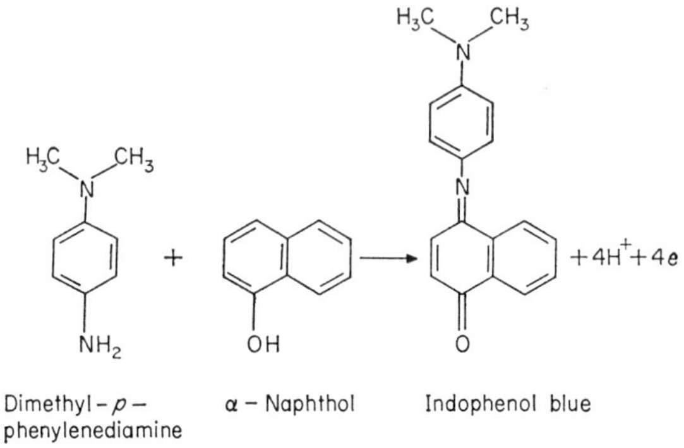

H₃C   CH₃

H₃C   CH₃

$$+ \quad \longrightarrow \quad +4H^+ + 4e$$

NH₂   OH   O

Dimethyl-*p*-phenylenediamine   α – Naphthol   Indophenol blue

The oxidase test can also be performed on reagent-impregnated paper strips (PathoTec-CO, Warner–Chilcott, Morris Plains, N.J., U.S.A.). This PathoTec-CO test is based on the same chemical reaction as described above. Narayan *et al.* (1967) have compared the PathoTec-CO test with the classical Kovac's oxidase test in 91 isolates. The correlation between both methods was excellent.

B. Catalase

(Hydrogen peroxide–hydrogen peroxide oxidoreductase: 1.11.1.6)

The test is valuable for differentiating, for example, lactic acid bacteria and many anaerobes (catalase negative) from other micro-organisms.

1. *Principle*

Catalase catalyses the reaction—

$$2H_2O_2 \rightarrow 2H_2O + O_2$$

2. *Test reagent*

10% hydrogen peroxide.

3. *Procedure*

Flood a plate culture of the organism in question with the H_2O_2 solution. Alternatively a drop of the reagent is placed on top of one or a few colonies. Development of gas bubbles is watched with a magnifying glass.

Mix 1 ml of H_2O_2 solution with 1 ml of culture withdrawn from a broth culture.

The evolution of gas bubbles, caused by the liberation of free oxygen, indicates the presence of catalase in the culture.

C. Urease

(Urea amidohydrolase: 3.5.1.5.)

Urease is characteristically produced by *Proteus*. *Klebsiella* and *Enterobacter* generally give a weak positive reaction.

In the classical urease test bacteria are inoculated on urea agar tubes of Christensen (1946) and incubated for 24 h. The colour change of the indicator is then recorded.

Reagent-impregnated paper strips are manufactured (PathoTec-U) for the quick detection of urease in intact, resting cells.

1. *Principle of the PathoTec–urease test*

Urease catalyses the reaction—

$$H_2NCONH_2 + H_2O \rightarrow 2NH_3 + CO_2$$

The formation of ammonia produces a rise in pH and a pink to red colour with phenolphthalein indicator, which is incorporated in the paper strip.

2. *Material*

PathoTec-U paper strips.

3. *Procedure*

Suspend a heavy loopful of the culture to be tested (grown overnight on, for example, a nutrient agar slant) in 0·2 ml saline in a small test tube. Insert a PathoTec-U test paper and incubate the test tube for 2 h in a water bath of appropriate temperature (37°C for Enterobacteriaceae). A positive reaction is indicated by a pink to red colour of the indicator.

4. *Comments*

Narayan *et al.* (1967) have compared the classical urease test according to Christensen (1946) with the PathoTec-U filter-paper test. Of the 67 isolates that were tested, 18 gave a false negative reaction in the PathoTec-U test. These strains belonged to the *Citrobacter* and *Enterobacter* groups. The correlation was however perfect for all *Proteus* strains. The so-called false negative results would imply that the PathoTec-U test is less sensitive than the classical Christensen (1946) test. It can however not be excluded that in these cases the classical test would be false positive, owing to the many side reactions that can interfere in Christensen (1946) medium. Further investigation is needed to explain the discrepancies.

D. Amino-acid Decarboxylases

(Amino-acid carboxylases: 4.1.1)

A detailed procedure will not be given here (see Holding and Collee, this Volume, p. 1). Some of the existing methods will be briefly discussed.

Amino-acid decarboxylases are currently used in the biochemical diagnosis of the Enterobacteriaceae. These tests are particularly important for the identification of *Salmonella*. The Møller (1955) method is normally used as the standard method for taxonomic work. The bacteria are incubated for several days in a medium containing indicator and one of the following basic amino-acids: arginine, L-lysine or L-ornithine (for full details, see Holding and Collee, this Volume, p. 1). Decarboxylation results in the formation of a diamine, which produces a rise in pH and a colour change of the indicator. The Møller method for lysine decarboxylase has recently been adapted as a quick paper-strip test for the presumptive identification of *Salmonella* (PathoTec-LD). The lysine present in the strip is decarboxylated by the enzyme to produce the diamine cadaverine with a rise in pH and a resulting blue colour of bromthymol blue according to the following reaction—

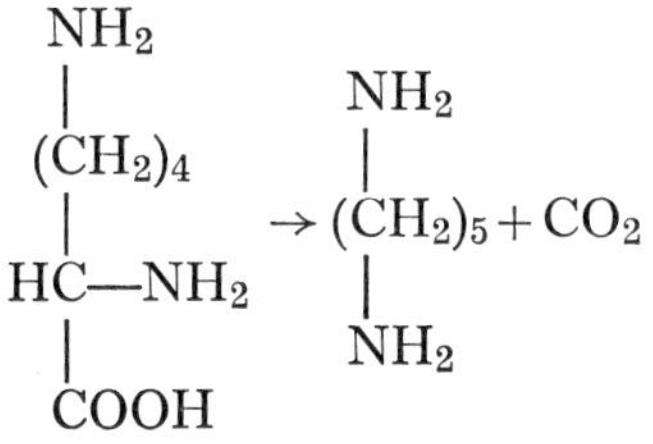

$$\begin{array}{c} NH_2 \\ | \\ (CH_2)_4 \\ | \\ HC-NH_2 \\ | \\ COOH \\ \text{L-Lysine} \end{array} \rightarrow \begin{array}{c} NH_2 \\ | \\ (CH_2)_5 \\ | \\ NH_2 \\ \text{Cadaverine} \end{array} + CO_2$$

The PathoTec-LD paper strips contain lysine and lactose, which should make this test more specific for *Salmonella* (lysine decarboxylase +, lactose −). Under these circumstances a negative lysine decarboxylase test is indeed manifested by typical *Escherichia coli, Klebsiella* and *Aerobacter aerogenes*, which produce lysine decarboxylase but ferment lactose. The alkalinity, due to the formation of cadaverine, is counteracted by the production of acids from lactose. The pH decreases and the colour changes to yellow.

Narayan *et al.* (1967) have compared the paper-strip lysine decarboxylase test with the classical decarboxylase test in 59 bacterial strains. Several discrepancies were observed: the PathoTec-LD papers gave rise to many false positive and a few false negative results. These apparent shortcomings of the paper strips interfered with a reliable identification of *Salmonella*-like Enterobacteriaceae.

The classical decarboxylase test has undoubtedly a great diagnostic value, but it is nevertheless obvious that the pH changes in both methods are not always exclusively the result of the amino-acid decarboxylase. Too many side reactions can indeed interfere and produce significant pH shifts. Diamine oxidase, arginase, arginine dihydrolase, deaminases, urease, etc., can theoretically act as strongly interfering enzymes. Amino-acid decarboxylases can only be determined unequivocally by manometric measurement of the CO_2 production or identification and assay of the reaction products (cadaverine, agmatine and putrescine).

E. Biochemical paper-disc tests

Clarke and Steel (1966) have developed several rapid and simple biochemical tests that can be used for bacterial identifications. Tests for esterase, glycoside hydrolase, tryptophanase and amino-acid oxidase will be described.

In contrast to the classical biochemical tests, the results with these paper-impregnated tests can be recorded after a maximum incubation of 2 h.

1. *General principle*

The test substrate is applied in the form of a paper disc on the surface of a nutrient agar plate. The cultures are incubated for a short time, depending upon the type of reaction under investigation. Enzyme activity is detected by using chromogenic substrates or by adding a reagent that reacts with the product of enzymic reaction to form a coloured compound.

2. *Cultures*

Grow the bacteria overnight on the surface of agar plates with suitable growth medium by spreading 0·2 ml of a broth culture over the agar surface.

3. *Preparation of paper discs*

Soak Whatman 3 MM paper in a substrate solution of appropriate concentration. After impregnation, cut the paper into discs of about 1 sq. cm. Store the paper discs in screw-cap bottles at room temperature. It is also possible to apply 5–25 μl of substrate solution to the discs with a micropipette.

4. *Esterases and lipases*

(Carboxylic ester hydrolase: 3.1.1.1)

(a) *Substrate.* Indoxyl acetate (0·05 mg/disc) applied from alcoholic solution. Other chromogenic substrates are available, e.g., indoxyl butyrate, β-naphthyl acetate, p-nitrophenyl laurate, caprylate β-naphthylester; laurate β-naphthylester.

(b) *Principle and procedure.* Certain esterases hydrolyse indoxyl acetate rapidly to indoxyl, which is spontaneously oxidized in air to indigo, which has a deep blue colour. Place the indoxyl acetate-containing paper disc on top of the growth on the agar plate. The colour reaction develops within a few minutes with cultures possessing a high esterase activity. Analogous tests for esterases in liquid medium were described by Bürger (1967a).

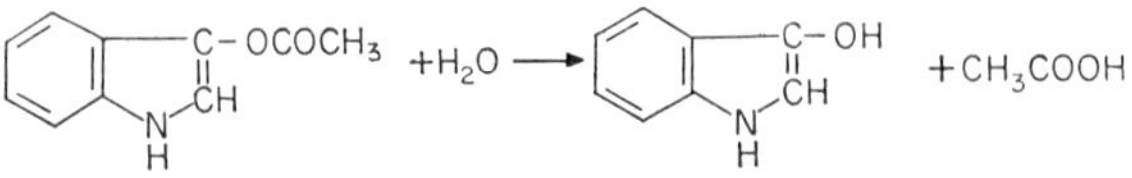

Indoxyl acetate   Indoxyl

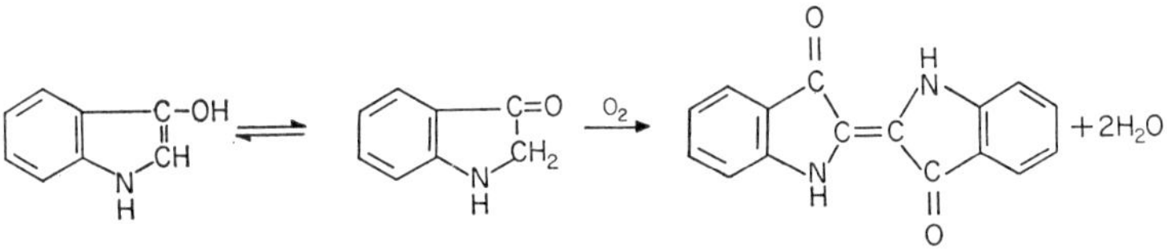

Indoxyl (enol)   Indoxyl (keto)   Indigo

5. *Tryptophanase* (*indole production*)

Indol production is used as diagnostic character for differentiating members of the Enterobacteriaceae.

(a) *Substrate and reagent.* Tryptophan (disc soaked in 1% (w/w) aqueous solution); Kovacs's (1928) reagent (5% (w/w) *p*-dimethylaminobenzaldehyde in 75 ml isopentanol + 25 ml concentrated HCl).

(b) *Principle and procedure.* Tryptophanase catalyses the following reaction—

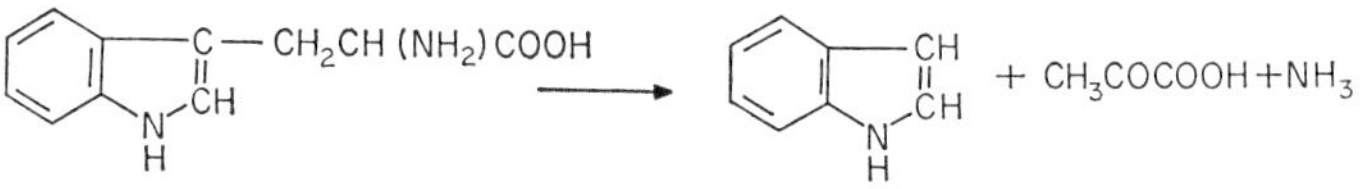

L–Tryptophan   Indole   Pyruvic acid

Incubate the disc on the nutrient agar plate for 2 h at the optimum growth temperature of the organism. Growth in the presence of glucose suppresses the formation of tryptophanase (Clarke and Cowan, 1952). After incubation, carry out the indole test by adding 1 drop of Kovacs's (1928) reagent. With positive cultures, the condensation of indole and *p*-dimethylaminobenzaldehyde yields a quinoidal red–violet compound. The colour is not stable and fades after about 15 min.

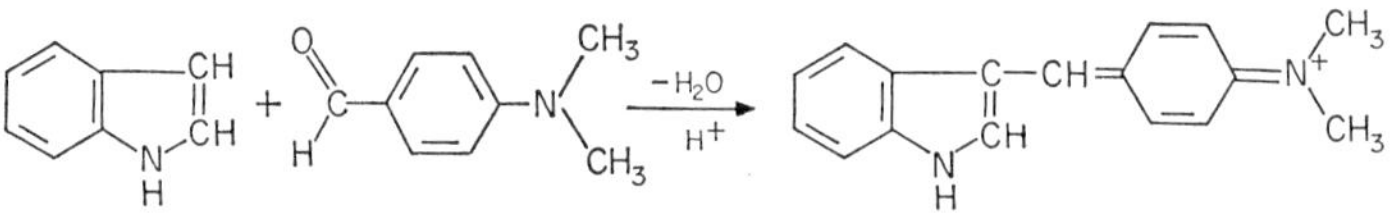

Indole   *p*-Dimethylaminobenzaldehyde

6. *Amino-acid oxidases*

(Amino-acid–oxygen oxidoreductase (deaminating): 1.4.3.2 and 1.4.3.3), e.g., L-phenylalanine oxidase.

The detection of phenylalanine deaminase is an important diagnostic biochemical reaction for the differentiation of the *Proteus-Providence* group from other Enterobacteriaceae.

(a) *Substrate and reagent.* L-Phenylalanine (disc soaked in 1% (w/w) aqueous solution); 10% (w/w) $FeCl_3$ in 0·1M HCl.

(b) *Principle and procedure.* Phenylalanine is oxidatively deaminated according to the following reaction—

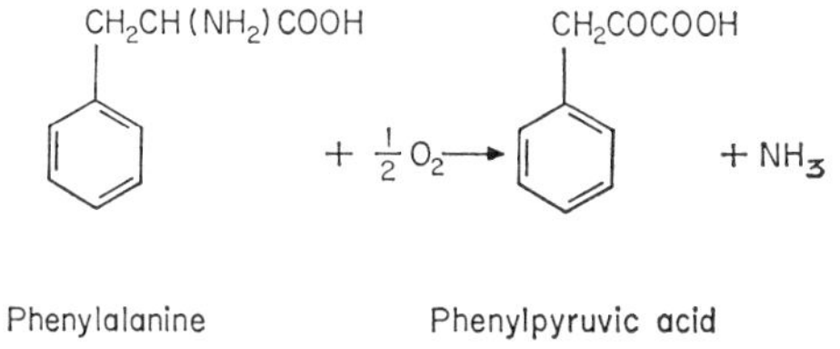

$$CH_2CH(NH_2)COOH \qquad CH_2COCOOH$$

Phenylalanine   Phenylpyruvic acid

Phenylpyruvic acid produces a characteristic deep green–blue colour with $FeCl_3$ in acid solution. The phenylalanine disc is incubated for 2 h on the agar plate. Phenylpyruvic acid is detected by adding one drop of $FeCl_3$ solution. A deep green–blue colour develops in about 1 min with positive cultures. This test can also be adapted to measure the oxidative deamination of other amino-acids, since most α-keto-acids give coloured complexes with ferric ions. Phenylalanine deaminase can even be detected in 10 min by the use of reagent-impregnated paper strips (PathoTec-PD). Rub a heavy loopful of the culture into an area of about 10 sq. mm of the indicator zone of the PathoTec-PD paper and leave it for 10 min, after which time the development or absence of a brownish to dark grey colour of that area is noted. Narayan *et al.* (1967) compared the classical phenylalanine deaminase test according to Ewing *et al.* (1957) with the quick reagent-impregnated PathoTec-PD paper strip test, and found an excellent correlation.

7. *Glycoside hydrolases (3.2.1)*

For example β-galactosidase (β-D-galactoside galactohydrolase: 3.2.1.23).

To detect an inducible enzyme, such as β-galactosidase, it is necessary to use a medium that encourages the synthesis of this enzyme. Therefore Clarke and Steel (1966) recommend the addition of a lactose-impregnated disc to the agar plate, followed after 2 h by a disc impregnated with the chromogenic substrate, *o*-nitrophenyl-β-D-galactoside, which is a substrate but not an inducer of the enzyme.

(a) *Inducer.* Lactose (15 mg/disc).

(b) *Substrate.* o-Nitrophenyl-β-D-galactoside (0·1 mg/disc).

(c) *Principle and procedure.* β-Galactosidase hydrolyses the chromogenic substrate, o-nitrophenyl-β-D-galactoside, producing yellow o-nitrophenol—

o - Nitrophenyl-β-D-galactoside β-D-Galactose o-Nitrophenol

Apply the inducer disc to the plate culture grown overnight, which is then incubated at the optimum growth temperature for 2 h to induce β-galactosidase. The substrate disc is then applied overlapping the lactose disc. With positive cultures the colour reaction develops after about 15 min.

Analogous simple tests in liquid medium were described by Lapage and Jayaraman (1964) and Bürger (1967a). The following glycosides can also be used for detecting β-D-glucosidases: aesculin, arbutin, D-salicin and indoxyl-β-D-glucoside.

F. Deoxyribonuclease

(Deoxyribonucleate oligonucleotido hydrolase: 3.1.4.5)

Most *Serratia* strains produce extracellular deoxyribonuclease. According to Rothberg and Schwartz (1965) this enzyme provides an auxilliary biochemical test for identifying non-pigmented *Serratia* strains. An extracellular deoxyribonuclease was not detected in *E. coli, Proteus, Klebsiella, Salmonella, Shigella*, the *Providence* group (Rothberg and Schwartz, 1965) and *Paracolobactrum* (Valu, 1966).

1. *Principle*

Deoxyribonuclease is determined according to the DNA–agar method of Jeffries *et al.* (1957). The micro-organisms are inoculated on an agar medium containing 2 mg DNA/ml. The enzymatic activity is assayed after incubation by flooding the plate with 1M HCl. This causes the DNA in the agar to form a diffuse, cloudy precipitate throughout the plate. A distinct clear zone is observed around the colonies which produce an extracellular deoxyribonuclease.

2. *Materials*

Deoxyribonuclease test agar (Difco) or any complex medium that produces good growth of the organisms under investigation, supplemented with

0·2% (w/w) DNA (from calf thymus or bull sperm; Sigma Chemical Co., St. Louis, Mo., U.S.A., or Worthington, Freehold, N.J., U.S.A.).

1M HCl.

3. *Procedure*

Inoculate heavy streaks of bacteria on the agar plates, and incubate them at 30°C for 18–36 h. Assay enzyme activity by flooding the plate with 1M HCl. A cloudy precipitate is formed in all parts of the plates, except where deoxyribonuclease is formed. The width of the clear zone is related to the amount of extracellular enzyme produced.

G. Arylsulphatase

(Arylsulphate sulphohydrolase: 3.1.6.1)

1. *Principle*

Arylsulphatase can be detected in dense suspensions of resting cells according to the method of Bürger (1967b). Arylsulphatase hydrolyses *p*-nitrophenylsulphate to *p*-nitrophenol, which is yellow in alkaline conditions—

p–Nitrophenylsulphate   p–Nitrophenol

It is possible to use other arylsulphates as substrate, e.g., phenolphthalein-disulphate and 2-hydroxy-5-nitrophenylsulphate (Bürger, 1967b).

2. *Reagents*

(a) *Bacterial suspension.* Suspend resting cells, harvested from a suitable solid or liquid medium, in physiological NaCl solution to give a concentration of 4–8 mg dry weight/ml.

(b) *Substrate solution.* 2·5 mM *p*-nitrophenylsulphate (Na or K salt) in 0·5M sodium acetate–acetic acid buffer, pH 5·8.

0·04M glycine–NaOH buffer, pH 10·5.

3. *Procedure*

Mix 0·3 ml of bacterial suspension and 0·3 ml substrate solution. After a maximum incubation of 6 h, the formation of *p*-nitrophenol is detected by the addition of 0·3 ml of glycine buffer. A yellow colour is formed when arylsulphatase is present. The reaction mixture remains colourless when the enzyme is absent.

4. *Sensitivity*

5–10 μg of p-nitrophenol are detectable.

H. Acid Phosphatase

(Orthophosphoric monoester phosphohydrolase: 3.1.3.2)

The presence or absence of phosphatases in dense suspensions of resting cells (4–8 mg dry weight/ml) can be determined according to the method of Bürger (1967a). The following substrates are currently used: α-naphthyl phosphate, p-nitrophenyl phosphate, disodium phenolphthalein diphosphate and ethanolamine–phenolphthalein phosphate. Phosphatase activity on p-nitrophenyl phosphate will be described here.

1. *Principle*

Hydrolysis of p-nitrophenylphosphate yields p-nitrophenol, which is yellow in alkaline solution—

p–Nitrophenylphosphate p–Nitrophenol

2. *Reagents*

0·01M p-nitrophenyl phosphate in 0·1M citrate buffer, pH 4·8.
0·04M glycine–NaOH buffer, pH 10·5.

3. *Procedure*

Mix 0·3 ml of a suspension of resting cells (see Section II G2a) with 0·3 ml of p-nitrophenyl phosphate solution and incubate it for a maximum of 6 h at 37°C. When acid phosphatase is present, a yellow colour will develop on addition of 0·3 ml of glycine–NaOH buffer. The solution remains colourless in the absence of phosphatase.

I. Alkaline Phosphatase

(Orthophosphoric monoester phosphohydrolase: 3.1.3.1)

Alkaline phosphatase can be determined by a procedure similar to that used for acid phosphatase. However, p-nitrophenyl phosphate is dissolved in 0·04M glycine–NaOH buffer, pH 10·5. The incubation mixture being alkaline, no further additions are required to render the product of the reaction visible.

J. Peptidases

(Peptide hydrolases: 3.4)

1. *Principle*

Peptidases can be detected according to the method of Bürger (1967b). The following naphthyl derivatives of amino-acids can be used as substrates: D,L-alanine-β-naphthylamide, L-leucine-β-naphthylamide, L-cystine-di-β-naphthylamide, N-γ-(α-naphthyl)-D,L-glutamine, etc. These naphthyl derivatives are hydrolyzed by peptidases according to the reaction—

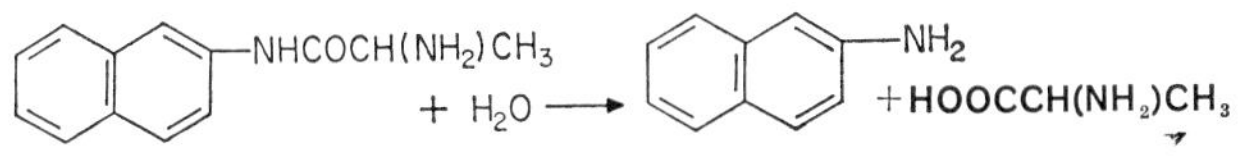

L-Alanine-β-naphthylamide β-Naphthylamine   L-Alanine

The resulting β-naphthylamine is diazotized and then coupled with β-naphthol—

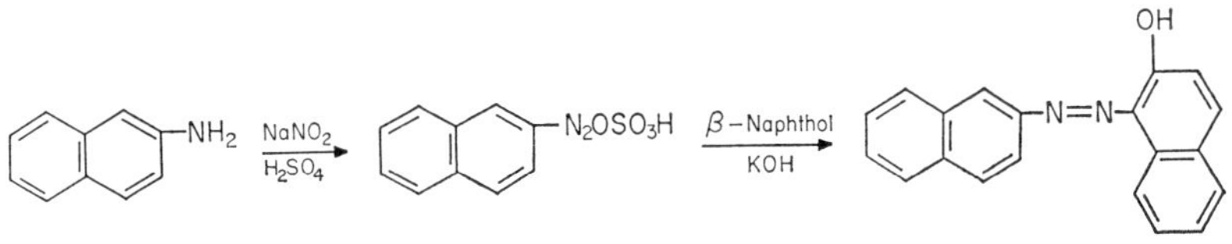

β-Naphthylamine

Orange-red azo dye

2. *Materials and reagents*

Dissolve 30 μmoles of D,L-alanine-β-naphthylamide or other amino acid-β-naphthylamide in 3 ml of 0·1M HCl and add to a mixture of 12 ml of 0·05M Tris buffer, pH 7·05, and 0·15 ml of M KOH. Adjust the pH of the solution to 6·5 with 0·1M KOH.

1·5M H_2SO_4.

4% (w/w) $NaNO_2$ 4M KOH.

4 mM β-naphthol in 0·05M KOH; this solution must be colourless.

3. *Procedure*

Mix 0·3 ml of substrate solution and 0·3 ml of resting cell suspension (see Section II G2a) and incubate it for a maximum of 6 h at 37°C. Thereafter add 0·1 ml of H_2SO_4, 0·2 ml of nitrite solution, 0·1 ml of KOH and 0·1 ml of β-naphthol, in that order, to the reaction mixture. β-Naphthylamine is detected by the formation of an orange–red colour 1–2 min after addition of the reagents. When peptidase is absent the solution remains yellow.

4. Sensitivity

20 μg of β-Naphthylamine produces an orange, 50 μg orange–red and 75 μg a red colour.

III. TESTS WITH CELL-FREE EXTRACTS

A. Fluorescence test of NAD- and NADP-linked dehydrogenases

1. Principle

Determinations of nicotinamide-linked dehydrogenases are usually based on the optical density at 340 nm or the fluorescence of the reduced cofactors, and are thus carried out spectrophoto- or fluorimetrically. The presence or absence of several nicotinamide-linked dehydrogenases in bacterial extracts can, however, be determined by a simple spot test on paper (Kersters, 1967), which is based on the fluorescence of NADH and NADPH.

The enzyme reaction is carried out on filter paper, which is then viewed in ultraviolet light. The activity of a given dehydrogenase is identified by the appearance of bright spots on a dark background resulting from the formation of the reduced cofactor.

2. Materials and reagents

Whatman No. 1 or similar filter paper sheets (20 × 20 cm); Tris–HCl buffer, 0·2M, pH 8·0, containing 10^{-3}M $MgCl_2$; 0·025M NAD and NADP solutions in 0·2M Tris buffer (the final pH is about 5·0); 0·4M substrate solutions in distilled water (glucose-6-phosphate, gluconate-6-phosphate, sugars, sugar alcohols, malate, iso-citrate, lactate, etc.); "soluble enzyme" fractions of the cell-free extract (5–10 mg protein/ml).

Prepare cell-free extracts by suspending 10 g of washed log-phase cells in 30 ml of 0·01 M phosphate buffer, pH 7·0, and disrupting them in a sonic oscillator for 10–20 min at 4°C. The cells can also be disrupted by other means, such as grinding with alumina or glass beads, rupture in a French pressure cell etc. (see Hughes et al., Volume 5B, p1).

Intact cells and large pieces of débris are removed by centrifugation at 15,000 g for 15 min at 4°C. The turbid supernatant is then centrifuged for 2h at 4°C and 105,000 g in an ultracentrifuge. The supernatant of this sedimentation contains the NAD- and NADP-linked dehydrogenases. This fraction will be called "soluble enzyme", and can usually be stored without loss for 2–4 days at −12°C. The gelatinous, brown–red precipitate contains the particulate oxidative enzymes (see Section IIIB). Centrifugation of the cell-free extract at 105,000 g is necessary to remove the particle-bound NADH oxidase, which interferes in the fluorescence spot test.

3. *Procedure*

Soak the sheets of filter paper for a few seconds in 0·2M Tris–HCl buffer, pH 8·0, containing 10^{-3}M $MgCl_2$, and air-dry them. Divide the buffered filter paper with the aid of a pencil into 1×1 cm squares. Pipette 1 μl of substrate solution onto the intersection of the pencil lines. The resulting spot, 4 mm in diameter, contains 0·4 μmole of substrate. One buffered 20×20 cm Whatman-1 paper can thus receive approximately 18 rows of 18 spots each of 18 different substrates. These "reagent papers" can be prepared in advance and are stable for at least 1 month when stored at $-12°C$ in dry, well closed containers. Just before assaying, mix 0·06 ml of soluble enzyme (5–10 mg/ml) with 0·02 ml of 0·025M NAD or NADH solution. With this mixture, place spots, about 4 mm in diameter, on the pencil-drawn intersections of the reagent paper, so that the whole series of substrates receives one given enzyme–cofactor mixture. Immediately place the paper between two glass plates to prevent evaporation. Press the plates firmly together with the aid of metal clamps. Allow the enzymic reaction on the paper to proceed for 15 min at 25°C, and then air-dry the paper, and view it under an ultraviolet lamp emitting at 360 nm. Fluorescence is quenched when the paper is still wet.

The presence of a given dehydrogenase in the bacterial extract is recognized by a characteristic fluorescent spot on the paper resulting from the reduced cofactor. The intensity of the fluorescence allows a rough estimation of the enzyme activity.

4. *Reliability of the fluorescence spot test*

It was demonstrated (Kersters, 1967) that the agreement between the fluorescence spot test and the classical dehydrogenase assay is excellent.

5. *Sensitivity*

Concentrations as little as 3×10^{-4} μmoles of NADH per spot of 4 mm in diameter produce a distinct fluorescence. The sensitivity of this assay for NAD- and NADP-linked dehydrogenases should prove sufficient for routine determinations.

6. *Limitations of the assay*

Intact cells cannot be used for this procedure, because most dehydrogenases will remain undetected, owing to permeability phenomena. Fluorescence assays with NAD as cofactor cannot be carried out with crude extracts, which usually display a high NADH oxidase activity. NADH oxidase is usually associated with the particulate fractions, however, and is thus removed by the centrifugation at 105,000 *g* (see Section IIIA2). With some bacterial extracts a fluorescence is produced by all the spots, including the blank. This is due to endogenous reduction of the cofactor and can usually be eliminated by appropriate dilution of the soluble enzyme.

B. Assay of particle-linked dehydrogenases

Many bacteria have been reported as oxidizing several organic substances by a particulate fraction of the cell extracts. These particle-linked dehydro-genases have been described in acetic acid bacteria, pseudomonads (De Ley, 1960) and a few other genera of aerobic micro-organisms. It was demon-strated for *Acetobacter liquefaciens* (De Ley and Dochy, 1960) and *Pseudomonas fluorescens* (Burrous and Wood, 1962) that these particles are derived from the cytoplasmic membrane during mechanical or ultrasonic breakage of the cell.

1. *Principle*

The presence of dehydrogenases on the particles is detected by the bleaching of the artificial electron acceptor 2,6-dichlorophenol–indophenol (2,6-D)—

$$\text{Reduced substrate} + 2{,}6\text{-D} \rightarrow \text{oxidized substrate} + \text{leuco-}2{,}6\text{-D}$$

2. *Reagents*

2,6-Dichlorophenol–indophenol (2,6-D) solution, $2 \cdot 5 \times 10^{-4}$M in $0 \cdot 02$M phosphate buffer, pH $6 \cdot 5$ (the solution is filtered and stored at 4°C); $0 \cdot 1$M substrate solutions (e.g., mono- and disaccharides, sugar alcohols, aliphatic alcohols, Krebs cycle intermediates, amino-acids).

Prepare the particles as described in Section IIIA2. Wash them twice with $0 \cdot 01$M phosphate buffer, pH $7 \cdot 0$; they can be stored as a gel without loss of activity for 3–5 days at -12°C.

3. *Procedure*

The test can be carried out for large routine determinations in plastic serological dilution trays, containing 96 cups, $0 \cdot 3$ ml each (Linbro Chemical Co., New Haven, Conn., U.S.A.).

Pipette $0 \cdot 1$ ml of the various substrate solutions in the different cups of the tray. Suspend the washed particles in 2,6-D solution to give a protein con-centration of approximately 5 mg/ml. Pipette $0 \cdot 1$ ml of this mixture into the substrate-containing cups of the tray. The swirl caused by the addition of the dye mixture produces an efficient mixing of the reagents. Cover the tray with a glass plate and incubate at room temperature. Compare the degree of bleaching visually with the blank (no substrate) after 10, 30 and 60 min.

The presence of a given dehydrogenase in the particulate fraction is indicated by the bleaching of the reaction mixture. The rate of bleaching allows a rough estimation of the enzyme activity.

C. Detection of the Enzymes of the Entner–Doudoroff pathway

Some Gram-negative micro-organisms catabolize glucose, mainly via the so-called Entner–Doudoroff pathway (Entner and Doudoroff, 1952), which can be summarized as follows—

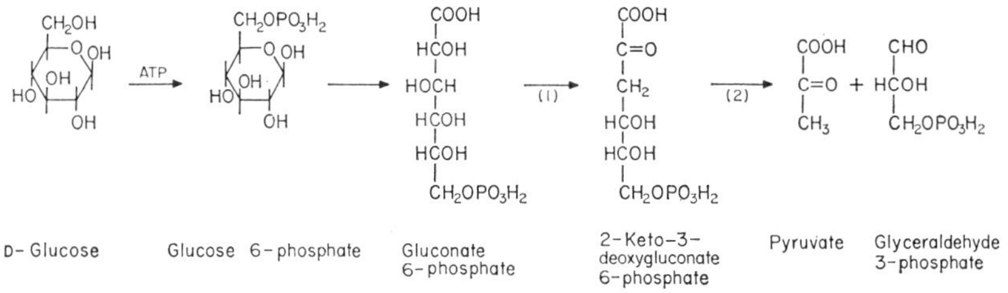

| D- Glucose | Glucose 6-phosphate | Gluconate 6-phosphate | 2–Keto–3– deoxygluconate 6-phosphate | Pyruvate | Glyceraldehyde 3-phosphate |

The key enzymes of this pathway, gluconate 6-phosphate dehydrase (1) and 2-keto-3-deoxygluconate 6-phosphate aldolase (2), respectively catalyse the following reactions—

Gluconate 6-phosphate $\xrightarrow{(1)}$ 2-keto-3-deoxygluconate 6-phosphate $+ H_2O$

2-keto-3-deoxygluconate 6-phosphate $\xrightarrow{(2)}$ pyruvate

$+$ glyceraldehyde 3-phosphate

1. *Principle*

The participation of the Entner–Doudoroff pathway in the overall catabolism of glucose can be detected by tracer techniques (Wang *et al.*, 1958) Cheldelin *et al.*, 1962) or by direct spectrophotometric measurement of the enzymes involved (Meloche and Wood, 1966a; Meloche *et al.*, 1966). These methods, however, require special instruments and/or purified enzymes. We have developed a simple method, based on thin-layer chromatography of the reaction products. The α-keto-acids 2-keto-3-deoxygluconate 6-phosphate and pyruvate are detected by the specific spray reagent o-phenylenediamine. This method detects separately the two key enzymes of the Entner–Doudoroff pathway (Kersters and De Ley, 1968a, b).

2. *Reagents and Materials*

0·2M Tris buffer, pH 7·5, 0·1M sodium gluconate 6-phosphate; 0·1M sodium 2-keto-3-deoxygluconate 6-phosphate (KDPG). (Prepare KDPG enzymatically with KDPG aldolase from *Ps. fluorescens* (Meloche and Wood, 1966b). It is not necessary to use the purified KDPG aldolase for this synthesis. Good yield of KDPG is obtained by performing the synthesis with the soluble enzyme fraction (see Section IIIA2) of *Ps. fluorescens*); 0·06M sodium arsenite, pH 7·5 (this compound inhibits the oxidative decarboxyla-tion of pyruvate); crude bacterial extract, 5–10 mg protein/ml (see Section IIIA2) (both enzymes being inducible, the bacteria should be grown in a gluconate-containing medium: 1% (w/w) calcium gluconate, 0·5% (w/w) peptone and 0·25% (w/w) beef extract or yeast extract). Dowex 50W (H$^+$), X-8; 20–50 mesh; thin-layer chromatography plates, coated with cellulose (MN 300, Macherey and Nagel, Düren, W. Germany), 0·3 mm thickness.

3. *Procedure*

The assay is carried out on a microscale, since the amount of KDPG available is limited. The serological dilution trays with 0·3 ml cups, are well suited for this purpose.

For the assay of gluconate 6-phosphate dehydrase or KDPG aldolase mix the following reagents in a total volume of 30 μl: 10 μl of Tris buffer, 5 μl of sodium arsenite, 5 μl of gluconate 6-phosphate (or 5 μl of KDPG) and 10 μl of crude bacterial extract.

After incubation at room temperature for 60–90 min, add a spatula point of Dowex-50 H$^+$ to the reaction mixture. The precipitated protein does not interfere on the thin-layer chromatograms. Apply 10 μl of the reaction mixtures on a thin-layer plate and develop the chromatogram with the solvent: n-propanol–ammonia (sp. gr. = 0·88)–water (6–3–1 v/v). Tailing can be suppressed by adding 0·1% (w/v) disodium ethylenediaminetetra-acetate. Spray chromatogram with a solution of 0·1% (w/v) *o*-phenylenedi-amine in 10% (w/v) trichloroacetic acid (Wieland and Fischer, 1949) and heat it for 2–3 min at 105°C. View the chromatogram under ultraviolet light (360 nm).

4. *Interpretation*

The R_f values of pyruvate, KDPG and 2-keto-3-deoxygluconate (KDG) are summarized in Table I. The formation of KDG, which is sometimes noticed on the chromatograms is probably due to the dephosphorylation of KDPG by a phosphatase in the microbial extracts.

Gluconate 6-phosphate dehydrase is present in a given bacterial extract when the formation of KDPG is demonstrated on the thin-layer chromato-gram, after incubation with gluconate 6-phosphate. KDPG aldolase is present in a given bacterial extract when the formation of pyruvate and dis-appearance of KDPG is demonstrated on the chromatogram, after incuba-tion with KDPG.

One of the advantages of this method is that only minute amounts (0·5 μmole) of KDPG are required. Under the described circumstances, 0·01 μmole of pyruvate and KDPG produce a distinct fluorescence.

TABLE I

Chromatographic data of intermediates of the Entner–Doudoroff pathway

	R_f values in n-propanol–ammonia–water (6–3–1) + 0·1% EDTA	Fluorescence in ultra-violet light after spraying with o-phenylenediamine –TCA
Pyruvate	0·64	Greenish yellow
KDPG	0·29	Light yellow
KDG	0·54	Light yellow

REFERENCES

Bergmeyer, H. U. (1962). "Methoden der enzymatischen Analyse". Verlag Chemie, Weinheim.
Bürger, H. (1967a). *Zentbl Bakt. ParasitKde, Abt. I, Orig.*, **202**, 97–109.
Bürger, H. (1967b). *Zentbl Bakt. ParasitKde, Abt. I, Orig.*, **202**, 395–401.
Burrous, S. E., and Wood, W. A. (1962). *J. Bact.*, **84**, 364–369.
Cheldelin, V. H., Wang, C. H., and King, T. E. (1962). *In* "Comparative Biochemistry" (Ed. M. Florkin and H. S. Mason), Vol. 3, pp. 427–502. Academic Press, New York.
Christensen, W. B. (1946). *J. Bact.*, **52**, 461–466.
Clarke, P. H., and Cowan, S. T. (1952). *J. gen. Microbiol.*, **6**, 178–197.
Clarke, P. H., and Steel, K. J. (1966). *In* "Identification Methods for Microbiologists" (Ed. B. M. Gibbs and F. A. Skinner), Part A, pp. 111–115. Academic Press, London.
De Ley, J. (1960), *J. appl. Bact.*, **23**, 400–441.
De Ley, J., and Dochy, R. (1960). *Biochim. biophys. Acta*, **40**, 277–289.
Entner, N., and Doudoroff, M. (1952). *J. biol. Chem.*, **196**, 853–862.
Ewing, W. H., Davis, B. R., and Reavis, R. W. (1957). *Publ. Hlth Lab.*, **15**, 153–167.
Ewing, W. H., and Johnson, J. G. (1960). *Int. Bull. bact. Nomencl. Taxon.*, **10**, 223–230.
Gaby, W. L., and Hadley, C. (1957). *J. Bact.*, **74**, 356–358.
Jeffries, C. D., Holtman, D. F., and Guse, D. G. (1957). *J. Bact.*, **73**, 590–591.
Kersters, K. (1967). *Antonie van Leeuwenhoek*, **33**, 63–72.
Kersters, K., and De Ley, J. (1968a). *Antonie van Leeuwenhoek*, **34**, 388–392.
Kersters, K., and De Ley, J. (1968b). *Antonie van Leeuwenhoek*, **34**, 393–408.
Kovacs, N. (1928). *Z. ImmunForsch. exp. Ther.*, **55**, 311–315.
Kovacs, N. (1956). *Nature, Lond.*, **178**, 703.
Lapage, S. P., and Jayaraman, M. S. (1964). *J. clin. Path.*, **17**, 117–123.
Meloche, H. P., and Wood, W. A. (1966a). *In* "Methods in Enzymology" (Ed. W. A. Wood), Vol. 9, pp. 653–656. Academic Press, New York.
Meloche, H. P., and Wood, W. A. (1966b). *In* "Methods in Enzymology" (Ed. W. A. Wood), Vol. 9, p. 51–53. Academic Press, New York.
Meloche, H. P., Ingram, J. M., and Wood, W. A. (1966). *In* "Methods in Enzymology" (Ed. W. A. Wood), Vol. 9, pp. 520–524. Academic Press, New York.
Møller, V. (1955). *Acta path. microbiol. scand.*, **36**, 158–172.

Narayan, K. G., Guinée, P. A. M., and Mossel, D. A. A. (1967). *Antonie van Leeuwenhoek*, **33**, 184–188.

Rothberg, N. W., and Schwartz, M. N. (1965). *J. Bact.*, **90**, 294–295.

Steel, K. J. (1961). *J. gen. Microbiol.*, **25**, 297–306.

Valu, J. A. (1966). *J. Bact.*, **91**, 467–468.

Wang, C. H., Stern, J., Gilmour, C. M., Klungsoyr, S., Reed, D. J., Bialy, J. J., Christensen, B. E., and Cheldelin, V. H. (1958). *J. Bact.*, **76**, 207–216.

Wieland, T., and Fischer, E. (1949). *Naturwissenschaften*, **36**, 219.

CHAPTER III

Analysis of Fermentation Products

E. A. Dawes, D. J. McGill and M. Midgley

Department of Biochemistry, University of Hull, Kingston-upon-Hull, England

I. INTRODUCTION

The products of a fermentation process may be few, as in the case of the classical yeast fermentation, or they may be tremendously diverse, which is typical of many bacterial fermentations. The analysis of fermentation may therefore present tasks ranging in magnitude from the relatively simple to the highly complex, involving the separation, identification and quantitation of a broad spectrum of compounds.

In the earlier days of fermentation studies chemical methods were the only means of analysis then available. In the 1940s isotopes came increasingly into general use and they extended the scope of analytical operations, while the last two decades have witnessed the gradual introduction of enzymes for the specific assay of biological materials. The present commercial availability of many of the enzymes employed in such methods has, of course, greatly accelerated their general adoption. The development of column, paper and thin-layer chromatography has had a major impact not

Unless stated to the contrary, all enzyme units are expressed as International Units, i.e. one unit of an enzyme is that amount which will catalyse the transformation of 1 μmole of the substrate per min at 25° and under optimum conditions.

only on the separation and identification of fermentation products but also on their quantitative determination, and the recent application of gas–liquid chromatographic techniques now enables many compounds to be determined in a single operation.

In this Chapter we consider first the general principles of fermentation balances, then discuss the apparatus and techniques for carrying out fermentation studies and, finally, the procedures involved in the separation, identification and quantitative analysis of the various compounds likely to be encountered in fermentation processes.

The only previous comprehensive treatment of this subject is the monograph by Neish (1952) which ante-dated the era of enzymic analyses and the development of gas–liquid and thin-layer chromatographic techniques.

II. FERMENTATION BALANCES

A. The construction of a fermentation balance

The construction of a fermentation balance is necessary for the formulation of a fermentation equation, the classical expression of fermentation data. It is customary to determine (a) the **carbon balance** and (b) the **oxidation-reduction balance** of the fermentation. The former requires accurate analysis of substrate consumed and products formed if it is to account for all the atoms of the substrate distributed amongst the products. Since the overall fermentation involves only substrate and water, and since a net uptake or loss of water may occur, the balance of H and O atoms must be obtained by comparing their ratio in the substrate and products. In this manner the oxidation-reduction balance is computed.

The following method for the preparation of a fermentation balance is based on Neish (1952) and W. A. Wood (1961). For construction of the balance the results are usually expressed as millimoles of product per 100 millimoles of glucose (or other substrate) fermented, and the millimoles of any product are multiplied by the number of carbon atoms in that molecule to obtain millimoles of C_1. The individual values are summed and compared with the amount utilized, i.e. glucose (100 mmol are equivalent to 600 mmol C_1).

This is illustrated in Table I, modified from Neish. Also indicated in this Table is C_1 unit recovery (HCOOH, CO_2 etc.) estimated from the number of C_2 units formed, and by comparing this with the actual C_1 units recovered. The oxidation-reduction balance is also indicated in Table I. The system used for its derivation is based upon a comparison of the ratio of H and O atoms in the products with that in water. When this ratio is 2, or CH_2O, the O/R state is zero. Each 2H in excess of this ratio is expressed as -1, whereas a decrease of 2H is expressed as $+1$. Table II indicates the oxidation-reduction number of some common products and substrates.

TABLE I

Anaerobic dissimilation of glucose by *Serratia marcescens*
(Neish, 1952)

Product	mmol of product per 100 mmol substrate fermented	mmol of C_1	O/R number	Milliequivalents of Oxidation $(+)$	Reduction $(-)$	Calculated C_1 units
2,3-Butanediol	51·45	205·80	-3		154·35	102·9
Acetoin	0·81	3·24	-2		1·62	1·62
Glycerol	4·54	13·62	-1		4·54	
Ethanol	42·24	84·48	-2		84·48	42·24
Lactate	33·09	99·27	0			
Formate	39·80	39·80	$+1$	39·8		
Succinate	3·41	13·64	$+1$	3·41		
CO_2	106·10	106·10	$+2$	212·2		
H_2	0·52	—	-1		0·52	
		565·9$_a$		255·4$_b$	245·5$_b$	145·9$_c$

$$\text{(a) }\% \text{ recovery} = \frac{565 \cdot 9}{600} \times 100 = 94 \cdot 5\%$$

$$\text{(b) Ratio O/R} = \frac{255 \cdot 4}{245 \cdot 5} = 1 \cdot 04 \qquad \text{(c) }\% \; C_1 \text{ recovery} = \frac{145 \cdot 9}{146 \cdot 8} \times 100 = 99 \cdot 4\%$$

TABLE II

**O/R numbers of some common products
and substrates**

Compound	O/R No.	Compound	O/R No.
Glucose	0	Butanol	-4
Acetate	0	Formate	$+1$
Lactate	0	Succinate	$+1$
2,3-Butanediol	-3	Glycerol	-1
Acetoin	-2	CO_2	$+2$
Ethanol	-2	H_2	-1
Propionate	-3	Methane	-2

Error may occur in the construction of such a balance if (a) excessive assimilation of carbon into cellular material occurs; (b) CO_2 fixation occurs, or (c) other ingredients in the medium contribute to the products.

Studies on the effect of pH, of the oxidation-reduction level of the substrate, and of the time course of fermentation on fermentation balances, can provide useful information especially as to the terminal reactions of the fermentation.

TABLE III

Typical fermentation balances

| Products | mmol/100 mmol of glucose fermented | | | | | |
	(a) *Clostridium butyricum*	(b) *Clostridium acetobutylicum*	(c) *Clostridium butylicum*	(d) *Propionibacterium arabinosum*	(e) *Leuconostoc mesenteroides*	(f) *Bacillus subtilis*
Butyric acid	76	4·3	17·2	—	—	—
Acetic acid	42	14·2	17·2	5·0	—	0·16
Lactic acid	—	—	—	—	88·8	17·61
2,3-Butanediol	—	—	—	—	—	54·60
CO_2	188	221	203·5	31·8	103·8	117·8
H_2	235	135	77·6	—	—	0·16
Ethanol	—	7·2	—	—	95·6	7·65
Butanol	—	56	58·6	—	—	—
Acetone	—	22·4	—	—	—	—
Acetoin	—	6·4	—	—	—	1·56
Isopropanol	—	—	12·1	—	—	—
Propionic acid	—	—	—	74·4	—	—
Succinic acid	—	—	—	3·9	—	1·08
Formic acid	—	—	—	—	—	1·32
Glycerol	—	—	—	—	—	56·8
Carbon recovery %	96	99·6	96·2	94	93·6	98
O/R balance	0·97	1·01	1·06	0·9	1·08	0·99

(a) A. J. Kluyver (1931)
(b) J. B. Van der Lek (1930)
(c) O. L. Osburn, R. W. Brown, and C. H. Werkman (1937)
(d) H. G. Wood and C. H. Werkman (1936)
(e) R. D. DeMoss, R. C. Bard, and I. C. Gunsalus (1951)
(f) A. C. Blackwood, A. C. Neish, W. E. Brown, and G. A. Ledingham (1947)

III. FERMENTATION TRAINS

A. Preparation and assembly of a fermentation train

The Fermentation Train technique is extremely useful for the accurate determination of a large number of gaseous and non-gaseous products in one system. It suffers from the disadvantage of the time required to carry out a single fermentation, but in some cases it is possible to incorporate a manifold system which permits a number of fermentation flasks to be flushed with gas simultaneously. A description of the train follows in the alphabetical order of vessels illustrated in Fig. 1.

Gas cylinder

Normally, fermentations are conducted under anaerobic conditions. In these cases specially purified nitrogen (White Spot Nitrogen containing less than 0·00001% O_2 by volume) is used to achieve anaerobiosis and flush out the gaseous products of the fermentation.

A. *Mercury pressure head*

The pressure head is necessary for fine control of the slightly pressurized gas entering the system. The apparatus consists of a T-junction of glass tubing, 5 mm i.d., connected to a mercury reservoir which is open to the atmosphere.

B. *Dreschel bottle containing water*

The Dreschel bottle (250 or 500 ml, B24 (24/40) joint) containing water is used to monitor the flow rate of gas entering the system, which should be regulated to about 12 ml per min per fermentation flask.

C. *Water absorption tube*

The water absorption tube contains anhydrous magnesium perchlorate to dry the influent gas. A tower containing other drying agents may be used but must be efficient enough to prevent water vapour entering D. A description of the special gas absorption tubes is given later.

D. *Reduced copper furnace*

The reduced copper furnace may be dispensed with if the nitrogen gas is highly purified (i.e. free from oxygen for the anaerobic fermentations). It consists of a quartz tube, about 30 mm o.d., packed for about 2 ft of its length with copper oxide wire. The oxide is reduced to copper by passing a slow stream of hydrogen through it at 350–450°C. Heating is achieved by

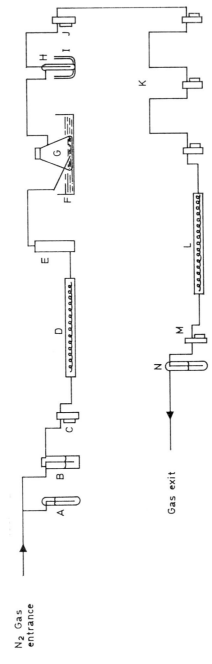

FIG. 1. Diagrammatic representation of a fermentation train (after Neish, 1952). A, Mercury pressure head; B, water wash bottle; C, water absorption tube; D, reduced copper furnace; E, soda-lime tower; F, water bath; G, fermentation flask; H, dry ice trap; I, thermos flask; J, water absorption tube; K, carbon dioxide absorption tubes; L, copper oxide furnace; M, water absorption tube; N, sulphuric acid bubbler.

a thermal tape wound round the tube and covered with asbestos lagging. A control unit is attached for temperature adjustment. When the reduction is complete excess hydrogen is flushed out with nitrogen. The temperature is raised to 500–600°C for use.

E. *Soda-lime tower*

The soda-lime tower (about 500 ml capacity) is filled with self-indicating soda-lime to remove any carbon dioxide from the incoming gas. Beyond this point a Dreschel bottle (250 ml) containing 100 ml of N NaOH may be inserted to help monitor the gas flow and to remove any residual carbon dioxide in the nitrogen which may have escaped the soda-lime treatment.

F. *Water bath*

The temperature of the water bath is controlled at that required for the fermentation.

G. *Fermentation flask*

The fermentation flask is illustrated in Fig. 2. The stopper is sterilized separately from the flask prior to starting an experiment. It may be greased with sterile silicone or, probably better, a PTFE sleeve which gives a good seat and is less trouble to set up. The stopper is attached to the flask with metal springs.

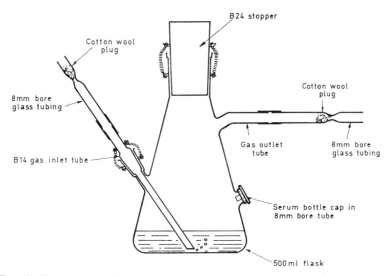

FIG. 2. Fermentation flask for continuous removal of gaseous products (after Neish, 1952).

H. *Dry ice trap*

The dry ice trap consists of a tube about 9 in. long and $1\frac{1}{2}$ in. i.d., closed at both ends and containing an internally sealed tube about 7 mm

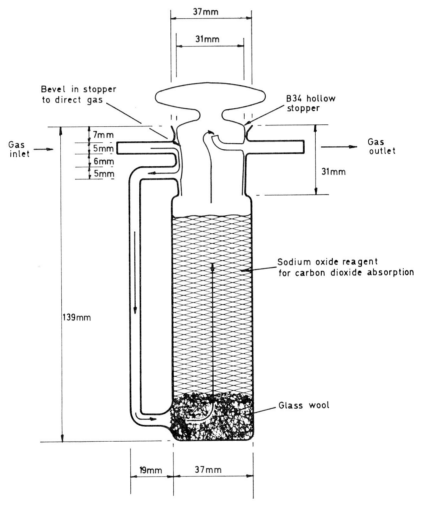

FIG. 3. Gas absorption tube (after Neish, 1952).

i.d., which comes to within about 2 in. of the bottom of the outer tube. Note that the fermentation gas enters at a side arm and escapes *up* the internal tube. The trap removes condensable volatile fermentation products,

I. *Thermos flask*

The thermos flask holds the trap around which are packed small pieces of dry ice.

J. *Water absorption tube*

The water absorption tube contains anhydrous magnesium perchlorate. Under the conditions described it should show no increase in weight. An increase in weight would indicate that the dry ice trap is not functioning efficiently, and water vapour from the fermentation flask is passing through. A slower gas flow rate or a multiple trap system should then be used.

K. *Carbon dioxide absorption tubes*

The gas absorption tubes are constructed as in Fig. 3. They are about 5 in. in height with the i.d. of a B34 ground glass stopper. The tubes have the advantage over conventional U-tubes in that a much greater cross-sectional area is presented to the effluent gases with consequently less resistance to flow. The best absorbent for carbon dioxide has been found to be a sodium oxide reagent "Carbosorb" which, unlike soda-lime, has a much greater capacity for holding the water produced on absorption of carbon dioxide. The stopcocks should be lightly greased when in use and can be secured to the body of the apparatus with rubber bands as a precaution against lifting in response to any increase of pressure within the system.

L. *Copper oxide furnace (determination of hydrogen)*

The copper oxide furnace comprises a quartz tube about 13 mm o.d. and is packed with wire form copper oxide (CuO) for about 6 in. of its length. It is maintained at a temperature of 450–550°C by a similar heating arrangement to that employed in D. The furnace is used to oxidize hydrogen in fermentation gases to water which can later be trapped in anhydrous magnesium perchlorate. The copper oxide may be regenerated by drawing air through the system at 450–550°C.

M. *Water absorption tube*

The water absorption tube contains anhydrous magnesium perchlorate which collects the water vapour resulting from the oxidation of hydrogen in furnace L.

N. *Sulphuric acid bubbler*

The sulphuric acid bubbler prevents water vapour entering the system from the distal end. The volume of the effluent gas can be measured to determine the flow rate through the apparatus. It is sometimes necessary to attach a water pump at this end of the apparatus since over an extended run of, say, 36–48 h changes in the resistance of the system to the influent gas occur.

Useful modifications to the system

1. Since it is not uncommon to find that a fermentation experiment extends over at least 48 h it is often convenient to be able to carry out more than one fermentation at a time. The insertion of a manifold arrangement after E can permit up to about six fermentations to be carried out simultaneously. In the case where, for example, the only product gas is carbon dioxide, separate dry ice traps and carbon dioxide absorption tubes may be used and the trains then rejoined with another manifold. It is inevitable that the apparatus will need constant attention under these conditions.

2. For volatile fermentation products which are extremely water soluble a water absorption system can often be effective. The water trap can be placed before the dry ice trap and cooled in ice.

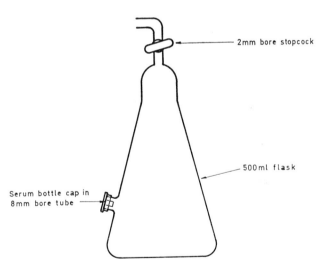

FIG. 4. Fermentation flask for small-scale closed system work (after Neish, 1952).

3. The determination of methane presents a difficult problem for an apparatus of this type. The method described could conveniently be applied after the hydrogen system together with a corresponding carbon dioxide

and/or water absorption tube. Usually, the methane system will be used instead of a hydrogen one.

B. Preparation of flasks for large scale and small scale fermentations

The flask for large scale fermentation work, i.e. with continuous removal of gaseous products, is shown in Fig. 2 and that for small scale work, i.e. for closed systems, shown in Fig. 4.

The fermentation train flask is best sterilized empty, plugged with cotton wool at the B24 joint instead of the stopper fitting. Autoclaving for 15 min at 15 p.s.i. is sufficient. Likewise, the closed system flask should have a cotton plug in its side port before sterilizing. Extremities of the fermentation flasks are wrapped with tin-foil.

The fermentation substrates are added at the cotton-plugged ports. For large scale work, 50 ml of sterile 15% w/v glucose is transferred into the flask, followed by nutrient solution and inoculum to a volume of 150 ml. The glucose concentration is then 5% w/v. The inoculum used may be 1 to 5 ml of a culture rapidly growing on a 1% (w/v) carbon source. The fermentation flask is now coupled to the system, the gas flow commenced and, after a short equilibration period (about 30 min) halted while the absorption tubes receive their initial weighing. The gas flow is then recommenced. Samples may be removed from the serum bottle-capped port with a syringe to monitor, for example, the utilization of the carbon source.

For small scale fermentations with the closed system, the carbon source (2·5 ml of a sterile 20% w/v solution) is pipetted into the side port followed by nutrient solution and inoculum to a volume of 10 ml. The inoculum should be about 0·1 ml of a culture grown as described for large scale fermentation. The sterile serum bottle cap is then fitted and the flask evacuated to about 0·5 atmosphere. It is flushed with the required gas supply through the cap. The process is repeated a number of times and the pressure in the flask finally adjusted to about 0·8 atmosphere, and the apparatus then left for the required period.

In all cases the fermentation may be stopped by the addition of the requisite amount of 2N HCl to decompose carbonates formed and adjust the pH to a value at which the fermenting organism is inactive.

C. Recovery of fermentation products in large and small scale fermentations

The fermentation train system, in which gaseous products are continually removed, will give final information about the stoicheiometry of carbon dioxide, hydrogen and methane produced during fermentation about 1 h after acidification of the fermentation medium. After removing the fermentation flask from the system and clearing the medium by preliminary centrifuging, the total supernatant plus distilled water washings may be added directly to the contents of the dry-ice trap and the whole deep frozen prior to analysis. Clearing of aliquots of the frozen and thawed medium may be carried out according to the procedure described in the relevant analytical method.

For the closed system fermentation, if a number of gaseous products, including carbon dioxide, have to be analysed the flask may be joined to the bead tower and thence to the hydrogen and methane analytical systems, and flushed slowly with nitrogen through the serum bottle cap using a syringe needle. The non-gaseous products are then collected by carefully washing out the contents of the fermentation flask with distilled water, followed by centrifuging to remove the organism. The supernatant fluid can be stored in a deep-freeze cabinet prior to analysis.

D. Fermentation in closed systems

In many ways the small-scale closed system fermentation is more suited to analysis by modern techniques than is the fermentation train technique. This is primarily due to the great accuracy now possible with analysis of small quantities of material and to the greatly increased use of isotopic tracers, especially ^{14}C, accompanied by scintillation counting methods. A further advantage of the closed system methods over train procedures is the considerable saving in time required for preparation and the small amount of attention the closed system requires. At the end of fermentation, however, parts of the train apparatus, e.g. the hydrogen, carbon dioxide and methane gas analysis systems, can profitably be used in conjunction with the closed fermentation system. The preparation of equipment and recovery of products from these fermentations are recorded in the appropriate sections.

IV. ANALYTICAL PROCEDURES

A. Initial treatment of fermentation liquors

1. Clarification

The presence of proteins in fermentation liquors leads to excessive frothing and foaming during distillation and extraction procedures. It is therefore essential to remove proteins by precipitation prior to analysis. The commonest technique has been that introduced by Somogyi (1930), involving the use of zinc sulphate and sodium hydroxide. However, Annison (1954) concluded that this method led to incomplete recoveries of steam-volatile fatty acids from various biological media and advocated the use of metaphosphoric acid as precipitant, as described by Phillipson (1947).

Method of Somogyi (*Neish*, 1952)

Principle: The pH of the sample is adjusted to 7–8 and then zinc sulphate solution, followed by an equivalent amount of sodium hydroxide solution, are added. The resulting precipitate of zinc hydroxide is centrifuged and protein and other interfering substances are sedimented with it. According to Annison (1954) the technique leads to low recoveries of steam-volatile fatty acids although Neish (1952) claimed that the process does not remove any of the common fermentation products.

Reagents:

Sodium hydroxide, 5N
Sodium hydroxide, 1N
Zinc sulphate, 25% (w/v) $ZnSO_4$, $7H_2O$ solution
Phenol red solution. 100 mg of phenol red is ground in a mortar with 28·5 ml of 0·01N-NaOH and diluted to 200 ml with water.

Procedure: Where the volume permits, it is best to add the zinc sulphate to the fermentation solution, insert a glass electrode and titrate with sodium hydroxide to pH 7·6–7·8. The volume of zinc sulphate solution added should be 1/10 to 1/20 to the volume of fermentation liquor. The solution is made up to a known volume and centrifuged, the supernatant being stored at 4°C for analysis.

With small volumes of solution the pH is adjusted to 7–8 with phenol red as indicator. Zinc sulphate solution is then added to 1/15 of the fermentation solution volume. After mixing, N-sodium hydroxide in an amount equivalent to the zinc sulphate is added with agitation and the mixture made up to a known volume. It is centrifuged and the supernatant stored as previously described.

The clarified supernatants so obtained are suitable for the analytical procedures to be described.

Method of Phillipson (1947)

Principle: Protein is precipitated by metaphosphoric acid and removed by centrifuging. The precipitate is washed once to remove adsorbed fermentation products and the washings added to the original supernatant.

4

Reagents:
Metaphosphoric acid, 25% w/v, freshly prepared
Potassium hydroxide solution, 5N

Procedure: After initial centrifuging, fermentation liquor is treated by the addition of one ninth of its volume of the metaphosphoric acid solution. It is mixed and allowed to stand for 20 min, and then centrifuged to remove protein. The sedimented protein is taken up in water to one quarter of the total volume of the original (medium plus metaphosphoric acid), centrifuged, and the supernatant added to that of the previous stage. The pH of the combined supernatants is adjusted to 8·0–8·5 with 5N-KOH and then they are concentrated by a rotary evaporator at 40°–60°C.

The concentrate is then made up to a specific volume, e.g., 10 ml, with or without further adjustment of pH, according to intended use.

2. Continuous ether extraction

Principle: Before continuous extraction of fermentation solutions can be carried out it is essential that they be cleared, otherwise emulsification will render the process either difficult or impossible. Extraction of a neutral cleared solution enables 2,3-butanediol to be extracted completely, together with about 15% of the glycerol present. Sugars, sugar alcohols and organic acids remain in the aqueous phase.

Acidification of the extracted aqueous phase with a highly ionized mineral acid, such as hydrochloric, converts organic acids to their unionized forms which are readily extracted by ether leaving the excess hydrochloric acid in the aqueous phase. The technique thus enables a neutral extract containing all of the 2,3-butanediol and an acidic extract containing all of the formic, acetic, propionic, butyric, succinic and lactic acids to be obtained. The residual aqueous phase, now free of these compounds, contains sugars and/or sugar alcohols and mineral salts and the remainder of the glycerol (about 85% of that initially present, some 15% being extracted into the ether).

Apparatus: Neish (1952) has surveyed various types of extractor and concludes that the most important factor is the amount of ether which passes through a given volume of aqueous phase per unit time. Consequently the extraction rate is approximately proportional to the rate of reflux of the ether. The capacity of laboratory condensers thus becomes the limiting factor and the most economical way to obtain rapid extraction is to use a small volume of the aqueous phase. For analytical work Neish advocates the 10 ml extractor shown in Fig. 5. This requires about 6 h to extract 2,3-butanediol.

Cold finger condensers are recommended since nearly all of the ether drops back down the centre into the dispersion tube. The dispersion tube contains 2 to 4 small holes, each about 1·0 mm in diameter at the bottom. These are made by drawing out a fine peak of glass, grinding off the end and then warming it gently in a small flame until it closes to the desired diameter. The holes should be fine enough so that the ether in the dispersion tube rises to 2–4 cm from the top when the extractor is operating at maximum rate. The extractors are best operated at 60°–70°C in a water bath.

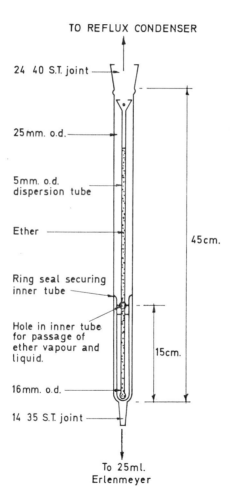

FIG. 5. Extractor for continuous ether extraction (10 ml capacity) (after Neish, 1952).

Extraction procedure (*Neish*, 1952)

A sample (10 ml) of the neutral cleared solution is pipetted into the empty extractor. The dispersion tube is then replaced and 0·5 ml of 5N-hydrochloric acid pipetted into it. The extractor is then connected to a 25 ml Erlenmeyer flask (with S.T. joint) containing about 12 ml of ether and 2–3 ml of water.

The extractor is run at the rate of about 5 ml/min for 6 h if all the 2,3-butanediol and organic acids are to be extracted, or 4 h if only the acids are required. (Alternatively the neutral solution could be extracted first to secure the 2,3-butanediol and then, after acidification, the acids. This is not customary now since ether extraction is primarily used to secure organic acids for partition chromatographic analysis and the presence of a small amount of the butanediol does not interfere.)

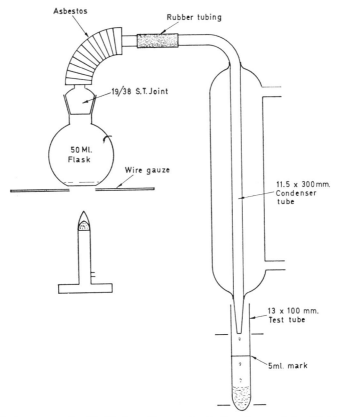

FIG. 6. Apparatus for distillation of neutral volatile solvents (after Neish, 1952).

The extract, containing the organic acids, is warmed on a steam bath until the ether phase is lost. A drop of phenol red is added and the total acids determined, by titration with N-NaOH from a micrometer syringe. The neutral solution is then carefully evaporated to dryness in a 100 ml beaker and dried overnight in a desiccator. The residual salts are held for determination of the individual acids.

3. Distillation of neutral volatile products

The neutral volatile products which may occur in fermentation media include the following groups of compounds:

1. Methanol, ethanol, isopropanol, butanol
2. Acetoin, diacetyl
3. Acetone, acetaldehyde
4. Pyruvic aldehyde

From the standpoint of identification and subsequent determination they fall into two groups, namely

(a) Those containing only an alcoholic group
(b) Those containing at least one carbonyl group

Separation of volatile products from fermentation media

The separation of volatile products from fermentation media is achieved by distillation after the pH has been adjusted to 7·0–7·5. A preliminary separation from the medium by this method offers a number of advantages in identification and determination of the volatile products.

Distillation of neutral volatile products

The procedure of Langlykke and Peterson (1937) (Neish, 1952) is used. Two modifications to the original description seem desirable, namely that the receiver should be cooled in an ice-bath to ensure recovery of extremely volatile products and that the end of the delivery tube should be below the level of a small volume (say 5 ml) of water in the graduated receiver.

Procedure: A portion (10 ml) of the cleared fermentation solution is accurately transferred to a dry 50 ml boiling flask, two glass beads added, and the solution distilled in the apparatus shown in Fig. 6. Exactly 5 ml of distillate is collected in the graduated receiving tube which is then stoppered and stored in the refrigerator until required. Each distillation occupies about 10 min.

Features to note in the assembly of the apparatus are the lagging to prevent reflux, and the presence of a hole about $\frac{1}{2}$ in. in diam. in the wire gauze to secure a hot spot and ensure even boiling. Cold water should be run through the condenser at a brisk rate.

Acetoin is the only common neutral volatile product which is not recovered completely in the first 50% of distillate collected in this procedure. A distillation correction factor must therefore be determined with standard solutions for the apparatus used. If no fractionation occurs (and the apparatus is designed to avoid significant reflux) the porportion of acetoin distilling bears a fixed ratio to the proportion of the water distilling. For the procedure described, Neish (1952) quotes a value of $53 \cdot 5 \pm 1\%$ for the acetoin in the first 50% of distillate.

Methyl glyoxal, which may be encountered in some fermentations, behaves in a similar manner to acetoin and the appropriate distillation correction factor must be determined.

Dilution factor: For subsequent calculation it is essential that the volume of distillate collected and volume of fermentation solution be accurately known. With the given procedure, a concentration factor of 2 is introduced for all neutral volatile products other than acetoin (and methyl glyoxal) in relation to the cleared fermentation solution.

4. *Distillation of volatile fatty acids*

A prime necessity for identification and determination of volatile fatty acids is their quantitative separation from the reaction medium. Such separation is most readily achieved by steam distillation, and the apparatus of Markham (1942) serves admirably for this purpose. To minimize the effect of interfering substances the distillation is carried out under conditions of minimum acidity.

Steam distillation of volatile fatty acids

Annison (1954) conducted a survey of the available methods for quantitative recovery of steam-volatile fatty acids from various biological media including sheeps blood, urine, gastric juice, saliva and cerebrospinal fluid. He found the best method of deproteinizing the medium to be that of Phillipson (1947) which employs metaphosphoric acid. Other methods, such as the Somogyi (1950) $ZnSO_4$-NaOH technique recommended by Neish (1952), did not give quantitative recoveries of volatile fatty acids from biological milieu. The deproteinized medium is then steam-distilled at pH $2 \cdot 8$–$3 \cdot 0$ to minimize the interfering effects of substances such as pyruvic and lactic acids and chloride, which are partially steam volatile under acid conditions. Annison (1954) established that at pH 3·0 some 5–8% of pyruvic acid steam distilled under the conditions he used for blood filtrates, whereas about 30% distilled at pH 1·5. At pH 3·0 chloride, lactic acid and β-hydroxybutyric acid, when present at concentrations similar to those encountered in blood, do not interfere. Scarisbrick (1952) employed a pH of 4·0 for the estimation of blood volatile fatty acids, but formic acid cannot be quantitatively steam-distilled at this pH, although at pH 3·0 complete recoveries of all the lower volatile fatty acids are obtained.

It is sometimes found that substances other than volatile fatty acids are contributing to the total acidity, a feature observed with urine (Annison, 1954). To obviate this problem a second distillation is carried out, after initially neutralizing the first distillate, concentrating and acidifying to pH 3·0. The titratable acidity of the second distillate is all accounted for as volatile fatty acid by subsequent chromatographic analysis.

Total volatile fatty acid determination (after Annison, 1954)

Reagents:

Metaphosphoric acid, 25% (w/v), freshly prepared
Potassium hydroxide, 5N
Sulphuric acid, 10N
Bromophenol blue indicator
Sodium hydroxide, 0·01N

Procedure: Fermentation medium, after centrifuging, is treated by the addition of one ninth of its volume of freshly prepared 25% (w/v) metaphosphoric acid, allowed to stand for 20 min, and then centrifuged to remove protein. The sedimented protein is taken up in water to one quarter of the total volume of the original (medium plus metaphosphoric acid), centrifuged and the supernatant added to that of the previous step. Concentration of the combined supernatants is achieved by a rotary evaporator at 40°–60°C after adjusting the pH to 8·0–8·5 with 5N-KOH. The resulting concentrate is then made to a specific volume (e.g. 10 ml) after adjustment of the pH to 2·8–3·0 with $10N-H_2SO_4$ (bromophenol blue indicator). A sample (5 ml) is then steam-distilled in the Markham still after the addition of 2·0 g of the $MgSO_4, 7H_2O$. Two 100 ml portions of distillate are collected and titrated with 0·01N–NaOH under CO_2-free conditions, the titre of the second distillate serving as a correction value for the first. Alternatively, rapid titration with more concentrated alkali (Neish, 1952) may be used.

Range: 5–20 μmoles of volatile fatty acid.

B. Analyses

GENERAL AND SPECIFIC ANALYSES DESCRIBED

The general and specific analyses described in this Section are listed below to aid location within the text.

1. General procedures

(i) Determination of total organic material (Johnson, 1949)

Principle: The majority of organic compounds encountered in the analysis of fermentation liquors are oxidized, to some extent, when heated with dichromate in the presence of a high concentration of sulphuric acid. Acetic acid is a notable exception. The trivalent chromium ion formed can be spectrophotometrically quantitated since it is green, and its absorption follows the Beer–Lambert laws when measured at 650 nm. At this wavelength there is little interference from the dichromate ion. A solution of dichromate, of known normality, is used and two additional tubes are run

TABLE IV

**Oxidation factors of some common compounds
encountered in fermentation liquors**
(Neish, 1952)

Compound	Milli-equivalent dichromate reduced per millimole	Milli-equivalent of compound per milli-equivalent reduced
Glycerol	13·9 (14)	6·46
Glucose	24·7 (24)	7·26
Acetoin	12·6	6·98
2,3-Butanediol	11·7	7·68
Lactic acid	4·7	19·1
Mannitol	24·8 (26)	7·29
Succinic acid	4·48	26·4
Citric acid	20·0	9·65
Formic acid	2·0 (2)	23·0
Butyric acid	15·2	4·86
Malic acid	13·5	9·94
Acetic acid	0·088	695·0
Ethanol	4·53	10·15
Acetone	4·20	13·8

through the procedure. The first contains water and oxidizing mixture and is used to set the slit width of the spectrophotometer to give zero extinction. The second is treated with bisulphite to reduce all the dichromate and thus serves as a standard.

Reagents:
Sodium bisulphite, 0·25M
Sodium metabisulphite (2 g), or sodium bisulphite (2·6 g) is dissolved in 100 ml of distilled water. This solution is prepared freshly each week.
Sodium dichromate oxidizing mixture
Sodium dichromate (5 g) is dissolved in 20 ml distilled water and diluted to 1 litre with conc. sulphuric acid. The normality of each batch is determined by diluting 5 ml with 100 ml of distilled water, adding crystals of KI and titrating the iodine released.

Procedure: 5 ml of sodium dichromate oxidizing mixture is added to sample (2 ml containing 0·5–2·5 mg organic material) in 25 × 100 mm test tubes. The reagent blank, containing water instead of sample, and the standard containing bisulphite are similarly set up. The tubes are heated for 20 min in a boiling water bath and then cooled to room temperature. Aliquots are transferred to suitable cuvettes and E_{650} is determined.

Calculation: The absorption of the bisulphite standard is usually approximately 0·7 and corresponds to 0·5 milli-equivalent of dichromate reduced. A calibration curve is constructed by joining this point to the origin on an extinction vs. concentration plot. Unknown samples are determined by reference to this graph.

The above method is useful for detecting unknown compounds present in the fermentation media. The experimentally obtained value is corrected for the quantities of known compounds present and the difference is thus a measure of the unknown compounds. Table IV, taken from Neish (1952), gives the experimentally determined oxidation factors of some of the substances likely to be found in fermentation media. Also, in some cases, the theoretical values calculated for the complete oxidation are shown in brackets. Sugars and sugar alcohols are completely oxidized.

(ii) *Determination of total carbon in fermentation solutions (Van Slyke and Folch, 1940)*

Principle: Organic compounds present in fermentation liquors are quantitatively converted to carbon dioxide by heating with Van Slyke–Folch combustion fluid. Determination, by any of various methods, of the carbon dioxide released thus allows total carbon to be quantitated. The

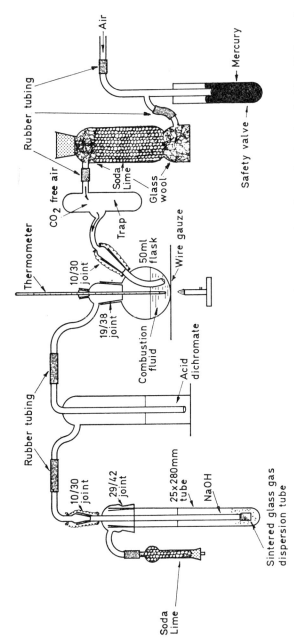

FIG. 7. Apparatus for wet combustion of organic compounds for total carbon determination by the Van Slyke and Folch (1940) procedure (after Neish, 1952).

gravimetric technique, involving precipitation as barium carbonate, is described here. Reliable results can be obtained even with volatile compounds such as acetone and ethanol.

Reagents:

Ammonium chloride, 4M
 Ammonium chloride (107 g) is dissolved in distilled water and diluted to 500 ml.
Barium chloride, 1M
 Barium chloride (104 g) is dissolved in distilled water and diluted to 500 ml.
Potassium iodate
 Powdered. Reagent grade.
Sodium hydroxide, 0·25N
 Sodium hydroxide (100 g) is dissolved in carbon dioxide-free water, and diluted to 1 litre. A 1 : 10 dilution of this, again with carbon dioxide-free water, gives the final solution which is stored in an aspirator fitted with a soda-lime tube.
Van Slyke–Folch combustion fluid
 Chromium trioxide (25 g), powdered potassium iodate (5 g) and 85% phosphoric acid (167 ml) are mixed in a 1 litre glass-stoppered flask. 333 ml of fuming sulphuric acid (20% SO_3) is added and the mixture is heated, with stirring, to 150°C. This is cooled with an inverted beaker over the flask mouth. The stopper is replaced. The reagent is stored with an inverted beaker over the lip to prevent accumulation of dust on the lip.
Carbon dioxide-free water
 This is prepared by aeration of distilled water with carbon dioxide-free air, produced by passage through a soda-lime column and sodium hydroxide.
Potassium dichromate
 Dry potassium dichromate (1·225 g) is dissolved in 10N sulphuric acid and the volume made up with this acid to 500 ml.

Procedure: The apparatus used is illustrated by Fig. 7. The acid dichromate trap is used to retain oxides of nitrogen and sulphur. The absorption tube is charged with 0·25N NaOH (40 ml) and then connected to the apparatus. Powdered KIO_3 (0·6 g) is added to the combustion flask followed by sample, 0·5–2·0 ml containing 2–20 mg of organic carbon. This is then connected to the absorption train. Lubrication of this joint, and the thermometer joint is achieved with syrupy phosphoric acid. Combustion fluid (10 ml) is then injected through the air inlet tube by means of a suitable syringe.

The trap is quickly connected. The combustion fluid-sample mixture is heated to 230°–250°C and at this temperature a slow stream of air bubbles is passed through the apparatus. The bubbler allows a check on the air flow which should be two bubbles per second. Heating is discontinued after 10 min but the carbon dioxide is swept out for 5 min further, using a more rapid airstream. The absorption tube is then lowered, with the air stream still passing, and the gas dispersion tube is rinsed with carbon dioxide-free water. Five ml of 4M ammonium chloride is mixed with the alkali, followed by 5 ml of 1M barium chloride. Precipitation is allowed to complete (3–5 min) and the barium carbonate is transferred to a tared sintered glass crucible, washed thoroughly with hot distilled water, and dried to constant weight at 120°C. The weight obtained is corrected for the appreciable amount of barium carbonate obtained in blank runs.

Calculation:
$$(\text{wt. of } BaCO_3 \text{ sample} - \text{wt. of } BaCO_3 \text{ blank}) \times 0\cdot06085$$
$$= \text{wt. of carbon in the sample.}$$

(iii) *Periodate analytical procedures*

Depending upon reaction conditions, periodate is capable of oxidizing quantitatively a wide variety of compounds containing cis and trans hydroxyl groups and also various carbonyl compounds. A selection of types of oxidation is given below together with reaction products.

1. $CH_3.CHOH.CHOH.CH_3 + HIO_4 \rightarrow 2CH_3.CHO + HIO_3 + H_2O$

2. $CH_3.CO.CHOH.CH_3 + HIO_4 \rightarrow CH_3.CHO + CH_3.CO_2H + HIO_3$
$$+ H_2O$$

3. $CH_3.CO.CO.CH_3 + HIO_4 \rightarrow 2CH_3.CO_2H + HIO_3 + H_2O$

4. $CH_2OH.CHOH.CH_2OH + 2HIO_4 \rightarrow 2HCHO + HCO_2H + 2HIO_3$
$$+ H_2O$$

5. $HO_2C.CHOH.CHOH.CO_2H + HIO_4 \rightarrow 2CHO.CO_2H + HIO_3$
$$+ H_2O$$

6. $CH_2OH.CHOH.CHOH.CHOH.CHOH.CO_2H + 4HIO_4 \rightarrow HCHO$
$$+ 3HCO_2H + CHO.CO_2H$$

7. a. $CH_2OH.CO.CO_2H \xrightarrow{NaBH_4} CH_2OH.CHOH.CO_2H$

   b. $CH_2OH.CHOH.CO_2H + HIO_4 \rightarrow HCHO + CHO.CO_2H + HIO_3$
$$+ H_2O$$

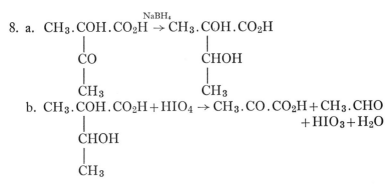

8. a. $CH_3.COH.CO_2H \xrightarrow{NaBH_4} CH_3.COH.CO_2H$

  with CO and CH_3 below first, $CHOH$ and CH_3 below second.

 b. $CH_3.COH.CO_2H + HIO_4 \rightarrow CH_3.CO.CO_2H + CH_3.CHO$
  $+ HIO_3 + H_2O$

  with $CHOH$ and CH_3 below.

From the above quantitative reactions it will be observed that the products may be formic acid, acetic acid, formaldehyde or carbonyl acids such as glyoxylate or pyruvate. In reaction 6 we see that 1 mole of gluconic acid can be converted stoicheiometrically to formaldehyde, formic acid, and 1 mole of glyoxylate. This is also true of the phosphorylated derivative, 6-phosphogluconate. Reactions 7 and 8 show that on reduction with borohydride, hydroxypyruvate and α-acetolactate can be quantitatively converted to carbonyl acids. This applies also to 2-ketogluconate and its phosphorylated derivative 2-ketogluconate-6-phosphate.

The products of the periodate reactions are readily estimated and thus can be used as a direct determination of the compound in question. We shall deal first with those compounds which yield carbonyl acids on periodate oxidation, viz, sugar acids, phosphorylated sugar acids, glycerate, tartronic semialdehyde and tartrate, and those which yield carbonyl acids with periodate only if a prior reduction with borohydride has been performed, viz., 2-ketogluconate, hydroxypyruvate and α-acetolactate. Fructose and fructose 6-phosphate, in a non-borohydride reduced system, will cause interference by the production of carbonyl acid. Galactose and glucose will also interfere in the non-reduced sample, but this is only evident when they are present in 50-fold excess over the carbonyl precursor that is being determined. 3-Phosphoglycerate, α-glycerophosphate, lactate, α-ketoglutarate, serine, threonine, tartronate, isocitrate, dihydroxyfumarate do not interefere to any significant extent. The methods given for the determination of carbonyl acids formed on periodate oxidation are assembled in three sections, which are:

1. Determination of carbonyl acids.
2. Determination of carbonyl acids produced on periodate oxidation.
3. Determination of carbonyl acids produced on periodate oxidation of borohydride-treated samples.

Other sections will deal with formaldehyde, formic and acetic acids and periodate estimations on periodate oxidation of compounds noted in reactions 1 to 4.

(a) Determination of formaldehyde formed on periodate oxidation (Glycerol Determination) (Neish, 1952)

By the following procedure polyols and aldonic acids may be determined.

Reagents:

Chromotropic acid reagent

Dissolve 1,8-dihydroxynaphthalene-3,6-disulphonic acid (chromotropic acid), (1 g), in 100 ml distilled water and filter. Conc. H_2SO_4 (300 ml) is added to 150 ml water. This is cooled and added to the filtrate to make the volume 500 ml. The reagent is stored in a brown bottle. It is prepared freshly every 2–3 weeks.

Glycerol standard

Dissolve mannitol (1·98 g) in water and make up to 200 ml.

1 g glycerol ≡ 1·98 g mannitol by this procedure.

Periodic acid, 0·1M

Prepared as described for carbonyl acid precursors (p. 84).

Sodium arsenite, 1M

Sodium hydroxide pellets (45 g) and arsenious oxide (arsenic trioxide), (100 g), are dissolved in water and made to 1 litre with water.

Sulphuric acid, 10N

Procedure: The test solution, containing 0·2 to 0·8 mg glycerol and not exceeding 20 ml in volume, is pipetted into a glass-stoppered 100 ml volumetric flask. Sufficient water to make the volume to 20 ml is added, followed by 10N H_2SO_4 (1 ml) with mixing. Periodate reagent (5 ml) is added and, after exactly 5 min, arsenite reagent (5 ml). After a further 5–10 min, the contents of the flask are made up to 100 ml with water. A sample (1 ml) is pipetted into a 25 × 200 mm Pyrex test tube, chromotropic acid reagent (10 ml) is added and the tube is then heated on a boiling water bath for 30 min in diffuse light. The tube(s) are cooled to room temperature and read in a spectrophotometer at 570 nm using 1 cm cuvettes. A blank and set of standards is run with each set of determinations.

For estimations on one-tenth of this scale the following procedure is used:

Test solution (2 ml), containing 20–80 μg glycerol, is pipetted into a 19 mm diameter test tube and 10N H_2SO_4 (0·1 ml) is added, followed by periodate reagent (0·5 ml). After 5 min arsenite reagent (0·5 ml) is added and mixed thoroughly. After 10–15 min the volume is made up to 10 ml with water and 1 ml is removed for estimation as above.

(b) Determination of acids formed during oxidation by periodate
(Neish, 1952)

Compounds such as glycerol, acetoin, diacetyl and mannitol are oxidized stoicheiometrically to carboxylic acids and other products. The increase in acidity is an index of the amount of a known compound present. Other compounds such as glucose (hexoses) are also oxidized but only to about 70% of the theoretical value.

Reagents:

2,3-Butanediol, (10% v/v) aqueous solution
   The diol used should be free of acids and acetoin, and is best prepared immediately prior to use.

Hydrochloric acid, 0·21N
Methyl red solution
   Methyl red powder (250 mg) is dissolved in 500 ml 50% (v/v) ethanol.
Phenolphthalein solution, 0·1% (w/v)
   Phenolphthalein powder (200 mg) is dissolved in 200 ml 50% ethanol.
Sodium hydroxide standard solution, 1N, carbonate-free
Sodium periodate, 0·1M
   A solution of periodic acid (11·5 g in 400 ml of water) is neutralized with N NaOH using methyl red indicator. The volume is adjusted to 500 ml.

Procedure: An aliquot (2–25 ml) of test solution is made up to a volume of approximately 40 ml with water. This is adjusted to the methyl red end point with dilute HCl and N NaOH. Periodate reagent (10 ml) is added and the solution mixed. The resulting solution is allowed to stand at room temperature for 1–3 h. A reagent blank is also run. After the required period butanediol reagent (5 ml) is added and the mixture is left to stand for 10 min. A few drops of phenolphthalein solution are added, and, with a micrometer syringe or a micro-burette, the solution is titrated with N NaOH to an end point. The blank titre is subtracted from the test.

1 mmol acetoin or glycerol gives 1 milli-equivalent of acid.

Note: For a spectrophotometric method for formic acid determination in periodate oxidation of carbohydrates see p. 132.

(c) Determination of periodate utilized in oxidation (Neish, 1952)

If compounds such as 2,3-butanediol, acetoin, diacetyl or glycerol are present singly in aqueous solution they may be directly determined by the amount of periodate used in their oxidation. For example, 1 milli-equivalent of periodic acid oxidizes

45 mg 2,3-butanediol,
44 mg acetoin,
43 mg diacetyl,
and 23 mg glycerol.

Alternatively, if a situation arises in which an unknown compound chromatographs as a single spot or band, a measurement of the amount of periodate utilized in its oxidation together with (in the case of a polyol) the amount of formaldehyde and formic acid produced, serves as a basis for its final identification.

Reagents:
Iodine standard solution, 0·1N
     Resublimed iodine (12·7 g) is weighed out on a rough balance and transferred to a glass stoppered Erlenmeyer flask, previously weighed to the nearest mg. The glass stopper is replaced quickly and the flask plus contents reweighed accurately. Potassium iodide crystals (40 g) are added to the flask, followed by water (25 ml). The flask is shaken until all the iodine enters solution. The contents of this flask are quantitatively transferred to a 1 litre volumetric flask and the volume is made up with distilled water. The solution is stored in a brown, glass-stoppered bottle.
     12·692 g iodine/litre solution = 0·1000N
Periodic acid, 0·1M
     Paraperiodic acid (H_5IO_6), (4·6 g) is dissolved in water (200 ml) and stored in a brown, glass-stoppered bottle.
Potassium iodide, 50% (w/v) aqueous solution
Sodium arsenite, 0·11N
     Sodium hydroxide pellets (45 g) and arsenious oxide (arsenic trioxide), (100 g), are dissolved in distilled water. The volume is adjusted to 1 litre. 55 ml of this solution and solid sodium bicarbonate (20 g) are added to distilled water (800 ml).
     The final volume is adjusted to 1 litre on solution of the bicarbonate.
Sodium bicarbonate solution, 6·8% (w/v)
Starch indicator solution
     Soluble starch (2 g) is mixed with sufficient water to make a paste which is diluted to 200 ml. This is heated to boiling followed by cooling and the addition of toluene (0·2–0·4 ml) as preservative. The solution is stored in a glass-stoppered bottle.
Sulphuric acid, 1N

Procedure: Periodate reagent (1 ml) and 1N H_2SO_4 (2 ml) are added to a 125 ml Erlenmeyer flask. The sample, containing up to 3·5 mg glycerol or

7 mg 2,3-butanediol, is then added followed by sufficient water to make the total volume to approximately 10 ml. The flask contents are mixed and allowed to stand at room temperature for 1 h or longer if convenient. Bicarbonate reagent (5 ml) is added and after thorough mixing the arsenite reagent (2 ml) is added. Two drops of KI solution are mixed in and the flask is allowed to stand at room temperature for at least 10 min. Starch indicator (four drops) is added and titration with 0·1N iodine to a definite blue colour, using a micrometer syringe or a micro-burette, is carried out.

Calculation: (Titre of sample − titre of blank) × Normality of iodine = milliequivalents of periodic acid reduced.

(d) Determination of carbonyl acids (Juni and Heym, 1962)

It is sometimes necessary to determine carbonyl acids present prior to periodate oxidation. The following method is part of the group procedure.

Reagents:

  p-Nitrophenylhydrazine, 0·1M solution in 10N sulphuric acid. *p*-Nitrophenylhydrazine hydrochloride (380 mg) is dissolved in distilled water to 10 ml. This is filtered (Whatman No. 1 Filter Paper) and to the filtrate is added an equal volume of 20N H_2SO_4. The reagent is prepared freshly each day and stored at 25–30° to prevent crystallization of *p*-nitrophenylhydrazine hydrogen sulphate.
  Ethyl acetate. Reagent grade
  Tris, 0·5M aqueous solution
  Sulphuric acid, 10N

Procedure: Sample (3 ml) and 10N H_2SO_4 (1 ml) are thoroughly mixed in 18 × 150 mm pyrex test tubes. For the blank, water replaces the sample.

  p-Nitrophenylhydrazine reagent (0·5 ml) is added. The contents are mixed, and the tubes are incubated in a 30°C water bath for 45 min.

After incubation the tubes are removed and ethyl acetate (5·0 ml) is added to each. The contents are mixed for 30 sec on a Vortex Junior Mixer. The phases are allowed to separate and as much as possible of the ethyl acetate layer is drawn off into a clean dry test tube. Further ethyl acetate (2 ml) is added to the extraction mixture, without further mixing. As much as possible of this layer is drawn off and pooled with the first ethyl acetate extract. A second 2 ml portion is added and the procedure repeated.

  0·5M Tris (4 ml) is added to the ethyl acetate extract, and the *p*-nitrophenylhydrazones are extracted for 30 sec using the Vortex mixer. The ethyl acetate layer is removed and Tris layer is washed with ethyl acetate (5 ml) using the Vortex mixer, again for 30 sec.

An aliquot of the Tris extract is transferred to a 1 cm cuvette and the extinction at 390 nm is determined against the blank.

The range of the estimation is 0·02 to 0·2 μmole carbonyl acid.

(e) Periodate oxidation of carbonyl acid precursors

This method is suitable for the determination of sugar acids, phosphory-lated sugar acids, glycerate, tartronic semialdehyde and tartrate. It may be necessary to carry out a preliminary determination of the carbonyl acids in the system.

Reagents:

The reagents given in the previous section for determination of carbonyl acids are required. In addition, the following are required.

Periodic acid or sodium periodate, 0·1M aqueous solution

Paraperiodic acid (H_5IO_6) (2·28 g) or sodium metaperiodate ($NaIO_4$) (2·14 g), are dissolved in distilled water to a final volume of 100 ml and stored in a brown bottle in the dark.

Thioacetamide, 0·867M aqueous solution

Thioacetamide (650 mg) is dissolved in distilled water to 10 ml. This is freshly prepared each day.

Procedure: Exactly 1·0 ml of periodate reagent is added to 18×150 mm pyrex test tubes containing 10N H_2SO_4 (1·0 ml) and the contents are mixed well. Sample (2 ml), containing 0·02 to 0·2 μmole carbonyl acid precursor, is added. If the volume of the sample is less than 2 ml then volume is made up with water which is added to the test tube prior to addition of the sample. The sample should be neutral or slightly alkaline. The reactants are thoroughly mixed and incubated in a 30°C water bath for 45 min. On completion of the incubation, thioacetamide reagent (0·5 ml) is added with gentle mixing by hand. The tubes are allowed to stand at room temperature for 5–10 min and the contents are then mixed using the Vortex mixer, for 30 sec. *p*-Nitrophenylhydrazine reagent (0·5 ml) is added. The remainder of the procedure is identical to that previously described. If the carbonyl acid produced is glyoxylate then gluconate is used as standard: otherwise pyruvate (freshly distilled) is used.

(f) Periodate oxidation of carbonyl acid precursors after borohydride reduction

This method is suitable for the determination of 2-ketogluconate, hydroxypyruvate and α-acetolactate. If carbonyl acids are present they do not interfere since they are reduced by the borohydride treatment.

Reagents:
The reagents given in the section on carbonyl acid estimation are required. In addition the following are required:
Sodium borohydride, 1·0M aqueous solution
Sodium borohydride (380 mg) is dissolved in distilled water to a final volume of 10 ml and the solution is filtered (Whatman No. 1 Filter Paper). It is prepared freshly each day.

Procedure: Borohydride reagent (0·1 ml) is added to samples (1·9 ml) contained in 18 × 150 mm pyrex test tubes. The contents are mixed and the tubes are incubated in a 30°C water bath for 30 min. After removal of the tubes from the bath, 10N H_2SO_4 (1·0 ml) is added with thorough mixing. The tubes are returned to the bath for a further 10 min at 30°C. The tubes are removed from the bath and mixed, using a Vortex mixer, for 30 sec. Periodate reagent (1·0 ml) is added and mixed in. The tubes are returned to the bath for a further 45 min. From this stage the procedure is identical to that previously described for carbonyl acid determination.

If the product of borohydride reduction is a sugar acid it will lactonize during the acid destruction of excess borohydride. The following procedure is then used.

Borohydride reagent (0·5 ml) is added to sample (5 ml), containing 0·15 to 1·5 μmole carbonyl acid precursor, and mixed. The solution is incubated for 30 min at 30°C. Excess borohydride is then destroyed by addition of 1·0N H_2SO_4 (1·0 ml) and incubation is continued at 30°C for a further 10 min, followed by mixing with a Vortex mixer for 30 sec. 2·5N NaOH (0·5 ml) is added and the tubes are allowed to stand for several minutes, thus achieving delactonization. 1·0 ml of this solution can now be used for the standard assay procedure described above. The small amount of alkali causes no interference in the determination.

2(a) *Specific analyses—Gases*

(1) *Determination of carbonate by titration* (Neish, 1952)

It is often useful when carrying out small scale radiochemical fermentations in closed systems where carbon dioxide is produced, to be able to collect this gas in alkali, and use aliquots for its estimation by titration followed by specific activity measurements using scintillation counting techniques.

Reagents:
Barium chloride, 1M
Barium chloride (104 g) is dissolved in water and diluted to 500 ml after neutralizing to the thymolphthalein end-point with N-NaOH.

Hydrochloric acid, 1N
Sodium hydroxide, 1N–carbonate free
Thymolphthalein solution (0·1% w/v)
   Thymolphthalein powder (100 mg) is dissolved in 100 ml 80% v/v
   ethanol.
Carbon dioxide-free water

Procedure: N-NaOH (20 ml, accurately measured) is added to the bead
tower, illustrated in Fig. 8. This volume of alkali should come about half
way up the bead tower bulb when it is in operation. If it does not, then the
required volume of CO_2-free water is added. The closed-system fermentation flask is connected to the bead tower and the stopcock opened a little,
allowing gas to escape into the bead tower at a slow rate by applying gentle
suction to the tower. Sufficient dilute hydrochloric acid is added, by syringe,
to the fermentation flask to decompose the carbonates. A hypodermic needle,
through which white-spot nitrogen is gently flowing, is pushed through the
serum-bottle cap of the fermentation flask and the gases are swept out for
about 30 min. Using carbon dioxide-free water, the alkali from the bead
tower is washed into the Erlenmeyer component. Barium chloride solution
(10 ml) is added, followed by 4–5 drops of thymolphthalein solution.
The resulting solution is titrated with N-HCl until the blue colour just
disappears. The amount of carbon dioxide absorbed is estimated by the
difference between the blank (20 ml N-NaOH) and the titre of the test.

(2) *Hydrogen*
The determination of hydrogen is described on p. 61.

(3) *Determination of ammonia in solution*
A wide variety of titrimetric procedures are available for determination
of ammonia in fermentation solutions. Most involve distillation from strong
base into boric acid and titration of the boric acid with standard acid.
However, for small scale work particularly, it is useful to be able to employ
small sample volumes and the methods to be described have been chosen
for this purpose.

*Determination of ammonia in solution without deproteinization (Wachsmuth
and Fritz,* 1965)

Reagents:
   Nessler's Reagent—available commercially (for preparation see Herbert,
      Phipps and Strange, this Series, Volume 5B).
   Phosphate buffer, 0·33M, pH 7·5.

Procedure: The sample (1 to 2 ml), containing 0·12 to 1·2 μmoles NH_3,
is placed in a micro-distillation apparatus containing water (2–3 ml) and

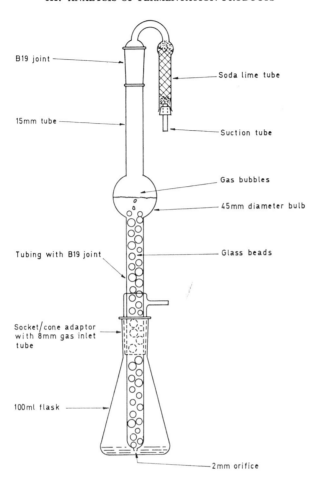

FIG. 8. Bead tower for determination of carbonate by titration (Neish, 1952).

0·33M buffer (2–3 ml). A total of 5 ml of distillate is collected and Nessler Reagent (0·1 ml) is added. After 3 min the extinction is measured at 436 nm against water. Reagent blanks and standards are also run.

Determination of ammonia by a phenol hypochlorite method (Mueller-Beissenhirtz and Keller, 1965).

Reagents:
    Trichloroacetic acid (TCA), 10% (w/v) solution
    Phenol-nitroprusside
        Phenol (1 g) and sodium nitroprusside (5 g) are dissolved in water and made up to 100 ml.

Hypochlorite

Na_2HPO_4, $12H_2O$ (90 g), sodium hydroxide (10 g) and 5% NaOCl solution (10 ml) are dissolved in water and made up to 1 litre with water.

Procedure

Deproteinization.

TCA solution (2 ml) is pipetted into a centrifuge tube, in iced water, followed by sample (2 ml). The mixture is kept at 0°C until required for analysis when it is centrifuged and the supernatant (0·5 ml) is removed for ammonia determination.

Determination.

Phenol-nitroprusside reagent (2 ml) is added to the supernatant (0·5 ml) contained in a test tube. The contents are mixed well and the hypochlorite reagent (2 ml) is added. The contents are thoroughly mixed before incubating the tubes in a water bath at 37°C for 30 min. The extinction is determined against water at 578 nm. Standards and reagent blanks are also put through the procedure. The standard ammonia solution should contain 200 μg of ammonia nitrogen per 100 ml.

(4) *Determination of methane*
(Murdock, Brooks and Zahn, 1948)

For the purpose of estimating methane as a fermentation product, a method which can be used in the "train" scheme was sought. Most combustion methods depend upon the presence of excess oxygen but Murdock *et al.* (1948) developed a method which involves combustion over hot copper oxide containing 1% iron oxide. Such a system should be readily accommodated in the fermentation train apparatus, immediately following the equipment for hydrogen determination, although the selectivity of the hydrogen system with respect to methane combustion would have to be determined should such a mixture be found. It is known that hydrogen is oxidized quantitatively at a much lower temperature than that used for methane. The method of Murdock *et al.* (1948) has been used by Stadtman and Barker (1951) for the estimation of methane produced during fermentation. Conditions, however, for quantitative recovery would have to be determined by the investigator, e.g., gas flow rates, optimum length of combustion tube and copper oxide reagent quantity. Methane for this purpose could be generated by adding water over the required period of time to an ethereal solution of $CH_3 . Mg . I$, but *only* if it could be fed through an adequate trapping system for ether.

Reagents:

Copper oxide–iron oxide

Appropriate weights of cupric nitrate and ferric nitrate to produce 100 g of 99 : 1 copper oxide–iron oxide mixture are dissolved in 3 litres of water to which is added 30% potassium hydroxide solution in slight excess. The resulting mixture is boiled for 20 min to convert the precipitated copper hydroxide to copper oxide. The precipitate is washed several times, by decantation, with water. It is then filtered and allowed to dry to a hard cake which is crushed and dried at 400°C. The resulting particles are reduced with hydrogen and reoxidized in a stream of air at 400°C.

Procedure: The oxide particles are packed into fused silica tubes about 120 mm in length and 3·5 to 4·0 mm diam. The tubes contain from 4–7 g of oxide depending on the mesh size used. The copper oxide–iron oxide packing is retained in the tubes with plugs of loosely rolled sheet asbestos. The tube is inserted into a furnace system at 700°C after the hydrogen system (or in place of) and is followed by (a) a gas absorption tube containing anhydrous magnesium perchlorate for water absorption and (b) an absorption tube of sodium oxide reagent (Carbosorb) for CO_2 absorption. A direct co-relation should exist between water and CO_2 absorbed. If this is sufficiently accurate at the gas flow rates predetermined by the operator, a single furnace at 700°C should suffice for both methane and hydrogen, the anhydrous magnesium perchlorate for hydrogen plus methane and the sodium oxide reagent for methane alone.

(5) *Gas–liquid chromatographic separation of gases produced during fermentation*

GLC techniques are applicable to closed fermentation systems, where following acidification to release carbon dioxide, a sample can be conveniently obtained for analysis. A GLC method for a mixture of CO_2, N_2, H_2 and CH_4 has been described (Chmielawski and Isaac, 1959) and a similar method is given below.

Method: Apart from a commercial GLC apparatus, a column (6 ft × ¼ in.) packed with activated charcoal (approximately 40 mesh) is required. This is operated at room temperature, using helium as the carrier gas. With a gas flow rate of 50 ml/min this will separate H_2, N_2, CH_4, and CO_2, fairly easily, in the order listed. The detection device used is a katharometer.

2(b) *Specific analyses—Identification and estimation of neutral volatile products of fermentation.*

In this section the analysis of the distillate, produced as described on p. 69, is dealt with. Identification procedures are first discussed, and for this purpose the neutral volatile products are divided into two classes of product, namely, those containing an alcohol group and those containing a carbonyl group. The analytical sections that follow are similarly divided. The determination of acetoin is described with the determination of diacetyl, which is found at the end of the carbonyl section.

(i) *Identification of volatile products which contain only an alcoholic functional group*

Alcohols may be identified by paper or thin layer chromatography of their 3,5-dinitrobenzoate esters. Gänshirt, Waldi and Stahl (1965) record the thin layer technique but the range of alcohols is not great and isopropanol is not represented. The paper chromatographic method described by Sundt and Winter (1957) separates all the alcohols of interest as their dinitrobenzoate esters. Holley and Holley (1952) have also recorded a paper chromatographic separation of these esters.

(1) *Preparation of 3,5-dinitrobenzoates*

(This technique is applicable to concentrations of ethanol as low as 0·001%.) To 10 ml of an aqueous solution containing the alcohols in a 100 ml volumetric flask, are added 0·1 ml of redistilled pyridine and 0·1 ml of benzene. The mixture is cooled in an ice bath and 11 g of anhydrous potassium carbonate added at such a rate that the temperature does not exceed 25°C. A solution of 0·5 g of 3,5-dinitrobenzoyl chloride in 2 ml of benzene is added in portions at room temperature with shaking. Three minutes after the addition of the acid chloride is complete, 30 ml of sodium-dried ether are added and the mixture shaken. The ether is decanted into a centrifuge tube. The extraction is repeated twice. The ether extracts are centrifuged, filtered through dry filter paper and evaporated at atmospheric pressure. The residue is heated at 70°–80°C under reduced pressure (20 mm Hg) until the odour of pyridine can no longer be detected. The residue is extracted with the solvent to be used for spotting plates or papers. The yield of ester under these conditions is about 20%.

The procedures described should serve to identify the alcohols encountered as fermentation products.

(2) *Column chromatography of 3,5-dinitrobenzoates of alcohols* (Holley and Holley, 1952)

Reagents and apparatus:

Column. This is a 1·8 × 40 cm borosilicate glass tube which is joined at the top to a 100 ml bulb which serves as a solvent reservoir. At the bottom of the tube is a borosilicate glass stopcock, which is not lubricated in order to avoid contamination with material absorbing at 240 nm.

Column packing. This is a 2 : 1 (by weight) mixture of silicic acid (Merck reagent grade) and Celite.

Petroleum ether. This is practical grade (e.g., Eastman No. P 513) that is specially purified to remove ultraviolet-absorbing impurities. The following procedure is adopted. Petroleum ether (2 kg) is washed with conc. sulphuric acid (500 ml) in a separatory funnel. It is then stirred overnight with fuming sulphuric acid (3 lb). Cautious addition of the fuming sulphuric acid is required since heat is evolved. The petroleum ether is then washed with water and sodium carbonate, followed by drying over calcium chloride and distillation. The fraction boiling at 65°–85°C is used and this should have no extinction at 228 nm.

Elution solvents: The composition of the solvents used in elution are given below:

Volume used (ml)	Petroleum ether % v/v	Ether % v/v
50	100	0
50	99	1
50	98	2
50	97	3
50	96	4
200	95	5
100	90	10

Pressure regulator: Since the column pressure is adjusted during the procedure some regulatory device must be used. That described on p. 116 will suffice.

Procedure: Preparation of column. Adsorbent (18 g) is added to the column, without suction and with the stopcock open. The adsorbent is supported on glass wool and a filter disc. The column is gently shaken and pressure (40 cm of mercury) is applied. The pressure is then gradually released and the top of the column is lightly tamped. Petroleum ether (50 ml) is added to the top of the column and forced through under approximately 50 cm pressure.

Application of sample. When the solvent emerges at the bottom of the column, the sample (in petroleum ether solution) of 3,5-dinitrobenzoates is applied. When all this solution has been forced on to the column development is commenced. The developer is forced through the column under approximately 50 cm pressure at a rate of 1·5 ml per min. The eluate is collected in 5 ml fractions. Fresh developer is added when approximately 5 ml of the previous solution remain above the adsorbent.

The 3,5-dinitrobenzoate content of the eluate is monitored spectrophotometrically at 240 nm in quartz cuvettes. Solutions are diluted so that the E_{240} does not exceed 0·7. In the results presented the authors often detected as a first peak some contaminant, (around 200 ml of effluent collected) which may be demonstrated to be such by using distilled water (10 ml) instead of sample.

Range of chromatography. Using the sensitive spectrophotometric method of detection of the derivatives the authors were able to detect as little as 100 μg of ester, and as much as 20 mg. The order of elution of some common DNB-alcohols is t-butyl, n-butyl, isopropyl and n-propyl, ethyl and methyl. Secondary and tertiary alcohols are generally required to be present at a higher concentration than primary alcohols since they are not so reactive.

The authors have shown that the concentration, or presence of other DNB derivatives, does not alter the peak position or shape, and thus these can furnish information as to the homogeneity and identity of the fractions. By selection of eluate fractions, it is possible, after evaporation of the solvent, to obtain the crystalline derivative and determine its melting point.

(3) Paper chromatography of 3,5-dinitrobenzoates of alcohols
(Sundt and Winter, 1957)

Materials:

Schleicher and Schüll chromatographic paper No. 2043b (or equivalent)
Chamber for descending chromatography
Filter paper sheets. The size of these depends on the size of tank used
Evaporating dishes (2)
N,N-dimethylformamide, 50% solution in acetone
Decalin (decahydronaphthalene)

Procedure: The paper is dipped in dimethylformamide solution and dried at room temperature to remove acetone. The sample and standards in chloroform are applied to this dimethylformamide impregnated paper in the usual manner, using micropipettes. The paper sheet is then placed in the chromatography tank, which has been lined with filter paper that has been moistened with dimethylformamide previously saturated with decalin. Two evaporating dishes, filled with mobile phase (decalin previously saturated with dimethylformamide), are placed in the bottom of the tank. At this stage the trough does not contain mobile phase.

After equilibration at 25°C, the chromatogram is developed. Under the conditions used by the authors the mobile phase travels 35 cm in 7 h. The chromatogram is removed from the tank and dried at 60°–70°C.

Visualization of the derivatives is achieved by exposing the chromatogram to daylight for 1–2 h, or irradiating it with ultraviolet for 10–15 min. Distinct violet spots are produced by both procedures.

Resolution: To secure good separation the authors advise the foregoing procedure for obtaining saturation of the tank atmosphere. They state that R_F values obtained vary slightly since it is impossible to duplicate all the conditions on different days (e.g., the amount of stationary phase fixed to the paper) and thus the values given below, for a 35 cm movement of solvent front at 25°C, should only be accepted as a rough guide. The following R_F values are reported by the authors: methanol, 0·21; ethanol, 0·40; 1-propanol, 0·50; 2-propanol, 0·52; and 1-butanol, 0·64. Approximately 5–10 µg were easily detectable with the system described.

(4) *Thin layer chromatography of 3,5-dinitrobenzoates of alcohols*
(Gänshirt, Waldi and Stahl, 1965)

Preparation of plates: Silica Gel G (25 g) is placed in a 10 cm diam. porcelain mortar and distilled water (35 ml) is added, with slow stirring, until a homogeneous mass is obtained. An additional 15 ml of distilled water is now added, with further stirring. The entire stirring period should not exceed 100 sec. The thin suspension is immediately placed in a spreader, and the plates spread. Five 20 × 20 cm plates (layer thickness approximately 250 µm) should be obtained. The plates are subjected to preliminary drying at room temperature, followed by 10 min drying by hot air in a vertical position, and finally they are placed in a 110°C oven for 30 min. The plates can be stored over blue silica gel.

Solvent. This is a cyclohexane-carbon tetrachloride–ethyl acetate mixture in the ratio of 10 : 75 : 15.

Chromatography. Separation chambers, lined with filter paper, are allowed to equilibrate before the plates are developed. The thin layer should be immersed in the solvent to a depth of approximately 0·5 cm, and the starting points should be 1·5 cm from the lower edge.

The plates are developed for a 10 cm solvent front migration, and visualization of the DNB-alcohols is achieved by spraying with Rhodamine B-reagent. This contains Rhodamine B (0·5 g) in 100 ml of ethanol. Apart from inspection in daylight, the DNB-esters can be recognized in ultraviolet light as dark spots on the red fluorescing plate. The speed of migration of the common DNB-esters is, in order of decreasing rate: *n*-butyl, *n*-propyl, ethyl and methyl.

(5) *Identification and determination of alcohols by gas–liquid*
chromatography

Gas–liquid chromatographic methods are finding increasing application for the identification and determination of alcohols in biological materials and the advantages of this technique cannot be overemphasized. Where a homologous series of compounds has to be determined satisfactory results are seldom obtained without recourse to gas–liquid chromatography which also offers one of the best methods for identifying components of the neutral volatile fraction.

Lyons and Bard (1964) have described a method for the determination of ethanol, n-propanol, isopropanol and acetone. Anhydrous calcium sulphate (Drierite) is used to absorb most of the water from the sample, followed by extraction of the alcohols from the solid absorbent by n-butanol. This technique avoids the complications of aqueous solutions and eliminates the necessity for a flame ionization detector; the apparatus is therefore relatively inexpensive.

Turner and Gilmour (1965) have applied gas–liquid chromatography as an aid in fermentation studies for the analyses of the non-gaseous products of a *Clostridium butylicum* fermentation. The apparatus requires a flame ionization detector but is capable of separating a wide variety of compounds with simultaneous determination. Freudiger and Vignau (1965) have also applied gas–liquid chromatography to the analysis of alcohols in body fluids and report the ready resolution of methanol, ethanol, isopropanol and acetone in blood.

Doelle (1966, 1967 and 1969a, b) has described a method that allows the detection and determination of C_1–C_7 alcohols and also acetone and diacetyl. This method is also described here.

The Turner and Gilmour (1965) method

Apparatus: A gas chromatographic apparatus equipped with a flame ionization detector and fitted with 6 ft glass columns of 4 mm i.d. was used. Column packings were prepared by dissolving 4 g of the stationary phase in 200 ml of chloroform and adding 16 g of support with stirring. After 1·5 h of stirring at room temperature the suspension was allowed to settle, the supernatant decanted, and the slurry thinly spread on a clean glass plate to dry at room temperature. Any residual chloroform was removed by shaking in a 2 litre beaker until the chloroform odour disappeared. Columns were packed with the aid of a vibrator (Burgess Vibrocrafters Inc.). A plug ($\frac{1}{2}$ in.) of glass wool was placed at the exit end and a $1\frac{1}{2}$ in. plug in the inlet.

The assembled columns were bled for 5 days at 20°–25°C above the temperature at which they were to be used.

Columns: The column for determining acetone, ethanol and n-butanol was packed with Hallcomid 180L on Chromosorb W (60/80 mesh acid washed).

For the determination of acetic and butyric acids the column was packed with 20% Tween 80 on Gas Chrome (60/80 mesh).

The column temperature and carrier flow rate were 115°C and 15/ml/min for the acids and 78°C and 42 ml/min for the alcohols. Nitrogen was the carrier gas. The authors report that both columns had been used intermittently over a 2-year period for the analysis of aqueous solutions without any deleterious effects.

Identification and determination: Identification was achieved by comparing the retention times of the fermentation products with those of the pure substances. The concentration of each substance was determined by measuring the area under elution curves (Said and Merton, 1963) and comparing it to the area under curves obtained when known quantities of the particular compound were injected.

Turner and Gilmour give examples of the separation of acetone, ethanol and butanol when 1 μl of a solution containing each substance in a concentration of 0·02% (v/v) was injected, and of acetic and butyric acids when 1 μl of a solution containing each acid at a concentration of 0·05% (v/v) was injected. It was shown that the detector response was linear for acetic acid, up to about 25×10^{-3} μM injected and for butyric acid up to about 16×10^{-3} μM injected. The authors state that similar data were obtained for acetone, ethanol and butanol, but do not record the concentration range employed.

The Method of Doelle (1966, 1967, 1969a, b)

Apparatus: The gas chromatograph used was a Shimadzu GC-4APFT (supplied in the U.K. by V. A. Howe & Co. Ltd., Analytical Division, London, England) equipped with a thermoconductivity cell connected in series with a dual hydrogen flame detector.

Column: A 6-ft stainless steel column, i.d. 3 mm, containing 30% polyethylene glycol 400 (Koch-Light Laboratories, England) on 60/80 mesh acid-washed Chromosorb W (Analabs Inc., Hampden, Connecticut, U.S.A.) was used.

Operating conditions: The following conditions were employed:
   Detector oven temperature: 250° C
   Injection port temperature: 150°C
   Helium gas flow rate: 100 ml/min
   Air flow rate: 400 ml/min
   Hydrogen flow rate: 70 ml/min
   Sample size: 5 μl

Temperature programme: The initial column temperature was 50°C, with a temperature programming rate of 10°C/min, commencing 5 min after injection.

Sensitivity: Quantities of 20 μg are reported to be easily detectable, with a variability of less than 3%. Quantitation was achieved by peak height measurement.

Separation: Compounds were detected in the following order: acetone, methanol, ethanol, diacetyl, *n*-propanol, *iso*-butanol, *n*-hexane and *n*-heptane. Ethanol could not be separated from *iso*-propanol.

(*ii*) *Identification of volatile products containing a carbonyl group*

The carbonyl compounds comprising the neutral volatile fraction are most readily identified as their 2,4-dinitrophenylhydrazones using thin-layer chromatographic methods, supplemented by visible spectroscopy.

1. *Preparation of derivatives*

Depending upon the reaction conditions, α-hydroxyl carbonyl compounds will form either the *mono-* or *bis*-2,4-dinitrophenylhydrazone, assuming an excess of reagent is present. In the case of acetoin, under the acid conditions to be described, the *bis*-2,4-dinitrophenylhydrazone of diacetyl would be formed. However, in ethanolic solution acetoin forms its own *mono*-derivative.

It is difficult to stipulate precise quantities of reagents for these identification procedures and a rough guide to conditions only can be given. Trial and error will enable a scheme to be worked out for individual cases. The method of Dagley, Trudgill and Callely (1961) employs a 100-fold excess of acid reagent for the determination of glycolaldehyde as the *bis*-2,4 dinitrophenylhydrazone of glyoxal. This method can be easily adapted to suit identification requirements for fermentation media.

In the present case it is advisable to fit a reflux condenser to a Quickfit flask containing the test solution (neutral volatile distillate, or a suitable dilution of this) and the reagent. The temperature of the water bath should be raised slowly over a period of about 20 min, in order not to lose any of the volatile products, and heated at 100°C on a boiling water bath for 1 h. The solution is allowed to cool and then filtered on a Buchner funnel. The derivatives are washed with water and small volumes of ice-cold ethanol to remove acid and unreacted 2,4-dinitrophenylhydrazine, air dried, and then taken up in benzene for thin layer chromatography (Byrne, 1965).

As previously noted, α-hydroxy carbonyl compounds react with acid 2,4-dinitrophenylhydrazine to give *bis*-2,4-dinitrophenylhydrazones. To permit distinction between compounds such as diacetyl and acetoin a method for preparing the derivatives in alcoholic solution is useful. Wolfrom and Arsenault (1960) use a three-fold excess of reagent over test compounds. The method involves the addition of an ethanolic suspension of 2,4-dinitrophenylhydrazine to an aqueous solution of the test sample and refluxing for 16 h.

Procedure: A suspension of 2,4-dinitrophenylhydrazine in ethanol is refluxed for 16 h with aliquots of the neutral volatile fraction such that the reaction is carried out in 90% ethanolic solution. The mixture is filtered while still hot; this removes unreacted 2,4-dinitrophenylhydrazine and most of the *bis*-2,4-dinitrophenylhydrazones. The filtrate is taken to dryness under reduced pressure (rotary evaporator) and the residue taken up in benzene for thin layer chromatography.

The thin layer chromatography of a comprehensive list of compounds as their 2,4-dinitrophenylhydrazones is described by Byrne (1965).

2. Thin layer chromatography of 2,4-dinitrophenylhydrazones (Byrne, 1965)

The preparation of plates, application of sample, and procedure for development are described on pp. 142–143.

Solvents: Two solvents, of equal merit, can be used, 80–100°C light petroleum-diethylether (70 : 30) and benzene-tetrahydrofuran (93 : 7).

Resolution: Approximate R_F values for some common derivatives are given below.

Light petroleum-diethylether: glyoxal (*mono*) 0·094, diacetyl (*mono*) 0·153, formaldehyde 0·173, pyruvaldehyde (*mono*) 0·193, acetaldehyde 0·220 and acetone 0·260.

Benzene-tetrahydrofuran: diacetyl (*bis*) 0·59, pyruvaldehyde (*mono*) 0·56, pyruvaldehyde (*bis*) 0·54, diacetyl (*mono*) 0·50, glyoxal (*bis*) 0·47, glyoxal (*mono*) 0·42 and acetoin 0·14.

All the values quoted are for a 15 cm front.

(iii) Determination of individual neutral volatile products

1. Methanol

Methanol is usually determined by oxidation to formaldehyde followed by determination of the formaldehyde produced with chromotropic acid. The reaction with chromotropic acid is reasonably specific for formaldehyde, but diacetyl and methyl glyoxal are known to interfere. The method described (Hindberg and Wieth, 1963) is the latest of the group which determines methanol as formaldehyde. The authors claim to have standardized the oxidation procedure, and the method has the advantage of requiring only simple apparatus.

5

Method of Hindberg and Wieth (1963)

Reagents:

Ethanol, 8·1% (w/v). 10 ml of 99% ethanol added to 90 ml of distilled water.

$KMnO_4$–H_3PO_4 solution. 15·8 g $KMnO_4$; 14 ml of 85% phosphoric acid and distilled water to 500 ml. This should give 0·99–1·01N (0·2M) $KMnO_4$. The solution can be stored.

Bisulphite solution. 5·0 g $NaHSO_3$ made to 100 ml with distilled water. Should be freshly prepared daily.

Phosphoric acid, H_3PO_4, 85%

Chromotropic acid reagent. 750 mg of chromotropic acid (1,8-dihydroxy-naphthalene-3,6-disulphonic acid), sodium salt, made up to 50 ml with distilled water.

Should be freshly prepared daily.

Sulphuric acid, 95%

Procedure: A sample (3 ml) of the solution is transferred to a 200 ml conical distillation flask which is stoppered by a closed tube which serves as a "cold finger", fitted with a B29 joint (Fig. 9). Approximately 2 ml of acetone is placed in the "finger" and sufficient dry ice added to secure a temperature of about − 80°C.

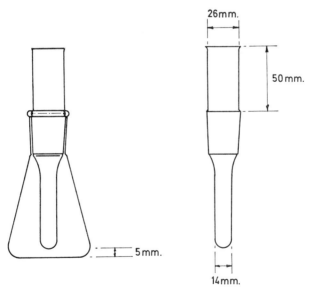

FIG. 9. Distillation flask and "cold finger" for methanol determination by the method of Hindberg and Wieth (1963).

The stoppered flask is transferred to a boiling water bath and kept in the vertical position. Distillation is continued until the water has been quantitatively removed from the sample and appears as a dense layer of ice on the outside of the "finger". The distillation should be complete within 15–20 min after which the "finger" is carefully transferred to a similar but dry flask taking care that ice is not lost during the manipulations.

One ml of the thawed distillate is transferred to a test tube and 1 ml of ethanol solution and 5 ml of $KMnO_4$-H_3PO_4 solution added, and the contents are thoroughly mixed. After oxidation for 10 min at room temperature 2·5 ml of $NaHSO_3$ solution are added, followed immediately by 0·5 ml of 85% H_3PO_4. The contents are mixed until they become colourless.

To 1 ml of the resulting reaction mixture 1 ml of chromotropic acid reagent and 8 ml of 95% H_2SO_4 are added. The tube, after carefully mixing the contents, is placed in a boiling water bath for 5 min. After cooling the extinction is read at 570 nm. A blank, in which 1 ml of distilled water replaces the sample, is taken through the oxidation and colour development steps. E_{570} of the blank in a 1 cm cuvette should not exceed 0·060.

Range of method: According to the authors the relationships between E_{570} and methanol concentration is linear up to about 700 μg/ml, which corresponds to an E_{570} of 1·35. They claim that reasonable accuracy is possible at higher concentrations since the coloured product may be diluted with concentrated sulphuric acid to the range where it can be read.

Hindberg and Wieth have used the method for blood and plasma and report the recovery of added methanol to plasma to be 100·6% ± 1·8.

Interference: Data on the interference by diacetyl may be found in Snell and Snell (1953) Volume III, and in the paper of Thornton and Speck (1950).

2. Ethanol

A number of non-specific methods for the determination of ethanol exist. A great many of these are useless in the presence of a volatile product other than ethanol. This is true of the Cavett (1937/38) method as modified by McGill (1966). Such a method, which is involved and time-consuming, has no advantage over the simple non-specific ceric ammonium nitrate method of Reid and Salmon (1955), which may be carried out within a few minutes. Unfortunately, the interferences which can occur with this ceric ammonium nitrate method have never been adequately worked out. Only a short note in the paper of Reid and Truelove (1952) is devoted to interfering substances which include certain oxidizing agents (organic peroxides), reducing agents, sulphate ions and compounds containing hydroxyl groups. However, if the compounds present in a neutral volatile distillate which contains an alcohol have been identified it may be worth while to check for interferences.

Reagent:
20 g of pure ceric ammonium nitrate is dissolved in 100 ml of standardized 4N-nitric acid, set aside for a day or two to clarify, and then decanted into a clean bottle.

The reagent is conveniently standardized as follows. 5 ml of the reagent is pipetted into a 250 ml conical flask and 50 ml of dilute sulphuric acid added. It is titrated with 0·1N-ferrous ammonium sulphate until the yellow colour is almost discharged. The ferrous solution is then added dropwise until the end-point is reached, using o-phenanthroline as internal indicator. The normality is adjusted to the requisite value of 0·36N, either by diluting with water or by adding the calculated weight of ceric ammonium nitrate.

Procedure: (As suitable for 4 cm cells of the Unicam SP 600 spectrophotometer; the quantities can be scaled according to the instrument used.) Ten ml of the sample are pipetted into a dry 4 cm cell and 4 ml of ceric ammonium nitrate reagent added; the solutions are mixed by means of a

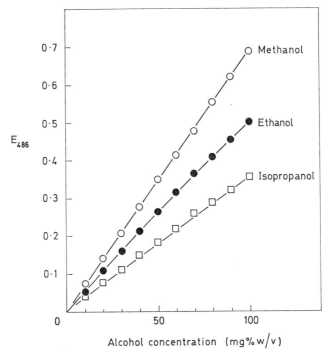

FIG. 10. Calibration curves for the estimation of alcohols by the method of Reid and Salmon (1955).

thin glass rod. A blank is prepared in a similar manner using 10 ml of distilled water.

Exactly 5 min after mixing, the extinction is read at 486 nm. Calibration curves are prepared for the various alcohols and examples plotted from the data of Reid and Salmon (1955) are shown in Fig. 10.

Range: The effective range investigated has been 0·1 to 1·0 mg/ml of the alcohol with an estimated accuracy of ± 0·02 mg/ml.

A specific method for the determination of alcohols as a group has been described by Stiller (1961) who based his technique on that of a spot test for alcohols given by Feigl (1957). This method, which involves the formation of a vanadium oxinate complex with the alcohol, may be used directly to determine a single alcohol present in a mixture of other types of compound, and may well be useful for the determination of a pair of alcohols if a completely specific method is available for one of them. Methanol, ethanol, butanol and amyl alcohol can be determined by this procedure. According to Mantel and Anbar (1964) the Stiller method is not applicable to microgram quantities of isopropanol but can be made so by suitable modifications (see p. 105).

Reagents:

Ammonium vanadate solution containing 1 mg of vanadium per ml
8-Hydroxyquinoline (oxine) solution, 2·5% (w/v) in 6% acetic acid
Acetate buffer solution, pH 4. (100 ml of acetic acid and 53·5 g of sodium acetate).
Benzene, analytical reagent grade
Sodium hydroxide, 1N

In this method the two phases are kept at fixed relative volumes, the ratio of the organic to aqueous phase being 2 : 1.

Procedure: Ammonium vanadate solution (1 ml) and 1 ml of the oxine solution are added to the test sample (containing 50–500 μg of alcohol) followed by buffer solution to a volume of 7 ml.

The mixture is shaken on a mechanical shaker (Stiller uses a Burrell wrist action shaker) with 15 ml of benzene for 20 min. After separation of the phases, extraction from the aqueous phase is repeated twice with fresh quantities of benzene and the other reagents.

The benzene extracts are collected and, after washing with 10 ml of N-NaOH, the extinction is read at 390 nm, at which wavelength the sensitivity is highest and the influence of oxine on the readings very small. A distilled water blank is put through the same procedure.

Range: A linear relation was shown to exist between E_{390} and concentration of the alcohol in the final benzene solution up to 16–20 μg per ml. The maximum deviation in results is reported to be ± 2·5%.

Stiller records that the smallest quantities of butyl or amyl alcohol that can be detected in the final benzene solution are 1 μg/ml (equivalent to 10 μg/ml in the original sample) and for ethanol or methanol 2–3 μg (equivalent to 20–30 μg/ml in the original sample).

Possible cation interferences were not studied.

A relatively specific method for ethanol

The enzymic method described by Bonnichsen in Bergmeyer (1963) is most useful and is very sensitive. There are interferences in the method from other alcohols, especially n-propanol and n-butanol but these may be easily overcome by the very different rates of oxidation of the interfering alcohols.

Determination of ethanol (Bonnichsen, 1963)

Principle: Ethanol is determined using ethanol dehydrogenase, the production of NADH being followed spectrophotometrically. The equilibrium of the reaction

$$\text{Ethanol} + \text{NAD}^+ \rightleftharpoons \text{acetaldehyde} + \text{NADH} + \text{H}^+$$

at pH 7 lies well to the left, but can be completely displaced, at a more alkaline pH, by trapping the acetaldehyde produced as its semicarbazone.

Reagents:

Pyrophosphate-glycine-semicarbazide buffer

$Na_4P_2O_7$, $10H_2O$ (33·33 g), semicarbazide hydrochloride (8·33 g), and glycine (1·66 g) are dissolved in doubly distilled water. 2N NaOH (ca. 33·33 ml) is added and the solution diluted to 1 litre with distilled water. The pH should be approximately 8·8. This solution is stable for a week when kept at room temperature. Absorption of CO_2 from the atmosphere must be prevented.

NAD solution

NAD (120 mg) is dissolved in doubly distilled water (1 ml). This solution is stable for one week when stored refrigerated.

Ethanol standard

Standard ethanol solutions (0·8–1·9 mg/ml) in ampoules are comercially available, and these should be used on the same day as opening.

Alcohol dehydrogenase, approximately 30 mg protein/ml

A commercially available preparation, such as that supplied by C. F. Boehringer und Soehne, should be used. The suspension supplied is used undiluted. It remains stable at $-20°C$ for several months.

If deproteinization of the sample is required then this is best achieved using perchloric acid. The precipitated protein is centrifuged and the clear supernatant is used for analysis.

Procedure: The wavelength used is 340 nm, cuvettes are of 1 cm light path, and the measurements are made against an air or water blank. The test cuvette contains buffer (3·0 ml); NAD solution (0·01 ml) and sample (0·04 ml). A series of standard cuvettes is also set up. These contain buffer (3·0 ml), NAD solution (0·01 ml), and standard ethanol solution (0·005 ml). The standards should be 4 μg, 6 μg, 7·5 μg and 9 μg of ethanol per cuvette.

The contents of the cuvettes are thoroughly mixed and E_1 is determined. Alcohol dehydrogenase (0·01 ml) is mixed into the cuvette, and this is allowed to stand for 70 min (at most 90 min) at 22°–26°C. E_2 is then determined.

Calculation: The calibration obtained is linear and varies little in slope for each series of determinations if the temperature is controlled adequately. The ΔE value (E_2–E_1) is converted to μg of ethanol per cuvette by consulting the calibration curve and knowledge of the sample dilution allows calculation of the concentration in the original sample. If the calibration obtained is not linear then this is usually due to too low an NAD concentration. Concentrations of ethanol as low as 1 μg/ml of sample can be estimated by this procedure, and the sensitivity can be further increased if the fluorescence of NADH is measured.

Specificity: Under the above conditions only primary and secondary aliphatic alcohols react.

3. Isopropanol

There is not a wide choice of method for isopropanol determination. The microdiffusion method of Neish (1952) following dichromate oxidation to acetone has appeared in various forms, with no substantial or important modification, and is useful. Acetone is determined simultaneously. Acetaldehyde interferes in this method.

Isopropanol plus acetone by microdiffusion (Neish, 1952)

Reagents:

Ferrous sulphate, 18% solution. 36 g of $FeSO_4$, $7H_2O$ is dissolved in water and the volume made to 200 ml. The solution should be freshly prepared daily.

Alkaline salicylaldehyde reagent. One volume of salicylaldehyde is dissolved in 4 volumes of absolute ethanol and filtered, if necessary. The reagent should be freshly prepared daily. One volume of the resulting solution is mixed with four volumes of 5N-NaOH.

Sodium dichromate, 2M. 119·2 g of $Na_2Cr_2O_7, 2H_2O$ is dissolved in water and the volume made to 200 ml. The solution is stored in a glass stoppered bottle.

Sulphuric acid, 19N. 1 litre of conc. H_2SO_4 is added cautiously to 1 litre of water with stirring.

Procedure:

(a) *Oxidation step.* The sample (1 or 2 ml) containing 1–4 mg of acetone and isopropanol is pipetted into a 100 ml volumetric flask, 1 ml of 2M-sodium dichromate added followed by 10 ml of 19N-H_2SO_4. The mixture is allowed to stand for 30 min at room temperature and is then treated with 20 ml of the 18% ferrous sulphate solution, made to volume with distilled water and mixed thoroughly. This procedure oxidizes the isopropanol to acetone and 1 or 2 ml portions of the final solution are taken for the determination of acetone by microdiffusion.

(b) *Microdiffusion analysis.* Two ml of the alkaline salicylaldehyde reagent is pipetted into the inner well of a Conway No. 1 microdiffusion unit. The lid is greased and placed lightly in position. One or 2 ml of the oxidized mixture is pipetted into the outer well and the unit sealed immediately. After standing overnight at room temperature the coloured contents of the centre well are transferred quantitatively to a 10 ml volumetric flask with distilled water and a Pasteur pipette. The volume is made to the mark and the extinction read at 530 nm.

Calibration and range: The oxidation procedure is applicable to samples containing 1–4 mg of acetone and isopropanol per ml and the microdiffusion analysis is suitable for 10–40 μg of acetone. The method is calibrated by putting standard solutions of acetone through the oxidation and microdiffusion procedures.

Wehle (1959) has described a fairly specific titrimetric method for isopropanol, which differs from methanol, ethanol and *n*-propanol in being oxidized by bromine in concentrated aqueous acid or in saturated aqueous $KHSO_4$ solution. The acetone produced is further brominated (acetone itself does not interfere). The bromine taken up in the further reaction can be determined iodometrically. By difference the amount of isopropanol can be determined with an accuracy of ± 3%.

Reagents:

Potassium bromide—potassium bromate solution, 0·1N with respect to each

Phosphoric acid, conc

Potassium iodide, 20% w/v solution

Sodium thiosulphate, 0·1N

Procedure: In a glass stoppered 250 ml flask are mixed 25 ml of 0·1N KBr-KBrO₃ solution, 5–15 ml of sample (neutral volatile distillate containing 0·2 to 0·3% isopropanol), and 10 ml of concentrated H₃PO₄. The flask is stoppered, contents mixed and heated for 1 h in a water bath at 40°C. After cooling and shaking to absorb all the bromine, 10 ml of 20% KI solution is added and the flask kept tightly stoppered in a water bath at 90°C for 15 min to liberate iodine equivalent to the bromine in the brominated acetone. The flask is cooled and the contents titrated with 0·1N sodium thiosulphate, and compared with a water blank carried through the same treatment.

Isopropanol: Mantel and Anbar (1964) have modified the Stiller (1961) vanadium oxinate method to permit the estimation of isopropanol. Neither of these publications furnishes data on the failure of the Stiller procedure for isopropanol. The modified method, which increases the sensitivity of the Stiller procedure by a salting-out step, involves the preliminary preparation of a benzene solution of vanadium oxinate, the use of acetate buffer and the salting-out of the isopropanol-vanadium-oxinate complex by a saturated lithium sulphate solution into the benzene layer.

Reagents:
   Acetate buffer, pH 4·3. Fifty-three g of sodium acetate are added to 100 ml of acetic acid and 10 ml of water. Solution is aided by gentle heat.
   Ammonium vanadate solution, containing 1 mg of vanadium per ml
   Benzene, analytical reagent grade
   Vanadium oxinate solution. Five ml of a 2·5% (w/v) 8-hydroxyquinoline solution in 6% acetic acid and 5 ml of the ammonium vanadate solution are transferred to a separatory funnel. Ten ml of acetate buffer is added and 150 ml of benzene. After shaking for 5 min the two layers are allowed to separate completely and the aqueous layer is discarded. The solution should be freshly prepared each day.
   Lithium sulphate, saturated solution; 34 g of AR lithium sulphate in 100 ml of water
   Sodium hydroxide solution, 1N

Procedure: The sample (10 ml, containing 1·5–30 μg isopropanol per ml) is pipetted into a separatory funnel and 3–4 g lithium sulphate are added, with shaking, to produce a saturated solution. The pH is adjusted to between 4 and 4·5. (If less than 10 ml of the sample is taken the volume is made up to 10 ml with saturated lithium sulphate solution).
   Ten ml of the vanadium oxinate reagent is added and the mixture

shaken for 20 min. After separation, the aqueous layer is discarded. The pink-coloured benzene solution is centrifuged for 5 min to eliminate turbidity and the authors read the extinction at 380 nm in a 2 cm light-path cell.

Calibration and range: 0·3 g of analytical grade isopropanol is accurately weighed and transferred to a 1 litre volumetric flask and diluted to the mark with distilled water. One ml of this stock solution is pipetted into a 100 ml volumetric flask and made to volume with distilled water. This solution contains 3 μg of isopropanol per ml. Quantities of 1 to 10 ml are taken through the analytical procedure. A linear calibration was obtained between 3 and 30 μg of isopropanol.

To increase the sensitivity of the method 15 ml of vanadium oxinate can be used and the extinction measured in 4 cm light-path cells; this extends the method down to 1·5 μg/ml of sample.

The accuracy of the method was tested at four different concentrations as given below:

Isopropanol in sample μg/ml	Relative standard deviation %
3·0	±10
6·0	±3·42
10·0	±3·28
20·0	±2·37

4. n-*Butanol*

Suitable methods for the determination of *n*-butanol are few and in most cases, where a mixture of alcohols is encountered, separation prior to estimation has been employed. Neish (1951) has separated simple aliphatic alcohols by chromatography on a celite-water column using carbon tetrachloride and chloroform as the developing solvents. Each alcohol can then be determined, in the presence of the developing solvent, by dichromate oxidation and measurement of the dichromate consumed. The method permits resolution of a mixture of methanol, ethanol, propanol or isopropanol, *n*-butanol and isoamyl alcohol. Diacetyl and acetoin are found in the butanol and isopropanol fractions and must be corrected for. Acetone also appears in the butanol fraction but does not interfere since it is not oxidized by dichromate under the conditions used by Neish.

However, with the availability of specific methods for ethanol and isopropanol it would seem possible in many circumstances to avoid the separation procedure. A general method for the determination of total alcohols combined with specific methods for individuals of the group should enable the determination of *n*-butanol by difference.

5. *Acetaldehyde*

Acetaldehyde can be determined by enzymic or by chemical methods.

Enzymic methods: The use of alcohol dehydrogenase from yeast permits the spectrophotometric determination of acetaldehyde by measuring the decrease in extinction at 340 nm of NADH under conditions where the equilibrium of the reaction

$$CH_3CHO + NADH + H^+ \rightleftharpoons C_2H_5OH + NAD^+$$

lies far to the right (Bergmeyer, 1963). The enzyme is not specific for acetaldehyde but other aldehydes react at considerably lower rates.

Yeast aldehyde dehdyrogenase has also been used (Lundquist, 1958) for spectrophotometric determination of acetaldehyde in the reaction

$$CH_3CHO + NAD^+ + H_2O \rightleftharpoons CH_3COOH + NADH + H^+.$$

Again, the enzyme is not specific for acetaldehyde.

Determination of acetaldehyde with yeast alcohol dehydrogenase (*Bergmeyer* 1963)

Principle: The consumption of NADH, in the reduction of acetaldehyde to ethanol, is spectrophotometrically monitored. At a slightly acid pH the reaction proceeds virtually to completion.

Reagents:
Phosphate solution
This must be of appropriate concentration and pH such that the addition of a small volume (e.g., 0·2 ml) to the sample produces a buffered solution approximately 0·25M and of pH 6·5. In the fermentation train procedure the acetaldehyde produced will be present in the dry ice trap and will thus be in aqueous solution. If this sample is combined with the centrifuged medium as advised (see p. 64) then obviously the nature of the medium and its final pH will determine the nature of the phosphate addition. If dilutions of the sample have to be made then this is probably best done with 0·25M phosphate buffer, pH 6·5, thus achieving the desired end.
NADH
NADH-Na₂ (2·5 mg) is dissolved in 1% NaHCO₃ to a final volume of 1 ml. This is stable for about 14 days at 0°–4°C, and about 4 weeks in the frozen state.
Alcohol dehydrogenase (ADH)
This enzyme is commercially available as preparations containing 10 mg protein per ml. It is diluted to a suitable activity with 2·4M

ammonium sulphate solution, containing 3% w/v $Na_4P_2O_7$ and glycine 1% w/v, pH ca. 8.

The ADH solution should not be stored frozen and it is stable at 0–4°C for several months.

Procedure: Sample preparation. Since acetaldehyde boils at 20·2°C it will be appreciated that in order to avoid acetaldehyde loss, the sample is best maintained cold until just prior to the assay, and that stoppered containers are used for handling the sample.

Spectrophotometric measurements. The assay is performed at room temperature, using 1 cm light path quartz cuvettes fitted with lids. For greatest sensitivity the wavelength used is 340 nm and measurements are made against a water or air blank.

The following are rapidly pipetted into the experimental cuvette: buffered sample (2 ml) and NADH solution (0·05 ml). The contents are quickly mixed with a glass rod, the cuvette lid is placed in position and E_1 is determined; ADH suspension (0·05 ml) is then mixed in and the cuvette lid is rapidly replaced. After 3–5 min the extinction E_2 is determined. If the presence of other substrates for the enzyme (see below) is suspected, it is best to check E_2 for any slow increase.

Calculation: The quantity of acetaldehyde per cuvette is given by

$$\frac{\Delta E \times 2 \cdot 1}{\epsilon} = \mu\text{moles of acetaldehyde}$$

where ϵ = extinction coefficient of NADH (ϵ_{340} = 6·22 $cm^2/\mu mole$)
      $\Delta E = E_2 - E_1$.

Sensitivity: If ΔE values of 0·010 can successfully be measured, then as little as 4×10^{-3} μmole of acetaldehyde can be quantitatively determined.

Specificity: Yeast ADH also reacts with the following aldehydes: glycolaldehyde, formaldehyde, propionaldehyde, butyraldehyde, valeraldehyde, isobutyraldehyde and glyceraldehyde. The reaction rate is considerably slower and the presence of these compounds leads to a non-constant end point. If this should occur then extrapolation to zero will give the true ΔE that corresponds to the acetaldehyde present.

In the presence of high concentrations of ethanol the reaction does not proceed to completion. However, the major source of error in this determination is the volatility of acetaldehyde and thus care must be taken to minimize any loss.

Chemical methods: Sodium nitroprusside gives an unstable blue colour with acetaldehyde in alkaline solutions and this can be quantitated in a spectrophotometer (Desnuelle and Naudet, 1945; Neish, 1952). As periodate and iodate do not interfere markedly, it is possible to determine the acetaldehyde produced by oxidation of 2,3-butanediol without prior separation. Another more suitable method is also colorimetric, involving reaction with p-hydroxydiphenyl as utilized in the determination of lactate by the method of Barker and Summerson (1941) with subsequent modification by Hullin and Noble (1953) and Nanni and Baldini (1964).

Method of Nanni and Baldini (1964)

The method is applicable to the determination of acetaldehyde in the absence of pyruvate and lactate.

Reagents:

p-Hydroxydiphenyl solution; 150 mg of recrystallized reagent is dissolved in 10 ml of A.R. ethanol. Should be freshly prepared every two weeks.

Sulphuric acid, conc.

Procedure: Samples (1 ml) are pipetted into glass stoppered tubes cooled to 8°–10°C. 6 ml of conc. H_2SO_4 is added carefully to each tube, followed by 0·1 ml of the p-hydroxydiphenyl solution, the stoppers immediately replaced and the tubes incubated in a water bath at $29 \pm 1°C$ for 30 min, followed by 90 sec in a boiling water bath. Immediately after this treatment the tubes are cooled in ice-water and the extinction of the resulting violet-coloured solution read at 568 nm against a blank of distilled water similarly treated.

Range: Calibration is linear over the range 0–6 μg of acetaldehyde (corresponding to approximately 0–12 μg of lactic acid in the full procedure and which the authors claim to be able to measure with an accuracy of $\pm 0·01$ μg).

6. Acetone

Acetone may be determined colorimetrically by reaction with salicylaldehyde in alkaline solution and the method is fairly specific. An enzymic method was partially developed by Jakoby and Fredericks (1962) using a secondary alcohol dehydrogenase purified from a species of *Pseudomonas.* This enzyme carried out the NAD-linked oxidation of secondary alcohols and the NADH-linked reduction of ketones; substrates included acetone, isopropanol and acetone.

Method of Snell and Snell (1953)

Reagents:

Salicylaldehyde solution. One volume of salicylaldehyde is dissolved in four volumes of absolute ethanol (commercial) and filtered if necessary.

Sodium hydroxide, 10n

Acetone standard. One ml of reagent grade acetone is dissolved in 200 ml of water and is standardized iodometrically. Store in refrigerator in a glass stoppered bottle.

Procedure: The sample, containing 10–40 μg of acetone is pipetted into a suitable test tube and the volume made to 5 ml with distilled water. Four ml of 10N-NaOH are added and mixed, followed by 0·1 ml of the salicylaldehyde reagent. The tube is heated at 45°–50°C for 20 min and then allowed to stand for 30 min at room temperature. The percentage light transmission is read at 530 nm (Neish uses 19 mm light path cuvettes). A series of standard solutions and a water blank are run in parallel with the unknowns.

Calibration: A linear plot is obtained for log percentage light transmission versus acetone concentration per tube and this is used for interpolation of the unknowns.

Interference: The colour intensity is increased slightly by the presence of acetoin or diacetyl in amounts some ten-fold that of the acetone. Under such circumstances the appropriate amounts of acetoin and diacetyl should be added to the standards.

The microdiffusion method of Neish (1952)

Neish (1952) has applied the salicylaldehyde reaction of Snell and Snell to microdiffusion thus permitting the determination of acetone in fermentation liquors without the necessity for prior distillation.

Reagents:
Alkaline salicylaldehyde solution. One volume of the salicylaldehyde reagent described in the previous method is mixed with four volumes of 5N-NaOH. It should be prepared daily.
Acetone standard, as for the previous method

Procedure: 2 ml of the alkaline salicylaldehyde reagent is pipetted into the centre well of a Conway No. 1 microdiffusion unit. The lid is greased with vaseline and placed lightly in position. One to two ml of a suitably diluted fermentation medium containing 10–40 μg of acetone is pipetted into the outer well and the unit immediately sealed. It is allowed to stand overnight at room temperature and the coloured contents of the inner well are quantitiatively transferred with the use of distilled water for rinsing, and the volume made to 10 ml. The percentage light transmission at 530 nm is measured (Neish uses 19 mm cuvettes).

Calibration: A series of acetone standards and a water blank are run in parallel with the unknowns. The plot of log percentage light transmission versus acetone concentration is linear over the range used (10–40 μg).

The microdiffusion method can also be used for the determination of acetone plus isopropanol (see p. 103).

7. Methyl Glyoxal

An enzymic method for the determination of methyl glyoxal has been described by Klotzsch and Bergmeyer (1963) but the authors state that the technique has been used only for pure solutions and the general value of the method is, therefore, not yet recorded. There are few chemical methods which offer specificity for methyl glyoxal but Dechary, Kun and Pitot (1954) have reported a colorimetric method based on reaction with 2,3-diaminophenazine in acid solution.

Method of Dechary, Kun and Pitot (1954)

Reagents:

Colour reagent. 21 mg of crystalline 2,3-diaminophenazine are dissolved in 50–60 ml of glacial acetic acid by gentle warming and stirring. After dissolution, the volume is made to 100 ml with glacial acetic acid.

The *o*-diamine is prepared by the method of Steigman (1946) and purified by the method of Fischer and Hepp (1889).

Acetic acid, 8·5N

This is prepared by mixing glacial acetic acid (1 vol) and water (1 vol). It is advisable to prepare 2 litres of this solution and use the same solution throughout the analyses.

Potassium nitrite solution, prepared by dissolving 20 mg of the C.P. salt in 100 ml of distilled water. The solution is chilled in an ice bath prior to use.

Hypophosphorous acid, purified 50% solution (Oldbury Electro-Chemical Co., 19, Rector Street, New York 6, N.Y.).

Standard methyl glyoxal solution. Methyl glyoxal may be prepared by the method of Neuberg, Faiker and Levite (1917) and analysed by iodometric titration (Kuhn and Hecksher, 1926).

Procedure: Samples (1.0 ml), containing not more than 1·2 μmoles of methyl glyoxal, are treated with the colour reagent (1 ml) in calibrated test tubes. These, together with a reagent blank, are heated in a boiling water bath for 10 min. The tubes are transferred to an ice water bath and, after equilibration, potassium nitrite (1·0 ml) and hypophosphorous acid solution (0·5 ml) are added. The tubes are then returned to the boiling water bath for 20 min. After cooling, the volume of the solutions is made up to 4 ml by the addition of glacial acetic acid, and the E_{610} of the solutions is determined against the reagent blank. Cuvettes of 1 cm light path are used.

Since the chromophore produced from methyl glyoxal is dependent upon the heating time and the acidity of the reagent it is best to construct a calibration curve and also to include several standards with each batch of samples.

Interference: The major source of interference may be ethanedial for whose estimation the procedure was originally devised. In the presence of this compound, which is best estimated at 600 nm, then methyl glyoxal can be determined at 715 nm.

8. *Estimation of acetoin and diacetyl*
(Brenner, Blick, Frenkel and Siebënberg, 1963)

Principle: Diacetyl is estimated by reaction with hydroxylamine to produce dimethylglyoxime whose concentration can be spectrophotometrically determined at 230 nm. Acetoin is also estimated by the above procedure, after prior conversion to diacetyl by oxidation with ferric chloride.

Reagents:

Ferric chloride C.P., 5% aqueous solution. For conversion of acetoin to diacetyl.

Hydroxylamine hydrochloride (A.R. Grade), 10% aqueous solution. For estimation of diacetyl.

Sodium tetraborate, A.R. Grade. An aqueous solution (1·91%) is prepared with freshly boiled distilled water. The final pH should be 9·1.

Dimethylglyoxime standard. Dimethylglyoxime (0·1348 g) is dissolved in distilled water to a final volume of 1 litre. One ml of this solution contains the equivalent of 100 μg of diacetyl.

Procedure:

(a) Conversion of acetoin to diacetyl.

A sample (25 ml) is added to ferric chloride solution (75 ml) in a 1-litre distillation flask. The mixture is distilled and the distillate is collected in a graduated tube containing 3 ml of distilled water. The delivery tube from the condenser dips below the water level in the tube. An accurately measured volume is distilled (15 ml) and the final volume is made up to 20 ml. The dilution that occurs here, and that on addition of ferric chloride solution, must be allowed for in calculating the acetoin content of the sample.

(b). Estimation of diacetyl.

Sample (10 ml) is pipetted into a calibrated test tube and hydroxylamine hydrochloride solution (1 ml) is added. The blank contains sample but no hydroxylamine hydrochloride solution. The tubes are placed in a bath containing a glycerol-water mixture at 80°C for 10–15 min, following which period the bath temperature is increased to 103°–104°C. The tubes are left in this bath until the volume is reduced to 3–4 ml. The tubes are then cooled to room temperature and borate solution (2 ml) is added. At this stage hydroxylamine hydrochloride solution (1 ml) is added to the blank. The final volume of all tubes is made up to 20 ml with distilled water and the E_{230} of the samples determined against the blank. Cuvettes of 1 cm light path are used.

Calibration: The method is calibrated over the range 0–100 μg of diacetyl per 20 ml sample. The standard solutions are made by appropriately diluting the stock solution. Borate is also included; for example to make a 50 μg solution, stock solution (0·5 ml), borate (2·0 ml) and water (17·5 ml) are mixed. The E_{230} is determined against distilled water.

For acetoin the range per ml of original sample will not extend as low as for diacetyl since considerable dilution occurs on addition of ferric chloride. This could presumably be overcome by increasing the concentration of the ferric chloride solution such that dilution is much reduced, while the final concentration of ferric chloride is maintained.

2(c) *Specific analyses—Organic acids*

Traditionally, the carboxylic acids produced in fermentation have been roughly divided into those that are steam-volatile and those that are not, although the line of demarcation is not always sharp. All organic acids can be obtained from clarified fermentation liquors by continuous ether extraction at an acid pH (Section IV A2). The residual ether is removed by warming the receiver on a steam bath until the ether phase just disappears, and the residue consists of a mixture of the total organic acids. These acids may now be separated by chromatographic techniques and determined by titrimetric or specific chemical or enzymic methods. In the present section we consider first a general chromatographic separation and determination which embraces both steam-volatile and non-volatile acids. Then follows a survey of methods for separation, identification and determination of organic acids which, for convenience of treatment, we have classified as (1) steam-volatile, (2) α-keto acids, and (3) other acids. The steam distillation of acids is described in Section IV A4.

(i) *General methods for separation and determination of carboxylic acids*

Although it is not now essential to have recourse to column chromatography for the separation of carboxylic acids, column methods generally permit greater accuracy of determination of individual acids in a complex mixture and, of course, allow larger quantities to be processed. Additionally, when radiochemical methods yield small quantities of highly radioactive acid intermediates, addition of substantial quantities of carriers and separation by column chromatography prior to isotopic assay is a useful technique. With these objectives in view, a column chromatographic method is presented.

Bové and Raveux (1957) have recorded a silicic acid column technique based on their intensive testing of systems used by previous workers.

1. Determination of C_1–C_6 carboxylic acids by chromatography on silicic acid columns

Raveux and Bové (1957) have studied the various factors involved in column chromatography of carboxylic acids on silicic acid. They have also (Bové and Raveux, 1957) described a column chromatographic technique which permits the separation and determination of a variety of C_1–C_6 acids with an accuracy within 5%. A silicic acid column is employed and elution effected with tertiary butanol-chloroform mixtures of six different compositions.

Acids separated: The acids studied include butyric, propionic, acetic, fumaric, pyruvic, glutaric, succinic, lactic, α-oxoglutaric, aconitic, oxalic, glycollic, malic, citric, isocitric, and tartaric. Also formic, itaconic, tricarballylic, nitric and phosphoric acids were investigated.

Succinic and lactic acids are not separated from one another and oxalic and glycollic acids are only partially separated. Nitric acid is eluted with isocitric acid and phosphoric acid is not retained.

Range and sensitivity: It is possible to detect 1–2 μ-equiv of each acid, and sometimes less than 1 μ-equiv in the case of acids which are the first to be eluted. A total of 1·5 m-equiv can be loaded on the column.

Apparatus: The chromatography tube is shown in Fig. 11. It terminates on a capillary tube closed by a stopcock. The internal diameter of the tube is 12 mm, the height is 40 cm and it is roughly graduated in cm.

The solvent reservoir (Fig. 12) is that used by Bulen, Varner and Burrell (1952).

Cylinder of nitrogen
Pressure regulator with gas bleed
Fraction collector of constant volume delivery type.

Reagents:
Silicic acid (Mallinckrodt, specially prepared for chromatography)
Chloroform. This should be washed twice with its own volume of
    CO_2-free distilled water and then passed through filter paper.
Tertiary butanol, pure
Sulphuric acid, 0·5N

Sodium hydroxide, 0·005N, CO_2-free, should be prepared immediately
before use.

Phenol red indicator. Phenol red, 100 mg; 6 ml of 0·005N NaOH and
94 ml of CO_2-free water.

Solvent mixtures. Six mixtures of tertiary butanol and chloroform of
varying composition are used, as given in Table V. The chloroform
should be washed as described above. Each solvent is equilibrated with
one tenth of its volume of 0·5N–H_2SO_4 for 2 min in a separatory funnel.
After separation the organic phase is passed through filter paper to
remove droplets of the aqueous phase which still remains in suspension.
The solvent mixtures are prepared the evening prior to the day of use.

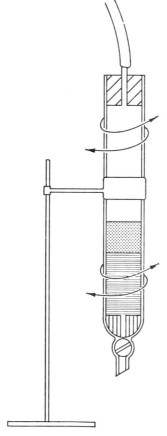

FIG. 11. Chromatography tube for separation of C_1–C_6 carboxylic acids by the
method of Bové and Raveux (1957).

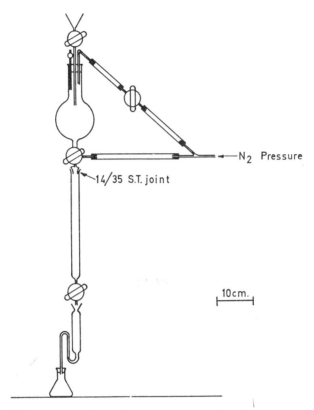

FIG. 12. Solvent reservoir and pressure system for chromatography (Bulen, Varner, and Burrell, 1952).

Preparation of the column: The efficiency of separation depends to a great extent on the method of preparing the column and the following method has been found to give the best results. Eight g of silicic acid is weighed (to within 10 mg), into a 150 ml Erlenmeyer flask and 5 ml of $0.5\text{N}-\text{H}_2\text{SO}_4$ is added in portions of 1 ml, stoppering the flask and shaking vigorously after each addition, to achieve uniformity. A white powder, which does not cling to the sides of the flask, should be obtained. Sixty ml of chloroform is added, the flask closed with a plastic stopper and shaken vigorously. This should yield a homogeneous suspension ready for pouring into the column.

A 12 mm diam. disk of Whatman No. 1 filter paper is placed at the bottom of the chromatography tube on the capillary, the stopcock is closed and 5 ml of chloroform introduced. 5.5 ml of the well-agitated silicic acid suspension is poured into the column, allowing the suspension to run down the walls in order to avoid introducing air bubbles. (5.5 ml of suspension corresponds to a height of 5 cm in a 12 mm diam. tube.) The sides of the tube are rinsed with chloroform, using a pipette. To remove any air bubbles the tube is rotated between index finger and thumb and tapped with a rubber-tipped glass rod. A pressure of 30 cm Hg is applied to the column, allowing the flow rate of chloroform to be about two drops per second, and continuing to rotate the column between thumb and index finger of both hands. The level of packed silicic acid is readily distinguished from that in suspension and it is essential to ensure that its surface remains horizontal. This is facilitated by placing an electric lamp behind the column.

TABLE V

Composition of solvent mixtures for elution of acids

Number of mixture	1	2	3	4	5	6
tert-Butanol, ml/100 ml mixture	8	13	20	28	35	40
Chloroform, ml/100 ml mixture	92	87	80	72	65	60
Volume of mixture used	120	120	100	100	100	120

When the level of silica in suspension is about 2 cm above the level of the packed column, the stopcock is closed and the pressure released. The next portion of 5·5 ml is added and the procedure repeated. By this means the surface of the packed column is not disturbed and different zones, unequally packed, are avoided. The procedure is repeated until all the 5·5 ml portions of suspension have been added. Towards the end, the Erlenmeyer flask is washed with a few ml of chloroform and the rest of the suspension is transferred to the tube; the packing procedure is then repeated. The stopcock is closed, the pressure released and, finally, 3 ml of chloroform is added very slowly down the side of the tube, taking care that the surface of the silicic acid column is not disturbed. By this means a uniform column, which should be 15·5 cm in height, is obtained.

Introduction of carboxylic acids. The sample of carboxylic acids in a 50 ml Erlenmeyer flask is concentrated to dryness in a current of nitrogen or compressed air, or over calcium chloride. If the acids are in the free state 0·5 ml of 1N–H_2SO_4 is added to the flask or, if they exist as Na or NH_4 salts, 0·5 ml of 5N-H_2SO_4 is used. Then 1 g of silicic acid is added and the flask contents are mixed thoroughly by agitation. Ten ml of chloroform are now added and the flask is stoppered and shaken vigorously. The contents are transferred to the column which already has 3 ml of chloroform on top, as previously described, pouring slowly down the walls. The flask is rinsed several times to transfer quantitatively all the silica to the column, the walls of the column are washed with chloroform and the chloroform meniscus is allowed to fall until it is just level with the packed silica. The silica containing the carboxylic acids now occupies 2 cm above the original column. Five ml of chloroform is poured very gently into the tube without disturbing the silica. A disk of filter paper is prepared as shown in Fig. 13 and, with the "teeth" upwards, is placed on the column and pressed lightly on the silica using a glass rod. A wad of glass wool is then placed on top of the paper disk.

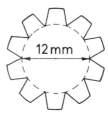

FIG. 13. Filter paper disk for placing on top of silicic acid column in the method of Bové and Raveux (1957).

Elution of the carboxylic acids. The chloroform meniscus is taken to the level of the glass wool and then 120 ml of the 8% tertiary butanol solvent is introduced. Elution is commenced by adjusting the pressure to deliver 2 ml every $2\frac{1}{2}$ min (14–15 cm Hg). The second solvent (13% tertiary butanol) is introduced when the meniscus of the first reaches the level of the glass wool and the process is continued for the other four solvent mixtures. The rate of flow decreases with the third or fourth solvent and the pressure can be progressively increased to 20 cm Hg to maintain the rate.

The authors give the column preparation as taking 2 h and passage of the first three solvents 7 h. If desired, elution may then be stopped overnight and recommenced next day, 7 h being taken for the last three solvents. The pressure should be released and the stopcock closed for the overnight period.

No significant diffusion of acids in the column occurs during the overnight period and there is no risk of their esterification with tertiary butanol.

The effluent is collected in 2 ml fractions. During the course of the elution, the silica immediately below that containing the sample becomes semitransparent and by the end of the elution extends for about 2 cm. Throughout, a hydration front exists which has not quite reached mid-column when tartaric acid is eluted. Sulphuric acid starts to be eluted when this front reaches mid-column.

Determination of eluted carboxylic acids: To each fraction a drop of phenol red indicator and 2–3 ml of CO_2-free water are added prior to titration with 0·005N–NaOH. Towards the end of the titration the solution should should be vigorously agitated. The blank values for the solvents are given in Table VI.

An accuracy of within 5% is achieved by this method. Non-volatile acids may be left for several hours before carrying out titration.

TABLE VI

Blank values for tertiary butanol solvents of various composition

Tertiary butanol content %	8	13	20	28	35	40
Acidity neutralized by the drop of indicator (μequiv.)	0·2	0·2	0·2	0·2	0·2	0·2
Acidity neutralized by the micro-burette (μequiv.)	0·1	0·2	0·3	0·4	0·6	1·2
Total mineral acid (μequiv.)	0·3	0·4	0·5	0·6	0·8	1·4

Capacity of the column. Up to a total of 1·5 m-equiv of carboxylic acids can be carried by the column described. This quantity is contained in 0·5 ml of sample which is mixed with 1 g of silicic acid for transfer to the column; this represents the maximum volume which can be handled on this column. For greater quantities of acids the authors recommend that the silica used for the transfer be placed in a desiccator over phosphorus pentoxide to remove part of the water initially present; it is then capable of absorbing a greater volume of sample and therefore more acids.

Separation. Table VII records the volume of effluent necessary to collect the various acids and the composition of the solvent mixtures which effect their elution.

The results of two separate chromatographic experiments are super-imposed in Fig. 14, each obtained with synthetic mixtures of acids. Complete separation, one from the other, is achieved in the order butyric, pro-pionic, acetic, fumaric, glutaric, succinic or lactic, α-oxoglutaric, *trans*-aconitic, pyrrolidine carboxylic, oxalic or glycollic, malic, citric, isocitric and tartaric.

Pyruvic is almost completely separated from fumaric and formic is almost completely separated from glutaric acid. Steam volatile fatty acids can, of course, be distilled and estimated separately.

2. Determination of eluted carboxylic acids

The most usual method for determination of carboxylic acids eluted from columns is by titration. This has certain disadvantages in being non-

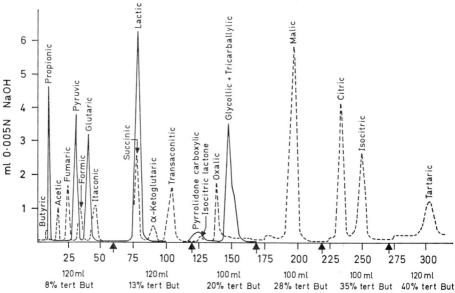

FIG. 14. Results of two separate chromatographic separations of synthetic mixtures of acids by the method of Bové and Raveux (1957).

TABLE VII

Acid	Quantity of acid separated μ-equiv	Volume of effluent in which the acid is eluted ml	Butanol content of effluent containing acid %
Fumaric	25	10	
Pyruvic	50	16	
Glutaric	50	16	8
Itaconic	25	18	
Succinic	50	18	
Lactic	100	22	13
α-Ketoglutaric	25	16	
Aconitic	50	22	
Oxalic	50	16	
		Volume of effluent containing 90% of the oxalic acid	20
Glycollic	50	16	
Tricarballylic	50	16	
Malic	200	30	28
Citric	100	20	35
Isocitric	50	30	
Tartaric	50	36	40

specific and also can be subject to error when more polar solvents are used in the elution programme, resulting in the leaching of mineral acid from the column.

Frohman and Orten (1953) have approached this problem by using the property of fluorescence of polycarboxylic acids on reaction with resorcinol. The method was rendered relatively non-specific since only one filter on the photofluorometer was used, but was standardized for each individual compound by its characteristic colour yield under the fixed conditions. The procedure is described for an eluate containing a carboxylic acid in tertiary amyl alcohol and chloroform but there is no reason why a dried (nitrogen stream in steam bath) aqueous sample of a carboxylic acid could not be put through the complete procedure. Of the monocarboxylic acids only α-keto acids interfere. Volatile fatty acids would be lost in the drying process.

Procedure of Frohman and Orten (1953)

Reagents:

Resorcinol, 0·4% w/v. Forty mg of freshly sublimed resorcinol is dissolved in 10 ml of absolute ethanol. The solution should be freshly prepared daily.

Quinine sulphate, standard solution. This contains 20 μg of quinine sulphate per 100 ml of distilled water.

Tertiary amyl alcohol–chloroform mixture. Twenty ml of redistilled amyl alcohol, boiling point 102°–103°C, is diluted with chloroform to 100 ml.

Sodium carbonate solution, 0·01%

Nitric acid, 1 : 1 by volume

Conc. H_2SO_4

NaOH, 1·5N

Conc. HCl

Diethyl ether

Following chromatography on silica gel, elution is effected with a mixture of tertiary amyl alcohol and chloroform, and 0·1 ml of 0·4% resorcinol is added to each fraction. Tubes containing known amounts of the acids to be used as standards and a tube used as a reagent blank are similarly treated. The samples are then evaporated to dryness in a bath of boiling salt water at 108°C which is sufficient to vaporize tertiary amyl alcohol. After heating for 20 min, each tube is aspirated for 2 min, while still in the bath, to remove the last traces of tertiary amyl alcohol vapour. After the tubes are dry 0·1 ml of conc. sulphuric acid is added and the tubes are heated for 20 min in a boiling water bath. The residue is dissolved in 5 ml 1·5N–NaOH and the fluorescence measured in a Coleman photofluorometer with a blue

TABLE VIII

Colour and intensity of fluorescence of acid

Acid	Colour of solution	Colour of fluorescence	Fluorescence relative to quinine sulphate standard
Fumaric	Colourless	Blue violet	24
α-Ketoglutaric	Yellow	Blue green	35
Oxaloacetic	Orange	Blue green	12
Succinic	Colourless	Yellow green	20
Aconitic	Colourless	Light blue	75
Malic	Colourless	Blue violet	22
Isocitric	Colourless	Light blue	58
Citric	Colourless	Sky blue	89

40 μg of each acid was used.

filter (B-2). The photofluorometer is arbitrarily set at 39 with the standard quinine solution, and the zero setting is adjusted with a reagent blank. The fluorescence of the sample is compared with a standard curve for the acid in question.

The method also lends itself to radiochemical counting procedures since the complexes are ether soluble.

Extraction method: After fluorescent determination of the acids 0·5 ml of conc. hydrochloric acid is added to each fraction which is then extracted twice with equal volumes of ether. The combined ether extracts are evaporated almost to dryness at room temperature in an aluminium planchette treated with 1 : 1 nitric acid. Before the last ether disappears, 1·0 ml of 0·01% Na_2CO_3 solution is added and drying completed in an oven at 80°C. The radio-activity can then be measured in a gas flow or Geiger counter. Alternatively the method could be adapted for scintillation assay.

(ii) Steam-volatile fatty acids

1. Thin-layer chromatography of straight-chain carboxylic acids

Lynes (1964) has described a thin-layer chromatographic separation of straight-chain carboxylic acids of low molecular weight which is very suitable for the analysis of steam distillates and sensitive to about 5 μg of an acid. The method is applicable to either the free acids or their ammonium salts, which are detected with methyl red after heating to remove excess ammonia.

Reagents:

Solvent system: methyl acetate-ammonia (2·5% vol aq), 95 : 5 v/v. As noted below, R_F values are greatly increased by allowing the solvent to stand in a stoppered flask for 24 h prior to use.

Spray reagent: methyl red, 0·1% alcoholic solution (industrial spirit is suitable). Solutions of reference carboxylic acids, 0·1% (w/v) in water or acetone.

Procedure: Separation of the acids is carried out in the standard fashion on 20 × 20 cm plates covered with silica gel. A layer thickness of 150 μm gives the best separations and Merck pre-coated plates are particularly suited to this purpose. When the solvent front has reached a line on the plate indicating the limit of travel, the plate is removed from the solvent tank and placed in an oven at 105°C for 2–3 min to evaporate the solvent and then allowed to cool.

If freshly-prepared solvent has been used the plate is replaced in the tank and again developed with the solvent. If, however, development is carried out with solvent which has been allowed to stand in a stoppered flask for 24 h the second development is not necessary. The R_F values of the acids increase with age of the solvent and therefore it is necessary to run mixtures of reference acids at the same time.

TABLE IX

R_F values of low molecular weight, straight chain carboxylic acids together with some branched chain acids for reference purposes. (Lynes, 1964)

	R_F		
	After double run in fresh solvent	After double run in solvent aged for 24 h	After single run in solvent aged for 24 h
Formic	0·05	0·07	0·03
Acetic	0·10	0·13	0·06
Propionic	0·15	0·30	0·15
n-Butyric	0·24	0·40	0·22
n-Valeric	0·39	0·50	0·30
n-Hexanoic	0·52	0·57	0·34
n-Heptanoic	0·55	0·60	0·39
n-Octanoic	0·58	0·66	0·43
n-Nonanoic	0·61	0·69	0·45
Trimethylacetic	0·57	0·71	0·47
α-Methylbutyric (dl)	0·39	0·65	0·39
β-Methylbutyric	0·34	0·53	0·31
Isobutyric	0·27	0·57	0·32

5 μl of 0·1% (w/v) solution of each acid, dissolved in acetone or water, used in this separation.

The plate is sprayed with alcoholic methyl red solution and heated in the oven at 105°C until the acids appear as dark red spots on an orange background. The R_F values, and the effect of solvent ageing on them, are given in Table IX.

A single separation takes about 30 min which enables complete analysis, including the time to prepare the plates, to be achieved within an hour.

2. Paper chromatography of volatile fatty acids

The factors governing the successful paper chromatographic separation of volatile fatty acids were studied by Lindqvist and Storgärds (1953) who showed that the quality of the paper, the concentration of volatile alkali in the atmosphere, the method and period of drying the paper, the concentration of the indicator and the solvent used, the construction of the sprayer and the manner in which spraying is carried out all affect the results obtained. Their paper should be consulted for full details of the effects of these factors. They developed a technique based on that of Hiscox and Berredge (1950), selected on account of its sensitivity.

Papers: Whatman no. 1 is used for the separation of higher acids and Munktell OB for the separation of formic, acetic and lactic acids.

Sprayer: The sprayer recommended by Lindqvist and Storgärds is one developed in the Department of Biochemistry at Uppsala and is shown in Fig. 15.

Reagents:
    n-Butanol. Commercial 98–100% *n*-butanol is treated with approx 10 g of KOH per litre and fractionally distilled through an efficient column. The fraction with b.p.$\geq$116°C contains water and is reworked, the fraction with b.p. 116°–118°C being used for the chromatography. The fraction with b.p. 118°–119°C is used for preparing the sample.

Water-saturated butanol: The fraction of b.p. 116°–118°C is shaken vigorously with about 25% of distilled water. The butanol is kept over water and can be used as soon as it is completely clear.

Butanol-saturated ethylamine: Thirty-three per cent ethylamine is diluted to 0·025N with butanol-saturated water, and checked by titration with 0·1N HCl using methyl red as indicator.

Indicator solution: 2·5 g of bromocresol green is dissolved in 500 ml of ethanol and 500 ml of butanol (b.p. > 118°C is suitable) is added.

Standard solutions of the acids: Approximately 0·1 equiv of acid is weighed into a 50 ml measuring flask, which is then filled to the

FIG. 15. Design of sprayer recommended by Lindqvist and Storgärds (1953).

mark with analytically pure methanol. The resulting solution is titrated with 0·1N-NaOH using phenolphthalein as indicator, and an appropriate amount to give a solution which will be eventually exactly N is transferred to a 50 ml flask. One drop of 1% bromothymol blue is added followed by 33% ethylamine until the colour turns blue, and the solution is diluted to the mark with butanol. (Lactic acid gradually decomposes and solutions of it change in concentration over a few weeks.) Solutions of 0·1, 0·050 and 0·025N are prepared from the N solutions by mixing the various acids and diluting with ethylamine-neutralized butanol. These normalities refer to the individual acids, not to the total concentration. It is convenient to make two mixtures, one containing lactic, formic and acetic acids, and the other acetic, propionic, butyric, valeric, capric and caprylic acids.

Silver reagent: 50 ml of 0·1N-AgNO$_3$ and 50 ml of 5N-NH$_4$OH are mixed. The solution should be freshly prepared each day.

Procedure:

Preparation of the sample. The acids in the sample should be isolated by distillation, neutralization, evaporation, acidification with NaHSO$_4$ solution and extraction with butanol. The butanol solution is finally neutralized to bromophenol blue (pH 7) with 33% ethylamine.

The concentration of the individual acids should be 0·025–0·050N, and the amount of butanol used for the extraction is decided upon with the help of titration data and a knowledge of the origin of the material (the number of acids present must be known or estimated).

Chromatographic procedure: Ethylamine solution is placed in the bottom of the tank to a depth of about 2 cm and the lid is replaced.

The papers are cut and lined. A sheet of Whatman no. 1 is used for the separation of the higher acids and a sheet of Munktell OB for the separation of formic, acetic and lactic acids. A pad of filter paper is attached to the lower edge of the latter sheet. This pad should weigh about five times as much as the chromatogram itself and is folded together tightly and attached by means of a number of staples.

About 3 μl of the sample is spotted onto the paper, its position being marked with a small cross. The two outer positions on the paper are reserved for standard solutions, usually 0·050N and 0·025N.

The paper is hung in the trough, kept in place with a glass rod, and the water-saturated butanol is run in. After 16–32 h the papers are removed and allowed to dry in air for 1 h. (The pad should be removed immediately after the paper is removed from the tank.)

The papers are sprayed evenly with the indicator solution.

The acid spots apparent on the Munktell paper are marked around the edges, the paper is sprayed with the silver reagent and heated for 1–2 h at 100°–125°C, during which time it should be allowed to hang freely. The indicator and the excess of silver reagent are removed by repeated washing with distilled water, and the paper is dried in the usual way.

Preservation of the papers: The chromatograms obtained as described can only be kept for a few hours. In order to preserve them for longer periods they should be sprayed with a 5% solution of paraffin in pure benzene. When the benzene has evaporated the paper is warmed until the paraffin melts and spreads evenly over the surface. The contrast is diminished by this procedure and unfortunately the weakest spots may disappear entirely.

If the treated chromatograms are kept between plain paper they may be preserved for up to several months but this method is really only satisfactory when large amounts of acids have been used. If a record is to be kept it is much better to photograph the chromatograms using panchromatic film or plates and a dense red-violet or orange filter.

3. *Identification and determination of volatile fatty acids by gas–liquid chromatography*

In recent years a variety of gas–liquid chromatography (GLC) methods have appeared in the literature for the simultaneous identification and determination of volatile fatty acids. Salwin (1965) has reported the results of a collaborative investigation carried out in eight laboratories on the quantitative determination of volatile fatty acids by GLC and by column partition chromatography. He concluded that the GLC method was as accurate, or possibly more accurate, than the partition chromatographic method and that it offered advantages of a single procedure for all the acids, improved specificity and sensitivity, rapidity and a permanent record of the analysis.

Initial problems encountered with volatile fatty acids, such as the necessity for applying the free acids in anhydrous state and the difficulty of detecting formic acid with ionization detectors, have now been virtually overcome. Lanigan and Jackson (1965) have described in detail a method for determining C_1 to C_6 acids in biological materials using a liquid phase of behenic and orthophosphoric acids and wet nitrogen as the carrier gas. The system tolerates the introduction of a small amount of water with the sample of acids and detection is carried out by titration using a glass electrode and pH-stat assembly. These authors used the method for analysing the components of the volatile acidic fractions from silages and rumen contents and reported recoveries of 96–102% of values obtained by titration of distillates, with a bias towards slightly low values.

Storry and Millard (1965) applied GLC to the volatile fatty acids in rumen liquor, blood plasma and milk fat using polyethylene glycol adipate-celite columns with non-aqueous samples; quantitative data for formic acid are not recorded. Carlström, Hallgren, Pehrson and Wallin (1965) have described a method for aqueous samples which does not permit analysis of formic acid; in this technique a substantial amount of formic acid is added to the sample to saturate the solid column support so that the other volatile fatty acids present cannot be adsorbed. This device eliminates the problem posed by aqueous samples, in which the water dissolves and removes adsorbed fatty acids thus preventing saturation of the column, which is a requisite for satisfactory operation and readily attained with non-aqueous samples. The flame ionization detector used by these authors is insensitive to formic acid and thus the added formate does not affect the recording of the other volatile fatty acids.

As the Lanigan and Jackson (1965) method permits the determination of formic acid this technique is described here. Recently Doelle (1969b) has surveyed 13 different columns to find a suitable combination for the separation and determination of micro quantities of C_1–C_7 branched and straight chain fatty acids. The method he recommends is capable of detecting and quantitating C_2–C_7 acids. Formic acid can be detected, but not quantitated by his procedure.

GLC Method of Lanigan and Jackson (1965)

Apparatus: The chromatographic apparatus was constructed by the authors in the laboratory (see Fig. 16) and consists of a water bubbler through which the carrier gas (nitrogen) can be passed before entering the column, a detachable sample heater, a straight chromatographic column, 0·4 cm i.d. by 125 cm long, within a cylindrical heating oven, a titration vessel

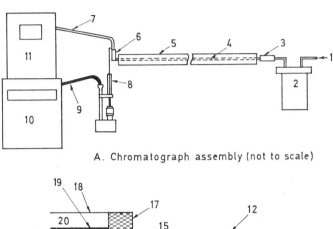

A. Chromatograph assembly (not to scale)

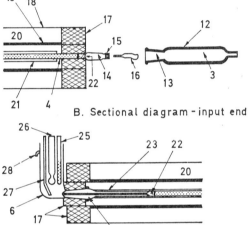

B. Sectional diagram – input end

C. Sectional diagram – titration end

FIG. 16. Gas–liquid chromatography apparatus of Lanigan and Jackson (1965). (For key, see Appendix, page 211.)

and the automatic titrator. With the exception of the oven, borosilicate glass is used for all parts. Demountable joints are secured by clamps or spring-loading so as to withstand an internal pressure of 25 lb/sq in. The heating element for the sample heater consists of an externally wound nichrome ribbon (40Ω total resistance) which is covered by an insulating layer of fibreglass adhesive tape. Operating at an applied potential of 18–20 V gives an internal temperature between 140°C and 160°C. The oven walls consist of two aluminium tubes approximately 125 cm long, an inner tube (2·5 cm diam.) being located coaxially with the outer (6·4 cm diam.) by means of cork spacing rings. The inner tube is wound with a 150 W heating tape, 183 cm long by 5 cm wide, and the space between the heating tape and the outer aluminium tube is packed with asbestos. The partitioning column is supported in the oven also by means of cork spacers, the one at the input end being split in order to facilitate assembly and dismantling. Within the oven, the column is enclosed in a loosely fitting glass tube which enables thermocouples to be held in a suitable position for column temperatures to be determined. Analyses are carried out with (rising) temperature programming. Adequate temperature control is obtained by means of a variable transformer. Although this method of control does not give linear programming, the temperature-time curve is sufficiently reproducible. Any effects of variations in this are insignificant.

Emerging acids are determined by means of the recording pH-stat assembly (Radiometer, Copenhagen: Titrator TTTIC, Titrigraph SBR2C and Syringe Burette SBUIC). When 0·02N alkali is used as titrant, the limit of readability on a titration curve corresponds to $\pm 0·01$ μmole.

Since the gas stream from the column tends to heat the titration cell contents, an upward slope in the baseline may be evident. The extent of the rise in baseline may be limited by starting an analysis with the titration liquid at 35°C and making use of the cooling effect of the nitrogen stream through the auxiliary bubbler which is employed to mix the cell contents. Allowance may readily be made for a rising baseline when reading results from the curve.

Stationary phase: The stationary phase consists of 20 g of behenic acid, 4 g of orthophosphoric acid, on 100 g of acid-washed Chromosorb W (F & M Scientific Corporation) 80–100 mesh. This mixture gives excellent separation of C_1–C_6 monocarboxylic acids, with wet nitrogen as the carrier gas. It has, moreover, a substantial tolerance of water vapour in the gaseous phase, a feature of basic importance to this technique. Reagent grade (syrupy) phosphoric acid may be used as received but laboratory grade behenic acid should be recrystallized from acetone. The column packing is prepared by dissolving the acids in acetone, adding the Chromosorb, then evaporating the solvent by heating over a steam bath with constant stirring. Columns are packed with the aid of a vibrator, to a density such that, at 90°–100°C, a flow rate of 50 ml/min is obtained with a head pressure of 18–20 lb/sq in. Before use, the packed column is conditioned by heating overnight at 100°C while passing through it a slow stream (10 ml/min) of wet nitrogen. Omission of this step results in low recoveries of formic acid, and high retention volumes with incomplete separation of formic and acetic acids during the first few analyses. The reason for this beneficial effect of hydration of the column packing on its performance is obscure.

Sample preparation: Volatile acids are distilled from biological material according to Friedemann (1938) and titrated to the phenolphthalein end point with 0·1N-NaOH. One ml excess of the alkali is added and the

6

sodium hydroxide solution concentrated by boiling. It is then made up to a volume such that the total concentration of acids is approximately M. A sample of this solution (10 μl) is transferred to a glass boat (see Fig. 16) by means of a micro-syringe. The syringe needle has a square cut tip and the last few mm of its outer surface are smeared lightly with silicone grease. Gentle suction is applied to the boat while it is warmed carefully with a micro-flame to dry the sample. A further 10 μl volume of the salts solution is then placed in the boat and similarly dried, the process being repeated until a sufficient quantity of salts has accumulated (5–10 μmoles). Best results are obtained when the salts are dried in a compact mass. Drying to the extent of removing water of crystallization from the salts is undesirable since this usually leads to loss by spattering. Boats containing dried salts can be stored, in a desiccator, without loss of fatty acids.

Chromatography. The column temperature is raised to 90°C and maintained at this level by appropriate adjustment of the applied voltage. At the same time, the sample heater is switched on (20 V). Reduced pressure equal to 0·5 atm is applied to the column via the titration vessel and a boat containing a sample of dried salts is attached to the input end by means of the perforated silicone rubber plug. Phosphoric acid solution (15 μl of 30% w/v) is dropped onto the salts in such a manner that the whole sample is wetted at the same time. The sample heater is then attached to the column and suction continued for 5 min. At the end of this period the vacuum is gradually replaced by a flow of wet nitrogen at 8–10 ml/min. Five minutes later, this flow rate is increased to 30 ml/min and the oven heater voltage raised to 180 V. Acids are neutralized as they emerge from the column and

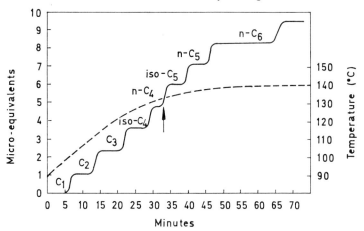

Fig. 17. Gas–liquid chromatogram of volatile fatty acids obtained with the apparatus of Lanigan and Jackson (1965).

the volume of alkali (0·02M) consumed is recorded with the pH-stat assembly. The volume of liquid in the titration vessel is 15 ml and the end-point setting pH 7·5.

Formic acid, if present, emerges from the column about 5 min after increasing the nitrogen flow to 30 ml/min. When *n*-butyric acid appears (31–32 min) the nitrogen flow is increased to 40–50 ml/min in order to keep the time required for the analysis to a minimum (60–70 min for caproic acid). The various acids present in the column can be identified by their time of emergence under standard conditions of operation and the amounts read directly in micro-equivalents from the chromatogram by means of the chart graduation lines (see Fig. 17).

Life of stationary phase: The useful life of the column was not determined but over 100 analyses were conducted without loss of efficiency.

Accuracy and reproducibility: Table X records results obtained in six replicate analyses of 10 μl portions of a synthetic mixture of sodium salts, the total acid content of this solution being determined by steam distillation and titration of a larger sample.

TABLE X

Analysis of a synthetic mixture of volatile fatty acids (6 replicates) by the Lanigan and Jackson method

Acid	Acid found (mean μmoles)	Standard deviation*
Formic	0·827	±0·008
Acetic	0·915	±0·011
Propionic	0·861	±0·012
Isobutyric	0·843	±0·009
n-Butyric	0·861	±0·010
Isovaleric	0·803	±0·005
n-Valeric	0·788	±0·008
n-Caproic	1·035	±0·006
Total acids	6·935	±0·025
Total acids taken (μmoles)	7·020	
Total recovery (%)	98·9	±0·35

* Differences between the standard deviations for individual acids were not significant.

4. Determination of individual volatile fatty acids

(a) *Formic acid*

Chromotropic acid method

Several methods of formic acid determination which depend upon reduction of the acid to formaldehyde, using magnesium ribbon and

conc. hydrochloric acid, with subsequent determination of the formaldehyde produced with chromotropic acid, have been published [e.g., Fabre
et al. (1954)]. They suffer from the disadvantage that the strongly acidic
conditions employed prevent the determination of acid-labile formyl
derivatives which are often found in biological materials.

The selected method here is that of Snell and Snell (1953). While relatively specific, it is best carried out on a steam distillate since compounds
such as diacetyl and pyruvic aldehyde, if not reduced, will interfere.

To a sample (0·5 ml) of steam distillate from acid medium contained in
a test tube and held in an ice bath, 80 mg of clean magnesium ribbon is
added. It is allowed to cool and then drops (0·05 ml) of conc. HCl are
added at intervals of 1–3 min until a total of 0·5 ml has been added. One
minute after the last addition the tube is removed from the ice bath and
1·1 ml of a reagent made by mixing 20 ml of 3% aqueous chromotropic
acid and 180 ml of conc. H_2SO_4 added. The tube is placed in a boiling
water bath, protected from bright light, for 30 min. After cooling and
centrifuging to remove the white precipitate, the extinction of the supernatant is read at 570 nm against a reagent blank.

Thiobarbituric acid method (Barker and Somers, 1966)

This technique was devised for the determination of formic acid produced by the periodate oxidation of carbohydrates. The formic acid is
heated with 2-thiobarbituric acid, under acidic conditions, to yield a
chromophore with an E_{max} of 450 nm. The method is free from interference from other acids and aldehydes, even when these are present
in a ten-fold excess, and is sensitive, permitting the determination of
formic acid in the range of 5 to 200 μg.

Reagents:
   Ethylene glycol, 10% (v/v) in distilled water (for samples taken from
      periodate oxidation).
   Sodium borohydride, 5% (w/v) in sodium tetraborate (0·05M)-hydro-
      chloric acid buffer, pH 8·0.
   Sulphuric acid, 8·0N, prepared from Micro-analytical Reagent conc.
      acid.
   2-Thiobarbiturate: a suspension of 2·5 g in 80 ml of distilled water is
      adjusted to pH 5·4 with 2N-sodium hydroxide to obtain complete
      dissolution at room temperature, and the solution is then diluted to
      100 ml with distilled water.
   n-Butanol, redistilled and containing 5% (v/v) of 11·6N-hydrochloric
      acid.

Formic acid, standard solutions, weighed as sodium formate to give a range of concentrations up to 12·5 mM.

Procedure: Samples (0·4 ml) containing 0 to 200 μg of formic acid are pipetted into clean, stoppered test tubes (125 × 16 mm) and, in the case of samples from periodate oxidation reactions, the periodate oxidation is terminated by the addition of ethylene glycol solution (0·05 ml). This step may be omitted in other cases. Standard solutions of formic acid are similarly treated.

After 5 min 0·1 ml of the sodium borohydride solution is added, excess of borohydride being destroyed after a further 5 min by the addition of 0·05 ml of 8·0N-sulphuric acid. 1·0 ml of 2-thiobarbituric acid solution is added followed by heating at 100°C for 20 min for colour development.

After the solution has cooled to room temperature the chromophore is quantitatively extracted into 1·5 ml of the acidic butanol reagent. After centrifugation at 1000 rpm for 3 min to clarify the solution, the extinction is measured at 450 nm. The authors used cuvettes of 10 mm light path for solutions containing 50–200 μg of formic acid and 40 mm cuvettes for those containing 5–50 μg of formic acid.

Calibration: A linear relationship between E_{450} and formic acid is shown up to 200 μg.

Interference: Acetaldehyde, formaldehyde, acetic acid, oxalic acid, glyoxylic acid, malonaldehyde and formylpyruvic acid do not react when present in ten-fold excess, and do not inhibit chromophore development from formic acid itself.

Enzymic assay

Rabinowitz and Pricer (1957) have described a sensitive enzymic assay for formic acid using the tetrahydrofolic acid formylase of *Clostridium cylindrosporum* and which is described in Bergmeyer (1963). As the enzyme must first be prepared and biochemicals such as tetrahydrofolic acid and ATP are required this would not be the method of choice for routine analysis of formic acid and is not therefore described here.

(b) *Acetic acid*

Acetic acid may be determined by enzymic or chemical methods, the former having a much greater sensitivity and therefore frequently being essential where acetate is to be determined in tissues. However, with fermentation media the concentration of acetate is often high enough for chemical methods to be used.

*Enzymic assay (Lundquist, Fugmann and Rasmussen, 1961;
Lundquist, 1963)*

Principle: The method is based on that of Soodak and Lipmann (1948) and Soodak (1957) employing an enzyme preparation from pigeon liver which catalyses the sequence of reactions

(1) Acetate + ATP → Acetyl-AMP + pyrophosphate

(2) Acetyl-AMP + CoA → Acetyl-CoA + AMP

(3) Acetyl-CoA + sulphanilamide → acetylsulphanilamide + CoA

Consumption of sulphanilamide in reaction (3) is determined colorimetrically and measures the acetate present. As the enzymes are inhibited by alkali-metal ions and interference from other compounds, e.g. acetoacetate, may be encountered, a microdiffusion step in a Conway unit is introduced. Anhydrous sodium sulphate is added to increase the vapour pressure of acetic acid and so ensure completion of diffusion within a reasonable time.

Reagents:

Sodium sulphate, anhydrous, acetate-free (p.a. Merck was the only source sufficiently pure, according to the authors). It is ground in a mortar with about 5% crystalline Na_2SO_4, $10H_2O$

Perchloric acid, 5% (w/v)

Trichloroacetic acid, 5% (w/v)

Hydrochloric acid, 0·1N and 0·9N solutions

Citrate buffer, 9·4 g of sodium hydroxide and 10·5 g of citric acid monohydrate are made up to 100 ml of distilled water and the reagent kept in a well-closed plastic bottle

Potassium hydroxide, 0·033N

Coenzyme-sulphanilamide mixture. Three hundred mg of disodium ATP and 5 mg of coenzyme A (both Sigma) are dissolved in 5 ml of water. Then 3 ml of 20 mM-sulphanilamide, 2 ml of M-potassium citrate and 0·5 ml of 0·1M-magnesium chloride are added and the mixture is distributed in vials and frozen at −20°C. It is stable for at least two months.

Buffer coenzyme reagent. *This is made up immediately prior to use* by mixing 2 vol of coenzyme-sulphanilamide mixture with 6 vol of M-tris-HCl buffer, pH 8·1, 1 vol of 0·5M-cysteine-HCl and 1 vol of 0·1M $MgCl_2$. This reagent is kept in an ice bath.

Conway unit sealing mixture. A mixture of three parts liquid and two parts solid paraffin is used.

Sodium nitrite solution, 0·1% w/v. This should be prepared daily.

Sulphamic acid, 0·5% w/v

N-Naphthylethylenediamine dihydrochloride, 0·1% w/v solution. This should be prepared freshly at monthly intervals and stored at 4°C.

Enzyme solution. The enzyme is prepared from pigeon liver according to the method of Soodak (1957). Livers from 12–15 animals were used for each batch of enzyme and it was observed that material from young pigeons gave the highest yield of enzyme.

Acetone-dried powder of pigeon liver (Tabor, 1955). Freshly extirpated pigeon livers are blended with 10 vol of cold (-10°C) acetone for 1 min in a Waring blendor. After filtering with suction on a Buchner funnel, the semi-dry filter cake is blended with 10 vol of acetone (-10°C) and again filtered. The filter cake is then broken up by hand, spread over a large surface and allowed to dry at room temperature. It is then stored at 0°C. The powder may be stored under these conditions for several weeks without loss of activity, but then gradually deteriorates.

Extraction of powder. Five g of acetone-dried powder is extracted with 100 ml of ice-cold 0·02M-KHCO₃ solution.

Ice-cooled extract (50 to 85 ml) is 70% saturated by addition of powdered ammonium sulphate (100% saturation is achieved by 65 g per 100 ml). After adding the ammonium sulphate the solution is allowed to stand at room temperature for 30 min and the precipitate then centrifuged in the cold. The supernatant is discarded and the precipitate dissolved by adding exactly 30 ml of ice-cold 0·02M-KHCO₃. The increase in volume is taken to be the volume of the 70% precipitate and its ammonium sulphate content is taken into account in the next step. More 0·02M-KHCO₃ is added to bring the volume to that of the original aged extract taken for fractionation. The solution is then brought to 40% saturation with solid ammonium sulphate. After allowing to stand for 30 min at room temperature is it centrifuged and the precipitate discarded. The supernatant is now raised to 70% saturation and the precipitate collected by centrifugation. This 40–70% saturation precipitate is dissolved in the minimum quantity of ice-cold 0·02M-KHCO₃ and dialysed overnight in the cold against 10 litres of a solution containing 50 g of KCl, 20 g of KHCO₃ and 2 g of cysteine hydrochloride. This dialysed fraction is the enzyme used for the assay. It is necessary to follow the entire procedure if the enzyme is to be essentially free of acetate.

The enzyme solution should be stored in glass ampoules at -20°C and is stable for about 1 year.

Procedure: Four steps are involved: deproteinization, diffusion in Conway units, enzymic reaction and determination of sulphanilamide. As the enzymic reaction does not go to completion it is necessary to include acetate standards in each analysis, together with a reagent blank.

1. Deproteinization. The sample is mixed with 1 vol of 5% (w/v) perchloric acid and centrifuged after 10 min. The clear supernatant is neutralized and buffered at pH 3 by the addition of 0·1 vol of the citrate buffer. Where protein is absent, the pH of the sample may be adjusted to 3 with citrate buffer and used immediately for the diffusion step.
2. Diffusion. Standard no. 1 Conway units are used. Ten g of the powdered sodium sulphate is distributed in the outer compartment of the unit. This operation is facilitated if the centre compartment is covered by a plastic cone which fits into the well while the salt is added. The powder is lightly compressed by means of a Perspex pestle shaped in the form of a ring and fitting into the outer chamber. The units are now placed at 4°C for 1 h before addition of the sample for analysis or, alternatively, the whole procedure may be carried out in the cold room.

   In the centre chamber is placed a plastic dish (external diameter, 32 mm; internal diameter, 29–30 mm; internal height, 4 mm; external height, 5 mm) made from Perspex rod, 35 mm in diam. With a Carlsberg constriction pipette, 0·003N-KOH (600 μl) is measured into the dish. 2 ml of the cold, neutralized perchloric acid filtrate is distributed evenly on the surface of the Na_2SO_4 layer and the unit is then sealed with the paraffin mixture applied to the rim of the unit by a glass syringe. The units are replaced at 4°C for approx 1 h to accelerate the crystallization of the sodium sulphate, and thereafter at room temperature (below 30°C) for 20–24 h. The plastic dishes are removed and held at 90°C for 30 min to remove all water and destroy any acetoacetate that may be present.
3. Enzymic reaction. Carlsberg pipettes are used to measure into the dried plastic dishes 200 μl of 0·1N-HCl followed by 250 μl of the buffer-coenzyme reagent. The contents are thoroughly mixed to dissolve all KOH and acetate and 400 μl is transferred to a small (7 ml) glass-stoppered centrifuge tube. To this is added 150–250 μl of enzyme and then nitrogen is blown through the solution for 20 sec. After incubation for 1 h at 37°C the solution is deproteinized with 2 ml of cold 5% (w/v) trichloroacetic acid and centrifuged for 10 min.
4. Sulphanilamide determination. The unreacted sulphanilamide is determined by the Bratton and Marshall (1939) method. Syringe pipettes are recommended for measuring the following reagents into a test tube: 9 ml of 0·9N-HCl, 1 ml of deproteinized supernatant from the enzymic reaction and 1 ml of sodium nitrite solution. These

are mixed and allowed to react for 2–3 min to destroy excess nitrite, and then 1 ml of sulphamic acid is added. The tube is shaken vigorously to facilitate the evolution of nitrogen and after a few minutes 1 ml of the N-naphthylethylenediamine reagent is added. The extinction of the solution is read at 540 nm.

Blank and standard analyses: These are carried through the complete procedure.

Blank: 5% Perchloric acid (1 vol) is neutralized with N-NaOH and made up to 2 vol with distilled water. 0·1 vol of citrate buffer is added. This "blank" mixture is run through the complete procedure. If the reagents are sufficiently pure, the extinction of the blank mixture subjected to enzyme action is only 0·020–0·030 lower than the extinction of an untreated blank mixture which corresponds to the initial sulphanilamide content.

Standard: This should be prepared for each assay. Fifty μl of 17·5 mM-acetic acid is added to 10 ml of blank mixture. Two ml of this solution corresponds to 10·5 μg acetic acid.

Range: A linear relation exists between E_{540} and acetate up to about 15 μg per assay. If the acetate concentration is higher the deproteinized sample must be diluted correspondingly.

Standard curves with 4, 8, 12, 14 and 16 μg of acetate per assay should be prepared every month (for this the diffusion step may be omitted).

Calculation: ΔE_{540} values for blank and unknown (ΔE_u) and for blank and standard (ΔE_s) are determined and, since the assays are carried out on 2 ml of deproteinized supernatant and 2 ml of standard solution contains 10·5 μg of acetate:

Acetate present (μg/2 ml of deproteinized sample)

$$= \frac{\Delta E_u}{\Delta E_s} \times 10·5$$

Interference: Formic and pyruvic acids do not interfere. Propionate, butyrate and valerate give respectively only about 0·7, 1·3 and 0·4% of the colour change obtained with an equivalent amount of acetate. Acetoacetate reacts with the pigeon liver enzyme but is eliminated by the diffusion technique, even when present in concentrations higher than 100 mg/ml. Acetyl CoA is stable in this method but acetyladenylic acid is labile and rapidly hydrolysed at pH values below 2; it is therefore determined as free acetate.

Chemical assay
Lanthanum nitrate method (Hutchens and Kass, 1949)

Lanthanum is a specific reagent for the detection of acetate which has been applied quantitatively by Hutchens and Kass (1949). A mixture of acetate, lanthanum nitrate, iodine and ammonium yields a jelly-like solution of basic lanthanum acetate on which the iodine is adsorbed, giving a blue to green colour. Inorganic interfering ions must be removed and therefore steam distillates, titrated to about pH 9·5, should be used.

Reagents:
   Lanthanum nitrate solution, 2·5% w/v
   Ammonium hydroxide, 0·1N
   Lanthanum nitrate reagent is prepared by mixing equal volumes of the
      above two solutions
   Iodine solution, 0·02N. 2·54 g of reagent grade iodine and 33·2 g of
      potassium iodide are made to 1 litre in distilled water.

Procedure: To a sample (1 ml) containing 0·08–0·25 mg of acetic acid in a stoppered test tube is added 2 ml of the lanthanum nitrate reagent. One ml of iodine solution is then added, the tube stoppered and placed in a boiling water bath for 5 min. After cooling the extinction is read at 625 nm against a reagent blank in which distilled water replaces the acetate sample. Poorly stoppered tubes result in a colour that fades rapidly.

Range: The relation between E_{625} and acetate concentration is linear up to 250 μg of acetate per ml.

Interference: Inorganic ions such as Cl^-, $SO_4^=$, $PO_4^\equiv$, Ca^{2+} and Mg^{2+} interfere. Hutchens and Kass give a precipitation technique for removal of these ions, but if steam distillates are used this is not necessary.

Modification of Artsybasheva and Favarskaya (1961)

To 1 ml of the sample, containing 0·08 to 0·25 mg of acetate, in a test tube are added carefully 1 ml of 2·5% lanthanum nitrate solution, 0·1 ml of 0·02N-iodine and 1 ml of 0·1N aqueous NH_3. After mixing, the tube is heated on a steam bath for 5 min, then cooled, and after 30 min the extinction is measured at 656 nm against a reagent blank.

The pH of the solution to be analysed should be between 8·2 and 10.

(c) Propionic and butyric acids

Specific chemical methods are not available for the estimation of propionic and butyric acids, so that where these occur together with formic and/or acetic acids they must be determined by difference. Formic and acetic acids may be determined by the specific methods previously described (pp. 131–138) and the values obtained subtracted from the titre for the total steam volatile distillate to yield the propionate or butyrate content. Should propionic and butyric acids be simultaneously present, however, separation must be carried out prior to titration. This can be achieved by the partition chromatographic system of Neish (1949, 1952).

Reagents:

Chromatography solvents

1. *n*-Butanol, 20 ml of reagent grade, is mixed with 380 ml of benzene. The mixture is shaken with 80 ml of $0.01N$-HCl in a separatory funnel for 2 min and the top layer separated and filtered through a dry filter paper.
2. *n*-Butanol, 40 ml of reagent grade, is mixed with 360 ml of $0.01N$-HCl and treated as for Reagent 1.
3. Chloroform, 400 ml of reagent grade, is shaken with $0.01N$-HCl in a separatory funnel for 2 min. The lower layer is separated and filtered through a dry filter paper. This reagent should be freshly prepared daily.

Celite (acid-washed). Celite 535 is slurried with conc. HCl and allowed to stand at room temperature overnight. It is washed twice by decantation with water and then on a Buchner funnel until free of acid. This is followed by washing with alcohol and then ether and the celite is dried first in air and then at 150°C overnight.

Sodium hydroxide, $0.01N$ prepared with CO_2-free water

Hydrochloric acid, $0.21N$

Hydrochloric acid, $0.01N$

Phenol red, 0.05% (w/v). One hundred mg of phenol red is ground in a mortar with 28.5 ml of $0.01N$-NaOH and diluted to 200 ml with water.

Alkaline phenol red. To 100 ml of the above phenol red reagent is added 1 ml of N-NaOH and the solution diluted to 1 litre with CO_2-free water.

Steam distillates: The steam distillate containing the volatile acids is titrated with NaOH to the phenol red endpoint. The total volatile acids are recorded and the neutralized distillate then evaporated to dryness on a steam bath, transferring to a 100 ml beaker near the end. The residual salts are dried in a desiccator overnight preparatory to separation on the column.

Chromatography: Three g of celite is wet with 2.5 ml of $0.01N$-HCl, slurried thoroughly in approx 30 ml of the chloroform reagent and poured into a chromatography tube. It is packed down by placing a filter paper disk on top and ramming with a glass plunger. 0.5 g of dry celite is slurried with chloroform and packed on top of the wet celite column, again with a filter paper disk on top.

The salts of the volatile acids are dissolved in 5 ml of $0.21N$-HCl per m-equiv and a portion (0·5 ml) is pipetted onto the column, on the paper disk, care being taken that it does not wet the walls of the column except for 1–2 mm above the top of the packing. (The sample should contain 0·05–0·10 m-equiv of total organic acids and sufficient hydrochloric acid to make the solution 0·01N; the procedure described for the dried salts ensures this requirement). As soon as the sample has been absorbed into the celite a clean 50 ml graduated cylinder is positioned to collect the column effluent and a portion (1–2 ml) of chloroform is added to the column and forced in by gentle air pressure using a rubber bulb and pressure flask. Development is commenced by filling the column with chloroform and applying sufficient air pressure to ensure a flow rate of 3–4 drops per second. The indicator is then adjusted to flow at approximately one tenth the rate of the column effluent by the device illustrated in Fig. 18.

When appreciable quantities of acid are being eluted the indicator is yellow; at other times it is red. The receiver is changed 2–3 ml after the

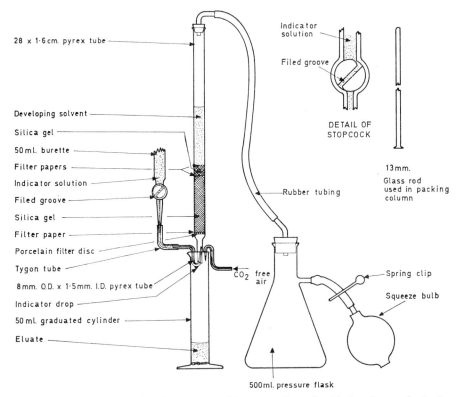

FIG. 18. Apparatus for chromatographic separation of acids by the method of Neish (1952).

indicator changes from yellow to red. Fractions of a definite volume are collected and titrated. The volume of effluent and of indicator in each fraction is recorded and four fractions are collected and titrated, as given in the example recorded by Neish.

Fraction no.	Acid	Solvent	Solvent + indicator ml
1	Butyric	Chloroform	15
2	Propionic	Butanol (1)	19
3	Acetic	Butanol (1)	35
4	Formic	Butanol (2)	40

When changing developing solvents, any of the previous solvent remaining is decanted from column before the new solvent is added.

Each fraction is washed into a 250 ml beaker, using at least two volumes of CO_2-free water, and then titrated with $0 \cdot 01N$-NaOH in a stream of CO_2-free air. Caution is necessary in the titration or error may result. If insufficient water is used the water-in-oil emulsion obtained may lead to overshoot. With the correct oil-in-water emulsion time must be allowed for the acids to be extracted from the organic phase as the endpoint is approached otherwise low results will be obtained. The titration should be carried to a definite pink colour which persists for at least 1 min in the vigorously stirred solution.

The determination can be simplified by omitting the indicator stream and collecting and titrating fractions of effluent of a predetermined volume.

Calculation: Both the acidity of the solvent and the base present in the indicator must be corrected for. One ml of indicator solution is equivalent to $0 \cdot 1$ ml of $0 \cdot 01N$-NaOH and the appropriate value must therefore be added to the volume of NaOH used in the titration. The solvent correction is determined by titration of 100 ml of CO_2-free water in the presence and absence of 20 ml of the appropriate solvent; the difference gives the correction to be used. The correction is negligible for chloroform but significant for the butanol solvents.

$$\text{Corrected titre} \times \text{ml of base} \times \text{normality of base} = \text{m-equiv of acid in portion analysed.}$$

(iii) α-Keto acids

1. Identification of α-keto acids

(a) Chromatography of 2,4-dinitrophenylhydrazones

Principle: The keto acids are converted to their 2,4-dinitrophenylhydrazones and identified by chromatography.

Reagents:
2,4-Dinitrophenylhydrazine, 0·2% w/v in 2N-HCl
Sodium carbonate, 10% (w/v) solution
Hydrochloric acid, 2N
Ethyl acetate
Benzene

Procedure: To a portion (1 ml) of aqueous solution containing carboxylic acids derived from continuous ether extraction of fermentation media, 3 ml of 0·2% (w/v) 2,4-dinitrophenylhydrazine in 2N-HCl is added and the tube is left for 1 h shielded from light (Dancis, Hutzler, and Levitz, 1963). If a precipitate forms it is centrifuged, washed with water and then taken up in ethyl acetate. If there is no precipitate the solution is extracted directly with ethyl acetate. To the ethyl acetate solution an equal volume of 10% (w/v) sodium carbonate is added and shaken to extract the keto acids into the carbonate layer. The organic layer is discarded. The sodium carbonate solution is acidified with 2N-HCl to about pH 2·0 and the 2,4-dinitrophenylhydrazones are extracted into benzene for chromatography by the method of Byrne (1965). Should an emulsion form, separation of the layers may be achieved by centrifuging briefly.

(b) *Thin layer chromatography of dinitrophenylhydrazine derivatives-α-keto acids* **(Byrne, 1965)**

In a comprehensive paper Byrne describes TLC methods for separation and identification of 41 dinitrophenylhydrazine derivatives (DNPHs), many of which are of interest to the fermentation biochemist. The method given below is the one he described specifically for keto acid DNPHs.

Materials and apparatus:
Shandon chromatography tank
Glass plates 20 × 20 cm
Desaga spreader
Silica gel G
30 g are dispersed in 60 ml of water.

Developing solvent:
This is benzene-tetrahydrofuran-glacial acetic acid in the ratio 60 : 36 : 4.

Preparation of plate: The glass plates are spread with a layer 250 μm thick of silica gel G using a Desaga spreader. They are then dried for 30 min at room temperature, followed by activation at 110°C for 2 h, or dried without heat.

Application of sample and development: Samples (and references) are applied in a line of small spots (0·5–1·0 mm in diam.) 1 cm from the edge of the plate, using drawn-out melting point tubes. The concentration of the samples should be between 0·01–0·1% and benzene is used as the solvent since, in conjunction with the use of drawn-out melting point tubes, this enables these small spots to be consistently obtained. After development this procedure results in spots having a diameter of 2–3 mm.

A Shandon chromatographic tank, lined with filter paper, is first equilibrated for 1 h with 100 ml of developing solvent. Development is commenced and after the solvent has ascended to a height of 10–15 cm the plate is removed from the tank and dried in a stream of warm air.

The DNPHs are best identified by running a series of known markers but the position of the following common derivatives, after the solvent front has run 15 cm, should provide a good guide to their identification: ketomalic acid, hardly any movement from the origin, α-ketoglutarate 2–3 cm, glyoxylic acid 5–6 cm, pyruvic acid 7–8 cm, and laevulinic acid 9–10 cm.

2. Chemical determination of α-keto acids

Principle: The commonly employed methods are based on the fact that the *p*-nitrophenylhydrazones of keto acids are soluble in, and are extracted from organic solvents by, sodium carbonate solution and give red to purple-brown colours on the addition of alkali. The 2,4-dinitrophenylhydrazones are usually formed by reaction with 2,4-dinitrophenylhydrazine in acid solution, extracted into ethyl acetate, re-extracted by 10% (w/v) sodium carbonate and the colour then developed by addition of sodium hydroxide. Friedemann and Haugen (1943) and Friedemann (1957) have used the faster rates of reaction of monocarboxylic keto acids with 2,4-dinitrophenylhydrazine relative to dicarboxylic keto acids, and differences in the distribution of the hydrazones between aqueous and organic solvents, as a means of determining different keto acids present in a mixture. For example, in the Friedemann technique, at a temperature of 25°C, the monocarboxylic keto acids (and ketones and aldehydes) react completely within 4 min whereas the dicarboxylic keto acids take about 20 min. From acid aqueous solution the monocarboxylic acid hydrazones are preferentially extracted by aromatic hydrocarbons and the dicarboxylic acid hydrazones by aliphatic and aromatic alcohols. Both groups of hydrazones are extracted by esters and ethers. On account of the instability of oxaloacetate in aqueous solution, the most commonly encountered keto acids in biological materials are pyruvic and α-ketoglutaric which, as examples of mono- and dicarboxylic keto acids respectively, may be readily determined in mixtures by these techniques.

Method of Friedemann (1957)

Reagents:

Trichloroacetic acid solution, 10% w/v. It should be prepared freshly each month and stored in the refrigerator.

Acetic acid, 5% solution

2,4-Dinitrophenylhydrazine, 0·1% w/v solution in 2N-HCl. It should be freshly prepared each month and stored in the refrigerator. The hydrazine should be recrystallized from ethyl acetate if it is not readily and completely soluble in the acid

Sodium carbonate, 10% w/v solution of the anhydrous salt. It should be filtered and stored in a Pyrex container

Sodium hydroxide, 1·5N

Solvents. Ethyl benzene, benzyl alcohol and ethyl acetate are used respectively for the three methods described. Alternatively benzene, *n*-butanol and dibutyl ether may be substituted respectively. All solvents should be distilled before use; dibutyl ether should be re-distilled at frequent intervals and stored at 4°C to prevent the accumulation of peroxides.

Keto acid standards. Pyruvic acid is redistilled at reduced pressure and used to prepare a stock solution (0·1–0·5N). A suitable quantity (8–25 g) of the acid is weighed accurately in a weighing bottle and transferred quantitatively to a volumetric flask (500 ml or 1 litre) with freshly boiled and cooled distilled water. The purity of the acid is checked by titration with standard alkali. Friedemann (1957) claims that such solutions have been stored for more than 1 year without apparent deterioration. It is, perhaps, safer to prepare fresh solutions at 6-month intervals.

α-Ketoglutaric acid as obtained commercially is recrystallized if titration indicates that it is not pure.

Standards for analysis are prepared by suitable dilution of the stock solutions with 5% acetic acid.

Procedure: If the sample has been deproteinized, then it may be analysed directly. If it is, for example, an enzyme reaction mixture then it should first be deproteinized by the addition of an equal volume of trichloroacetic acid solution. After centrifuging, the supernatant is analysed.

Samples (3·0 ml) are pipetted into 150 × 23 mm SB 19, glass-stoppered test tubes, and reagent blanks containing 3·0 ml of either water, acetic acid or trichloroacetic acid, to correspond with the samples are also set up. All the tubes are incubated in a water bath at 25 ± 2°C for 10 min and then, at accurately timed intervals (20 or 30 sec), 1·0 ml of the hydrazine reagent is added to each tube. The incubation at 25°C is continued for the precise time stipulated for the particular analysis (see below) and then the exact volume of the appropriate solvent is added from a burette to each tube at the timed intervals. Extraction is effected immediately by agitating the mixture for 2 min with a rapid stream of air or nitrogen through a capillary pipette inserted into each tube (Friedemann recommends 10 mm o.d. glass tubing drawn out to give an upper portion of 4 in. and a lower portion of 8 in. length with fine, square-cut tip, capillary). An alternative extraction method, possible with the glass–stoppered tubes, and in our experience much better, is to agitate mechanically, e.g., on a Vortex Junior Mixer (Scientific Industries, Queen's Village, New York).

If an emulsion forms the tubes are centrifuged to separate the phases (ethyl benzene and ethyl acetate separate readily without this treatment). The lower aqueous reaction phase is then removed by Pasteur pipette, or by the capillary pipettes used in the gaseous agitation technique. The tubes should be swirled to dislodge any drops of aqueous phase adhering to their walls.

Six ml of sodium carbonate solution is added to each tube and the extraction procedure repeated for 2 min.

If necessary, the tubes are centrifuged. A 5·0 ml pipette is introduced rapidly into the aqueous phase and any solvent which may have entered is blown out prior to transferring 5 ml of the carbonate extract to a colorimeter tube held at 25°C. At accurately timed intervals, 5·0 ml of 1·5N-NaOH is added to each tube and, after 5 min, the extinction is read at 435 nm, against blanks, preserving the same time intervals between reading each tube.

Method 1. For pyruvic and other monocarboxylic keto acids. The procedure is as described above, the sample for assay being incubated with the hydrazine reagent for precisely 5 min. Then 3·0 ml of ethyl benzene is added.

Method 2. For α-ketoglutaric and other dicarboxylic keto acids. The sample is incubated for precisely 25 min with the hydrazine reagent and then 8·0 ml of benzyl alcohol is added. The procedure is continued as described above.

Method 3. For total keto acid determination. The sample is incubated for precisely 25 min with the 2,4-dinitrophenylhydrazine reagent and the reaction mixture is then extracted with 8·0 ml of ethyl acetate. The procedure is continued as described above.

Calculations: Analysis of standard solutions of each keto acid permits the extinction per μmole at 435 nm to be evaluated for each of the three methods. If these are p_1, p_2, p_3, and g_1, g_2, g_3 for pyruvic and α-ketoglutaric acids for methods 1, 2 and 3 respectively and P and G represent

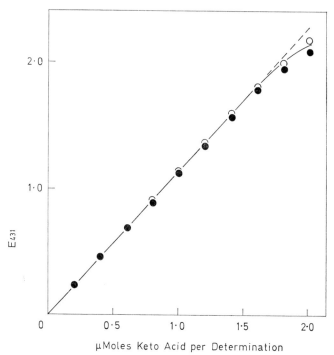

Fɪɢ. 19. Calibration curve for the 2,4-dinitrophenylhydrazones of pyruvic and α-ketoglutaric acids in 0·7N-sodium hydroxide solution. Pyruvic, ○; α-ketoglutaric, ●. (E. A. Dawes and W. H. Holms.)

the amounts (μmoles) of pyruvic and α-ketoglutaric acids present in 3 ml of the analysed sample, then where the observed extinctions in Methods 1, 2, and 3 are E_1, E_2, and E_3.

$$E_1 = p_1P + g_1G$$
$$E_2 = p_2P + g_2G$$
$$E_3 = p_3P + g_3G$$

By using any two of the methods and by solving the respective equations for P and G, the amounts of the individual acids may be evaluated. The most accurate results are obtained with Methods 1 and 2 which give a sharp separation of the hydrazones.

Modified method for pyruvic and α-ketoglutaric acids (Dawes and Holms). For samples which contain only pyruvic and α-ketoglutaric acids an alternative method developed by Goodwin and Williams (1952) and, independently, by E. A. Dawes and W. H. Holms (unpublished) simplifies the Friedemann procedure. Alkaline solutions of the 2,4-dinitrophenylhydra-

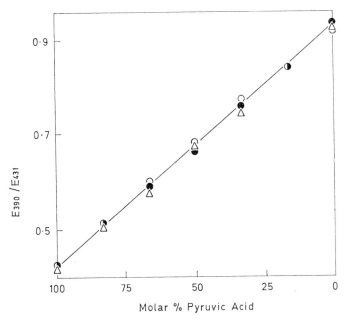

FIG. 20. The ratio E_{390}/E_{431} as a function of the molar proportions of pyruvic and α-ketoglutaric acids in the original reaction mixture. Total concentration of keto acids per determination: 0·2 μmole, $\bigcirc$; 0·4 μmole, $\bullet$; 0·8 μmole, $\triangle$. (E. A. Dawes and W. H. Holms.)

zones of these acids display an isosbestic point at 431 nm. Consequently an extinction measurement at this wavelength permits the total molar concentration of keto acid in the sample to be measured. If a second extinction measurement is made at a wavelength where the spectra of the two hydrazones are widely divergent, e.g., at 390 nm, this value depends on the relative molar proportions of the two keto acids. As the proportion of α-ketoglutaric acid in the mixture is increased the E_{390}/E_{431} ratio increases in a linear manner from the value characteristic of pure pyruvic acid to that for pure α-ketoglutaric acid. Calibration curves are thus prepared with standard mixtures of the keto acids which are put through Method 3 of Friedemann for total keto acid determinations. The E_{390}/E_{431} ratio is determined for each and calibration curves drawn for total keto acids (E_{431}), and for E_{390}/E_{431} as a function of the composition of the mixtures (Figs 19 and 20).

Accuracy: Total keto acids may be measured to an accuracy of $\pm 1\%$ and the determination of the relative proportions of pyruvic and α-ketoglutaric acids to $\pm 5\%$. It should be noted that in techniques of this type it is vitally important that a constant slit width is used for all measurements made at one given wavelength. Ideally these should be as narrow as possible.

Other methods: A salting-out extraction method which permits the separation of the 2,4-dinitrophenylhydrazone of α-ketoglutaric acid from other hydrazones has been described by Katsuki *et al.* (1961a). The hydrazones of monocarboxylic keto acids are completely removed from sodium carbonate–sodium sulphate solution by repeated extractions with ethyl acetate–amyl alcohol mixtures, leaving the hydrazone of α-ketoglutaric behind. The method involves some seven extraction procedures.

The same workers (Katsuki *et al.*, 1961b) have also published a modified method for pyruvate estimation.

3. *Enzymic methods for pyruvic and lactic acids*
(Rosenberg and Rush, 1966)

Principle: Rabbit muscle lactate dehydrogenase in the presence of its coenzyme NADH reduces pyruvate to lactate. Although the reaction is reversible, at pH 7·5 the formation of lactate predominates ($K = 10^{12}$)

$$CH_3COCOOH + NADH + H^+ \rightleftharpoons CH_3CHOHCOOH + NAD^+$$

However, lactate may be determined under conditions which permit its oxidation, namely an alkaline medium (pH 10) with an excess of NAD^+ and removal of the pyruvate product as its semicarbazide. Measurement of the change in extinction at 340 nm permits pyruvate or lactate to be determined according to the stoicheiometry of the above equation.

Reagents:

Sodium hydroxide 2N

Nicotinamide adenine dinucleotide. 98% pure NAD is used and 266 mg dissolved in 10 ml of distilled water. The pH is adjusted from 3·0 to 6·0 by carefully adding 4–5 drops of 2N-NaOH (a pH meter is used to monitor the addition). If the NAD solution is inadvertently made alkaline it should be discarded because of the instability of NAD in weak alkaline solutions. The final volume is made to 20 ml. The solution should be prepared daily and therefore the volume prepared should be in accord with the number of assays to be performed.

Glycine-semicarbazide buffer. This is prepared daily by dissolving 1·5 g of glycine and 2·2 g of semicarbazide hydrochloride in 80 ml of distilled water. The pH of the solution is adjusted to 10·0 with 2N-NaOH (about 10 ml) using a pH meter and magnetic stirrer. The solution is then diluted to 100 ml.

Phosphate buffer, pH 7·5. This solution is prepared by mixing 84·1 ml of 0·1M-Na_2HPO_4 and 15·9 ml of 0·1M-KH_2PO_4.

Reduced nicotinamide adenine dinucleotide. NADH, 95% pure (e.g., Sigma Chemical Company) is stored at 4°C and protected from light and moisture by keeping the vial in an air-tight and water-tight bag which also contains anhydrous calcium chloride granules. Immediately prior to use, a sufficient quantity of NADH is weighed out and added to 0·1M phosphate buffer to give a concentration of 1 mg per ml.

Lactate dehydrogenase (rabbit muscle) is obtained commercially as a crystalline suspension in ammonium sulphate, e.g., Sigma Chemical Company. As supplied, the enzyme solution usually contains about 65 mg of protein per ml (1 mg will convert approximately 60 mmol of NADH to NAD at pH 7·5; and 37°C). The enzyme is diluted with distilled water to give a concentration of 2 mg of protein per ml for lactate analysis, and 5 mg/ml with 0·1M-phosphate buffer for pyruvate analysis within 72 h of being used. It is stored at 4°C.

Procedure:

Pyruvic acid: Two ml of protein-free sample, together with pyruvate standards and appropriate blanks, are pipetted into a series of spectrophotometer cuvettes (1 cm light path) or colorimeter tubes. Phosphate buffer, pH 7·5 (0·7 ml) and the buffered NADH solution (0·2 ml) are added to each cuvette and the extinction at 340 nm recorded (E_1). 0·1 ml of the lactate dehydrogenase preparation, containing 5 mg/ml of protein in 0·1M-phosphate buffer, is then added to each and E_{340} determined 1 min later (E_2). The reaction is carried out at room temperature.

Lactic acid: 2·8 ml of the glycine-semicarbazide solution is pipetted into each cuvette or tube followed by 0·6 ml of NAD solution and 0·2 ml of the sample for analysis, standard lactate or water blank. The cuvettes or tubes are inverted five times after being covered with Parafilm and E_{340} determined (E_1). 0·4 ml of lactate dehydrogenase (2 mg protein/ml) is added to each and the mixture incubated at 40°C for 1 h when E_{340} is again read (E_2).

Calculations:

Pyruvic acid: Rosenberg and Rush use the following formula to determine the pyruvate

$$\Delta E = 0·97E_1 - E_2$$

The reagent blank does not undergo significant change and may be neglected. Knowledge of ΔE for the standards permits calculation of the pyruvic acid content of the unknown samples.

Lactic acid: The net change in extinction, ΔE, as a result of NADH formed by oxidation of lactate to pyruvate is obtained from the formula

$$\Delta E = (E_2 - 0.9E_1) - (B_2 - 0.9B_1)$$

where E_1 and E_2 and B_1 and B_2 are the readings before and after incubation of samples and blanks respectively.

Range:

Pyruvic acid: A linear relationship between ΔE and pyruvic acid concentration up to 0·10 μmole per ml is illustrated by Rosenberg and Rush (corresponding to a mean ΔE of 0·252), but linearity extends beyond this concentration and up to 0·4 μmole per ml could be analysed accurately without dilution. Concentrations as low as 0·01 μmole per ml can be measured.

Lactic acid: Linearity between ΔE and lactic acid concentration is obtained between 0·2 and 3·0 μmole per ml, corresponding to ΔE of about 0·8. Concentrations less than 0·2 μmole per ml are too close to the blank value to be significant.

(iv) Other acids

1. Identification of dicarboxylic acids by chromatographic methods

Methods: For speed of separation and sensitivity, thin layer chromatographic methods are more suitable than paper chromatographic techniques for the identification of carboxylic acids. However, a series of solvents is given by Resnik, Lee and Powell (1955), together with R_F values of a number of dicarboxylic acids and citric acid. The method does not recommend whether descending or ascending chromatography should be used but the running time (overnight) of the amyl alcohol solvent would suggest that the descending method is used. A note on the use of 8-quinolinol as an aid to visualization of acids on paper chromatograms is given by the same authors.

Rasmussen (1967) has developed a thin layer method from a paper chromatographic method for the separation of fumaric, succinic, malic and citric acids. Dichlorofluorescein was incorporated into the organic layer of the solvent to aid ultraviolet detection of the acids on the developed plate.

Ting and Dugger (1965) have developed a thin layer chromatographic system for α-ketoglutaric, citric, fumaric, lactic, malic and succinic acids using an ether-formic acid solvent with silica gel plates. The method suffers from the disadvantages of lack of reproducibility and the fact that acids in a mixture may mutually affect their R_F values. However, coupled with the use of other systems it may serve as an aid to identification of dicarboxylic acids, citric and lactic acid. Paper chromatography of lactic acid has been discussed by Lindqvist and Storgärds (1953) in connection with paper chromatography of volatile fatty acids.

2. Separation and detection of organic acids on silica gel
(Ting and Dugger, 1965)

Principle: Water-soluble organic acids are separated and identified by thin-layer chromatography. The solvent used is diethyl ether-formic acid (7 : 1) and detection is achieved either by use of a pH indicator or by acid ammonium molybdate.

Reagents:

Plates—Commercially available glass plates are coated, to a thickness of 250 μm, with silica gel H (Stahl, 1962), using an adjustable applicator (Desaga). The plates are dried for 3–4 h and stored in a desiccator until used. Subsequent heat activation is unnecessary.

Solvent—Water-saturated diethyl ether and 88% formic acid are mixed in a ratio 7 : 1 by volume in a separatory funnel and small quantities of distilled water are added with shaking until saturation is achieved. The lower aqueous layer is discarded.

Indicator. Bromophenol blue, 0·3% w/v, and methyl red, 0·1% w/v, are dissolved in 95% ethanol.

Ammonium molybdate. This consists of 5 ml of 60% w/w perchloric acid, 25 ml of 4% w/v ammonium molybdate solution, 10 ml of N-HCl, and 60 ml of distilled water.

Procedure: Solvent, to a depth of 1 cm, is added to a developing chamber lined with filter paper. The chamber is sealed with adhesive tape prior to development, to prevent solvent changes due to evaporation. Super-saturation is achieved by shaking immediately prior to development. Lining, taping and shaking are desirable to maintain a uniform solvent front and to prevent secondary front formation. For a 14 cm front development the time is about 1 h.

Samples, 10 μl containing 30 μg of acid (or its salt), are applied in ethanolic solution 2·5 cm from the bottom of the plates and 2–3 cm apart.

After development, plates are air-dried in a hood for a few minutes to remove ether, and then heated in an oven (80°C) to evaporate formic acid. Alternatively, to prevent loss of keto acids, the plates may be air-dried for about 4 h, or until all traces of formic acid are removed.

Many pH indicators can be used for acid detection but a mixture of 0·3% bromophenol blue and 0·1% methyl red in 95% ethanol gives good contrast and lasts for several weeks before fading. The acids appear as yellow spots against a blue background. A good demonstration of some acids can be achieved by spraying with acid ammonium molybdate until just moist, air drying, irradiating with ultraviolet light for 15 min. The acids appear as blue spots against a white background.

Sensitivity and reproducibility: Usually 30 μg samples of acid are applied. The R_F values obtained are variable, even when great care is taken to maintain identical conditions. The high and low R_F values are generally more reproducible than those in the intermediate range. R_F values tend to increase slightly with increasing acid concentration, and are also altered by the presence of other components in the mixture. Hydroxy acids, e.g.,

TABLE XI

R_F values and colour reaction with ammonium molybdate on silica gel H developed with a water-saturated diethyl ether-formic acid (7 : 1) solvent

Acid[a]	R_F[b]	Colour[c]	Comments
α-Ketoglutaric	0·56	B	
Ascorbic	0·30	B	Sodium salt applied
Aspartic	0·04	FB	
β-Hydroxybutyric	0·81	FB	
cis-Aconitic	0·61	FB	
Citramalic	0·64	B	
Citric	0·37	B	
Citraconic	0·91	FB	
Fumaric	0·96	LB	Sodium salt applied
Galacturonic	0·06	B	
Glucuronic	0·09	B	Sodium salt applied
Glutamic	0·05	FB	
Glutaric	0·91	NR	
Isocitric	0·42	B	Sodium salt applied
Isocitric lactone	0·63	B	
Lactic	0·65	B	
Malic	0·53	B	
Malonic	0·69	FB	
Oxalic	0·07	B	Usually streaks
Phosphoric	—	Y	R_F increases with increasing concn.
Succinic	0·86	FB	Sodium salt applied
Tartaric	0·23	B	
Tartronic	0·06	B	Streaks
Sudan Red G	0·88	—	Standard dye

(a) 30 μg applied in 10 μl of ethanol solution.
(b) Average of four determinations.
(c) B = blue, LB = light blue, FB = faint blue, Y = yellow, NR = no apparent reaction.

tartronic, citric, isocitric and malic, tend to show tailing at high concentration, and since all these have similar R_F values their concentration must be satisfactorily controlled for good separation.

Despite the variability in R_F values they are constant enough for identification purposes. Table XI lists some acids and R_F values.

3. Separation and quantitation of esters of tricarboxylic and related acids by gas–liquid chromatography

Introduction: The method given here is that of Harman and Doelle (1969), in which esters of the tricarboxylic acids and related compounds are separated on a $24 \times \frac{1}{4}$ in. o.d. column of 10% Reoplex 400 on acid-washed Chromosorb 400, the choice from 13 different columns surveyed. An alternative procedure, using trimethylsilyl-derivatives has also been published (Doelle and Manderson, 1969).

Instrument: The instrument used was a Beckman GC-M linear-programmed gas chromatograph fitted with a thermo-conductivity cell and a dual flame ionization detector.

Column: The column is $24 \times \frac{1}{4}$ in. o.d. packed with 10% Reoplex 400 on acid-washed Chromosorb W (60–80 mesh). Reoplex 400 (polypropylene glycol adipate) was obtained from Griffin & George Ltd., London, England. Chromosorb W was obtained from Analabs Inc., Hampden, Connecticut, U.S.A.

Operating conditions: The following conditions were used:
    Detector oven temperature: 250°C
    Injection port temperature: 150°C
    Helium gas flow rate: 100 ml/min.
    Hydrogen flame ionization detector: hydrogen flow rate, 35·5 ml/min; air, 40 p.s.i.
    Sample size: 5 μl.

Temperature programme: The range of 50°–200°C was programmed at a rate of 5°C/min, commencing at the time of injection.

Preparation of esters: The acids (10 mg to not more than 100 mg) are dissolved in 3 ml of 51% boron trifluoride-methanol (British Drug Houses Ltd, London, England) in a stoppered sample bottle. Methylation is achieved by shaking the tubes overnight in a water bath at 28°C. The remaining boron trifluoride-methanol complex is hydrolysed by the addition of 5 ml of distilled water and the esters are then extracted by shaking the solution vigorously with two separate volumes (2 ml) of chloroform each for 2 min. The esters must be extracted within 5 min of the addition of distilled water.

The combined chloroform extracts are dried over anhydrous sodium sulphate and the resulting solution is injected into the gas chromatograph.

The efficiency of esterification by this procedure approaches 100% for dimethyl esters, with a replicate variation of $\pm 2\%$, while mono- and tri-esters yield a constant 50–55% recovery, with a variation of $\pm 3\%$ amongst replicates. Table XII indicates the efficiency for some of the tricarboxylic acid cycle acids and related acids.

TABLE XII

Percentage recovery of tricarboxylic acid cycle acids and related acids from the esterification procedure of Doelle

Free acid	Percentage recovery
Pyruvate	52
Lactate	55
Oxalate	100
Succinate	100
Fumarate	96
Malate	90
α-Ketoglutarate	102
Citrate	52

Separation and sensitivity: The column used separates the following acids, as esters: pyruvate, lactate, glyoxalate, fumarate, succinate, malate, α-keto-glutarate, *cis*-aconitate, citrate, isocitrate, oxalate, glycollate, itaconate, tartrate, malonate, maleate, adipate, and acetoacetate. In an analysis of a mixture of all 18 acids only glycollate, oxalate and glyoxalate, and itaconate and maleate, are eluted as combined peaks.

For the separation of acetoacetate from pyruvate the standard conditions given are used, but 5 min after injection the rate of temperature programming is increased to 10°C/min.

The ester of oxaloacetate decomposes on the column to give three breakdown products that appear as small peaks between glyoxalate and fumarate, succinate and malate, and *cis*-aconitate and citrate respectively. The appearance of these peaks can be taken as an indication of the presence of oxaloacetate in the sample. Harman and Doelle (1969) report that this ester can be quantitated on a 6 ft column of 15% Dow-Corning silicone grease SE 30 on acid-washed Chromosorb W (60–80 mesh).

Calibration using peak height measurements, is linear over the range of 5–25 μg, at an attenuation of 2×10^3. An attenuation of 1×10^2 enabled samples of 0·25 μg to be determined, and 0·10 μg was detectable.

4. Determination of individual acids
(a) *Estimation of lactic acid*

Lactic acid can be estimated chemically by the method of Hullin and Noble (1953), as modified by Nanni and Baldini (1964).

Several enzymic methods have been described and lactate dehydrogenases, both NAD-linked and non-NAD-linked, are commercially available. The colorimetric method of Schön (1965) makes use of yeast lactate dehydrogenase, and is given here. An ultramicro method using the same enzyme, but a different electron acceptor, has been described by Rutowski and De Baare (1966).

The method of Rosenberg and Rush (1966), for the simultaneous determination of lactic and pyruvic acids, is described in the section on keto acid estimation (p. 148).

Method of Nanni and Baldini (1964)

Principle: The deproteinized sample is treated with $CuSO_4$, $5H_2O$ and $Ca(OH)_2$ to remove interfering pyruvate. Further $CuSO_4$, $5H_2O$ is added, together with conc. H_2SO_4, which, under the influence of heat, converts lactic acid to acetaldehyde. This is reacted with p-hydroxydiphenyl to produce a violet chromophore, having an absorption maximum at 568 nm.

Reagents:
> Standard lactic acid. 0·2133 g of dry lithium lactate is dissolved in 100 ml of distilled water, and 1 ml of conc. H_2SO_4 added. The final volume is made up to 1 litre, using distilled water. This is diluted to the appropriate range for calibration.
> p-Hydroxydiphenyl solution. 150 mg of p-hydroxydiphenyl is dissolved in 10 ml of absolute ethanol.
> Copper sulphate solutions. $CuSO_4$, $5H_2O$, 20% (w/v) and 15% (w/v).
> Calcium hydroxide.
> Sulphuric acid, conc.

Method: Protein-free solution (1 ml), containing 10–200 μg of lactic acid, is pipetted into 110×15 mm centrifuge tubes which are graduated exactly at 10 ml. One ml of 20% copper sulphate is added and the mixture made up to a final volume of 10 ml with distilled water. $Ca(OH)_2$ (1 g) is added after which the tubes are stoppered and shaken vigorously for 30 sec periods, at intervals of 5 min for 30 min. The stoppers are then removed and the tubes are centrifuged.

One ml of each supernatant solution is pipetted into a series of 180×15 mm ground glass-stoppered Pyrex tubes. The bottoms of the tubes are placed in an ice bath and 0·05 ml of 15% $CuSO_4$ is added, followed by 6 ml of conc. H_2SO_4, added slowly with continuous shaking, dropwise from a burette. When all the acid is added the tubes are shaken vigorously. The stoppered tubes are transferred to a water bath ($60° \pm 1°C$) for 30 min, then removed and cooled to $8°-10°C$. 0·1 ml of alcoholic p-hydroxydiphenyl solution is added, and mixed by vigorously shaking.

The tubes are then incubated in a water bath at $29° \pm 1°C$ for 30 min, followed by 90 sec in a boiling water bath, a treatment which removes excess p-hydroxydiphenyl. Immediately after this treatment the tubes are cooled in ice water and the extinction at 568 nm determined against a blank prepared by taking distilled water through the whole procedure. The violet colour is stable for at least 2 h.

Calibration: The calibration obtained for 10–120 μg lactic acid is linear ($E = \mu g \times 0·054$).

Range and sensitivity: The range, per ml of initial sample, is 10–200 μg. Samples containing above 120 μg of lactic acid can be diluted, prior to reading the extinction, with H_2SO_4/H_2O (6 : 1 v/v). When working below 120 μg per ml an accuracy of $\pm 1\%$ is obtainable.

Interference: The most probable interfering compound present in the sample is pyruvic acid. The initial treatment is designed to reduce interference from this, but Hullin and Noble (1953) report that this procedure, although it does remove a considerable amount of pyruvate present, does not result in reproducible results and they recommend a total of three copper-lime treatments, since this reduces the contribution of pyruvic acid to the extinction to a small, constant amount. They showed, using three such treatments, that up to 600 μg/ml of pyruvic acid can be tolerated.

The Hullin and Noble (1953) treatment of the supernatant is as follows. Six ml of the supernatant from the first copper-lime treatment is pipetted into a second tube containing 0·6 ml of 20% $CuSO_4$ and 0·6 g of solid $Ca(OH)_2$ is added. After centrifuging the procedure is repeated with 3 ml of supernatant, 0·3 ml of 20% $CuSO_4$ and 0·3 g of $Ca(OH)_2$. The supernatant from this third treatment is then carried through the procedure described by Nanni and Baldini.

Enzymic estimation of $L(+)$ lactic acid (Schön, 1965)

Principle: Lactate dehydrogenase from yeast is a ferroflavoprotein very specific for its substrate, $L(+)$ lactic acid. The natural electron acceptor is cytochrome c but for routine work a number of artificial electron acceptors are adequate. The o-phenanthroline-Fe^{3+} complex is used here and the overall reaction is

$$L(+)\text{lactate} + 2[Fe(\text{phenanthroline})_x]^{+++} \longrightarrow$$
$$\text{pyruvate} + 2[Fe(\text{phenanthroline})_x]^{++}$$

The o-phenanthroline-Fe^{+++} complex is yellow, whereas the o-phenanthroline-Fe^{++} complex is pink, with an absorption maximum at 510 nm. The extent of reduction is monitored spectrophotometrically at this wavelength.

Reagents:
For preparation of sample:
  Perchloric acid. The normality used depends upon the sample volume taken since the final concentration should be 0·3M.
  Bromocresol purple. 0·04% w/v in ethanol.
  Potassium hydroxide, 3N

For assay of sample:
  Yeast L(+) lactate dehydrogenase is obtainable commercially as a powder. Schön also describes a method of preparation. The final concentration should be around 10 units/ml (1 unit = that amount of enzyme that will oxidize 1 μmole of lactate/min under the assay conditions used).
  Solution 1: phosphate buffer, 0·1M, pH 7·0.
  Solution 2: $FeCl_3$, saturated aqueous solution (approximately 2·5M).
  Solution 3: o-phenanthroline monohydrate, 0·006M. This is stable for at least one week when kept refrigerated.
  Solution 4: this is prepared by mixing 20 ml of solution 3 with 2·5 ml of a freshly prepared 1 : 400 dilution of stock solution 2, and making the volume up to 40 ml with distilled water. This solution must be prepared freshly every day and be kept cold prior to use.
  Lithium or zinc lactate, 0·01M in 0·01N H_2SO_4 for calibration. The standard is appropriately diluted with distilled water.

Procedure:
Preparation of sample: If the sample to be analysed contains protein it must first be deproteinized, preferably with perchloric acid (0·3M final concentration). Three ml of perchloric acid extract is mixed with 0·01 ml of bromocresol purple (0·04% in ethanol), and then neturalized with KOH (3N). After 15 min in an ice bath the perchlorate is removed by centrifuging. Adequate removal of perchlorate must be achieved to avoid further precipitation during incubation.

Assay of the sample: The sample (0·5 ml), containing between 10–70 nmoles of lactic acid, is pipetted into a test tube, followed by solution 1 (1 ml) and solution 4 (1 ml). A blank, containing water instead of sample, is also set up. The reaction is initiated by the addition of the appropriate amount (usually 0·02 ml) of enzyme preparation, diluted previously with phosphate (0·1M, pH 7·0) so as to contain about 10 units/ml. A control tube, to measure the amount of non-enzymic reduction occurring due to the presence of reducing substances in the sample, and its blank are set up. These contain, respectively, sample but no enzyme and neither sample nor enzyme.

All tubes are incubated for 30 min at room temperature (18°–20°C) after which time their extinction at 510 nm is recorded. The colour developed is stable for at least another 30 min but on prolonged standing tends to rise. Blank values should always be well below $E = 0.05$.

Calibration: A calibration curve is prepared using a solution (0·01M) of lithium or zinc L(+) lactate in 0·01N H_2SO_4, diluted 1 : 50 prior to use. The method is calibrated from 0–80 nmoles (E_{510} 0–approx. 0·70) over which range it is linear.

Calculation: The extinction of the test is corrected using the appropriate blank (enzyme but no sample). The extinction of the control tube, to correct for non-enzymic reduction, is corrected using its blank (no enzyme or sample). The blank-corrected test can now be corrected against the blank-corrected control. This final figure represents the amount of enzymic reduction which has occurred and thus the amount of lactic acid can be read from the calibration curve.

Interference: The deviation in duplicate and triplicate determinations falls below 3%.

The following substances, when tested at the level of 1·0 μmole in the presence of 50 nmoles of lactic acid, did not interfere: glucose, pyruvate, malate, α-ketoglutarate, succinate, β-hydroxybutyrate, glutamate, 3-phosphoglycerate, α-glycerophosphate.

Reducing agents such as ascorbate, cysteine and reduced glutathione reduce the phenanthroline complex non-enzymically. Ascorbate does this quantitatively within 10 min, the latter two rather more slowly at rates which permit corrections to be applied.

The enzymic reaction is inhibited strongly by EDTA even at 0·1 mM concentration; the presence of this compound in samples should therefore be avoided.

(b) Estimation of succinic acid

Succinic acid can be estimated enzymically by the method of Rodgers (1961), and also by the method of Kmetec (1966). It can be determined chemically by the method of Swann (1957).

Chemical method of Swann (1957)

Principle: The method is based upon the reaction of succinic anhydride with hydroquinone to form dihydronaphthazarin, the concentration of which is estimated spectrophotometrically at 520 nm.

Reagents:
Hydroquinone
Sulphuric acid, concentrated
Benzene
Succinic acid

Procedure: The sample to be analysed, containing between 4 and 25 mg of succinate, is transferred to a glass-stoppered 25 ml Erlenmeyer flask and dried in an oven at a temperature below 100°C. Exactly 1·000 g of hydroquinone is added, followed by 2 ml of concentrated sulphuric acid. The stopper is inserted and the flask is placed in an oven at 105°–110°C for 30 min. It is then transferred to a pre-heated oven, at 135°C, for 2 h. Gentle agitation is required, two or three times, during this period. The oven used should have a quick recovery to the reaction temperature when the door has been opened. The temperature control should be very fine and not exceed by 1°C the temperature stipulated for the reaction.

On cooling, the sample is carefully diluted with small portions of water and transferred to a separatory funnel. The final volume should be 25–30 ml. Approximately 30 ml of benzene is added and the contents of the funnel thoroughly agitated to extract the red dihydronaphthazarin. The aqueous layer is drawn off and extracted with a further 10 ml of benzene. The benzene portions are worked separately with water until acid free, and are then combined. The benzene extract is then passed through a filter previously dampened with benzene into a 50 ml volumetric flask. The volume is made up with benzene and the extinction read at 520 nm.

Calibration: A calibration is prepared in the range 4–25 mg using standard succinic acid.

Interference: o-Phthalic acid interferes.

Enzymic estimation of succinic acid

The enzymic methods used are based upon the reduction of artificial electron acceptors, such as dichlorophenol indophenol, in the presence of a succinate dehydrogenase preparation obtained from a variety of sources. The success and ease of the method depend to a great extent upon the characteristics of the preparation used. The method of Rodgers (1961) is described here but the procedure of Kmetec (1966) has many advantages and is favoured if muscle strips from *Ascarus lumbricoides* var. Suis (pig ascarus) are obtainable.

Method of Rodgers (1961)

Principle: Succinate is extracted from the sample by ether. Phosphate buffer is added to this extract and the ether distilled off. The sample is treated with semicarbazide to prevent subsequent interference by α-keto-glutarate. Succinate is then estimated using a pigeon breast preparation whose limited dehydrogenase activity is ensured by successive, thorough washing during its preparation. This procedure removes many coenzymes. Further, most coenzymes are ether-insoluble and are thus not introduced in the sample. For the assay of fermentation liquors the acid-ether extract (p. 66) should be used directly.

The amount of succinate present in the sample is estimated by follow-ing the enzymic reduction of 2,6-dichlorophenolindophenol, measured at 600 nm, in the presence of cyanide, to ensure that this reduction is not interfered with by oxygen.

Reagents:

Succinic acid, standard solution 0·1 mM. Succinic acid (A.R.) is dissolved in KH_2PO_4-Na_2HPO_4 buffer, 0·06M, pH 7·0.

Perchloric acid 3% w/v, for deproteinization, if required.

Diethyl ether. This is shaken with acidified saturated $FeSO_4$ solution and redistilled immediately prior to use.

Potassium phosphate-sodium phosphate buffer. KH_2PO_4: Na_2HPO_4 0·06M, pH 7·0 and 0·01M pH 7·4. A.R. reagents are used.

Semicarbazide, 50 mM. 557·5 mg of semicarbazide hydrochloride (A.R.) is dissolved in 50 ml of 0·06M phosphate buffer, pH 6·0, readjusted to pH 6·0 with N-NaOH, and diluted with water to 100 ml.

Cyanide reagent. 2·72 g of KH_2PO_4 (A.R.), 1 g of crystalline bovine plasma albumen and 60 mg of EDTA are dissolved in 900 ml of water. The pH is adjusted to 7·0 with KOH. 780 μg of KCN is added and the mixture diluted to 1 litre. The reagent is stable for at least 8 months when stored at 3°C.

2,6-Dichlorophenolindophenol. A stock solution of 0·15% w/v is diluted 1 : 10 with 0·06M phosphate buffer, pH 7·0, immediately before use.

Procedure:

Preparation of the enzyme: Pigeon breast muscle (50–100 g) is minced and washed four times with 10 vol ice-cold phosphate buffer, 0·01M, pH 7·4. The suspension is filtered through muslin under reduced pressure after each wash. At this stage the preparation can be stored for several weeks at −15°C. For use it is resuspended in 10 vol of phosphate buffer, 0·06M, pH 7·0, and homogenized for 2 min in a Waring Blender. This homogenate remains active for at least five days when kept at 5°C.

Preparation of the sample: This depends on the nature of the sample to be analysed. For fermentation media the acid-ether extract (p. 66) will contain the succinic acid and the ether extraction given below, for extraction of intracellular succinic acid, can be eliminated.

The sample is ground with acid-washed sand and 12 ml of 3% $HClO_4$ in a mortar. The suspension is filtered, using Whatman no. 30 paper, and portions of it are extracted with ether in a Kutscher-Steudd type extractor, whose efficiency is previously determined by extracting known amounts of succinic acid. Two ml of phosphate buffer (0·06M, pH 7·0) is added to the ether extract and the ether is removed by distillation. Any $HClO_4$ extracted into the ether is neutralized at this stage, using N-KOH with phenol red as an indicator. The extract is transferred to a stoppered Pyrex test tube and made up to 5 ml with phosphate buffer, 0·06M, pH 7·0. It is maintained at 5°C for 1 h, allowing the $KClO_4$ to separate out.

The supernatant is transferred to a second stoppered tube and is treated to prevent subsequent interference from α-ketoglutarate and oxaloacetate by addition of semicarbazide. The pH of the sample is adjusted to around 6·0 with 0·1 ml N-HCl and 0·2 ml of the 50 mM semicarbazide solution is added. The mixture is incubated for 2 h at 37°C, or overnight at 18°C. The pH is then readjusted to about 7·0 with 0·1 ml N-NaOH.

Estimation of succinic acid. The sample (total volume not exceeding 1·5 ml) is mixed with 1 ml of cyanide reagent, 1 ml of 0·015% 2,6-dichlorophenolindophenol solution, and 0·06M phosphate buffer, pH 7·0, such that the final volume, contained in a 10 ml stoppered Pyrex tube, is 4 ml. Enzyme (2 ml) is added and the tube is shaken. After 20 min a portion of the reaction mixture is transferred to a 1 cm cuvette and the extinction at 600 nm measured against a mixture containing 1 ml of cyanide reagent, 3 ml of 0·06M phosphate buffer, pH 7·0, and 2 ml of enzyme. The measurement is repeated at intervals until the rates of reduction of dye are the same for blank and sample. Enzyme preparations that take longer than 20 min to complete the oxidation of 0·1 μmole of succinic acid should be discarded. A blank without succinate is run in parallel with the sample, or batch of samples. The extinction of each sample or standard is corrected for the extinction change in the blank over the same time period.

The assay can also be carried out in a recording spectrophotometer. The total volume per cuvette is 3·0 ml (0·5 ml of cyanide reagent, 0·2 ml of 0·075% 2,6-dichlorophenolindophenol, sample up to 0·75 ml, 1 ml of enzyme preparation and 0·06M phosphate pH 7·0). The blank contains all the above, with the exception of succinate which is replaced by buffer.

Calibration: The method is calibrated over the range 0·02–0·2 μmole, in which region the standard error for the direct spectrophotometric assay is recorded as ± 0·004 μmole. Although the calibration is linear, the slope varies with each enzyme preparation, and from day to day with the same

7

preparation. Consequently it is necessary to run a series of standards (0·02, 0·1 and 0·2 μmole of succinic acid) with each batch of samples. The blank value of the preparation increases with its age.

Interference: Ether-insoluble materials, such as glucose 6-phosphate, glycerol 1-phosphate and most amino acids, do not interfere since they are not extracted. Acetate, acetoacetate, β-hydroxybutyrate, L-glutamate, lactate, pyruvate, citrate, isocitrate and fumarate, at a concentration of 10 μmoles, do not reduce the dye nor do they interfere with the recovery of succinate when treated alone and at the same concentration in the presence of succinic acid (0·1 μmole). Fumarate causes an increase in the reaction time although the amount of dye reduced does not alter. L-Malate decreases the recovery of added succinate when present in amounts greater than 0·2 μmole, but is not itself oxidized.

(c) *Estimation of fumaric acid*

Enzymic assay (Singer and Lusty, 1963)

Principle: By the combined action of fumarate hydratase, malate enzyme and lactate dehydrogenase, fumarate is converted to L-lactate with the elimination of one mole of CO_2 per mole of fumarate converted. The reactions are:

$$\text{Fumarate} + H_2O \rightleftharpoons \text{L-malate}$$

$$\text{L-Malate} + NAD^+ \rightleftharpoons \text{pyruvate} + CO_2 + NADH + H^+$$

$$\text{Pyruvate} + NADH + H^+ \rightleftharpoons \text{L-lactate} + NAD^+$$

$$\text{Sum: Fumarate} + H_2O \rightleftharpoons \text{L-lactate} + CO_2$$

By suitable choice of conditions the overall reaction proceeds quantitatively from left to right and the CO_2 evolved can be measured manometrically. By using a pH of 5·5 CO_2-retention is negligible and the necessity for acid-tipping is eliminated.

If the sample contains L-malate, the sum of the fumarate + L-malate is obtained. The amounts of the individual acids can be determined by omitting fumarate hydratase from a second assay. The difference between the two assays gives the fumarate content of the sample.

Reagents:

Potassium acetate buffer, approx. 2M, pH 5·5.

An approximately 2M solution of potassium acetate containing 196 g per litre is titrated with approximately 2N-acetic acid (115 ml of acetic acid diluted to 1 litre), or with 2N-hydrochloric acid, to pH 5·5 determined with a pH meter. It may be stored at 4°C for several months.

Manganous chloride, approximately 0·045M. 0·89 g of MnCl, 4H$_2$O is dissolved in distilled water and made to 100 ml.

Fumarate standard solution, 0·05M, pH 5·5. 0·58 g of fumaric acid A.R. is dissolved in 50 ml of distilled water, adjusted to pH 5·5 with 0·1N-KOH (pH meter) and made to 100 ml. It should be stored frozen, in which state it is stable for months.

Fumarate hydratase (fumarase), 250 units per ml. The enzyme from pig heart is available commercially as a crystalline suspension in ammonium sulphate from Sigma and from Boehringer. One unit, according to Massey (1955), is the amount of enzyme contained in a 3 ml assay mixture which changes E_{300} by 0·010 in 1 min at pH 7·3.

Malate enzyme—lactate dehydrogenase. An homogenate of lyophilized cells of *Lactobacillus arabinosus* is used as a source of these enzymes. One hundred mg of cells are homogenized in 1 ml of distilled water in a glass-Teflon homogenizer. Growth of the organism is described below.

Procedure: The samples for analysis should be deproteinized prior to assay and the pH adjusted to 5·5, at which value the retention of CO_2 is insignificant. As fumarate hydratase and malate enzyme are not optimally active at pH 5·5, however, it is necessary to provide a sufficient excess of these enzymes if the reaction is to proceed to completion within a reasonable period.

Five Warburg flasks are required, comprising two for a duplicate assay of the sample, two for the standard fumarate solution and one for the fumarate-free control.

All the flasks receive:

Main compartment	*Side-Arm*
0·6 ml acetate buffer	0·15 ml acetate buffer
0·1 ml manganous chloride solution	0·40 ml *L. arabinosus* homogenate

The experimental flasks additionally receive (main compartment)
   0·1 ml fumarate hydratase solution
   1·65 ml distilled water

The standard fumarate flasks receive (main compartment)
   0·1 ml fumarate hydratase solution
   0·1 ml and 0·2 ml fumarate standard solution
   1·55 ml and 1·45 ml distilled water

The control flask receives
   1·75 ml distilled water

The flasks are attached to the manometers and equilibrated at 38°C for 10 min. The taps are closed, the reading taken, and then the side-arm contents tipped into the main compartment. Readings are continued until the rate of CO_2 release in the unknown and standard flasks is the same as that in the control. This takes about 15–25 min if the fumarate is within the range 1–10 μmoles. The CO_2 evolved endogenously by the control is about 5–7 μl.

To determine fumarate rather than the total fumarate + L-malate, two additional flasks with unknown samples are set up with fumarate hydratase omitted from each. The CO_2 evolved from these flasks corresponds to the L-malate content of the sample and so, by difference from the flasks which contain fumarate hydratase, the fumarate content may be determined.

Calculation:

$$\frac{(\mu l \ CO_2 \text{ produced in experimental flask}) - (\mu l \ CO_2 \text{ produced in control})}{22 \cdot 4}$$

$$= \mu\text{moles (fumarate + L-malate) in experimental flask}$$

Sensitivity: This depends on the volume of the Warburg flasks used. With flasks of 15–30 ml the lower limit for the determination is 1 μmole (fumarate + L-malate), whereas with 5 ml flasks it is about 0·3 μmole.

Interference: Pyruvate present in the sample is decarboxylated by the malate enzyme and so interferes. Addition of semicarbazide, to give a final concentration of 0·02M (pH 5·5), prevents the decarboxylation of pyruvate and should be used if the presence of this keto acid is suspected.

To check for the presence of substances in the unknown which might inhibit the enzymes used in the assay additions of standard fumarate solution are made to the sample and recovery is checked; it should be 96–100%.

Preparation of Lyophilized Cells of L. arabinosus

Organism: *Lactobacillus arabinosus* (*plantarum*) 17–5 (ATCC 8014; NCIB 8026; NCTC 6376).

Growth media: For maintenance stab cultures: yeast extract, 1%; glucose, 1%; and agar, 1·5%. Transfers are made every 3 to 4 weeks, with incubation for 24 h at 30°C.

For subculture: yeast extract, 1%, and glucose, 1%. Incubation at 30°C.

For large-scale culture: Nutrient broth, 1%; yeast extract, 1%; glucose 2%; DL-malic acid, 2%; sodium acetate trihydrate, 1%; KH_2PO_4, 0·1% and 5 ml of salts solution (see below). The medium is sterilized without the glucose and salts solution. The glucose is sterilized as a 20% solution and added aseptically to the rest of the (sterile) medium. The sterile salts solution is also added aseptically.

Salts solution: NaCl, 2 mg; $MgSO_4$, $7H_2O$, 40 mg; $MnSO_4$, $4H_2O$, 2 mg and $FeSO_4$, $7H_2O$, 2 mg, are dissolved in distilled water and made to 1 litre. The solution is sterilized by Seitz or Millipore filtration.

Growth of bacteria: Bulk medium is given a 1–5% v/v inoculum of the subculture and incubated at 30°C for 24 h. The medium is agitated continuously by passage of nitrogen through a coarse sintered glass sparger. Cells are collected by centrifuging and washed with distilled water until the supernatant is clear and colourless. The cells are then lyophilized and may be stored for several months in a desiccator below 0°C. The yield is about 9 g of lyophilized cells from 10 litres of culture.

Chemical Determination of Fumarate (*Hartford*, 1962)

Principle: The Furth and Hermann reaction, that is the production of a chromophore by reaction with acetic anhydride and pyridine, is used. The following acids can be estimated individually: itaconate, citrate, aconitate, and fumarate. The following mixtures of acids can be accurately estimated by determining the extinction at 435 and 385 nm: itaconate and citrate, itaconate and aconitate, fumarate and citrate, and fumarate and aconitate. With these mixtures one acid produces a chromophore that has negligible extinction at 435 nm (fumarate or itaconate) and a measurable extinction at 385 nm, whereas the chromophore produced from the other acid (citrate or aconitate) absorbs at this wavelength, and the concentration is found by the 435 nm determination. This allows calculation of this acid's contribution to the extinction at 385 nm, and thus, by difference, the extinction contribution of the other component. The chromophores from citrate and aconitate have a broad peak in the spectral region considered, the value of the 385 nm determination being 65% and 67% respectively of the 435 nm determination, for a 100 μg sample. The chromophores produced from fumarate and itaconate have very little absorption in the 435 nm region (for itaconate 1% of the 385 nm value), absorbing strongly at 385 nm. These spectral characteristics thus allow only the mixtures indicated to be determined.

Reagents:
   Fumaric acid, anhydrous, or its salts
   Pyridine
   Acetic anhydride

Procedure: The sample to be analysed (1 ml), containing between 25–1000 μg of fumaric acid, is pipetted into a test tube, followed by pyridine (1·3 ml). The contents of the tube are mixed by swirling. The pyridine should be added from a microburette, or an automatic pipette. Acetic anhydride (5·7 ml) is added in a similar manner, the tube swirled once and immediately placed in a constant temperature bath at 32°C. Colour development is complete after 30 min and remains relatively constant for 15 min, at 32°C. The extinction at 385 nm is determined against a reagent blank containing water instead of sample.

Calibration: A calibration curve can be prepared by taking known amounts of fumaric acid through the above procedure, in the range indicated (25–1000 μg).

Sensitivity: The lower limit given here is not the ultimate limit of the method but is the range of greatest accuracy of determination. Samples of fumaric acid can be assayed with a reproducibility of 0·3%.

Determination of a mixture of acids, e.g., fumarate and citrate: Using the procedure described above two calibration curves for citric acid are constructed, one at 385 nm and one at 435 nm. Both deviate from Beer's Law to a different extent. By measuring the extinction at 435 nm citrate is estimated, and by consulting the 385 nm curve, its contribution to the extinction here can be accurately assessed. For both 385 nm and 435 nm determination the blank is set at zero extinction.

A mixture of fumarate and aconitate can be similarly analysed.

The recommended ranges for the various acids are:

citrate   5–200 μg
aconitate 5–200 μg
itaconate 1–100 μg

When trans-aconitate alone is being analysed, the recommended time of incubation is between 15–25 min, since after this period the extinction of the chromophore declines.

Isocitric acid is reported as giving approximately 25% of the colour developed with citric acid.

(d) *Estimation of malic acid*

The estimation of malic acid is usually carried out enzymically and the method of Hohorst (1963b) is given here.

Principle: Malate is estimated spectrophotometrically by following the reduction of NAD in the presence of malate dehydrogenase. Since the reaction has an unfavourable equilibrium constant it must be pulled over to obtain quantitative oxidation. This is achieved by carrying out the reaction at an alkaline pH, effectively removing the protons produced, and by removing oxaloacetate as its hydrazone.

Reagents:

If deproteinization of the sample is necessary, for example in an enzyme incubation mixture, then this should be performed with perchloric acid, subsequently precipitating the perchlorate to give a neutral solution.

Hydrazine-glycine buffer, pH 9·5

7·5 g of glycine, 5·2 g of hydrazine sulphate and 0·2 g of EDTA $Na_2H_2, 2H_2O$ are added to a small volume of distilled water. 2N-NaOH (51 ml) is added and the final volume made up to 100 ml with distilled water. This solution is 0·4M with respect to hydrazine and 1M with respect to glycine. It is stable for one week when kept at 0 to 4°C. A stock solution of glycine, hydrazine sulphate and EDTA can be stored practically indefinitely, bringing it, as required, to the correct pH as described above.

NAD, 50 mM

Malate dehydrogenase. The preparation used should contain approximately 5 mg of protein/ml, having a specific activity of 37 International Units/mg.

Procedure: The assay is carried out using a spectrophotometer set at 340 nm. The components of the assay system are pipetted into the cuvette in the following order: hydrazine-glycine buffer (0·45 ml), NAD (0·05 ml) and sample (0·5 ml). The contents are mixed thoroughly and allowed to come to room temperature. The extinction (E_1) is determined twice, with an interval of 3 min, against a water blank. The reaction is initiated by the addition of malate dehydrogenase (0·01 ml), and should be complete within 10–20 min after which period the extinction (E_2) should be determined, twice, with an interval of 3 min. Alternatively a recording spectrophotometer may be used to follow continuously the course of the reaction.

Changes in the initial extinction, due to dilution by the addition of enzyme, are usually negligible in comparison with the extinction difference, $\Delta E(E_2-E_1)$. If the reaction is not complete 20 min after the addition of enzyme, then, provided there are no interfering substances present, the enzyme activity is too low. To check that the assay is working correctly, 0·01 ml of 0·002M L(−) malate solution can be added to the experimental cuvette. The increase in extinction, at 340 nm, that should be complete in 10–20 min is 0·123.

Range and specificity: Since it is advisable to limit ΔE to below $1\cdot0$ then at 340 nm the maximum capacity per cuvette is $0\cdot16$ μmole, and is $0\cdot3$ μmole at 366 nm.

The enzyme is highly specific for L($-$) malic acid and thus this can be assayed in a complex mixture of metabolites.

Calculation: Since malate reacts quantitatively the amount can be calculated from the following formula

$$\frac{\Delta E \times \text{dil.}}{\epsilon \times d} = \mu\text{mole malic acid}$$

where
$$\Delta E = E_2 - E_1$$
$$\text{dil.} = \text{total dilution of sample}$$
$$\epsilon = \text{extinction coefficient (cm}^2/\mu\text{mole)}$$
$$d = \text{light path (cm).}$$

(e) Citric acid

Determination of citric acid with citrate lyase (Moellering and Gruber, 1966)

Principle: The enzyme citrate lyase produces oxaloacetate and acetate from citrate. The oxaloacetate produced is estimated by following the oxidation of NADH in the presence of malate dehydrogenase. Nonenzymic decarboxylation of oxaloacetate, to pyruvate, is allowed for by the addition of lactate dehydrogenase. Due to the coupling to these enzyme reactions the equilibrium of citrate lyase is shifted in the direction of complete splitting of citrate. Prior to the determination of citrate, pyruvate and oxaloacetate can be assayed in the sample. The enzyme is conveniently prepared from *Aerobacter aerogenes* and is now commercially available.

An alternative procedure using crude extracts of *A. aerogenes* has been described (Dagley and Dawes, 1953). The extract also contains an active oxaloacetate decarboxylase which converts oxaloacetate to pyruvate and CO_2. The pyruvate may be estimated by the method of Friedemann and Haugen, or by following the oxidation of NADH in the presence of a commercial preparation of lactate dehydrogenase (Dagley, 1963).

Reagents:
Triethanolamine buffer, $0\cdot1$M, pH $7\cdot6$
β-NADH, $0\cdot01$M. This can be stored for 3 weeks at $0°$C in the dark
Zinc chloride, $0\cdot03$M
Perchloric acid, $0\cdot6$M, for deproteinizing if necessary
Lactate dehydrogenase. Two mg of protein/ml (360 IU/mg). This is stable for several months at $0°$C.
Malate dehydrogenase. Two mg protein/ml (720 IU/mg). This is also stable for several months at $0°$C.

Citrate lyase. Ten mg protein/ml (10 IU/mg)
This preparation loses around 10% of its activity within one month when stored in the cold.
The above three enzymes are available from Boehringer.

Procedure:

Sample preparation: Deproteinized samples of fermentation media should be used. For enzyme incubation mixtures, perchloric acid should be used for deproteinizing.

Assay: Glass cuvettes, of 1 cm light path, at a temperature of 25°C, have been used but the authors suggest that greater accuracy can be achieved by working at 340 nm rather than 366 nm.

The reagents are pipetted into the cuvette in the following order: buffer (2·0 ml), NADH (0·06 ml), $ZnCl_2$ (0·01 ml), and sample (0·02–0·9 ml). Water is added to obtain a volume of 2·97 ml and E_1 is read; then 0·01 ml of lactate dehydrogenase suspension, and 0·01 ml malate dehydrogenase are mixed in. These enzymes remove pyruvate and oxaloacetate. The endpoint in extinction, E_2, is reached within 3 min, and can be used to calculate pyruvate + oxaloacetate present. Alternatively, the concentration of each compound can be determined individually by the separate addition of the enzymes.

0·01 ml of citrate lyase suspension is then added and mixed. Citrate is completely decomposed within 5–10 min, and E_3 is read. The extinction due to citrate is

$$\Delta E \text{ citrate} = E_2 - E_3,$$

and the amount of citrate is calculated from this value using the following formula

$$\frac{\Delta E.V.M.}{\epsilon\, d\, v} = \frac{\text{mg citrate}}{\text{ml sample}}$$

where ϵ = extinction coefficient of NADH, at the wavelength used
d = light path of the cuvette (1 cm)
V = assay volume (3 ml)
v = the sample volume (0·02–0·9 ml)
M = molecular weight (192·1).

Since the enzymic reaction goes to completion no standards should be required, but it is advisable to run a standard citric acid solution and probably citrate additions to samples to check that complete utilization is in fact achieved, especially if the assay conditions are altered (see below). The range of the method is limited by the change in extinction of

NADH that can be measured. In the assay described the maximum amount of citrate estimated per cuvette must be less than 0·6 μmole, the amount of NADH present. The range can probably be extended upwards, if the sample is slightly above this level, by successive additions of NADH, until oxidation is complete and some remains. Any dilution occurring must be allowed for when calculating the amount of citrate present.

The lower limit of the system, when working at 366 nm, is reported as 0·02 μmole, with an accuracy of ± 5%. This can be improved by working at 340 nm.

The concentration of Zn^{2+} present in the assay system must be limited in the presence of phosphate, or carbonate, in the sample to avoid precipitation. To compensate for any reduction in the concentration of Zn^{2+} the authors advise that the concentration of citrate lyase should be proportionately increased.

Interference: This, to a great extent, depends upon the specificity of the citrate lyase preparation, and this is reported as absolute. None of the following exhibited any interference with speed or accuracy of the citrate determination: isocitrate, cis-aconitate, oxalate, succinate, fumarate, α-ketoglutarate, L-glutamate, tartrate, lactate, malate, acetate, ascorbate, glucose, fructose and ethanol, all at concentrations similar to that of citrate.

The presence of high concentrations of pyruvic acid and/or oxaloacetic acid could conceivably cause difficulties but this can be overcome by successive additions of NADH until these are completely reduced.

Chemical estimation of citric acid (*McArdle*, 1955)

Principle: Citrate is oxidized to pentabromoacetone using a bromide-bromate-vanadate solution. Excess bromine is removed by reaction with ferrous sulphate. The pentabromoacetone is extracted with petroleum ether and estimated by the production of a chromophore obtained on reaction with a solution of thiourea-borax-sulphide.

Reagents:
Sulphuric acid (A.R.) 1N and 33N solutions
Bromide-bromate-vanadate solution. 19·836 g of KBr, 5·44 g of $KBrO_3$ and 12·0 g of $NaVO_3$ are dissolved in distilled water and made up to 1 litre. This solution is stable for several months at room temperature. It yellows with age.
Ferrous sulphate solution. Twenty-two g of $FeSO_4$, $7H_2O$ are dissolved in 100 ml of 1N H_2SO_4. The solution should be freshly prepared each day.
Thiourea-borax-sulphide solution. Two g of sodium borate is dissolved in 100 ml of distilled water, to which is added 4 g of thiourea, followed

by 2 ml of a 10% Na_2S (5 g in 50 ml) solution, freshly made up. The sulphide solution is added not long before use, although at least 30 min before. If the Na_2S is moist then it may be contaminated with thio-sulphate, which causes low, irregular results. This can be avoided by washing and drying; however, recrystallization may be necessary.

Na_2SO_4–anhydrous

Light petroleum (b.p. 80°–100°C)

Citric acid standards, in the range 0·10–0·75 μmole/5 ml sample

Procedure: The sample (5 ml) is added to 33N–H_2SO_4 (5 ml) in a glass-stoppered Quickfit tube (150 mm × 29 mm), which has been previously boiled in 10% (v/v) nitric acid, well rinsed with distilled water and dried. The sample and acid are mixed thoroughly and allowed to cool. Bromide–bromate–vanadate solution (5 ml) is added and the tubes placed in a water bath at 30°C for 20 min.

The tubes are removed and $FeSO_4$ solution (3 ml) is added. The contents are mixed by swirling and left for at least 5 min. The tubes are inverted in order to remove any last traces of bromine from the airspace. The stopper and neck of each tube are wiped with tissue to remove any solution not reduced by $FeSO_4$. The colour at this stage is emerald green.

Light petroleum (7·5 ml) is added and the contents mixed for 2 min on a Vortex mixer. The lower aqueous layer is removed by suction, using a Pasteur pipette attached to a water pump. The sides of the tubes are washed down with distilled water, approximately 15 ml, and the contents mixed by a 20 sec period on the Vortex mixer. The aqueous layer is then removed in a similar fashion as before. A spatula end of anhydrous Na_2SO_4 is added to remove the last traces of water. Petroleum extract (5 ml) is pipetted into test tubes, followed by thiourea-borax-sulphide solution (4 ml). The contents of the tube are mixed on the Vortex mixer (20 sec period). The aqueous layer is drawn off and its extinction at 435 nm, or 500 nm, determined against a reagent blank. The orange-yellow colour produced is stable for 3 h.

Range and sensitivity: The range is 0·1–0·75 μmole of citrate/5 ml sample. The coefficient of variation, at low citrate concentrations is $\pm 3·9\%$.

The calibration curve is linear in the region of concentration used but it may not pass through the origin and the slope may vary from day to day. Consequently, it is necessary to run at least two standards with each batch of samples.

Interference: Glucose and acetoacetic acid interfere in that they cause production of 435 nm-absorbing material. Their contribution to the extinction at 500 nm is negligible, however, and thus citrate can be estimated in their presence. For instance, when read at 435 nm 1 mg/litre of acetoacetic acid is equivalent to 30 μg of citric acid, whereas at 500 nm 1 mg/litre is equivalent to 0·65 μg of citric acid.

2(d) *Specific analyses—Carbohydrates*

(*i*) *Separation and identification by chromatography*

The analysis of individual carbohydrates in complex biological media can present difficulties. In the examination of such milieu for unknown compounds considerable advantage may be gained by a chromatographic technique capable of resolving the mixture into "type" groups. One such method is the paper chromatographic procedure of Gordon, Thornburg and Werum (1956).

1. *Paper chromatography of complex mixtures of carbohydrates and related compounds* (*Gordon, Thornburg and Werum,* 1956)

Apparatus: Tank for ascending chromatography.

Chromatography paper: Whatman No. 4 paper.

Solvent for washing paper: Distilled water, pyridine (spectroscopic grade) and glacial acetic acid are mixed in the ratio 80 : 15 : 5 by vol.).

Developing solvent: Isopropanol, pyridine, glacial acetic acid and water (8 : 8 : 1 : 4 by vol).

Detection reagents:

Method 1: Solution A. Benzidine, 0·01M. 184 mg. of benzidine is dissolved in a mixture of 0·6 ml of glacial acetic acid, 4·4 ml of water and 95 ml of acetone to give a yellow solution which keeps indefinitely.

Solution B. Periodic acid, 0·1M aqueous solution, is diluted 1 ml to 20 ml with acetone; the resulting solution is stable for about 3 h.

The paper strip to be developed is dipped in Solution B and allowed to dry for 3–4 min, after which it is dipped in Solution A when white or yellow spots on a blue background appear, indicating that the compound(s) under investigation may contain *cis*-glycol group(s).

Method 2: 2-Aminobiphenyl hydrogen oxalate solution, 0·1M. 1·69 g of 2-aminobiphenyl and 0·9 g of anhydrous oxalic acid (or 1·26 g of oxalic acid dihydrate) are dissolved in a mixture of 5 ml of glycerol, 10 ml of water and 84 ml of acetone. The solution keeps indefinitely and is specific for all carbohydrates pyrolysable to furfural derivatives.

The paper strip requiring development is dipped through the reagent and allowed to dry in air for 10 to 15 min. It is then placed in an oven at

110°C for 5 min. The background is pale yellow while pentoses give red, hexoses greenish brown and uronic acids purple coloured spots.

Gordon *et al.* (1956) were able to draw some useful generalizations from the data they compiled on the R_F values of many carbohydrate compounds. As a rule deoxyaldohexoses have R_F values ranging from 0·75 to 0·83, aldopentoses from 0·70 to 0·76, ketohexoses from 0·69 to 0·70 and aldohexoses from 0·63 to 0·70. Monophosphoric esters have R_F values ranging from 0·37 to 0·43 unit lower than those of the parent carbohydrates (e.g. of glycerol, glucose or adenosine). Carboxylic acids have R_F values 0·20 to 0·30 lower than the parent glycol but also commonly display a strong lactone spot with an R_F value 0·20 higher than that of the parent glycol.

Addendum: Gordon *et al.* (1956) found a 10% v/v solution of pyridine in water to be a useful extractant for sugars and sugar acids. However, on application of this solution to chromatograms it must not be heated. To prevent possible interference from cationic components of complex milieu without recourse to formal desalting techniques, the above authors applied 1 μl of a 1M solution of pyridinium sulphate 0·5 to 1 mm in front of the spot origin so that the chromatographed material passes through this area, the test material being applied in the same volume to the origin after this application.

Preliminary chromatography of milieu containing unknown carbohydrate compounds may permit their division into groups. Further chromatographic methods may then be used as an aid to their identification.

2. Paper chromatography of carbohydrate compounds

Solvents for development: The following solvents are useful for the classes of compound indicated.

(a) Disaccharides, hexoses, pentoses, trioses and polyols
    (i) Ethyl acetate-pyridine-water, (120 : 50 : 40 by vol).
    (ii) Isopropanol-water, (160 : 40 by vol).
(b) Uronic acids
    Acetone-ethanol-isopropanol-borate buffer, 0·05M, pH 10·0, 3 : 1 : 1 : 2 by volume. This solvent, developed by Mukerjee and Sri Ram (1964), will separate glucuronic and galacturonic acids. Chromatography is carried out on Whatman No. 1 sheets which are developed at room temperature for 24 h by the descending technique.

Detection methods:

(a) Periodate-benzidine reagent (see p. 172).
(b) 2-Aminobiphenyl reagent (see p. 172).

3. *Thin layer chromatography of carbohydrate compounds* (*Method of Hay, Lewis and Smith*, 1963).

Pentoses, hexoses, polyols and dissacharides may be separated on silica gel G plates by this method.

Procedure: Plates are prepared by slurrying 30 g of silica gel in 66·5 ml of water and drying the spread plates overnight at 135°C.

Solvent: butanol-acetic acid-ether-water (9 : 6 : 3 : 1 by vol.)

Detection: After drying plates in air:
1. Spray with conc. H_2SO_4 and heat at 100°C for 5–10 min for reducing sugars. For polyols heat the sprayed plates at 150°C for 5–10 min.
2. $KMnO_4$ (0·5% w/v) in N-NaOH. Heat at 100°C for 0·5–2 min.

Method of Bomhof and Tucker (1965)

These authors have developed a thin layer system using cellulose coated plates. They tested dissaccharides, ketohexoses, aldohexoses and pentoses.

Procedure: Plates are prepared by slurrying 3MN cellulose (Macherey Nagel) in small portions at a time in a methanol-water (5 : 1 by vol) mixture, 15 g of cellulose to 90 ml of methanol-water being used. Plates 0·37 mm thick were used (Desaga applicator), dried in a hood for 2 h and then transferred to a desiccator overnight before use.

Detection of compounds: The 2-aminobiphenyl reagent previously described (p. 172) was used.

4. *Identification of carbohydrate compounds.*

The chromatographic methods described are useful for the preliminary identification of a wide variety of carbohydrate compounds. Final identification must rest ultimately on the preparation of derivatives of the pure compounds, or for example, by periodate methods (see pp. 78–85). To apply these techniques satisfactorily adequate quantities of material must be made available either by the use of preparative thin layer plates or by column methods. The column method of Walborg, Christensson and Gardell (1965) is useful in this connection.

5. *Ion exchange column chromatography of neutral monosaccharides* (*Walborg, Christensson and Gardell*, 1965)

Apparatus: Jacketed glass columns, having an internal diameter of 6 mm and a length of 155 cm, are used. The external diameter of the water jacket is 25 mm. The water jacket extends to within 5 mm of the end of the column, so that the temperature of the entire column of resin can be controlled. A piece of small plastic tubing (internal diameter of approximately 1 mm) is inserted into the lower end of the column. The columns are constructed in this manner in order to minimize mixing of the eluate after passage through the resin.

Buffers:
- A. 0·4M-Boric acid, 1·0M-glycerol and 0·5 ml of toluene per litre, adjusted to pH 6·80 ± 0·05 at 50°C with NaOH (approximately 70 m-eq per litre required for adjustment).
- B. 0·4M-Boric acid, 1·0M-glycerol, 0·050M-NaCl and 0·5 ml of toluene per litre, adjusted to pH 6·80 ± 0·05 at 50°C with NaOH. The buffers are filtered prior to use.

Preparation of resin for chromatography: Dowex 2-X8 of 200/400 mesh medium porosity, total capacity 3·0 ± 0·3 m-eq per dry gram is used (Fluka A. G. Buchs, S. G., Switzerland).

To 500 g of moist resin in a 4 litre beaker is added 3·5 litres of water. The resin is stirred and allowed to settle for 30 min. After settling the fine particles are decanted. This procedure is continued until most of the fine particles have been removed, and these fines are designated as Fraction I. The remaining resin is suspended, stirred and allowed to settle for 7 min. The particles in suspension are decanted and saved. The procedure is repeated until the supernatant liquid is clear. The 7 min supernatant particles are designated Fraction II (25–50% of the starting material). Fraction III is the fraction sedimenting within 7 min.

One hundred and fifty ml of settled Fraction II (enough for 2 columns) is treated in the following manner:

1. Transfer the resin to a sintered glass filter and wash with 1 litre of 2N-NaOH in 4 portions.
2. Wash the resin with 2 litres of distilled water to remove excess NaOH.
3. Wash the resin with 2 litres of Buffer B in 4 portions. The final pH of the slurry should be 6·50 or less.
4. Suspend the resin in 250 ml of Buffer B which has been warmed to 50°C and the pH adjusted to 6·80 ± 0·05 at 50°C.
5. Equilibrate at 50°C with 3 × 250 ml changes of Buffer B.
6. Equilibrate finally by adding 350 ml of Buffer B, warming to 50°C and de-aerating under reduced pressure.
7. After allowing the resin to settle the total volume is adjusted to 450 ml giving a slurry consisting of one part of settled resin to two parts of buffer. This slurry is kept at 50°C while packing the columns.

Packing and equilibration of columns: The columns at 50°C are packed in

4–5 sections by gravity flow, a fine pad of glass wool being placed at the bottom of the column to prevent resin particles obstructing the outlet. The initial height of the columns should be 150–153 cm. To aid in de-aerating the buffer before it enters the resin, a small plug of fine glass wool is inserted in the column about 3 cm above the resin. The column is equilibrated at a flow rate of 3.0 ± 0.2 ml/h at 50°C with buffer de-aerated under reduced pressure. Further packing of the column occurs on equilibration, to give a height of 145–150 cm.

Procedure for analysis: The sample to be analysed is dissolved in Buffer A (volume of sample 200 μl or 1 ml) and added to the column by gravity flow. A 200 μl sample is washed on to the column with 200 μl each of Buffers A and B respectively. A 1 ml sample is washed on to the column with 0.5 ml each of Buffers A and B respectively. Elution is effected with Buffer B at 50°C with a flow rate of 3.0 ± 0.2 ml/h using a constant volume pump and collecting 1 ml samples. Between samples the column should be allowed to equilibrate with 100 ml of Buffer B. The void volume is determined by adding a sample (1 ml) of water to the column, following the prescribed washing procedure and noting the depression in the blank as indicated by the aniline/acetic orthophosphoric reagent for estimation of sugars (see below).

Sugars are eluted from the column in the order: rhamnose, mannose, lyxose, fucose, ribose, arabinose, galactose, glucose, xylose, fructose, with greater than 90% recovery in all cases.

Analysis of samples: 3 ml of aniline/acetic orthophosphoric reagent are added to each 1 ml fraction, the samples heated for 2 h at 100°C, and the extinction read at 370 and 360 nm.

6. *Determination of sugars by an aniline/acetic orthophosphoric acid method* (*Walborg and Christensson*, 1965)

Reagent:
  Glacial acetic acid (200 ml) is added to 6 ml of redistilled aniline followed by 100 ml of 85% orthophosphoric acid.

Aniline is prepared for use by twice distilling analytical grade aniline from sodium hydroxide and zinc dust under nitrogen. The colourless aniline is stored in a glass-stoppered amber bottle at 4°C and is suitable for use for at least 2 months.

Procedure: To 1 ml of sugar solution (5–50 μg sugar) in 17–18 × 160 mm test tubes is added 3 ml of reagent. The samples are mixed and placed in a water bath at 100°C for 2 h. The level of water in the bath should be low enough to prevent excessive heating of the upper part of the tubes which are covered with glass marbles to cut down further evaporation. The samples are then cooled for at least 20 min in a water bath at 30°C (not lower). The extinction of the samples is read against water as a blank in 1 cm cuvettes at 360 and 370 nm. Should the extinction be too high (above 0·8), the sample may be diluted with a mixture containing two parts of glacial acetic acid to one part of 85% orthophosphoric acid. Up to four-fold dilutions may be performed in this manner.

Comment: Aldopentoses absorb maximally at 355 nm, aldo- and keto-hexoses at 365 nm, and 6-deoxyaldohexoses at 370 nm. This may afford a useful qualitative classification of the unknown sugar eluted from the columns.

Reference should also be made to the general method described by Herbert, Phipps, and Strange (this Series, Volume 5B).

(ii) Determination of individual carbohydrates

1. Determination of hexoses

A wide variety of methods is available for the determination of hexoses. The Nelson (1944) and the anthrone procedures are commonly used colorimetric procedures. The anthrone method depends upon the use of concentrated sulphuric acid and therefore, as applied to complex organic milieu, has great disadvantages as to its specificity and interference from non-carbohydrate compounds. The Nelson (1944) procedure, and indeed all methods using an arsenomolybdate reagent, have recently been criticized on two counts (Marais, de Wit and Quicke, 1966), namely the variability of the absorption maximum of the complex formed, and the relationship between the amount of sugar present and the volume of reagent necessary to achieve a proportional reaction. These facts militate against the extensive use to which the Nelson (1944) and Somogyi (1952) methods have been put. In the last few years there has been a movement towards the use of more specific methods of sugar determination generally not dependent upon concentrated sulphuric acid or upon copper ion reduction for their action.

The most effective methods used to date for glucose determination are the *o*-toluidine and the glucose oxidase procedures. These two methods are compared for their value in determining blood glucose by Relander and Räihä (1963), the *o*-toluidine method being favoured because of the speed of determination and the fact that it is not liable to interference from compounds such as glutathione as is the glucose oxidase method. The *o*-toluidine method is specific for aldoses.

2. Determination of glucose

(a) Determination of glucose by the o-toluidine method (Dubowski, 1962)

Reagents:

o-Toluidine reagent. This is a 6% (v/v) solution of o-toluidine (redistilled) in glacial acetic acid.

Trichloroacetic acid, 3% w/v, for deproteinization if required.

Procedure: If deproteinization of the sample is necessary, as with bacterial extracts, this may be achieved by the addition of 1·8 ml of 3% w/v trichloroacetic acid solution to 0·2 ml of sample. After setting aside for 5–10 min, the solution is filtered through a 5·5 cm Whatman no. 2 filter paper. To 1 ml of the filtrate in a test tube is added 3 ml of 6% v/v o-toluidine in glacial acetic acid. The tube is stoppered and, after mixing well, heated in a water bath at 100°C for 10 min. After cooling, the extinction is measured at 630 or 635 nm against a reagent blank. If the sample does not contain protein 1 ml of a suitable dilution of the sample is used for the determination. If the deproteinizing procedure above is adopted then the range is 0·1–0·6 mg of glucose/ml of original sample.

Note: The procedure described is applicable to the determination of aldohexoses.

(b) Determination of glucose by glucose oxidase (Barton, 1966)

Principle: Glucose is oxidized by a highly purified glucose oxidase preparation, to produce hydrogen peroxide and gluconate. The hydrogen peroxide formed oxidizes, in the presence of a horse-radish peroxidase preparation, o-dianisidine to produce a chromophore, the concentration of which can be estimated by its extinction at 525 nm.

Reagents:

o-Dianisidine hydrochloride (10 mg), horse-radish peroxidase (10 mg, Worthington Biochemical Co.) and 0·1 ml of purified glucose oxidase (Miles Chemical Co.) containing 1000 units/ml are dissolved in 0·1M-acetate buffer, pH 5·5, and made to a volume of 100 ml. One unit of enzyme is that amount which utilizes 0·447 μmole of D-glucose per min at 30°C and pH 5·5, measured titrimetrically.

Sulphuric acid, 10N

Procedure: Reagent (4·0 ml) is pipetted into a 25 × 150 mm test tube, placed in a 30°C water bath and allowed to equilibrate to bath temperature. 2·0 ml of the test solution, containing up to 200 μg of glucose, is pipetted into the reagent and mixed. At a reaction time of precisely 5 min 8·0 ml of 10N-H_2SO_4 is added. The extinction is read against water plus reagent at 525 nm.

For very accurate work a series of standards should be included with each set of determinations.

Calibration: Standard solutions of glucose (40–400 μg per 2 ml sample) are taken through the procedure given above. The calibration obtained is linear, and does not vary from day to day.

Specificity: Glucose oxidase preparations may contain maltase, in which case the validity of the method depends upon the absence of maltose in the samples to be analysed. Otherwise, the method is specific for glucose.

Interference: Cystathionine, cysteine and ascorbic acid in the reduced form inhibit glucose oxidase and thus their presence should be avoided.

A procedure using the "Glucostat" enzyme kit is described by Herbert, Phipps and Strange (this Series, Volume 5B).

3. Determination of galactose

Determination of galactose with galactose oxidase (Roth, Segal and Bertoli, 1965)

Principle: The estimation of galactose by the galactose oxidase method is similar in principle to that for glucose oxidase. The chromophore used is, however, measured in the ultraviolet and steps must therefore be taken to ensure that the extinction at 310 mμ of the sample prior to estimation is minimal.

Reagents:

Galactose oxidase. Suitable sources of supply are Worthington Biochemical Corporation, Freehold, New Jersey, 6000 units/g (Avigad *et al.*, 1962); Ames Research Laboratories, Elkhart, Indiana, 35,000 to 43,000 units/g (Scott, 1953). Both preparations are supplied as a dry powder to be stored at $-15°$C. One unit of either preparation yields approximately the same amount of activity under the conditions described for the assay. The enzyme units employed are defined by these respective authors.

The enzyme is made up in an aqueous solution containing 35 units/ml. It is divided into individual portions of 1 ml which are stored at $-15°$C until used. These are stable for at least 12 months.

Horse-radish peroxidase. Type II. Available from Sigma Chemical Co., St. Louis, Missouri, it should be stored at $-15°$C.

The enzyme is made up of an aqueous solution containing 1 mg/ml. It is stored at 4°C and keeps for about 30 days.

Benzidine. The base is recrystallized from hot water after treatment with activated charcoal and subsequent filtration.

One hundred mg of the recrystallized compound is dissolved in 10 ml of absolute ethanol and stored at $-15°C$. It is stable for 30 days.

Glycine buffer. 0·05M-Glycine, pH 8·3, is stored at 4°C and is stable for one month. This buffer is prepared by diluting 1 : 10 0·5M-glycine buffer (7·5 g glycine dissolved in water, adjusted to pH 8·4 with 5N-NaOH and made to 200 ml).

Hydrochloric acid, 5N

Reagent for analysis. Prepare reagent 15 min before use by mixing 10 ml of 0·05M-glycine buffer, 1 ml of galactose oxidase solution, 0·5 ml of horse-radish peroxidase and 0·25 ml of benzidine solution. For the period of analysis this reagent may be kept at room temperature.

Procedure for preparation of culture media for analysis

Samples (10 ml), containing not more than 0·5 mg galactose per ml, are treated with 1 g hydrated aluminium silicate and 300 mg of activated charcoal (roughly measured by spatula). The samples are allowed to stand for 30 min at room temperature with gentle agitation and are then filtered through Whatman No. 1 filter paper. The extinctions at 310 nm of 2 : 1 dilutions of the filtrates are then measured as blanks to be subtracted from the final extinctions on analysis, and also as a check that most of the ultraviolet-absorbing material has been removed. If a great deal of ultra-violet-absorbing material remains the above procedure should be repeated on fresh portions of a higher dilution. Galactose is removed from solution by this procedure by a factor of 0·5 of the total, and thus a set of standards should be run to run to determine the loss.

Procedure: Samples (0·5 ml) of treated filtrate, or standard solutions containing 0–150 μg galactose are added to 5 ml test tubes and brought to 37°C in a water bath. To each tube is added 0·5 ml of the reagent solution, followed by brief mixing. The tubes are incubated for exactly 30 min at 37°C when the reaction is stopped by adding one drop of 5N-HCl. The samples are transferred to 1 ml cuvettes and the extinction at 310 nm against water is read. The extinction at 310 nm is stable for approximately 30 min after acidification. For more concentrated solutions (extinction greater than 0·7 and less than 2·0) dilution of the sample with water prior to reading is necessary.

For measurement of smaller concentrations of galactose with higher sensitivity the following variation of procedure is used. The reagent mixture is made up to contain 10 ml of glycine buffer, 1 ml of galactose oxidase solution, 0·5 ml of horse-radish peroxidase and 0·08 ml of benzidine base. Standard and unknown samples, both 0·5 ml, are incubated at 37°C. 0·5 ml of reagent mixture is added and the reaction terminated after 120 min by the addition of one drop of 5N-HCl. The solution is transferred to a

1 ml cuvette and the extinction at 295 nm is recorded. The calibration in the range 0–20 μg is linear.

Interference: This is encountered with materials absorbing in the ultra-violet at 310 nm, high salt concentration, peroxides, and cyanide and fluoride ions. High concentrations of organic compounds (glucose, glycine, tris, sucrose) will also inhibit the enzyme.

A procedure using the "Galactostat" kit is also described by Herbert, Phipps and Strange (this Series, Volume 5). Boehringer also offer a convenient galactose ultraviolet test based on a NAD-linked galactose dehydrogenase.

4. Determination of aldopentoses

Many methods for the estimation of aldopentoses have appeared in the literature since about 1950. The majority of these depend upon a phenol to supply part of the chromophore and it has been found that upon the choice of phenol often depends the specificity of the reaction. For example, orcinol has been widely used in the determination of aldopentose (Bial's reaction) but it is subject to considerable interference from glucose, aldoheptoses and a variety of other compounds. This is not so of the method developed for aldopentoses by Dische and Borenfreund (1957) who employed phloroglucinol as the part chromophore. In fact Lind (1957) applied the phloroglucinol reaction with sugars as an aid to their classification since aldohexoses, aldopentoses, uronic acids and other sugar types all have characteristic absorption maxima.

Details of the orcinol method are described by Herbert, Phipps and Strange (this Series, Volume 5B).

The phloroglucinol procedure of Dische and Borenfreund (1957) has been modified to give it greater sensitivity by Bolognani, Coppi and Zambotti (1961).

(a) *Phloroglucinol method of Bolognani, Coppi and Zambotti* (1961)

Principle: Reaction of sugars and their derivatives, for example nucleotides, with phloroglucinol produces a variety of chromophores having different spectral characteristics and extinction coefficients. These differences are exploited to enable quantitative estimation of aldopentose, notably ribose.

Aldopentoses produce an intense red chromophore, with a sharp absorption maximum at 552 nm while aldohexoses, and ketohexoses, produce, at higher concentrations than the pentose, a faint brown chromophore with a maximum absorption at 553 nm, and a stronger maximum in the blue region. Ketopentose and ketoheptose produce green chromophores both having two absorption maxima, the ketopentose at 610 and 450 nm, the ketoheptose at 640 and 450 nm. Aldoheptoses produce a chromophore having a maximum absorption at 550 nm. The sensitivity of reaction for the above sugars is only 2–10% of that for aldopentose. 2-Deoxyribose produces a chromophore similar to aldopentose, but it is more brownish and possesses two well defined absorption maxima at 552 nm and at 470 nm. With DNA appreciable extinction is evident at a concentration of 1 mg/ml.

The chromophores produced from hexuronic acids show the 552 nm absorption but the spectra differ significantly from that of aldopentose.

The extinction at 552 nm produced by aldopentose is proportional to the concentration of the aldopentose, but in the presence of a large excess of other sugars it would be impossible to determine the pentoses accurately, because of the contribution by the chromophores from the other sugars at this wavelength. The influence of keto sugars, and DNA, can be eliminated by reading at a second wavelength at which the absorption of the respective keto sugars differs very little from that at 552 nm, whereas for aldopentose the difference is considerable. The wavelength used is 510 nm and $E_{552} - E_{510}$ is a measure of the concentration of the aldopentose. This difference for keto sugars is small enough to be negligible. Ketoheptose and keto-hexose, when present at a concentration comparable to that of the aldo-pentose, deepen the colour produced by a few per cent and it is advisable when using bacterial extracts, for example, to run internal standards.

Aldopentose derivatives, the most common of which are ribose nucleo-tides, also produce chromophores with the phloroglucinol reagent; for example adenosine produces the same extinction difference as an equi-molar solution of ribose, while AMP gives double the extinction difference. For further details the paper of Dische and Borenfreund (1957) should be consulted.

Note: One of the important features of the phloroglucinol reaction is that ketopentose is differentiated from aldopentose, the peaks for keto-pentose being used at 450 and 610 nm; also the ketohexose, fructose, does not absorb to any extent at 610 nm.

Procedure: The sample should be deproteinized prior to analysis. Tri-chloroacetic acid (3% w/v) may be used for this purpose but, if so, the same amount of this acid must be present in the blank (reagent and water). Details of the reagents and procedure are described by Herbert, Phipps and Strange (this Series, Volume 5).

(b) *Determination of aldopentose by the* o-*toluidine method* (*Ghetie and Cioba*, 1964)

Principle: o-Toluidine reacts with a variety of aldoses giving different absorption maxima depending upon the exact class of sugar involved, i.e.

whether pentose or hexose. Pentoses display their maxima at 500 nm whereas the glucose derivative yields maxima at 420 and 600 nm. Deoxyribose gives no colour.

Reagents:
  Solution 1. *o*-Toluidine (4% w/v) and thiourea (1% w/v) in anhydrous glacial acetic acid. The reagent should be set aside for 24 h before use. At room temperature and shielded from direct light, the reagent is stable for 2–3 months.
  Trichloroacetic acid, 3% w/v

Procedure: Solution 1 (3·9 ml) is added to 0·1 ml of the sample, containing 50–2000 μg of pentose, in a test tube. The mixture is heated for 3 min in a boiling water bath, cooled rapidly and the stable extinction measured at 500 nm against water as blank. If the sample contains protein it should be deproteinized with 3% w/v trichloroacetic acid.

Specificity and interference: Hexoses do not interfere in the standard procedure if their concentration does not exceed 20% of that of the pentose. If the sample contains higher concentrations of hexose the heating time should be shortened to 1 min; glucose then gives practically no colour and arabinose gives just over half the extinction produced by heating for 3 min.

5. Determination of fructose

The most commonly employed procedures for the determination of fructose comprise modifications of the method originally described by Roe (1934). The method depends on the colour reaction of ketoses with resorcinol. Recently Yaphe and Arsenault (1966) have investigated the resorcinol procedures and found that the wavelength of maximum absorption is dependent on the presence or absence of acetaldehyde in the reagent. In the absence of acetaldehyde λ_{max} is at 480 nm whereas either in the presence of impure acetic acid or ethanol, or these two purified compounds plus acetaldehyde, the λ_{max} shifts to 555 nm. It was also shown that the concentration of acetaldehyde was important for the product of the reaction to conform to Beer's Law at the 555 nm wavelength. The acetaldehyde concentration should be equal to, or greater than, that of the fructose concentration to be determined.

Yaphe and Arsenault (1966) developed an improved resorcinol method by incorporating acetaldehyde in the reagent employed.

(a) *Determination of fructose by the resorcinol method* (*Yaphe and Arsenault*, 1966)
Principle: This method is based on the Seliwanoff test for ketoses, that is

the reaction with resorcinol in the presence of hydrochloric acid. 1,1-Diethoxyethane is added to the reagent as a source of acetaldehyde (see above).

Reagents:

   1,1-Diethoxyethane (acetal) stock solution. 0·822 g (6·96 mmol; about 1 ml) of the compound is weighed in a 100 ml volumetric flask and diluted immediately to volume with distilled water. The solution is prepared weekly and stored in a brown bottle.

   Resorcinol reagent. 100 ml of conc. HCl (s.g. 1·188–1·192) is added to 9 ml of resorcinol stock solution and to this mixture is added 1 ml of the aqueous solution of acetal (1,1-diethoxyethane). The reagent develops a colour on standing but is stable for at least 3 h. The resorcinol stock solution contains 150 mg of resorcinol (boiling point 109°–111°C) in 100 ml of distilled water. This is prepared weekly and stored in a brown bottle.

Procedure: The sample (2 ml), containing up to 0·25 μmole of fructose in the free or combined state, is transferred to a boiling tube, 25×150 mm, and covered with a glass marble. The tube is placed in an ice bath and 10 ml of the resorcinol reagent added. The contents are mixed in the ice bath and cooled for at least 3 min but not longer than 30 min. The tube is placed in a water bath at 20°C for 4 min and then heated for 10 min at 80°C. It is then cooled for 1·5 min in an ice bath and the extinction measured within 15 min at 555 nm. The reaction is carried out in diffuse light since the colour fades on exposure to sunlight.

Calibration: A calibration curve in the concentration range 0·025–0·25 μ-mole of fructose/2 ml sample should be prepared. This is linear.

Interference: The authors give the impression that the method must be carried out with great care. The method has also been used to determine 3,6-anhydro-L-galactose, which gives 92% of the colour for fructose. Sorbose interferes but glucose, galactose, mannose, fucose, rhamnose, xylose, arabinose and ribose do not interfere to a significant extent (ribose yields 5% of the fructose colour and all others give 2·5% or below). It is stated by Sheth and Rao (1963) that tryptophan interferes in the Roe resorcinol method.

   The method of Roe is given by Herbert, Phipps and Strange (this Series, Volume 5B).

(b) *Determination of fructose with p-anisidine*

Hessler (1959) published a method for fructose determination which depended on reaction with p-anisidine. The method as published appeared to require some refinements and these were effected by Guyot in 1961.

p-*Anisidine method of Guyot* (1961)

Reagent:

p-Anisidine (0·5%) in phosphoric acid.

Procedure: The reagent (4 ml) is heated in a boiling water bath for 15 min with 2 ml of a solution containing 5 to 80 μg of fructose or 10–160 μg of sucrose. The extinction of the cooled solution is read after 1·5 h at 393 nm against a reagent blank plus water. The results are reproducible to within ±2%.

Interference: Glucose, lactose, maltose or galactose at concentrations equal to that of fructose give an error of approximately +2%, glucuronic acid +5% and ascorbic acid +13%. Gluconic acid and sorbitol do not interfere. Vanillin, piperonal, benzaldehyde, *p*-dimethylaminobenzaldehyde and benzylidine-acetone also give a yellow colour with the reagent. KNO_3 does not interfere but $NaNO_2$ and $NaClO_3$ produce a violet colour.

(c) *Determination of fructose with β-indoleacetic acid (Heyrovsky*, 1956)

Principle: Fructose reacts with β-indoleacetic acid, when incubated at 37°C in the presence of concentrated hydrochloric acid, to give a purple chromophore.

Reagents:

β-Indoleacetic acid. 0·5% w/v solution in ethanol.

Hydrochloric acid, conc. A.R.

Fructose standard solution, 0·6 mM.

Procedure: The sample (1 ml), containing up to 0·6 μmole of fructose, is transferred to a narrow test tube ($6 \times \frac{1}{2}$ in. or narrower) and 0·2 ml of the β-indoleacetic acid reagent added, followed by 10 ml of conc. hydrochloric acid. The tubes are sealed with Parafilm, inverted to mix, and incubated at 37°C for 1 h. The extinction is then read at 530 nm.

Calibration: A calibration curve over the range 0–0·6 μmole of fructose should be prepared. This is linear. It is desirable that standards be included with each batch of analyses. The method works equally well with fructose phosphates and other bound forms of fructose. Heyrovsky reports reproducibility to be of the order of 1–2% and that the method is insensitive to a large excess of aldose.

In 1957 A. St.-J. Huggett carried out a comparison of the resorcinol and β-indoleacetic acid methods and provided the following assessment (personal communication). The resorcinol method is more sensitive but is interfered with to a greater extent by the presence of glucose, which produces a chromophore in both methods. Rhamnose and ribose were noted to produce chromophores by the β-indoleacetic acid method, the extinction and spectra differing from those produced by fructose. The fumes from conc. HCl were noted as troublesome.

(d) *Identification of ketoses on paper chromatograms*

Percheron (1962) has developed a method for the detection of ketoses on paper chromatograms.

Principle: Ketoses are detected by conversion to a furfuraldehyde type structure which reacts with thiobarbituric acid to produce a chromophore, whose characteristics depend upon the original sugar.

Reagent:

Thiobarbituric acid, 0·5 g, 100 ml of ethanol and 2 ml of 85% H_3PO_4 are mixed.

Procedure: After drying, the chromatograms are sprayed with the thiobartituric acid reagent and then heated in an oven at $100°-105°C$ for 5–7 min. Ketoses and oligosaccharides containing ketoses give bright yellow to orange to brown spots. Sedoheptulose gives a green colour. Aldohexoses and their glycosides do not react.

Sensitivity: 3–25 μg of ketose can be detected.

(e) *Other methods for determination of fructose*

The method in Bergmeyer (1963) is an example of the current procedures for fructose determination.

Principle: Glucose 6-phosphate dehydrogenase, hexokinase, and phosphoglucose isomerase are used in this method. Hexoses (glucose, fructose and mannose) are phosphorylated, in the presence of ATP, to produce the corresponding hexose 6-phosphate. Any glucose 6-phosphate produced is oxidized with concomitant reduction of NADP. Addition of phosphoglucose isomerase converts fructose 6-phosphate to glucose 6-phosphate which is then oxidized with a further reduction of NADP. Mannose 6-phosphate is not isomerized and thus remains as such. The equilibria of the kinase and dehydrogenase lie far to the right so that the reaction as a whole proceeds stoicheiometrically. NADPH production is followed spectrophotometrically at 366 nm or 340 nm.

Reagents:

Triethanolamine buffer, 0·05M, pH 7·6

9·3 g of triethanolamine hydrochloride is dissolved in 22 ml of

N-NaOH and diluted to 1 litre with distilled water. The pH is checked using a glass electrode.

Magnesium chloride, 0·1M

ATP, 0·017M

NADP, 0·012M

Hexokinase, 1 mg protein/ml
  The specific activity should be at least 140 units/mg.

Glucose 6-phosphate dehydrogenase, 1 mg protein/ml
  The specific activity should be at least 70 units/mg.

Phosphoglucose isomerase, 1 mg protein/ml
  The specific activity should be at least 390 units/mg.

The three enzymes are obtained from yeast and are commercially available as suspensions, in ammonium sulphate, from Boehringer. Any dilution of the enzymes should be made using ammonium sulphate solution of the same concentration in which the enzyme is suspended. The purity of these enzymes is crucial for specific quantitative assay of fructose and it is recommended that, relative to their own specific activities, hexokinase, glucose 6-phosphate dehydrogenase and phosphoglucose isomerase should contain no more than 0·1% NADPH oxidase, 6-phosphogluconate dehydrogenase, or phosphoglucomutase, and no more than 0·01% invertase. In addition, hexokinase and glucose 6-phosphate dehydrogenase must contain no more than 0·5% hexose isomerase.

Procedure: If deproteinization is necessary, then this is best carried out with perchloric acid, as previously described (p. 157).

The assay is carried out in a 4 ml cuvette, of 1 cm light path, at room temperature. The extinction changes (at 340 nm or 366 nm) are read against a blank containing buffer (2·88 ml) and sample (0·02 ml).

The contents of the experimental cuvette are buffer (2·65 ml), MgCl₂ solution (0·01 ml), ATP solution (0·10 ml), NADP solution (0·10 ml), sample (0·02 ml) and hexokinase (0·01 ml). At this stage the contents are mixed thoroughly and the extinction (E_1) determined. Glucose 6-phosphate dehydrogenase suspension (0·01 ml) is mixed in and the extinction determined after 10, 12, 14 and 16 min, and extrapolated to the time of addition of the dehydrogenase to obtain E_2 (alternatively a recording spectrophotometer can be used). Phosphoglucose isomerase (0·01 ml) is then mixed in and the reaction followed to completion to obtain E_3.

Calibration and range: Since the reaction is stoicheiometric, no calibration is required. E_2 is determined by extrapolation and since even highly purified preparations of glucose 6-phosphate dehydrogenase and hexokinase contain traces of phosphoglucose isomerase it is advisable to check this operation by using a standard fructose solution instead of sample.

The range and sensitivity depends upon the largest extinction change, and the smallest extinction change respectively, that can be accurately determined on the instrument used. Measurement of fructose in the presence of a much higher concentration of glucose will cause difficulties.

The total extinction change $(E_3–E_1)$ is due to the oxidation of the following substrates: glucose, fructose, glucose 6-phosphate (G6P) and fructose 6-phosphate (F6P).

Thus

$$E_2 - E_1 = \Delta E \, (\text{glucose} + \text{G6P})$$

and

$$E_3 - E_2 = \Delta E \, (\text{fructose} + \text{F6P})$$

These amounts of F6P (and G6P) can be estimated by setting up a second experimental cuvette in which hexokinase is replaced with distilled water, and measuring as described above. If the equivalent extinction changes are indicated by E_1', E_2' and E_3'

Then

$$E_3' - E_1' = \Delta E \, (\text{G6P} + \text{F6P})$$

$$E_2' - E_1' = \Delta E \, (\text{G6P})$$

$$E_3' - E_2' = \Delta E \, (\text{F6P})$$

and this allows the determination of ΔE (fructose), viz.:

$$\Delta E \, (\text{fructose}) = \Delta E \, (\text{fructose} + \text{F6P}) - \Delta E \, (\text{F6P})$$

Since the final volume is 3 ml, thus

$$\text{at 340 nm} \quad \frac{\Delta E \, (\text{fructose}) \times 3}{6 \cdot 22} = \mu\text{moles fructose/cuvette}$$

$$\text{at 366 nm} \quad \frac{\Delta E \, (\text{fructose}) \times 3}{3 \cdot 3} = \mu\text{moles fructose/cuvette}$$

6. Determination of ketopentoses by enzymic methods

The determination of ketohexose and ketopentose in a mixture of both is a problem not yet resolved by colorimetric procedures. The solution of this difficulty probably lies in some of the methods already described but no detailed procedure is yet available. Thus, recourse to enzymic methods of analysis is necessary. D-Ribulose may be estimated by the Nordlie and Fromm (1963) procedure. Methods for the estimation of other ketopentoses are also given in Bergmeyer (1963).

(a) *Determination of* D-*ribulose* (*Nordlie and Fromm* 1963)

D-Ribulose can be estimated enzymically by at least two procedures. The method described here uses a purified ribitol dehydrogenase preparation derived from *A. aerogenes*. For details of the second method, in which ribulose is converted to ribulose 5-phosphate, by reaction with ATP in the presence of D-ribulokinase, which is then estimated enzymatically, Bergmeyer (1963) should be consulted.

Preparation of Ribitol Dehydrogenase.

Bacterium: Aerobacter aerogenes (ATCC 9621) is the organism used by the authors.

Reagents:
Salts solution
KH_2PO_4, 1·5 g; Na_2HPO_4, 13·5 g; $MgSO_4$, $7H_2O$, 0·2 g; NH_4Cl, 2 g; $CaCl_2$, 10 mg; and $FeSO_4$, $7H_2O$, 0·5 mg, are dissolved in doubly-distilled water to a volume of 900 ml.
Sugar solution
Glucose (400 mg) and ribitol (60 mg) are dissolved in doubly-distilled water to a final volume of 100 ml.
Tris buffer, 0·1M, pH 7·4
Tris-hydroxymethylaminomethane (12·11 g) is dissolved in doubly-distilled water (about 50 ml). The pH is adjusted to 7·4 by addition of 2N HCl (42·5 ml). The pH is checked with a glass electrode and the final volume is made up to 100 ml. This buffer is 1·0M and is required in the assay. A 1 : 10 dilution of this buffer is used to wash the bacterial culture during harvesting.
Tris buffer, 1·0M, pH 8·5
The above procedure is followed except that only 15 ml of 2N HCl are added.
Streptomycin, 5% w/v
Streptomycin sulphate (1·25 g) is dissolved in doubly-distilled water to a final volume of 25 ml.
Acetic acid, 0·1N
Glacial acetic acid (5·72 ml) is diluted to 1 litre with doubly-distilled water.
Potassium hydroxide, 0·1N
KOH (0·56 g) is dissolved in doubly-distilled water to a final volume of 100 ml.
Calcium phosphate gel suspension
This contains 21·5 mg dry wt/ml and is prepared according to the method of Keilin and Hartree (1938).

Growth and harvesting of the organism: Except where otherwise stated all operations are carried out at 30°C. The organism is grown with shaking in 2 litre flasks at 37°C. The final volume of medium is 400 ml, composed of 360 ml of salt solution and 40 ml of sugar solution, which have been sterilized by autoclaving and, on cooling, mixed aseptically.

The organism is harvested, 48 h after inoculation, by centrifuging. The pellet is resuspended in tris buffer (0·1M, pH 7·4) at 3°C and recentrifuged. This procedure is repeated twice.

Preparation of ribitol dehydrogenase: Cells (10 g wet weight) are suspended in 30 ml of tris (0·1M, pH 7·4) and to this suspension is added glass beads (30 g). The suspension is then exposed to a 10 kc sonic oscillator for 30 min.

The sonicate (30 ml) is mixed with 35 ml of tris (0·1M, pH 7·4) and streptomycin solution (13 ml) is slowly stirred in. The resulting solution is allowed to stand for 10 min after which period it is centrifuged at 10,000 g for 10 min. The supernatant is separated from the precipitate and adjusted to pH 6·2 (glass electrode) with acetic acid. The resulting solution is placed in a water bath at 40°C and is stirred vigorously for 20 min. At the end of this period the solution is centrifuged at 10,000 g for 10 min and the supernatant is saved for the next stage, which is ammonium sulphate fractionation.

The pH of the supernatant is slowly adjusted to 7·15 (glass electrode) using 0·1N-KOH. Solid ammonium sulphate is slowly stirred into solution until 30% saturation is achieved. The solution is allowed to stand for 5 min after which period it is centrifuged at 13,000 g. The precipitate is discarded. Further solid ammonium sulphate is added to bring the percentage saturation to 45. At this stage the solution is allowed to stand for 10 min, followed by centrifuging at 13,000 g. The precipitate is dissolved in 0·1M tris buffer (pH 7·4) to give a protein concentration of about 8 mg/ml. The resulting solution is dialysed for 6 h against 0·01M tris buffer (pH 7·4) on a rocking dialyser. The slightly turbid solution obtained is centrifuged at 15,000 g for 15 min and the precipitate is discarded.

The supernatant is diluted with 0·01M tris buffer (pH 7·4), such that the final protein concentration is 3·70 mg/ml. To each 1 ml of solution is added cold calcium phosphate gel suspension (11 ml). The pH of the resulting suspension is adjusted to 6 (glass electrode) with acetic acid and allowed to stand for 20 min followed by centrifuging at 2500 g for 5 min. The supernatant, which no longer contains ribitol dehydrogenase activity, is decanted. The gel is stirred up with 10 ml of 1·0M tris buffer (pH 8·5) and allowed to stand at about 8°C for 20 min. The supernatant obtained after centrifuging at 2500 g for 10 min contains the major portion of ribitol dehydrogenase and this solution is used in the assay described below.

Principle: The oxidation of NADH in the reduction of ribulose to ribitol is spectrophotometrically monitored. In the presence of excess NADH there is virtually quantitative reduction to ribitol.

Reagents:

NADH solution. NADH–Na$_2$ (7·82 mg) is dissolved in doubly-distilled water to a final volume of 10 ml. This should be made freshly each week and stored in the frozen state.

Tris buffer, 1·0M, pH 7·4. This is as described on p. 189.

Tris buffer, 1·0M, pH 8·5. This is as described on p. 189.

Ribitol dehydrogenase preparation. If prepared as described above then the eluate from the calcium phosphate gel should contain approximately 1 mg protein/ml. The enzyme solution keeps for longer than one month at 3°C but repeated freezing and thawing lead to a large loss of activity. The better enzyme preparations show an approximately 320-fold increase in specific activity compared with crude extracts.

Procedure: Silica cuvettes of 1 cm light path are used and the wavelength monitored is 340 nm.

The following mixture is prepared for both control and experimental cuvette: sample (3 ml) containing approximately 0·1 μmole D-ribulose/ml, NADH solution (1·5 ml), tris buffer (1·0M, pH 7·4, 3 ml) and doubly-distilled water (1·2 ml). These are mixed and allowed to come to room temperature. 2·9 ml of the mixture is pipetted into both control and experimental cuvettes. To the experimental cuvette is added the ribitol dehydrogenase preparation (0·1 ml) and to the control tris buffer (1·0M, pH 8·5 0·1 ml). The solutions are mixed well and the reaction is allowed to go to completion (40–60 min) after which period E_1, control cuvette against experimental cuvette, is determined. Although the authors do not mention it, it would seem advisable to include a control containing all reactants except the substrate D-ribulose.

The extinction of the enzyme preparation is determined for each preparation by measuring the extinction of 0·1 ml enzyme solution + 2·9 ml doubly-distilled water against 0·1 ml tris buffer (1·0M, pH 8·5) + 2·9 ml doubly-distilled water. This is usually around 0·005.

Calculation: E_1 + the extinction of the enzyme is the ΔE_{340} corresponding to NADH oxidized and since the reaction proceeds virtually stoicheiometrically

$$\mu\text{moles D-ribulose/ml} = \frac{\Delta E_{340} \times 3}{6\cdot22}$$

$$= \Delta E_{340} \times 0\cdot482$$

since 6·22 is the molar extinction coefficient of NADH at the wavelength and pH utilized.

Specificity: Ribitol 1-phosphate, L-ribulose, D-fructose, D- and L-arabinose, D-sorbitol, dulcitol, and D-xylitol do not interfere with the assay, or react with the enzyme.

7. Determination of glucuronic acid (Nir, 1964)

Principle: Glucuronic acid is estimated by reaction with a naphthoresorcinol reagent to produce a pink-bluish chromophore whose extinction, at the wavelength utilized, 580 nm, obeys the Lambert–Beer Law. The conditions used by Nir are such that the stability of the reagent is greatly increased, giving reproducible results over a period of three months.

Reagents:
> Naphthoresorcinol. This should be crystallized from an aqueous acidified solution of sodium chloride and washed with cold water.
> Hydrochloric acid, concentrated
> Ethyl acetate, redistilled
> Sodium hydroxide, 0·5N
> Phosphoric acid 10% (w/v)
> Sodium bisulphite.
> Glucuronic acid, or glucuronolactone
> Naphthoresorcinol reagent. Naphthoresorcinol (200 mg) is dissolved in distilled water (approximately 80 ml) and sodium hydroxide (0·5N) is slowly added until the pH is between 8–8·5. The solution should be deep yellow and is allowed to stand for 15 min. Phosphoric acid 10% (w/v) is added until the pH is between 2–2·5.
>> The solution should now be a light yellow. Sodium bisulphite (100 mg) is added and the volume made up to 100 ml. The reagent is filtered and stored at 5°C, in the dark.

Procedure: The following solutions are pipetted into a conical, glass-stoppered 50 ml centrifuge tube: glucuronic acid solution (2 ml, containing between 10 and 90 μg D-glucuronic acid), naphthoresorcinol reagent (2 ml), and hydrochloric acid (2 ml). A blank is prepared by replacing the glucuronic acid solution with water. The tubes are stoppered, shaken and placed in a boiling water bath for 30 min. It is advisable to prevent the stoppers jumping out during this period by covering with a wet towel. After 30 min the tubes are transferred to an ice bath for 10 min followed by the addition of ethyl acetate (10 ml). They are then vigorously shaken for 30 sec. An aliquot of the ethyl acetate layer is removed and E_{580} is determined against the blank. The chromophore remains stable in ethyl acetate for at least 1 h.

Calibration: A calibration curve can be constructed by taking samples containing 10–100 μg of glucuronic acid through the above procedure. The calibration is linear and highly reproducible from day to day, as is the blank value.

According to Green, Anstiss, and Fishman (1962) glucose and ascorbic acid interfere in the naphthoresorcinol method. This would suggest that other reducing agents may be similarly active. Unless, therefore, it can be clearly shown that no constituent of the fermentation medium interferes, and only glucuronic acid is being determined, a chromatographic separation of the uronic acid as previously directed should be made prior to analysis.

The carbazole method of Dische and the decarboxylation method are described by Herbert, Phipps, and Strange (this Series, Volume 5B).

8. *Determination of gluconic acid in complex biological media*
(Tholey, Frey and Wurtz, 1965)

Principle: Gluconic acid is oxidized by a gluconate dehydrogenase preparation from *Pseudomonas fluorescens*, ferricyanide acting as the electron acceptor. The production of ferrocyanide is monitored spectrophotometrically at 600 nm. Since enzymatic, the assay is highly specific and sensitive and, provided glucose oxidase is absent, glucose does not interfere.

Organism: The requisite strain is not deposited in any culture collection, but may be obtained, on request, from Professor B. Wurtz, Laboratoire de Biochimie Microbienne, Université de Strasbourg, France. It is an R-type mutant of *P. fluorescens* which has a tendency to revert to an S-type and it is therefore necessary to check the strain fairly frequently (about three weekly intervals) by plating on non-glucose nutrient agar and, in the case of reverse mutation, re-isolating the R-type from the R and S colonies (see Meyer and Wurtz, 1964). Type R produces well defined, opaque colonies with a rough surface, while type S produces translucent, smooth colonies.

Cultivation:

Medium: The medium used has the following composition per litre distilled water: Liebig meat extract, 5 g; Difco peptone, 10 g; sodium chloride, 5 g. The medium is heated to 100°C to aid solution and then filtered; the pH is adjusted to 6·0 with 0·1N-NaOH and 10 g of glucose is added to give 1% final concentration. The medium is sterilized at 115°C for 30 min.

Inoculation and growth: Growth is secured at 27°C in 1 litre flasks containing 500 ml of medium which are shaken at 120 oscillations per min. Each flask is inoculated with 1 ml of a 24 h culture which has been grown from a

8

colony isolated on non-glucose nutrient agar. Under these conditions the end of the exponential phase occurs after about 24 h. After 60 h (i.e., 36 h in the stationary phase) the glucose oxidase activity of the cells has virtually completely disappeared while the gluconate dehydrogenase activity persists.

The cells are centrifuged at 4°C, washed twice with distilled water and then resuspended in distilled water (80 ml for 2 litres of culture).

Preparation of enzyme: The bacterial suspension, in distilled water, is poured dropwise into 10 volumes of acetone at $-20°C$ with constant stirring. The precipitate is collected on a Buchner funnel, washed with ether at $-10°C$, dried rapidly in air, and then under vacuum at room temperature. A 2 litre culture should yield approximately 1 g of acetone-dried powder which may be stored in the cold (probably means deep frozen) until required, or extracted in the following manner: 2·5 g of powder are ground in a mortar then added in portions to 40 ml of 0·05M sodium bicarbonate buffer (pH 9·1). The cells in suspension are disintegrated in a Mickle shaker with glass beads for 10 min at 0°C and treated with a further 80 ml of the bicarbonate buffer. The mixture is then left at 4°C for 12 h followed by centrifugation for 30 min at 18,000 rpm at 1°C. The supernatant is adjusted to pH 7·2 with acetic acid (0·05M) and 21 g of crystalline ammonium sulphate is added (30% saturation). The precipitate which forms in 12 h is centrifuged and discarded. To the supernatant is added 20 g of ammonium sulphate (55% saturation) and the mixture is left for 12 h at 4°C. The 12 h precipitate obtained at 55% saturation (centrifuged at 4°C) is taken up in 160 ml of cold distilled water.

The resulting solution serves as the gluconate dehydrogenase preparation. It may be stored frozen until required, preferably in small portions.

Reagents:
  Potassium ferricyanide, 0·1M
  Sodium acetate, 0·5M, pH 5·5
  Ferric sulphate reagent, $Fe_2(SO_4)_3$, H_2O (5 g), and sodium lauryl sulphate (3 g) are added to 85% H_3PO_4 (95 ml). The volume is then made up to 1 litre with distilled water.

Assay of gluconic acid: To test solution (1 ml) is added successively potassium ferricyanide (0·1 ml), acetate buffer (0·5 ml) and enzyme (1 ml), containing not less than 600 μg protein.

The mixture is incubated at 37°C in a water bath, and after 20 min the reaction is stopped by addition of ferric sulphate (1 ml). The colour is allowed to develop for 5 min and then the volume of the solution is made up to 5 ml with distilled water. Its extinction at 660 nm is determined against a reagent blank.

Range of estimation: The range is 20–70 μg/ml of gluconic acid, and this gives a linear response. A calibration curve may also be constructed with 15–76 μg/ml potassium gluconate.

Specificity: Even when a preparation free from glucose oxidase is obtained, glucose still contributes to the E_{660} change. Since this is non-enzymatic it can be compensated for by running a suitable control containing sample but no enzyme. Similarly, arabinose and glucuronate have been shown to contribute, non-enzymically, to the E_{660}. A 2% glucose solution gave a ΔE_{660} of 0·010, while arabinose 1% and glucuronate 1% gave a ΔE_{660} of 0·040 and 0·016 respectively. Succinic acid and lactic acid, at a concentration of 20 mg/100 ml, did not interfere with the assay, or contribute to the E_{660}.

9. Estimation of 2-keto-3-deoxy-6-phosphogluconate
(Srinivason and Sprinson, 1959)

Principle: This method was initially developed to estimate 3-deoxy-D-*arabo*-heptonic acid 7-phosphate and is based on the production of an intense pink chromophore by reaction of thiobarbituric acid with β-formyl-pyruvic acid, which is derived from the oxidation of the above sugar phosphate by periodate. Similar compounds, for example 2-keto-3-deoxy-galactonic acid and 2-keto-3-deoxygluconic acid 6-phosphate (KDP), also produce β-formylpyruvic acid on periodate oxidation and can thus be similarly estimated. Under the conditions of the assay both gluconic acid and gluconic acid 6-phosphate also yield spectra identical with that given by 2-keto-3-deoxygluconic acid 6-phosphate and therefore interfere with the assay.

Reagents:
Periodic acid, 0·025M in 0·125N–H_2SO_4.
Sodium arsenite, 2% in 0·5N HCl.
Thiobarbituric acid solution. Thiobarbituric acid (300 mg) is dissolved in distilled water (70 ml) with the aid of 1N–NaOH (3 ml). 1N–HCl (2·5 ml) is added and the pH is adjusted to 2 in a final volume of 100 ml.

If deproteinization of the sample is necessary then this is performed with trichloroacetic acid, final concentration ca. 4%.

Procedure: Sample (0·25 ml), containing between 0·01–0·05 μmole of KDP, is treated with periodate (0·25 ml) for 45 min at room temperature. At the end of this time arsenite reagent (0·5 ml) is added, to destroy excess periodate, for a period of 2 min at room temperature. Thiobarbituric acid solution (2 ml) is added and the tubes are placed in a boiling water bath for 5 min. After cooling in a water bath (40°C) the E_{549} is immediately determined, against a reagent blank (water instead of sample).

Scope of the assay: Simple aliphatic aldehydes, α, β-diketones, β-oxo acids, and β-formyllactic acid (derived from periodate oxidation of 3-deoxy-D-*arabo*-heptonic acid 7-phosphate) do not yield coloured products in the above assay. Glycolaldehyde and glyoxal give brown solutions with very low extinctions at 517 and 546 nm respectively.

The molar extinction coefficient for the chromophore produced by 2-keto-3-deoxygluconic acid 6-phosphate is $7 \cdot 2 \times 10^4 \, \text{cm}^2 \, \text{mol}^{-1}$ (Srinivason and Sprinson, 1959).

10. *Fluorometric determination of 2-deoxy-D-glucose* (Blecher, 1961)

Principle: The quinaldine reaction for acetaldehyde, which leads to the formation of a fluorescent product, has been adapted for the estimation of 2-deoxyglucose, based upon the green fluorescence in ultraviolet light of 2-(1-glycerol)-5-carboxy-7-aminoquinaline, the probable reaction product of the acid-catalysed condensation of 3,5-diaminobenzoic acid with 2-deoxyglucose.

Reagents and apparatus:
   Diaminobenzoic acid reagent
      Diaminobenzoate is obtained as the hydrochloride, and is recrystallized from hot water following decolorization with Norit A. The dihydro-chloride is precipitated from concentrated aqueous solution by addition of conc. HCl. This precipitate is isolated by vacuum filtration and washed with cold 10N–HCl. The white, crystalline dihydrochloride is dried *in vacuo* at 100°C over P_2O_5. The uncorrected decomposition point is recorded as 235°–240°C.
      The reagent is a 0·01M solution of the dihydrochloride in 5·0M H_3PO_4.
   Quinine reference standard
      This contains quinine sulphate at a concentration of 1·056 μg per ml of 0·10N–H_2SO_4.
   Phosphoric acid. H_3PO_4, 2·5M

Photofluorometer: The author used a Coleman Electronic photofluorometer (Model 12C). Matched cuvettes (19 × 105 mm) were used. Details of the filters used are primary filter: Coleman No. 14–216 (Corning No. 5976); this filter has a 35% transmittance at 400 nm (the approximate excitation maximum) and less than 0·2% transmittance above 430 nm, thus eliminating interference with emitted light. The secondary filter should be a sharp-cut filter which does not transmit below 430 nm, and thus eliminates interference due to scatter. Such a filter (C.S. 3–72, No. 3387, 3 mm thick) can be obtained from Corning Glass Works, Corning, N.Y.

Procedure: Sample, containing between 8 and 300 nmole 2-deoxyglucose, in a volume of up to 3 ml, is made up to a volume of 3 ml with distilled water. Diaminobenzoate reagent (3 ml) is added and the mixture heated in a boiling water bath for 15 min. Following a 20 min period at 15°–17°C (preferably in the dark in order to minimize destruction of fluorescence resulting from ultraviolet light) either 1·0 or 2·0 ml (depending on the minimal volume required by cuvettes for maximal sensitivity) of H_3PO_4 (2·5 M) is added.

The photofluorometer is set at zero fluorescence with a reagent blank, and the fluorescence of the unknown solutions determined against this. As a check on reagents and the linearity of the method a series of standard solutions of 2-deoxyglucose should be run simultaneously with the unknowns. The standard reaction mixtures are checked against the quinine reference solution.

Range: Fluorescence is reported to be proportional to the concentration of 2-deoxyglucose between 2·8 and 125 nmoles/ml of final solution. Fluorescence obtained with lower concentrations than this are reported as being erratic, but the author believes that the range could be extended to lower concentrations by use of a more sensitive instrument. Over the range of concentration of 2-deoxyglucose specified the precision ranged between ± 0·4 and ± 2·4% on five replicate determinations of each of four concentrations of 2-deoxyglucose.

Interference: High concentrations of glucose alone develop a small fluorescence but, in the presence of a low concentration of 2-deoxyglucose, fluorescence due to glucose is completely quenched.

Deoxyribose alone develops a fluorescence which, at its maximum, is approximately 10% of that produced by the same amount of 2-deoxyglucose. Fluorescence produced when both deoxy sugars are present is the approximate sum of that produced separately. The fluorescent product of diaminobenzoate and deoxyribose is maximally excited at 420 nm and, since the primary filter used by the authors transmitted less than 2% of the light of this wavelength, this probably explains the low fluorescent value obtained with deoxyribose. Tissue blanks, produced by the deproteinization of material such as liver, diaphragm and thymus (30 mg used) developed no fluorescent product while the deviation for theoretical recovery of 2-deoxyglucose averaged about 2·6% over a wide range of concentrations. The deproteinizing agent used was trichloroacetic acid (final concentration 5%). Only small amounts of freshly prepared acid should be used since large quantities of freshly prepared acid cause an increase in fluorescence, while "old" acid causes marked decreases in fluorescence.

The cysteine-H_2SO_4 method is described by Herbert, Phipps and Strange (this Series, Volume 5B).

11. *Determination of 2-deoxyribose*
(Waravdekar and Saslaw, 1957)

Principle: Deoxyribose is oxidized by periodate to produce malonaldehyde which is estimated by reaction with 2-thiobarbituric acid.

Reagents:

Periodate reagent. 0·025M in 0·125N sulphuric acid.

Arsenite reagent. Sodium arsenite (1·0 g) is dissolved in 0·5N HCl (50 ml).

Thiobarbituric acid reagent. The thiobarbituric acid is purified by passing a 3% solution, in hot water, through a column of Woelm acid aluminium oxide (activity grade I) and is allowed to crystallize at room temperature. The white rectangular crystals are washed with cold water and air dried.

The reagent is a 0·6% w/v solution of this, adjusted to pH 2 with 1·0N NaOH and 1·0N HCl.

Procedure: Periodate reagent (0·5 ml) is added to sample (3·5 ml) contained in test tubes. The contents are mixed well and allowed to stand 20 min at room temperature. At the end of this period arsenite reagent (1 ml) is added and the tubes are briefly shaken. After 2 min an aliquot (1 ml or less) of the resulting solution is transferred to 15×125 mm test tubes containing thiobarbituric acid reagent (2 ml). The volume is adjusted to 3 ml and the contents of the tubes are mixed. The blank is prepared at this stage by addition of distilled water (1 ml) to thiobarbituric acid reagent (2 ml). All tubes are fitted with pear-drop condensers and immersed in a boiling water bath for 20 min. After cooling in tap water at room temperature for 2 min the E_{532} of the resulting pink solutions is determined. The colour is stable for at least one hour.

Range and calibration: The range is 0·2–12·5 μg deoxyribose per 3·5 ml sample and the extinction is proportional to concentration up to 2·5 μg of deoxyribose per ml.

Determinations with the diphenylamine reagent are given by Herbert, Phipps and Strange (this Series, Volume 5B).

2(e) *Specific analyses—Polyhydroxy compounds*

Separation and determination of polyhydroxy compounds

In practice, it is unlikely that more than two polyols would be present as fermentation products in a medium. However, in a situation where this occurs and glycerol is not one of the polyols, a method requiring separation prior to determination is necessary.

(i) Ion exchange chromatography of polyols (Spencer, 1967)

Principle: The borate complexes of the polyols are separated by column chromatography. Relatively concentrated borate buffer is used since this sharpens the elution profile.

Preparation of resin: De-Acidite ff (3–5 cross linked, passing 200 mesh; Permutit Co. Ltd.,) is washed well with water and fines are removed by decantation. The resin is poured into a large column and regenerated by passing 2N NaOH (5 volumes) through it. Excess alkali is removed from the column by washing with water and it is finally converted into the borate form by passing through five column volumes of 0·5M potassium tetra-borate. Excess borate is washed from the resin with distilled water and the resin then extruded and stored moist.

Preparation of columns: The analytical columns are of the jacketed type measuring 60 cm in length with an i.d. 0·8 cm; the resin is thoroughly degassed at 40°–50°C on a vacuum pump and is then poured as a thick slurry (0·5 vol water) to give a column 50–55 cm in length. Water is continuously circulated through the column jacket, at a temperature of 35°C, throughout this operation and subsequent chromatography.

Preparation of samples for analysis: Sample (10 ml) is added to 15 ml moist Bio-deminrolit (converted to the HCO_3^- form by passing an excess of CO_2 through a suspension in water) and the resulting slurry is magnetically stirred for 30 min. The resin is filtered off, washed well with water and the filtrate and washings freeze-dried and kept in a deep freeze cabinet prior to analysis.

Application of sample and chromatography: The sample, dissolved in 1–2 ml of 0·1M borate, pH 9–10, is applied when excess liquid has just drained to the top of the resin bed; 1–2 ml washings are applied in the same way. Eluting buffer is then immediately pumped on to the column via a small de-aeration tube placed in a circulating water bath at 35°C. The pump is adjusted to give a column flow rate of 25 ml per h, and 5 ml fractions are collected. Eluting buffers used are:

1. 0·18M boric acid, pH 9, adjusted with triethylamine (up to fraction 80).
2. 0·36M boric acid, pH 9, adjusted with triethylamine as above.

The order of elution is glycerol, threitol, erythritol, xylitol (ends at fraction 50), arabitol, ribitol, glucitol (fraction 100), galactitol and mannitol. The first four polyols and glucitol are completely separated in a synthetic mixture.

Identification of eluted polyols: Fractions that on analysis are found to contain a solute peak are combined. Triethylamine is removed with Zeo-Carb 225 (Permutit Co. Ltd.) and the boric acid is distilled off, as methylborate, by repeated evaporation to dryness in the presence of methanol. The resulting residues are taken up in water (0·1 ml) and chromatographed in the descending manner on Whatman 3 MM papers for 18 h, using ethyl acetate–pyridine–water (saturated with boric acid) (120 : 50 : 40 by vol) as the solvent system. The chromatograms are allowed to dry in air, and polyols and sugars are revealed by the periodate-benzidine dip, described previously for sugar visualization (page 172).

Glycerol may not be identified by this method since the boric acid distillation procedure results in complete loss of this compound. The author relied upon the elution position of glycerol for identification, its peak fraction number being 12 (the average of five determinations).

For the determination of glycerol see p. 80 and p. 201.

Analysis of column effluent:

Reagents:

All reagents are freshly prepared
Sodium metaperiodate, 0·01M in 1N sulphuric acid
Sodium bisulphite, 10% w/v, prepared from ampoules supplied by B.D.H. Ltd
Chromotropic acid, 2·0% w/v aqueous solution
Sulphuric acid, conc

Procedure: Sodium metaperiodate (0·5 ml) is added to the sample (2 ml) in a Pyrex test tube. After mixing, the solutions are allowed to stand for at least 10 min at room temperature. Sodium bisulphite (0·2 ml) is added with immediate mixing, followed by chromotropic acid reagent (0·2 ml). Finally conc. sulphuric acid (3 ml) is added from a burette and the solution is mixed well using a Vortex mixer. The test tubes are then placed in a boiling water bath for 1 h. After approximately 10 min in the boiling water bath the tubes are removed briefly and remixed using the Vortex mixer; incomplete mixing at this stage results in the formation of a precipitate which interferes with the spectrophotometric measurement. After cooling the E_{570} is determined.

Borate inhibits colour development to an extent proportional to the amount of borate present. Hence all solutions are diluted prior to analysis so that they are 0·18M with respect to borate.

Recoveries: The procedure adopted for desalting, which is that used for urine samples, results in losses of polyols to an extent dependent on the polyol involved. The method requires improvement but for a particular group of compounds it may be calibrated to give results within 10% of the true value, on one determination. Recoveries for urine samples range from a mean of 40% for mannitol to 66% for glycerol of the untreated sample.

H. D. Graham (1965) has published details of a spectrophotometric method based on the reaction of an aromatic aldehyde (*p*-hydroxybenzaldehyde or *p*-dimethylaminobenzaldehyde) in the presence of thiourea and concentrated sulphuric acid. The following order of reactivity was observed: sorbitol > dulcitol > mannitol > erythritol > xylitol > arabitol > ribitol > glycerol > inositol. Recovery from complex media, after treatment to remove interfering material, is reported as 95–102%.

(*ii*) *Determination of glycerol by a direct dehydrogenase method* (*Himms-Hagen and Hagen*, 1962, 1965)

Principle: Glycerol is oxidized by an NAD-dependent glycerol dehydrogenase preparation from *Aerobacter aerogenes*. Under the optimum culture conditions described below a good preparation lacking other alcohol dehydrogenases can be obtained.

Reagents:
Preparation of glycerol dehydrogenase: Organism. The authors used their laboratory strain of *A. aerogenes*.

Medium and Growth Conditions. The medium contains $(NH_4)_2SO_4$, 3·6 g; KH_2PO_4, 16·2 g; $MgSO_4$, $7H_2O$, 1·2 g; glycerol, 45 g and one drop of A.F. 60 silicone antifoam (General Electric, Waterford, New York) in 3 litres of tap water. The pH is adjusted to 7·2 with 10N NaOH. This medium is placed in a 5-litre round-bottomed flask, with three neck openings, which stands in a heated mantle fitted with a powerstat regulator. (In the earlier paper the authors used a New Brunswick batch fermentor for growth of the organism and noted that a good preparation could be obtained without aeration, stirring at 300 rpm). An umbrella stirrer is inserted through a teflon-lined gland in the central flask opening and this is driven at 60 rpm by a small motor. A thermometer is inserted in another neck while the third is plugged lightly with non-absorbent cotton wool. The medium is then boiled for 30 min, and allowed to cool to 37°C, at which temperature it is maintained. The medium is then inoculated with *A. aerogenes* (size of inoculum unstated). Culture is continued for 5 days at 37°C. During this period further additions of glycerol and salts are made as indicated in Table XIII.

Additions of 10N NaOH, to maintain the pH above 6, are made over the 5 day period; a total of 60 to 70 ml of NaOH is required. No air is bubbled through the culture, but it is not excluded from the flasks. These culture conditions lead to slow growth and relatively poor yields of bacterium, but if the culture is highly aerobic then contamination of the enzyme preparation with other alcohol dehydrogenases results, and high blanks occur.

On the sixth day the culture is harvested and washed ($\times 3$) in cold distilled water in a conventional manner. Finally the bacteria are resuspended in cold distilled water to give a volume of approximately 50 ml. This is then treated for 40 min in a water-cooled 9-kilocycle Raytheon sonic oscillator (power output, 200 W), and centrifuged at 35,000 rpm for 60 min in a No. 40 rotor of the Spinco model L. The clear supernatant, containing

TABLE XIII

Medium for the culture of *Aerobacter aerogenes* on glycerol

Day		Glycerol	(NH$_4$)$_2$SO$_4$	MgSO$_4$, 7H$_2$O	KH$_2$PO$_4$	Water
0		45	3·6	1·2	4·0	3000
1	9 a.m., culture inoculated					
2	9 a.m.	45	3·6	—	—	100
	12 noon	45	3·6	1·2	—	100
	3 p.m.	45	3·6	—	4·0	100
	6 p.m.	45	3·6	—	—	100
	9 p.m.	45	3·6	—	4·0	100
3	9 a.m.	90	7·2	—	4·0	100
	6 p.m.	90	7·2	1·2	—	100
4	9 a.m.	90	7·2	—	4·0	100
	6 p.m.	90	7·2	1·2	—	100
5	9 a.m.	90	7·2	—	4·0	100
	6 p.m.	90	7·2	1·2	—	100
6	9 a.m., bacteria collected					

Note: Values given are the grams of each compound added.

the enzyme, is decanted and frozen until it is convenient to carry out further purification.

The purification procedure follows closely that of Burton (1955) except that a second precipitation step, to ensure removal of glycerol carried over from the growth medium, is included. All manipulations are carried out in a cold room.

(a) *First ammonium sulphate precipitation.* The sonicate supernatant is diluted with water to approximately 10 mg of protein per ml; it is brought to 40% saturation with ammonium sulphate by the addition of a saturated solution of this salt, stirred for 5 min, and then centrifuged for 60 min at 9500 rpm at 2°C (International HR-2, rotor No. 856). The supernatant is discarded. The sediments are resuspended in a total of 15 ml of 0·05M potassium phosphate buffer (pH 7·6), pooled in one tube, and recentrifuged for 30 min. The supernatant is placed on ice: the sediment is resuspended in a further 10 ml of buffer, recentrifuged, and the supernatant pooled with the first supernatant.

(b) *Second ammonium sulphate precipitation.* The supernatant from (a) is brought to 50% saturation with ammonium sulphate solution, stirred for 5 min, and then centrifuged for 15 min at 9500 rpm. The supernatant is discarded and the sediment dissolved in 20 ml 0·05M potassium phosphate buffer, pH 7·6.

(c) *Calcium phosphate gel adsorption.* Calcium phosphate gel (prepared according to Keilin and Hartree, 1938) is added to the solution to yield a gel to protein ratio of 1·5 (dry weights), stirred for 15 min, and then centrifuged for 15 min at 9500 rpm. The single batch of gel used in these preparations was from 1 to 3 years old at the time of use.

(d) *Heat treatment.* The supernatant from (c) is heated for 5 min at 60°C, cooled rapidly on ice, and then centrifuged for 30 min at 30,000 rpm (Spinco model L, rotor No. 40). The supernatant, which contains the glycerol dehydrogenase, is decanted.

(e) *Storage.* The extent of dilution of the supernatant from (d) that will be required for the glycerol estimation is determined by measuring the reduction of NAD by 0·1 μmole of glycerol in the presence of 0·1 ml of 1 in 5, 1 in 10 and 1 in 20 dilutions of the enzyme solution as described before (Himms-Hagen and Hagen, 1962). The dilution that will bring the reaction almost to completion in 25 to 30 min is chosen. The solution is frozen in 0·2 ml (or 0·1 ml) lots, which are to be thawed and diluted appropriately as required.

The above procedure is stated by the authors to have been followed on three separate occasions with reproducible results. When stored in a frozen state, the enzyme preparation retains full activity for at least 1 year. The enzyme blank (change in extinction at 340 nm in the absence of added glycerol) is usually 0·005 and always less than 0·01. Interference with the glycerol assay by glyceraldehyde 3-phosphate, fructose 1,6-diphosphate, and ethanol (0·1–1·0 μmole) is negligible with this enzyme preparation. Very large amounts of ethanol (10–100 μmoles in the sample to be tested) do cause a small increase in extinction (0·03–0·04) in the presence of the enzyme.

NAD-glycine buffer. 6·65 mg NAD per ml of 0·1 M-glycine, pH 9·5. Prepare fresh daily.

Procedure: If deproteinization is required then this is achieved by addition of 2N perchloric acid (0·5 ml) to test solution (0·5 ml). Precipitated protein is removed by centrifugation. The supernatant is neutralized with KOH, the solution chilled and the potassium perchlorate is removed by centrifugation. The volume of the sample is now made up to 2 ml with distilled water.

Both test and control tube contain NAD-glycine reagent (0·5 ml) and sample (0·4 ml); water (0·1 ml) is added to the control tube and enzyme (0·1 ml) is added to the sample tube at zero time. Incubation is carried out at 30°C and, near to 30 min, the contents of sample and control tube are transferred to microcuvettes and, at exactly 30 min after enzyme addition, the E_{340} of the test is determined with the control set at zero. This corrects for any 340 nm absorbing material present in the sample.

Calibration: A series of standards containing 0·005, 0·010, 0·020, 0·030, 0·040 μmole are run with each batch of samples to give a calibration curve. This range of calibration can be extended upwards if desired since 0·06 μmole of glycerol gives a ΔE_{340} of 0·20 approximately.

2 (f) *Specific analyses—Determination of triose phosphates*

This section deals with the determination of L-glycerol 1-phosphate, dihydroxyacetone phosphate, D-glyceraldehyde 3-phosphate, D-1,3-diphosphoglycerate, D-3-phosphoglycerate (3PG), D-2-phosphoglycerate (2PG) and phosphoenolpyruvate (PEP). All the determinations described are enzymic since, when working with biological material probably containing a mixture of these triose phosphates, extreme specificity is necessary. For the estimation of $p$mole quantities the fluorescent assays, based on the same principles and described in "Methods in Enzymology", should be consulted.

(*i*) *Estimation of* D-1,3-*diphosphoglycerate* (*Negelein*, 1963)

Principle: In media free from inorganic phosphate the reaction catalysed by glyceraldehyde 3-phosphate dehydrogenase, shown below, proceeds virtually quantitatively from right to left. Glyceraldehyde 3-phosphate + NAD$^+$ + P$_i$ ⇌ 1,3-diphosphoglycerate + NADH + H$^+$. An excess of NADH is present and its oxidation is followed at 340 nm.

Reagents:

If deproteinization is necessary the solution should be made only weakly acidic (about pH 2) because of the lability of 1,3-diphosphoglycerate, and then rapidly neutralized. Storage at 0°C in slightly alkaline media (pH 7–9) results in a 6% loss in 24 h.

Pyrophosphate buffer, 0·01 mM, pH 7·9. $Na_4P_2O_7$, 10 H_2O (4·47 g) is dissolved in distilled water (90 ml) followed by the addition of 1N HCl (6·0 ml). The final volume is made up to 100 ml. This should be free from orthophosphates and must, therefore, not be stored for more than a few days.

NADH solution. Disodium NADH (4·1 mg) is dissolved in distilled water and made up to a final volume of 2·0 ml. This should be stored at 0°C and kept for only a few days before discarding.

D-Glyceraldehyde 3-phosphate dehydrogenase. This is a yeast or skeletal muscle preparation. The crystalline suspension should be diluted with distilled water to around 1 μg protein/ml. This is prepared freshly each day and maintained at 0°C.

Procedure: The wavelength used is 340 nm, with cuvettes of light path 0·5 cm. The experimental cuvette is read against a blank containing pyrophosphate buffer (0·83 ml) and distilled water (1·67 ml).

The experimental cuvette contains pyrophosphate buffer (0·83 ml), NADH solution (0·20 ml), distilled water (1·24 ml) and sample (0·20 ml). The sample should not contain more than 0·4 μmole of 1,3-diphosphoglycerate. The extinction E_1 is determined and then enzyme solution (0·03 ml) is mixed in. The course of the reaction is followed; this should be complete within a short period. If it is not then the enzyme concentration is increased. The final extinction E_2 is determined.

If more than 90% of the NADH is oxidized then it is advisable to repeat the estimation on a dilution of the sample. If the concentration of 1,3-diphosphoglycerate is very low increased sensitivity can be obtained by using cuvettes with a longer light path.

Calculation: The ΔE value $(E_2 - E_1)$ obtained has to be corrected for the dilution on addition of enzyme. In this case the factor is 0·987, and the concentration of 1,3-diphosphoglycerate can be calculated from the following where $\epsilon = 6·22$ cm^2/μmole:

$$1,3\text{-diphosphoglycerate } \mu\text{mole/ml} = \frac{\Delta E \text{ (corrected)} \times \text{assay volume}}{\epsilon \times \text{light path} \times \text{sample volume}}$$

Stability of 1,3-diphosphoglycerate: 1,3-Diphosphoglycerate is a labile compound which spontaneously decomposes to give 3-phosphoglycerate and inorganic phosphate. The best stability seems to be achieved by storage in the frozen state in slightly alkaline solution; under these conditions a 3% loss is recorded in 24 h. At pH 7·2 and 38°C the half-life of decomposition is 37 min.

(ii) Estimation of L-glycerol 1-phosphate (Hohorst, 1963a)

Principle: Glycerol 1-phosphate dehydrogenase catalyses the following reaction:

glycerol 1-phosphate + NAD^+ ⇌ dihydroxacetone phosphate + $NADH + H^+$

Unfortunately the position of equilibrium lies well to the left, but the reaction can be manipulated so that complete oxidation occurs. This is ensured by (a) trapping dihydroxyacetone as its hydrazone and (b) by carrying out the reaction in an alkaline buffer, effectively removing the released protons. The course of the reaction is followed spectrophotometrically, monitoring NADH production.

Reagents:

If deproteinization of the sample is necessary then this is best performed with perchloric acid (about 6% w/v), neutralizing with potassium carbonate (about 5M) using a methyl orange indicator.

Hydrazine-glycine buffer; 0·4M hydrazine, 1M glycine, pH 9·5.
Hydrazine sulphate (5·2 g), glycine (7·5 g) and EDTA Na₂H₂, 2H₂O (0·2 g) are suspended in a small volume of distilled water. 2N NaOH (51 ml) is added and the final volume made up to 100 ml. When stored in the cold this is stable for 1 week and it may be more advisable to prepare a stock solution of hydrazine sulphate, glycine and disodium EDTA. This is stable for a much longer period and can be adjusted to pH 9·5 as required.

NAD. NAD (40 mg) is dissolved in distilled water (1 ml). This is stable for several weeks, in the cold, and does not require neutralization as the buffering capacity of the hydrazine-glycine buffer is high.

Glycerol 1-phosphate dehydrogenase, about 6 mg protein/ml. This should have a specific activity of 36 I.U./mg.

Procedure: The experimental cuvette (light path 1 cm) contains hydrazine-glycine buffer (0·45 ml), NAD solution (0·05 ml), and sample (0·5 ml). The E_{340} measurements are usually read against a water blank.

The contents of the cuvette are thoroughly mixed and allowed to come to room temperature. The initial extinction is then determined two or more times at intervals of 3 min (E_1). The assay is initiated by the addition of enzyme suspension (0·01 ml) to the experimental cuvette. The reaction should be complete within 10–20 min, depending on the glycerol 1-phosphate concentration, and the endpoint is judged by reading to a constant extinction (E_2) (or to a very small increase during the 3 min interval of taking readings). If a stable extinction is not reached after 20 min then the activity of the enzyme is probably too low. To check the assay it is advisable to add 0·002M glycerol 1-phosphate (0·01 ml) to the experimental cuvette on completion of the reaction. The E_{340} should be 0·123 and this increase should be complete in 10–20 min.

Calculation: Since glycerol 1-phosphate reacts quantitatively the amount can be calculated from the following expression:

$$\frac{\Delta E \times \text{dil.}}{\epsilon \times d} = \mu\text{moles of glycerol 1-phosphate}$$

where $\Delta E = E_2 - E_1$.

  dil. = total dilution of sample.

  ϵ = extinction coefficient [$cm^2/\mu mole$].

  d = light path.

Range and specificity: The upper limit per cuvette is approximately 0·1 μmole. The assay is specific for L($-$) glycerol 1-phosphate: the dextro-rotatory isomer does not react.

Sources of error: The initial extinction may not be constant and this can be a result of (1) the cuvettes not being brought to room temperature, (2) the hydrazine-glycine buffer being more than 8 days old, or (3) impure NAD solution. If a bacterial extract is being used then this may cause similar effects but can be compensated by employing a blank containing all the components of the experimental cuvette except enzyme.

If the addition of enzyme causes a sharp change in extinction then its absorption is too high and the preparation should be discarded. If the extinction decreases on addition of enzyme the pH of the buffer is probably too alkaline.

(iii) Estimation of D-glyceraldehyde 3-phosphate and dihydroxyacetone phosphate (Bücher and Hohorst, 1963)

Principle: Glyceraldehyde 3-phosphate is estimated by conversion to glycerol 1-phosphate by triose phosphate isomerase and glycerol 1-phosphate dehydrogenase (GDH). NADH is consumed during the second step of this sequence.

Dihydroxyacetone phosphate can be similarly estimated, requiring only the presence of glycerol 1-phosphate dehydrogenase. The equilibrium of GDH is such that quantitative reduction occurs, in both assays.

Reagents:

If deproteinization of the sample is required then this is achieved by the addition of perchloric acid followed by subsequent neturalization with potassium carbonate. Chilling and centrifuging will remove the protein and precipitated perchlorate.

Triethanolamine buffer. 0·4M, pH 7·6.

Triethanolamine hydrochloride (18·6 g) is dissolved in approximately 200 ml of distilled water. 2N NaOH (18 ml) and EDTA-Na_2H_2, $2H_2O$ (3·7 g) is added; the final volume is made up to 250 ml with distilled water.

NADH reagent. NADH, disodium salt (7 mg), is dissolved in triethanolamine buffer, the final volume being 1·5 ml. The solution is stable for 2–3 weeks when stored between 0°–4°C.

Glycerol 1-phosphate dehydrogenase. Commercial crystalline suspension is diluted with distilled water to approximately 1·5 mg protein/ml. The specific activity should be at least 36 I.U./mg.

Triose phosphate isomerase. The commercial crystalline suspension is diluted to a concentration of 100 μg protein/ml. This should have a specific activity of $3·6 \times 10^3$ I.U./mg.

Potassium dichromate, approximately 1%.

Procedure: The experimental cuvette (of light path 5 cm) contains buffer (2·0 ml), sample (2·5 ml) and NADH solution (0·01 ml), and its E_{340} is determined against a blank (light path 1 cm) containing buffer (2·0 ml), and, to compensate for the absorption of the sample, potassium dichromate solution (ca. 0·02 ml). The contents of both cuvettes are thoroughly mixed and allowed to come to room temperature. The E_{340} of the experimental cuvette is determined two or more times at 3 min intervals.

For the determination of dihydroxyacetone phosphate glycerol 1-phosphate dehydrogenase solution (0·01 ml) is mixed into the experimental cuvette. The reaction should be complete within 6–9 min and is monitored at 3 min intervals. On completion of the reaction a further addition of enzyme will allow the increase in E_{340} due to the enzyme to be measured, if any.

Glyceraldehyde 3-phosphate is then estimated by addition of triose phosphate isomerase (0·005 ml); the reaction should reach completion in 3–5 min and is monitored at 3 min intervals. A further addition of the enzyme will allow its contribution to E_{340} to be measured.

Calculation: The difference in extinction at the various stages of the assay, when corrected for the increase in extinction on addition of the enzyme preparations, gives a direct measure of the amounts of triose phosphates that are present per cuvette. Knowing the sample dilution, if any, and the molar extinction coefficient of NADH at 340 nm, the amount of either triose phosphate can be computed.

(*iv*) *Estimation of phosphoenolpyruvate, D-3-phosphoglycerate and D-2-phosphoglycerate (Czok and Eckert, 1963)*

Principle: This method is based on the enzymic conversion of the triose phosphates to lactic acid, via pyruvic acid, following the oxidation of NADH spectrophotometrically. The equilibria and enzymes involved are as below.

$$3\text{-phosphoglycerate} \underset{\text{mutase (PM)}}{\overset{\text{phosphoglycerate}}{\rightleftarrows}} 2\text{-phosphoglycerate}$$

$$2\text{-phosphoglycerate} \overset{\text{enolase}}{\rightleftarrows} \text{phosphoenolypyruvate}$$

$$\text{phosphoenolpyruvate} + \text{ADP} \underset{\text{kinase (PK)}}{\overset{\text{pyruvate}}{\rightleftarrows}} \text{pyruvate} + \text{ATP}$$

$$\text{pyruvate} + \text{NADH} + \text{H}^+ \underset{\text{dehydrogenase (LDH)}}{\overset{\text{lactate}}{\rightleftarrows}} \text{lactate} + \text{NAD}^+$$

The equilibria of the last two reactions are such that quantitative conversion is assured.

Reagents:

Doubly distilled water is used throughout.

Triethanolamine buffer, 0·2M, pH 7·6. Triethanolamine hydrochloride (9·3 g) is dissolved in approximately 200 ml of distilled water. Disodium EDTA (3·7 g) is added and the pH is adjusted to 7·6 with 2N NaOH. The final volume is made up to 250 ml.

Potassium chloride, 2M. KCl (14·9 g) is dissolved in distilled water and made up to a final volume of 100 ml.

Magnesium sulphate, 0·5M. MgSO$_4$, 7H$_2$O (12·3 g) is dissolved in distilled water and made up to 100 ml.

Manganous sulphate, 0·005M. MnSO$_4$, 4H$_2$O (1·11 g) is dissolved in distilled water and made up to 1 litre. This should be prepared freshly for each series of determinations.

ADP, approximately 0·01M. Trisodium ADP (51·1 mg) is dissolved in distilled water and made up to 10 ml.

NADH. Disodium NADH (7 mg) is dissolved in 1 ml of distilled water. This should be made weekly.

2,3-Diphosphoglycerate, ca. 0·01M. The brucine salt is prepared from pig blood according to Greenwald (1925), or from D-3-phosphoglycerate and ATP with an extract of acetone-dried chicken breast muscle according to Grisolia and Joyce (1958) or as the barium salt according to Baer (1950).

To make up the reagent 30 mg of the (brucine)$_5$-salt is suspended in distilled water (1·5 ml). The brucine is precipitated with 1N NaOH (3·06 ml), and the curd-like precipitate collected by centrifuging for 5 min at 3000 g. The precipitate is washed with 0·5 ml distilled water which, after further centrifuging, is added to the initial supernatant. The combined supernatants are extracted twice with 10 ml portions of diethyl ether by shaking for a 5 min period each time.

The aqueous phase is separated off and residual ether is removed by evacuation, achieved by means of a water pump. The pH is adjusted to 6–7, using ca. 0·01 ml 1N HCl and indicator paper.

Lactate dehydrogenase, 15 mg protein/ml. The enzyme should have a specific activity of at least 350 I.U./mg. It is a rabbit skeletal muscle preparation as are the other enzymes below. It may be used as a suspension, or centrifuged and the sediment dissolved in distilled water (the same volume as the original suspension). This also applies to the other enzymes below.

Pyruvate kinase (PK), 10 mg protein/ml. This should have a specific activity of at least 120 I.U./mg.

Enolase, 5 mg protein/ml. This should have a specific activity of at least 25 I.U./mg.

Phosphoglycerate mutase (PM), 10 mg protein/ml. This should have a specific activity of at least 30,000 I.U./mg.

Procedure: For high sensitivity it is advisable to use a wavelength of 340 nm, although 366 nm, can also be used. Cuvettes of 1 cm light path are employed and the measurements are made against air.

The contents of the experimental cuvette are added in the order indicated: buffer (0·50 ml), KCl solution (0·075 ml), MgSO$_4$ solution (0·032 ml), ADP solution (0·050 ml), 2,3-diphosphoglycerate (0·025 ml); NADH solution (0·020 ml) and sample (0·50 ml), deproteinized with perchloric acid if necessary. The assay mixture is equilibrated at 25°C in a constant temperature cuvette holder and the assay is initiated by the mixing in of LDH suspension (0·001 ml). The reaction (the reduction of free pyruvate to lactate) is allowed to proceed to completion and E_1 is determined. PK suspension (0·002 ml) is now mixed in and, on completion of the reaction (5–10 min), E_2 is determined. This should be constant but if a small constant drop occurs then it is best to extrapolate to find the extinction at the end of the reaction. Finally, PM (0·002 ml) is mixed in and E_4 is determined after 10–15 min.

Biological materials may contain 10 times more 3PG than 2PG, PEP and pyruvate, and to increase the sensitivity for the latter group it may be necessary to determine 2PG and PEP separately from 3PG in larger samples.

For the determination of 3PG the phosphate concentration must be less than 10^{-3}M, although this effect can be largely overcome if $MnSO_4$ solution is substituted in the reaction mixture for $MgSO_4$ solution.

Range and calculation: The optimum concentration of all three metabolites is 0·03 to 0·2 μmole/cuvette, when using 340 nm light; at 366 nm it is double these figures.

The extinction differences observed represent the following:

$$E_1 - E_2 = \Delta E_{PEP}; \quad E_2 - E_3 = \Delta E_{2PG}; \quad E_3 - E_4 = \Delta E_{3PG}$$

and can be inserted in the following expression:

$$\frac{\Delta E \times \text{assay volume}}{\epsilon \times \text{sample volume} \times \text{light path}} = \mu\text{mole 3PG, 2PG or PEP/ml of sample}$$

to give the amounts of the triose phosphates present.
For this formula the values of ϵ at 340 nm and 366 nm are respectively 6·22 and 3·30.

Specificity: Both enolase and pyruvate kinase are highly specific and these ensure the specificity of the assay.

APPENDIX

Key to Fig. 16, page 128. Gas–liquid chromatography apparatus of Lanigan and Jackson (1965).

Note that Figs. 16B and 16C are approximately one quarter of the actual size.

1. Gas inlet
2. Water bubbler
3. Sample heater
4. Chromatographic column
5. Column oven
6. Titration vessel
7. Electrode leads
8. Micro-burette
9. Flexible drive
10. Recorder
11. pH-meter titrator
12. Insulated heater (40 Ω)
13. Ground glass socket-B10
14. Modified glass cone-B10
15. Silicone rubber plug
16. Glass sample boat
17. Cork spacers
18. Aluminium tube
19. Aluminium tube with heating tape (150 W)
20. Asbestos packing
21. Glass tube for thermocouples
22. Glass yarn plug
23. Capillary end of column
24. Glass cone and socket-B7
25. Calomel electrode
26. Glass electrode
27. Bubbling tube
28. Vacuum connection

REFERENCES

Annison, E. F. (1954). *Biochem. J.*, **58**, 670.
Artsybasheva, Y., and Favarskaya, I. A. (1961). *Zhur. Anal. Khim.*, **16**, 370.
Avigad, G., Amaral, D., Ansensio, C., and Horecker, B. L. (1962). *J. biol. Chem.*, **237**, 2736.

Baer, E. (1950). *J. biol. Chem.*, **185**, 763.
Barker, S. A., and Somers, P. J. (1966). *Carbohydrate Res.*, **3**, 220–224.
Barker, S. B., and Summerson, W. H. (1941). *J. biol. Chem.*, **138**, 535.
Barton, R. R. (1966). *Anal. Biochem.*, **14**, 258–260.
Bergmeyer, H.-U. (1963) (ed.) "Methods of Enzymatic Analysis". Academic Press, New York.
Blackwood, A. C., Neish, A. C., Brown, W. E., and Ledingham, G. A. (1947). *Canad. J. Res.*, **B25**, 56.
Blecher, M. (1961). *Anal. Biochem.*, **2**, 30–38.
Bolognani, L., Coppi, G., and Zambotti, V. (1961). *Experimentia*, **17**, 67–68.
Bomhof, D. W., and Tucker, T. C. (1965). *J. Chromatog.*, **17**, 300–306.
Bonnichsen, R. (1963). In "Methods of Enzymatic Analysis" (Ed. H.-U. Bergmeyer), pp. 285–287. Academic Press, New York.
Bové, J., and Raveux, R. (1957). *Bull. Soc. Chim.*, 376–381.
Bratton, A. C., and Marshall, E. K. J. (1939). *J. biol. Chem.*, **128**, 537.
Brenner, M. W., Blick, S. R., Frenkel, G., and Siebënberg, J. (1963), pub (1964). *European Brewery Convention, Proceedings Congress*, **9**, 233.
Bücher, T., and Hohorst, H-J. (1963). In "Methods of Enzymatic Analysis" (Ed. H.-U. Bergmeyer), pp. 246–252. Academic Press, New York.
Bulen, W. A., Varner, J. E., and Burrell, R. C. (1952). *Analyt. Chem.*, **24**, 187–190.
Burton, R. M. (1955), In "Methods in Enzymology" (Eds S. P. Colowick and N. O. Kaplan), Vol. 1, 397–400. Academic Press, New York.
Byrne, G. A. (1965). *J. Chromatog.*, **20**, 528.
Carlström, G., Hallgren, W., Pehrson, B., and Wallin, O. (1965). *Acta Vet. Scond.*, **6**, 52.
Cavett, J. W. (1937–38). *J. Lab. Clin. Med.*, **23**, 543.
Chmielawski, J., and Isaac, P. C. G. (1959). *Nature, Lond.*, **183**, 1120–1121.
Czok, R., and Eckert, L. (1963). In "Methods of Enzymatic Analysis" (Ed. H.-U. Bergmeyer), pp. 224–228. Academic Press, New York.
Dagley, S. (1963). In "Methods of Enzymatic Analysis" (Ed. H.-U. Bergmeyer), pp. 313–317. Academic Press, New York.
Dagley, S., and Dawes, E. A. (1953). *Enzymologia*, **16**, 226–230.
Dagley, S., Trudgill, P. W., and Callely, A. G. (1961). *Biochem. J.*, **81**, 623.
Dancis, J., Hutzler, J., and Levitz, M. (1963). *Biochim. biophys. Acta*, **78**, 85–90.
Dechary, J. M., Kun, E., and Pitot, H. C. (1954). *Analyt. Chem.*, **26**, 449–452.
DeMoss, R. D., Bard, R. C., and Gunsalus, I. C. (1951). *J. Bacteriol.*, **62**, 499.
Desnuelle, P., and Naudet, M. (1945). *Bull. Soc. chim. Fr.*, **12**, 871.
Dische, Z., and Borenfreund, E. (1957). *Biochim. biophys. Acta*, **23**, 639–642.
Doelle, H. W. (1966). *Ant. van Leeuwenhoek J. Microbiol. Serol.*, **32**, 373–380.
Doelle, H. W. (1967). *J. Gas Chromatog.*, **5**, 582–584.
Doelle, H. W. (1969a). *J. Chromatog.*, **42**, 541–543.
Doelle, H. W. (1969b). *J. Chromatog.*, **39**, 389–401.
Doelle, H. W., and Manderson, G. J. (1969). *Ant. van Leeuwenhoek J. Microbiol. Serol.*, **35**, 467–478.
Dubowski, K. M. (1962). *Clin. Chem.*, **8**, 218–235.
Fabre, R., Truhant, R., and Singerman, A. (1954). *Ann. Pharm. Franc.*, **12**, 409.
Feigl, F. (1957). *Spot Tests in Organic Analysis*. Elsevier, Amsterdam.
Fischer, O., and Hepp, E. (1889). *Ber.*, **22**, 356.
Freudiger, J. B., and Vignau, J. A. (1965). *J. Forensic Sci.*, **10**, 73.
Friedemann, T. E. (1938). *J. biol. Chem.*, **123**, 162.

Friedemann, T. E. (1957). *In* "Methods in Enzymology" (Eds S. P. Colowick and N. O. Kaplan), Vol. 3, pp. 414–418. Academic Press, New York.

Friedemann, T. E., and Haugen, G. E. (1943). *J. biol. Chem.*, 147, 415.

Frohman, C. E., and Orten, J. M. (1953). *J. biol. Chem.*, 205, 717.

Gänshirt, H., Waldi, D., and Stahl, E. (1965). *In* "Thin-Layer Chromatography" (Ed. E. Stahl), pp. 356–357. Springer-Verlag, Berlin.

Ghetie, S., and Cioba, A. (1964). *Rev. Roumaine Biochim.*, 1, 285–291.

Goodwin, T. W., and Williams, G. R. (1952). *Biochem. J.*, 51, 708.

Gordon, H. T., Thornburg, W., and Werum, L. N. (1956). *Analyt. Chem.*, 28, 849–855.

Graham, H. D. (1965). *J. Food. Sci.*, 30, 846.

Green, S., Anstiss, C., and Fishman, W. H. (1962). *Biochim. biophys. Acta*, 62, 574–575.

Greenwald, J. (1925). *J. biol. Chem.*, 63, 339.

Grisolia, S., and Joyce, B. K. (1958). *J. biol. Chem.*, 233, 18.

Guyot, H. (1961). *Bull. Trav. Soc. Phar. Lyon*, 5, 19–23.

Harman, M. A., and Doelle, H. W. (1969). *J. Chromatog.*, 42, 157–169.

Hartford, C. G. (1962). *Analyt. Chem.*, 34, 426–428.

Hay, G. W., Lewis, B. A., and Smith, S. (1963). *J. Chromatog.*, 11, 479–486.

Hessler, L. E. (1959). *Analyt. Chem.*, 31, 1234–36.

Heyrovsky, A. (1956). *Chem. Listy*, 50, 1593–97.

Himms-Hagen, J., and Hagen, P. B. (1962). *Can. J. Biochem., Physiol.*, 40, 1129.

Himms-Hagen, J., and Hagen, P. B. (1965). *Can. J. Biochem.*, 43, 122.

Hindberg, J., and Wieth, J. O. (1963). *J. Lab. Clin. Med.*, 61, 355–362.

Hiscox, E. R., and Berredge, N. J. (1950). *Nature, Lond.*, 166, 522.

Hohorst, H.-J. (1963a). *In* "Methods of Enzymatic Analysis" (Ed. H.-U. Bergmeyer), pp. 215–219. Academic Press, New York.

Hohorst, H.-J. (1963b). *In* "Methods of Enzymatic Analysis" (Ed. H.-U. Bergmeyer), pp. 328–334. Academic Press, New York.

Holley, A. D., and Holley, R. W. (1952). *Analyt. Chem.*, 24, 216.

Hullin, R. P., and Noble, R. L. (1953). *Biochem. J.*, 55, 289.

Hutchens, J. O., and Kass, B. M. (1949). *J. biol. Chem.*, 177, 571.

Jakoby, W. B., and Fredericks, J. (1962). *Biochem. biophys. Acta*, 58, 217.

Johnson, M. J. (1949). *J. biol. Chem.*, 181, 707.

Juni, E., and Heym, G. A. (1962). *Analyt. Biochem.*, 4, 143–181.

Katsuki, H., Kanayuki, H., Yoshida, T., and Kawano, C. (1961a). *Analyt. Biochem.*, 2, 421–432.

Katsuki, H., Kawano, C., Yoshida, T., Kanayuki, H., and Tanaka, S. (1961b). *Analyt. Biochem.*, 2, 433–440.

Keilin, D., and Hartree, E. F. (1938). *Proc. Roy. Soc. London*, B, 124, 397.

Klotzsch, H., and Bergmeyer, H.-U. (1963). *In* "Methods of Enzymatic Analysis" (Ed. H.-U. Bergmeyer), pp. 283–284. Academic Press, New York.

Kluyver, A. J. (1931). "Chemical Activities of Micro-organisms". University of London Press, London.

Kmetec, E. (1966). *Analyt. Biochem.*, 16, 474–480.

Kuhn, R., and Hecksher, R. (1926). *Z. physiol. Chem.*, 160, 116.

Langlykke, A. F., and Peterson, W. H. (1937). *Ind. Eng. Chem. Anal. Ed.*, 9, 163.

Lanigan, G. W., and Jackson, R. B. (1965). *J. Chromatog.*, 17, 238.

Lind, N. O. (1957). *Ark. Kemie.*, 10, 569–576.

Lindqvist, B., and Storgärds, T. (1953). *Acta. Chem. Scand.*, 7, 87.

Lundquist, F., Fugmann, U., and Rasmussen, H. (1961). *Biochem. J.*, **80**, 393.
Lundquist, F. (1958). *Biochem. J.*, **68**, 172.
Lundquist, F. (1963). In "Methods of Enzymatic Analysis" (Ed. H.-U. Berg-meyer), pp. 303–307. Academic Press, New York.
Lynes, A. (1964). *J. Chromatog.*, **15**, 108.
Lyons, H., and Bard, J. (1964). *Clin. Chem.*, **10**, 429.
McArdle, B. (1955). *Biochem. J.*, **60**, 647.
McGill, D. J. (1966). In "Carbohydrate Metabolism of *Zymomonas anaerobia*". Ph.D. thesis, University of Hull.
Mantel, M., and Anbar, M. (1964). *Analyt. Chem.*, **36**, 936.
Marais, J. P., De Wit, J. L., and Quicke, G. V. (1966). *Anal. Biochem.*, **15**, 373–381.
Markham, R. (1942). *Biochem. J.*, **36**, 790.
Massey, V. (1955). In "Methods in Enzymology" (Eds S. P. Colowick and N. O. Kaplan), **1**, 727. Academic Press, New York.
Meyer, E. and Wurtz, B. (1964). *Compt. rend.*, **158**, 369–376.
Moellering, H., and Gruber, W. (1966). *Anal. Biochem.*, **17**, 369–376.
Meuller-Beissenhirtz, W., and Keller, H. (1965). *Klin. Wschr.*, **43**, 43–49.
Mukerjee, H., and Sri Ram. (1964). *J. Chromatog.*, **14**, 551–552.
Murdock, R. E., Brooks, F. R., and Zahn, V. (1948). *Analyt. Chem.*, **20**, 65–67.
Nanni, G., and Baldini, I. (1964). *Ital. J. Biochem.*, **13**, 135.
Negelein, E (1963). In "Methods of Enzymatic Analysis" (Ed. H.-U. Bergmeyer), pp. 234–237. Academic Press, New York.
Neish, A. C. (1949). *Can. J. Res.*, **B27**, 6.
Neish, A. C. (1951). *Can. J. Chem.*, **29**, 552.
Neish, A. C. (1952). Analytical Methods for Bacterial Fermentations N.R.C.C. Report No. 46-8-3.
Nelson, N. (1944). *J. Biol. Chem.*, **153**, 375.
Neuberg, C., Faiker, E., and Levite, A. (1917). *Biochem. Z.*, **83**, 244.
Nir, I. (1964). *Anal. Biochem.*, **8**, 20–23.
Nordlie, R. C.,and Fromm, H. J. (1963). In "Methods of Enzymatic Analysis" (Ed. H.-U. Bergmeyer), pp. 182–185. Academic Press, New York.
Osburn, O. L., Brown, R. W., and Werkman, C. H. (1937). *J. biol. Chem.*, **121**, 685.
Percheron, F. (1962). *Bull. Soc. Chim. Biol.*, **44**. 1161–1165.
Phillipson, A. T. (1947). *J. expt. Biol.*, **23**, 346.
Rabinowitz, J. C., and Pricer, W. E. Jnr. (1957). *J. biol. Chem.*, **229**, 321.
Rasmussen, H. J. (1967). *J. Chromatog.*, **26**, 512–514.
Raveux, R., and Bové, J. (1957). *Bull. Soc. Chim.*, 369–376.
Reid, V. W., and Salmon, D. G. (1955). *Analyst*, **80**, 704.
Reid, V. W., and Truelove, R. K. (1952). *Analyst*, **77**, 325–328.
Relander, A., and Räihä, C. E. (1963). *Scand. J. Clin. Lab. Invest.*, **15**, 221–224.
Resnik, F. E., Lee, L. A., and Powell, W. A. (1955). *Analyt. Chem.*, **27**, 928–931.
Rodgers, K. (1961). *Biochem. J.*, **80**, 240–244.
Roe, J. H. (1934). *J. biol. Chem.*, **107**, 15.
Rosenberg, J. C., and Rush, B. F. Jnr. (1966). *Clin. Chem.*, **12**, 299–307.
Roth, H., Segal, S., and Bertoli, D. (1965). *Anal. Biochem.*, **10**, 32–52.
Rutowski, R. B., and De Baare, L. (1966). *Amer. J. Clin. Pathol.*, **46**, 405–407.
Said, S. A., and Merton, A. R. (1963). *J. Gas Chromatog.*, **1**, 7.
Salwin, H. (1965). *J. Assoc. Offic. Agr. Chem.*, **28**, 628.
Scarisbrick, R. (1952). *Biochem. J.*, **50**, xxiv.
Schön, R. (1965). *Anal. Biochem.*, **12**, 413–420.

Scott, D. (1953). *J. Agr. Food Chem.*, **1**, 727.
Sheth, A. R., and Rao, S. S. (1963). *Experimentia*, **19**, 362–363.
Singer, T. P., and Lusty, C. J. (1963). *In* "Methods of Enzymatic Analysis" (Ed. H.-U. Bergmeyer), pp. 346–349. Academic Press, New York.
Snell, F. D., and Snell, C. T. (1953). *Colorimetric Methods of Analysis*, **3**, pp. 285–293. D. Van Nostrand Company Inc., New York.
Somogyi, M. (1930). *J. biol. Chem.*, **86**, 655.
Somogyi, M. (1952). *J. biol. Chem.*, **195**, 19.
Soodak, M. (1957). *In* "Methods in Enzymology" (Eds S. P. Colowick and N. O. Kaplan), **3**, p. 266. Academic Press, New York.
Soodak, M., and Lipmann, F. (1948). *J. biol. Chem.*, **174**, 37.
Spencer, N. (1967). *J. Chromatog.*, **30**, 566–571.
Srinivason, T. R., and Sprinson, D. B. (1959). *J. biol. Chem.*, **234**, 716–722.
Stadtman, T. C., and Barker, H. A. (1951). *J. Bact.*, **61**, 67.
Stahl, E. (1962). Dunnschicht-Chromatographie, Springer-Verlag, Berlin.
Stahl, E. (1965). Ed. *In* "Thin Layer Chromatography, A Laboratory Handbook". Academic Press, New York.
Steigman, A. (1946). *Brit. J. Phot.*, **93**, 256.
Stiller, M. (1961). *Anal. Chim. Acta.*, **25**, 85.
Storry, J. E., and Millard, D. (1965). *J. Sci. Fd. Agric.*, **16**, 417.
Sundt, E., and Winter, M. (1957). *Anal. Chem.*, **29**, 851.
Swann, M. H. (1957). *Anal. Chem.*, **29**, 1352–1353.
Tabor, H. (1955). *In* "Methods in Enzymology" (Eds S. P. Colowick and N. O. Kaplan), **1**, p. 609. Academic Press, New York.
Tholey, G., Frey, L., and Wurtz, B. (1965). *Path-Biol. (Paris)*, **13**, 689.
Thornton, B. J., and Speck, J. C. (1950). *Anal. Chem.*, **22**, 899.
Ting, I. P., and Dugger, W. M. Jnr. (1965). *Anal. Biochem.*, **12**, 571–578.
Turner, R., and Gilmour, M. (1965). *Anal. Biochem.*, **13**, 552.
Van der Lek, J. B. (1930). Ph.D. Thesis Technische Hoogeschool, Delft, Holland.
Van Slyke, D. D., and Folch, J. (1940). *J. biol. Chem.*, **136**, 509.
Wachsmuth, E. D., and Fritz, I. (1965). *Klin. Wschr.*, **43**, 53–54.
Walborg, E. F., Christensson, L., and Gardell, S. (1965). *Anal. Biochem.*, **13**, 177–185.
Walborg, E. F., and Christensson, L. (1965). *Anal. Biochem.*, **13**, 186–193.
Waravdekar, V. S., and Saslaw, L. D. (1957). *Biochim. biophys. Acta*, **24**, 439.
Wehle, H. (1959). *Z. Anal. Chem.*, **169**, 241.
Westerfeld, W. W. (1945). *J. biol. Chem.*, **101**, 495.
Wolfrom, M. L., and Arsenault, G. P. (1960). *J. Org. Chem.*, **25**, 206.
Wood, H. G., and Werkman, C. H. (1936). *Biochem. J.*, **30**, 48.
Wood, W. A. (1961). *In* "The Bacteria", Vol. II (Eds I. C. Gunsalus and R. Y. Stanier). Academic Press, New York.
Yaphe, W., and Arsenault, G. P. (1966). *Anal. Biochem.*, **13**, 133–148.

CHAPTER IV

Evaluation of Methods Used to Determine Metabolic Pathways

S. Dagley and P. J. Chapman

Department of Biochemistry, University of Minnesota, St. Paul, U.S.A.

I. INTRODUCTION

A. General aspects of metabolism

We shall attempt to evaluate some of the methods used to investigate the main metabolic pathways found in micro-organisms. Details of most of these procedures are given elsewhere in these Volumes, and many of them make use of principles that have also been fruitfully applied to other forms of life. In some instances, however, the methods find unique application to the bacterial cell which is, in the phrase of Stephenson (1949) "the most plastic of living material [and] is immensely tolerant of experimental meddling." It is due to the convenience with which a wide range of experimental methods may be applied to *Escherichia coli* that many discoveries of fundamental importance to biochemistry have been made with this particular organism. The statement of Watson (1965) may be amply justified, that "*E. coli* is the best understood organism at the molecular level." Clearly, this understanding would be less valuable if the central metabolic processes of bacteria were found to differ radically from those of other organisms. However, despite great differences in their capacities to synthesize or degrade particular metabolites, most forms of life utilize similar chemical sequences for the release of energy from foodstuffs or for the biosynthesis of cell constituents, thereby displaying a biochemical unity that doubtless reflects a common ancestry.

We may therefore gain perspective for an evaluation of methods of investigating the metabolism of bacteria or any other form of life by posing this question: what are the salient features which distinguish the chemistry of living matter from that of other chemical systems? For when these features are recognized, some of the difficulties attending their study will emerge.

First, it appears that when life began to emerge on this planet some 5×10^9 years ago, the element hydrogen was much more abundant than it is now, with carbon in its most highly reduced form, methane. During the passage of time much hydrogen escaped from the earth, and most of the terrestial carbon now exists (as $CaCO_3$) in a more oxidized form than that of living matter. For life to be maintained it is therefore necessary for carbon to be reduced by hydrogen to the level of reduction of living-cell constituents. This highly endergonic process is achieved by photosynthetic organisms which, in so doing, harness the very reaction that would doom life to extinction if sufficient hydrogen were lost to outer space: namely, the photolysis of water.

A second contrast between the chemical condition of living matter and its environment emerges when we consider the changes in entropy that have to be accomplished. In general, the events that occur spontaneously in inanimate Nature are those that entail a loss of ordered arrangements of atoms and an increase in disorder; but living matter needs continually to reverse this trend. For example, when pseudomonads are introduced into a solution that contains molecules of acetic acid and a few species of inorganic ions they rapidly assemble atoms of carbon, hydrogen, oxygen, nitrogen and phosphorus into those complex and ordered arrangements that constitute the macromolecules of their progeny. As Lewis (1926) observed, living organisms "alone seem to breast the great stream of apparently irreversible processes. These processes tear down, living things build up. While the rest of the world seems to move toward a dead level of uniformity, the living organism is evolving new substances and more and more intricate forms." Nevertheless, no thermodynamic mystery is involved. The overall decrease in entropy that occurs is compensated by the energy released when food-stuffs are degraded; and its ultimate source is the solar energy harnessed in photosynthesis when CO_2 is converted into carbohydrate.

In biosynthetic sequences, hydrogen atoms are usually transferred to carbon from NADPH whereas in degradations they are received by NAD. Energy is usually transferred through the agency of ATP, which is formed in degradative sequences and utilized in biosynthesis. This metabolic device may have had its origin in the use of inorganic polyphosphates as energy sources by early forms of life, since these molecules exhibit two properties essential for that function. Thermodynamically, they are energy-rich: that is, they liberate a relatively large amount of free energy when hydrolysed; and kinetically they are stable in neutral solution, so that energy is preserved for long periods until the molecule can take part in phosphorylation reactions. In any event, the need of biosynthetic sequences for the energy, reducing power and chemical material supplied by degradation requires that metabolic pathways be linked at many points. The controlled release of energy and hydrogen atoms likewise requires that sequences of both types shall proceed in many steps, each of which entails a relatively small modification of the participating molecules. In consequence, a metabolic map shows a network comprised of a great many reactions, few of which proceed in isolation from the rest. The art of investigating such a system lies in resolving the paradox, on the one hand, that *reaction chains must be broken up and the individual enzymes identified*, and, on the other, that *an assessment must be made of the significance of each integrated pathway for the metabolism of the cell as a whole.*

Two other distinguishing features of the chemistry of living matter have called for the development of specialized experimental approaches and methods: namely, the extreme rapidity by which reactions of the metabolic network are catalysed, and the means by which the regulation of their rates is accomplished. It has long been appreciated that enzymes owe their specificity and effectiveness of action to the fact that they are proteins. When it takes up a particular configuration, such a macromolecule provides sites of suitable shape for the effective binding of a substrate, and also chemical groups that are free to participate in the events of catalysis. However, it is only during the last decade that we have come to appreciate fully the relevance for enzyme action of the physicochemical properties of proteins. The configuration of an enzyme, and therefore the efficiency of its catalytic centre, may be profoundly altered when metabolites other than substrates or products are bound to the protein molecule. This recognition of allosteric behaviour now permits a description of mechanisms by which many metabolic pathways may be regulated.

B. Biosynthesis and degradation: their regulation in micro-organisms

Within the same cell, synthesis and degradation of an essential metabolite often proceed simultaneously. Accordingly, many cell constituents are in a dynamic state and the concentration of a particular compound remains, in general, nearly constant because its rate of synthesis is balanced by a similar rate of degradation. This state of affairs calls for a very effective regulation of reaction rates. Control is achieved in part by the sensitive responses of allosteric enzymes to changes in their environment, and in part is due to the fact that a particular metabolite is rarely synthesized by the same set of enzymes that serve for its degradation. It is evidently advantageous for the cell to be able to regulate each of these pathways separately. Adjustments of metabolism do not have to wait until such time as reverse reactions are favoured by a build-up of reaction intermediates.

From numerous reactions that would illustrate the separation of anabolic from catabolic routes we may choose one example. The overall conversion of palmityl coenzyme A into eight molecules of acetyl coenzyme A is represented by the following equation; and the synthesis of one molecule of palmityl coenzyme A is given by the same equation written in reverse—

$$CH_3(CH_2)_{14};CO \cdot SCoA + 7HSCoA + 7H_2O = 8CH_3CO \cdot SCoA + 28[H]$$

Nevertheless, in any particular organism, sets of completely different enzymes are found to catalyse the two metabolic routes, and different co-enzymes are also involved. In degradation, the hydrogen atoms are received by FAD and NAD and in synthesis they are donated by NADPH; the bacterial synthetase enzymes employ acyl derivatives of "acyl-carrier protein" and not those of coenzyme A directly; and whereas D-β-hydroxy-acyl derivatives are intermediates in biosynthesis, the L-isomers are formed during degradation. Most significantly, although the hydrocarbon chain is shortened by fission of one molecule of acetyl coenzyme A at each turn of the fatty acid "spiral", in biosynthesis it is lengthened by a sequence of con-densations with malonyl acyl-carrier protein. This derivative of malonic acid is formed when malonyl coenzyme A reacts with acyl-carrier protein, and malonyl coenzyme A is synthesized, in turn, from acetyl coenzyme A by the enzyme acetyl coenzyme A carboxylase. This biotin-enzyme is power-fully inhibited when there is an accumulation of the end product of the biosynthetic sequence, palmityl coenzyme A. From the point of view of metabolic regulation, therefore, this biosynthetic route possesses the great advantage of being very sensitive to feed-back regulation. On the other hand it may be pointed out that the participation of malonyl derivatives satisfies a thermodynamic requirement of synthesis. The equilibrium of the reaction between two molecules of acetyl coenzyme A lies heavily in favour of fission rather than condensation, whereas the participation of malonyl coenzyme A in the initial reactions of biosynthesis assures conditions that are energetically favourable by bringing in a molecule of ATP when CO_2 is fixed and by liberating CO_2 when condensation occurs.

In the example discussed, anabolic and catabolic sequences differed in the detailed chemistry of the reactions they employed: thus, two-carbon units were added as malonyl coenzyme A which lost CO_2 in the process. In other systems, such as those concerned with the bacterial metabolism of tryptophan, leucine, isoleucine, valine and lysine, degradation and bio-synthesis differ at almost every point with regard to the chemical reaction intermediates which participate. Such differences between synthetic and degradative routes might be anticipated on thermodynamic grounds. How-ever, in certain instances micro-organisms "distinguish" between the catabolic and anabolic functions of a *single reaction* by elaborating two dif-ferent enzymes. Some examples are as follows—

$$5\text{-Dehydroquinate} = 3\text{-dehydroshikimate} + H_2O \tag{1}$$

$$\text{L-Threonine} = \alpha\text{-oxobutyrate} + NH_3 \tag{2}$$

$$2 \text{ Pyruvate} = \alpha\text{-acetolactate} + CO_2 \tag{3}$$

$$\text{L-Arginine} = \text{agmatine} + CO_2 \tag{4}$$

$$\text{L-Ornithine} = \text{putrescine} + CO_2 \tag{5}$$

Each one of these reactions serves a biosynthetic function. However, in dif-ferent circumstances each one may lie on a pathway of degradation or may operate as a side reaction whose only function appears to be that of assisting the attainment of conditions more tolerable to the cells. In each case the micro-organisms synthesize two enzymes, one used for biosynthesis and the other not so used; and each reaction proceeds from left to right whether or not it is used for biosynthesis. Reaction (1) lies on the synthetic aromatic pathway to chorismate, but Giles *et al.* (1967) have shown that it is catalysed by a second, inducible enzyme in *Neurospora* mutants that grow with quinic acid as an aromatic supplement. *E. coli* elaborates two different threonine dehydratases (reaction 2). The biosynthetic enzyme is inhibited by iso-leucine but the catabolic enzyme is not, and is induced only under rather specialized conditions that include the presence of serine or threonine and the absence of fermentable carbohydrate (Umbarger, 1961). A similar situation exists with regard to reaction (3). *Aerobacter aerogenes* and other organisms possess a constitutive enzyme, concerned with the biosynthesis of valine, which is inhibited by this amino-acid. A second enzyme is induced below pH 6, is not inhibited by valine and has various physical properties that differ from those of the biosynthetic enzyme (Halpern and Umbarger, 1959). Morris and Pardee (1966) have shown that when *E. coli* is grown at neutrality, constitutive enzymes are present that catalyse reactions (4) and (5). They appear to function for the biosynthesis of putrescine which, in *E. coli* at least, probably serves an important metabolic purpose along with the polyamines spermidine and spermine; these compounds appear to assist in stabilizing membranes and ribosomes and also stimulate DNA-directed RNA polymerase (Fox *et al.*, 1964; Raina and Cohen, 1966). It has long been known (Gale, 1940) that enzymes for reactions (4) and (5) can be induced in *E. coli*, their sole function apparently being to catalyse the decarboxylation of arginine and ornithine when cultures grow increasingly acidic. The physical properties of these two catabolic enzymes differ from those of their bio-synthetic counterparts (Morris and Pardee, 1966).

An organism may also catalyse one reaction by two separate enzymes in order to achieve more effective regulation of its metabolism. Thus, *E. coli* contains two aspartate kinases, one inhibited competitively by lysine and the other non-competitively by threonine (Stadtman *et al.*, 1961). The product of this reaction, 4-phospho-L-aspartate, is the starting material for separate biosynthetic pathways leading to lysine and threonine. The operation of two enzymes for one reaction assures that excess of one amino-acid will not abolish the synthesis of the other.

Again, two enzymes may be found to catalyse one reaction because each is derepressed by a different inducer and is the expression of a different gene. Thus Cánovas *et al.* (1967) showed that β-oxoadipate enol-lactone hydrolase (EHL) and β-oxoadipate succinyl-CoA transferase (TR) are co-ordinately derepressed, along with other enzymes of the pathway, when *Moraxella calcoacetica* is grown with benzoate as source of carbon. Now β-oxoadipate and its enol-lactone, but not the compounds that proceed their formation from benzoate, are obligatory intermediates in the degradation of proto-catechuate by this organism. Accordingly, when *Mor. calcoacetica* is grown with *p*-hydroxybenzoate, EHL and TR must again be synthesized. In this case the two enzymic activities are derepressed co-ordinately with other enzymes of the protocatechuate pathway which are not those used for the degradation of benzoate. In fact the pair of enzymes, EHL and TR, which are derepressed when this organism grows with benzoate, differ in their physical properties from the pair that is found in *p*-hydroxybenzoate-grown cells, although they catalyse the same two reactions.

The examples given will suffice to justify the observation that *a metabolic pathway is not completely described by the chemical equations for the reactions that constitute the sequence. It is also necessary to identify the enzymes that participate.*

C. Cellular organization and metabolism

The complete elucidation of the chemical reactions and their enzymes, which together constitute a metabolic pathway in a microbe, follows a pattern that emerges repeatedly in other areas of biochemical investigation. The study begins with the intact organism and continues with the progressive dismantling of its enzymic apparatus. Thus, our understanding of the "spiral" of reactions, by which fatty acids are oxidized, stems from the experiments of Knoop which suggested that, when fed to animals, the hydrocarbon chains of ω-substituted fatty acids were degraded by fission of two carbon atoms at a time. Later the livers of diabetic animals were isolated and perfused by Embden who supported the theory of β-oxidation by showing that fatty acids, containing an even number of carbon atoms, gave rise to greater quantities of ketone bodies than did those containing an odd number. Next, slices of liver were shown to oxidize fatty acids; but attempts to isolate the enzymes, and hence the intermediates of the reaction chain, met with failure for many years. It was the introduction of the homogenizer, and the preparation of breis capable of oxidizing butyrate, that enabled Leloir and Muñoz (1939) to dispel the belief that the oxidation of a fatty acid depended in some way upon the maintenance of the structure of the intact cell. Progress in the isolation of the relevant enzymes was then dependent upon the results of a long series of investigations in other areas: first, in the field of cytology, culminating in the recognition of the mitochondrion, and second in the application of techniques of centrifugation by which these organelles could be isolated. Kennedy and Lehninger (1949) found that mitochondria readily oxidized fatty acids and Drysdale and Lardy (1953) showed that extracts of isolated rat-liver mitochondria provided a rich source of the enzymes concerned, far superior to extracts obtained by homogenizing whole cells. The stage was then set for the isolation and purification of the enzymes of the fatty acid "spiral" by workers in various laboratories.

We may take this system as an example to discuss how, in general, studies of metabolic pathways in mammals may resemble or differ from those concerned with microbes. With organisms of both kinds, some limited information can be obtained by relating the compounds excreted by the organism to those supplied in its diet. Such experiments are more readily undertaken with micro-organisms, since they can often be grown in mineral salts media containing single sources of carbon which may give rise to products of degradation that can be isolated from the culture fluids. Whole cells of bacteria are more conveniently handled than intact animals: thus, their ability to oxidize substrates in a respirometer can give valuable information. Nevertheless, with microbes as with mammals, the study cannot be completed until the system under investigation is isolated from the vast number of enzymes that catalyse the complex network of reactions inside the cell. The procedures used to disrupt microbial cells and to fractionate their contents are described elsewhere in this Series, Volume 5B. Because the structural organization of microbes is generally less complex than that of mammalian cells, the problem of locating the enzymes—as we described for the fatty acid metabolism of mammals—does not arise in this case. The enzymes of interest are either almost completely soluble when the cells are disrupted or else they remain bound to the cytoplasmic membrane.

However, this comparative ease of extraction is not entirely advantageous. We might isolate a series of enzymes from a crude, soluble extract and hopefully each one might be crystallized; but this in itself is no guarantee that they function together as an integrated system inside the cell in the way we might conjecture. Had it been necessary first to locate them in a particular structure of the cell, the difficulties of isolation would probably have been increased, but so would our confidence that they functioned together as a unit to catalyse one particular reaction sequence. For these reasons, although the study of a metabolic pathway usually begins with the intact microbial cell it should finish at the same point. It is only when the reactions of isolated enzymes can be shown to occur as a sequence within the cell that we can claim to have elucidated a pathway of metabolism. Fortunately, biochemists who work with microbes possess a singular advantage at this stage. They may isolate, with relative ease, mutant organisms that lack specific enzymes in the reaction sequence and the metabolic consequences of such deficiencies provide a direct test of the correctness of the pathway proposed.

II. CATABOLISM

A. Isolation from culture fluids of chemical intermediates of metabolic sequences

For many years the only methods available for studying microbial metabolism were those that depended upon painstaking analyses of fermentation products. Many valuable results were thereby obtained, notably for the alcoholic fermentation of glucose by yeast whereby the foundations were laid of our understanding of glycolysis. Proof that heterotrophic as well as autotrophic organisms could fix CO_2, a very surprising observation at the time when it was made, was first obtained by Wood and Werkman (1936) who showed that propionic acid bacteria fixed CO_2 in amounts comparable with those of the substrate they consumed during growth, namely glycerol. However, the general limitations of experiments which rely upon determining the overall conversions of nutrients into fermentation products were well expressed by Stephenson (1930). "We are indeed in much the same position," she wrote, "as an observer trying to gain an idea of the life of a household by a careful scrutiny of the persons or materials arriving at, or leaving the house: we keep an accurate record of the foods and commodities left at the door and patiently examine the contents of the dustbin, and endeavour to deduce from such data the events occurring behind closed doors."

In many cases it will be immediately evident that a compound which accumulates in a liquid growth medium is not necessarily a reaction intermediate in the metabolic pathway that leads from the source of carbon to the simpler molecules formed by degradation. For example when conditions are anaerobic, an organism will obtain energy by transferring hydrogen atoms from its growth substrates to other metabolites, and this process will give rise to a variety of fermentation products. Thus when *Clostridium kluyveri* grows with ethanol and acetate as carbon sources, hydrogen is transferred to reaction intermediates of the biosynthetic route to butyric and hexanoic acids, and these compounds consequently accumulate as the fermentation proceeds. However, most aerobic bacteria utilize the tricarboxylic acid cycle as the hub of their metabolism, and hydrogen atoms are transferred, through coenzymes, to oxygen by the energy-harnessing reactions of the electron transport chains present in these organisms. Consequently, when the supply of oxygen does not limit growth, any compounds detected in the culture medium are likely to be those that lie on the metabolic pathway by which the carbon source is oxidized completely to CO_2 and H_2O. The accumulation will be transitory, rising to a maximum and decreasing as the primary source of carbon is consumed (Fig. 1).

The first step in the elucidation of a metabolic pathway for aerobic bacteria has often consisted of isolating compounds from culture fluids. This is particularly true for the reaction by which aromatic compounds are degraded. The reactions that initiate such sequences place a heavy demand upon the supply of oxygen to the cells since the benzene nucleus must contain two hydroxyl groups before it can be cleaved, and hydroxylation and ring cleavage both consume molecular oxygen. In consequence, when the overall rate of metabolism is limited by the concentration of dissolved oxygen available to the two types of enzyme systems, the rate of formation of a dihydric phenol may sometimes exceed its rate of oxidation, depending upon the values of the respective Michaelis constants for oxygen. Thus catechol (Evans, 1947), protocatechuic acid (Ribbons and Evans, 1960), gentisic acid (Sugiyama *et al.*, 1958) and homogentisic acid (Kluyver and van Zijp, 1951) have all been isolated from culture fluids. Each compound is a ring-fission substrate common to several different pathways of degradation. In some cases, washed non-proliferating suspensions of organisms have been used instead of growing cultures. The technique of Kluyver and van Zijp (1951) in which organisms are grown in liquid media in stationary

9

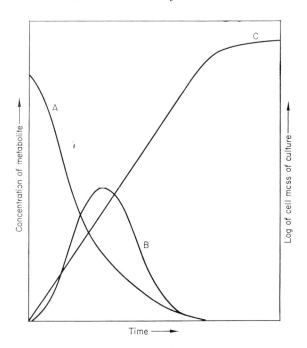

Fig. 1. Transitory appearance of a catabolite during the growth of a bacterial culture. Concentrations of primary growth substrate A, and catabolite, B, are shown during the exponential growth of the culture, C.

flasks has also proved useful for assisting the isolation of compounds formed in cultures of fungi (Henderson and Farmer, 1955; Henderson, 1957). It was the isolation of β-oxoadipate by Kilby (1951) from cultures metabolizing phenol and benzoate which paved the way for much of the later work on bacterial aromatic metabolism.

Taken by itself, however, the observation that a metabolite is excreted by cells is of limited value in assigning the compound a place on a pathway of degradation. Indeed we may make the generalization that the easier it is to isolate a compound from metabolism fluids, the greater the caution to be exercised before we assign to it the status of a degradative intermediate; for such a role implies rapid removal as well as rapid formation. For example, gluconic and 2- and 5-oxogluconic acids have been proposed as intermediates of a main pathway for glucose oxidation in *Acetomonas* (Acetobacter) *suboxydans*. This organism produces copious amounts of 5-oxogluconic acid that crystallize out of the medium as the calcium salt. However, DeLey and Stouthamer (1959) have presented strong evidence that gluconic and oxogluconic acids are formed by a side pathway. When an abundance of reduced NADP becomes available, specific and reversible dehydrogenases, which these workers have isolated, are able to reduce the oxo-acids; and the resulting gluconate, after phosphorylation and conversion into ribulose 5-phosphate is oxidized through the hexose monophosphate cycle. This cycle, and not a route of oxidation through gluconate, appears to be the main oxidative process in *Acetobacter*.

The best criteria to support the assigned status of a compound as an intermediate in degradation are those supplied by a study of enzymes isolated from the organism. However, it is not sufficient merely to establish that the relevant enzymes are present. They must also be present in large enough amounts to catalyse the formation and degradation of the proposed intermediate at rates that will account for the overall rate of degradation of the growth substrate. Techniques which employ intact cells, such as simultaneous adaptation, are also useful but less conclusive in deciding the status of a proposed intermediate. It is also valuable to study kinetics of accumulation of a compound isolated from a culture, since its appearance and removal should follow a course similar to that shown in Fig. 1. This was done by Evans (1947) when he showed that phenol was oxidized to catechol and by Dagley *et al.* (1965), who followed the transient accumulation of 2,3-dihydroxyphenyl-β-propionate in cultures of *Achromobacter* growing with β-phenylpropionic acid as a source of carbon. Webley *et al.* (1955) showed that *Nocardia opacia* oxidizes this substrate by an alternative pathway that leads to the transient appearance of cinnamic acid. However, the kinetics of Fig. 1 may still be shown for a compound that does not arise *directly* from the substrate by degradation. Thus Dagley *et al.* (1952) showed that α-oxoglutarate, but not pyruvate, accumulated in this manner from phenylacetic acid supplied to cultures of "Vibrio 01" (later identified as a species of *Moraxella*). It might be argued that since both of these oxo-acids are metabolites related to the tricarboxylic acid cycle, the sole accumulation of α-oxoglutarate provides evidence that this compound is formed from phenylacetate before the cycle is entered. From other investigations, this is known not to be the case: the cycle intermediates arising from phenylacetic acid are acetyl coenzyme A and fumarate. Indeed, when the same species of *Moraxella* is grown with acetate as sole source of carbon, α-oxoglutarate (but no pyruvate) again accumulates (Dagley and Patel, 1955) and in this case the growth substrate cannot undergo prior degradation to this metabolite. These observations may simply reflect the proportions of the various enzymes of the cycle, and related reactions, which were synthesized in response to the metabolic requirements of growing cultures. One metabolite might therefore be readily identified and another escape detection although both occurred in the same reaction sequence.

B. The use of inhibitors of metabolism

A chemical intermediate in a reaction sequence may accumulate, as we have seen, until such time as its rate of degradation becomes equal to its rate of formation; and thereafter its concentration will diminish with time. It is evident that isolation of the metabolite will be assisted by adding to the culture an inhibitor of the degradative processes. It is not our purpose to discuss the wide range of known inhibitors. Many have been used to elucidate the mode of action of the enzymes they inhibit, but these are seldom the compounds that aid the delineation of a metabolic pathway. If such a study has reached the stage of experimenting with active cell-free extracts, modern methods of fractionating proteins usually provide a better means of interrupting the reaction sequence at specific points. This, admittedly, is not always the case and exceptions occur as, for example, when the action of one particular enzyme dominates a sequence. Thus, proof that oxaloacetate arose from tartrate by dehydration was long delayed because extracts of tartrate-grown pseudomonads contained a powerful decarboxylase that converted oxaloacetate into pyruvate as fast as it was formed. Oxaloacetate was made to accumulate, and a study of the dehydratases of the tartrate isomers became possible, when ethylenediaminetetra-acetate was added to extracts to inhibit oxaloacetate decarboxylase (Shilo, 1957). It was 8 years later that Hurlbert and Jakoby (1965) accomplished a partial purification of an unstable tartrate dehydratase and were able to study its properties. Historically, the use of iodoacetate and NaF to inhibit triosephosphate dehydrogenase and enolase, respectively, was of great value in earlier studies of the glycolytic sequence.

Nevertheless, the use of inhibitors for investigating new pathways of degradation is now largely confined to those preliminary experiments in which metabolites are made to accumulate as a consequence of blocking specific reactions in intact cells. The information so obtained then serves as a guide for studies at the cell-free level. A preliminary approach of a similar nature was also fruitful in a few of the early studies of biosynthesis in bacteria. Thus, when the growth of $E.$ $coli$ was partially inhibited by sulphanilamide, 4-amino-5-imidazolecarboxamide was excreted into the culture (Shive et $al.$, 1947). As its ribotide, this compound is an intermediate in the biosynthesis of purines when it receives a one-carbon fragment donated by formyl N^{10}-tetrahydrofolate. Likewise when poisoned with azaserine, bacteria excreted N-formylglycinamide (Tomisek et $al.$, 1956) which again is related to an intermediate in purine biosynthesis. In this case Hartman et $al.$ (1956) showed that the L-isomer of azaserine interfered with the transfer of an amide group from glutamine to N-formylglycinamide ribotide. Two further illustrations may be given to the use of inhibitors for aiding the identification of intermediates in a biosynthetic sequence. First, much of our knowledge of the nature of bacterial cell walls stems from the observation that various nucleotides involved in their biosynthesis were made to accumulate when *Staphylococcus aureus*, *Streptococcus faecalis* or *E. coli* were treated with antibiotics such as penicillin, bacitracin, novobiocin or oxamycin (Strominger, 1962). Second, diphenylamine was found to stop normal carotenoid synthesis in *Rhodospirillum rubrum* growing photosynthetically; several carotenoids more saturated than lycopene accumulated in the culture and were identified. When diphenylamine was removed and the cells were incubated anaerobically in the light an endogenous synthesis of normal carotenoids took place at the expense of the accumulated precursors (Jensen *et al.*, 1958). Such observations as those we have quoted have been valuable as early indications of the nature of the compounds that functioned in the various biosynthetic pathways. However, since the precise point of action of an inhibitor is not always known, auxotrophic mutants are now preferred for such investigations because their use does not entail this kind of uncertainty.

For use with intact cells, an inhibitor must be able to gain access to their enzymes. Thus, permeability barriers often rendered malonate useless for studies of the tricarboxylic acid cycle in bacteria. By contrast, sodium arsenite has been widely used to inhibit degradative pathways by blocking the oxidative decarboxylation of α-oxo-acids. However, if pyruvate or α-oxoglutarate accumulate, caution must be exercised when interpreting the significance of the observation, as we have previously indicated. This may be illustrated from experiments with non-proliferating suspensions of two species of *Pseudomonas* that oxidized L-arabinose and nicotinic acid, respectively. Weimberg and Doudoroff (1955) found that in the presence of arsenite, 90% of the L-arabinose accumulated as α-oxoglutarate. It is now known that this organism converts the pentose directly into α-oxoglutarate by a pathway that includes L-arabonate, L-3-deoxy-2-oxoarabonate and α-oxoglutarate semialdehyde (Stoolmiller and Abeles, 1966). On the other hand, Behrman and Stanier (1957) found that the species of *Pseudomonas* they used gave 65% yields of pyruvate from nicotinic acid in the presence of arsenite. In this case, pyruvate arises from the tricarboxylic acid cycle which is entered through fumarate; the pyridine nucleus is cleaved to give *N*-formylmaleamic acid, and fumarate is formed from maleic acid after loss of ammonia and formate. Pyruvate does not appear on the metabolic route that leads from nicotinate into the cycle.

If the compound that accumulates can be formed, in principle, by alternative routes a choice may be possible by using a radiotracer. Thus Smith and Kornberg (1967) found that when arsenite-inhibited suspensions of *Micrococcus denitrificans* oxidized L-malate or propionate, pyruvate accumulated in 80% yields. However, when sodium [^{14}C]bicarbonate was present, the pyruvate formed from propionate became highly labelled, whereas that from L-malate did not. This observation showed that the utilization of propionate involved its prior carboxylation to succinate, which gave rise to pyruvate via fumarate, malate and oxaloacetate.

Arsenite appears to inhibit the oxidative decarboxylation of α-oxo-acids by combining with the two sulphur atoms of lipoic acid, one of the cofactors of the enzyme system, to form a cyclic arsenite. In principle, many reagents that combine with prosthetic groups or coenzymes might be used to block the metabolism of whole cells, but their use is restricted when they interfere with a broad spectrum of reactions. Thus, a large number of enzymes show requirements for metal ions and in consequence are inactivated by a general chelating reagent, such as ethylenediaminetetra-acetate. However a chelating reagent may be useful for work with intact cells if it is fairly specific for the metal in question, and if the dependent reaction occurs so early in the degradative pathway that the inactivation of later enzymes is of no consequence for the investigation. o-Phenanthroline and α,α'-dipyridyl are both known to combine strongly with ferrous ions and they inhibit the colourless dioxygenases that catalyse early reactions in several aromatic degradative pathways, namely the *meta* cleavages of catechol and protocatechuate. By contrast, Tiron is a chelating agent for trivalent iron and it inactivates the red dioxygenases concerned with *ortho* cleavage of the benzene nucleus. α,α'-Dipyridyl has been used to accumulate phenolics in cultures of *Pseudomonas* when they oxidized 3-methylphenol (*m*-cresol) and its derivatives bearing alkyl substituents in the 5- and 6-positions of the benzene nucleus. First, it appears that the methyl group in position 3 was oxidized to carboxyl and second, the 3-hydroxybenzoic acid (or alkyl-substituted derivative) so formed was then hydroxylated to give gentisic acid (3,6-dihydroxybenzoic acid) or an alkyl-substituted gentisate. The following pairs of compounds were isolated from cultures, separated by chromatography and identified: 5-methyl-3-hydroxybenzoate and 3-methylgentisate; 4-methyl-3-hydroxybenzoate and 4-methylgentisate; 4,5-dimethyl-3-hydroxybenzoate and 3,4-dimethylgentisate; 5-ethyl-3-hydroxybenzoate and 3-ethylgentisate. These isolations (Hopper, 1967) supported the view that *m*-cresol and certain of its alkyl-substituted derivatives are converted into gentisic acids before the benzene nucleus is cleaved. They also provided a source of substrates, several of which were difficult to synthesize by purely chemical means, for use in experiments which show that further degradations by cell-free extracts follow the "gentisic acid pathway" elucidated by Lack (1959).

One feature of work with inhibitors may be stressed; namely, that it is rarely possible to use an inhibitor so specific in its action that, of all the enzymes functioning in the complex metabolic network of a bacterial cell, only one—or even one type—will be inactivated. Sites of inhibitor action are often uncertain, and sound deductions only follow when the metabolic consequences of inhibition have been established. It is of little value merely to show that inhibition occurs. Thus, the reasonable assumption that *o*-phenanthroline inhibits metapyrocatechase because it chelates with the ferrous ion cofactor has been questioned by Nozaki *et al.* (1966), who point out that *m*-phenanthroline, which does not chelate with metals, is a stronger inhibitor of the enzyme than the *ortho* isomer. A further example was provided by experiments that were undertaken to demonstrate the existence of the tricarboxylic acid cycle in a species of *Moraxella*. It was found that sodium monofluoroacetate inhibited respiration and some citrate was formed, in agreement with the accepted view that fluorocitrate is "lethally biosynthesized" from fluoroacetate and blocks metabolism by inactivating aconitase (Peters, 1952). However, it was also observed that under the same conditions substantial amounts of pyruvate accumulated from certain members of the tricarboxylic acid cycle (Dagley and Walker, 1956). It appears that in these cases fluoromalate may have been biosynthesized from the added fluoroacetate, since Dixon *et al.* (1960) showed that fluoroacetyl coenzyme A can react with glyoxylate in the presence of malate synthase, presumably to give fluoromalate. This compound, like fluoropyruvate, is a powerful inhibitor of pyruvate oxidation (Callely and Dagley, 1959).

A degradative sequence of reactions may also be broken by an inhibitor that acts by combining with a reaction intermediate. Classical examples are provided by sodium bisulphite which "traps" acetaldehyde formed in glycolysis, whereas hydroxylamine combines with acyl compounds of coenzyme A and prevents their further metabolism. Semicarbazide may be used to trap α-oxo-acids; but other compounds may accumulate instead, as this reagent can combine with pyridoxal phosphate and so inhibit enzymes that require this cofactor. Since they usually encounter permeability barriers, trapping agents are seldom used with intact cells, although they have been useful in experiments with cell-free extracts. The use of acrylic acid to inhibit β-oxidation in cultures of *Pseudomonas* oxidizing alkanes may furnish an example of this approach. Hexanoic acid and penta-2-one accumulated from *n*-hexane when acrylate was added, and heptanoic acid, hexa-2-one and penta-2-one were formed from *n*-heptane (Thijsse, 1964). It was suggested that acrylic acid combined with coenzyme A inside the cells and prevented the functioning of acyl-CoA synthetase and 3-ketoacyl-CoA thiolase: the ketones would then arise by loss of CO_2 from the β-oxo-acids whose metabolism was blocked.

C. Partial catabolism of substrates and their analogues

The enzymes of a particular pathway of degradation may differ in their substrate specificities. Accordingly, the first three enzymes, for example, might catalyse the oxidation of an analogue of the substrate but the fourth might not, so that the partially oxidized analogue would then accumulate in the medium. Under these conditions, good yields of the accumulating compound are obtained, and after identification it can be assigned a position in the catabolic sequence. For example, a species of *Pseudomonas* oxidized *p*-cresol to *p*-hydroxybenzoate, but this was difficult to establish because *p*-hydroxybenzoate was rapidly hydroxylated to give protocatechuate. However, when a second methyl group was introduced into the molecule of *p*-cresol, a methyl-substituted *p*-hydroxybenzoic acid readily accumulated in the culture fluid (Dagley and Patel, 1957). This method of approach has also been used with cell-free extracts. Such extracts from pseudomonads grown with benzoate usually contain a catechol dioxygenase that is so active, and so difficult to remove, as to prevent a direct demonstration of the conversion of benzoate into catechol. However, Ichihara *et al.* (1962) found that both benzoate and *m*-chlorobenzoate were attacked by extracts, whereas 3-chlorocatechol, the product derived from the chlorinated benzoate, was not. This compound therefore accumulated and its identity was established.

The use of sodium arsenate in classical experiments on the glycolytic sequence had a similar rationale. Arsenate could replace phosphate in the metabolism of 3-phosphoglyceraldehyde by phosphate-depleted yeast juice, resulting in the formation of 1-arseno-3-phosphoglyceric acid. This compound was then unable to react with ADP and instead gave rise to accumulations of 3-phosphoglyceric acid by a non-enzymic decomposition.

When intact cells are used, enzymes for a separate degradative pathway may be derepressed by a compound as soon as it begins to accumulate in the culture. Accordingly, the compound will cease to accumulate and will then disappear. These events can be prevented if non-proliferating cell suspensions are used and if chloramphenicol is added to prevent the synthesis of new enzymes. Thus, it appears that a species of *Moraxella* degraded dicarboxylic acids by a process of β-oxidation: those acids having an even number of carbon atoms greater than 4 gave rise to the tricarboxylic acid cycle intermediates, succinate and acetate; whereas those having odd numbers of carbon atoms greater than 5 gave acetate and glutarate. The last-named compound was degraded by a set of enzymes different from those of β-oxidation; and these enzymes were present in cells grown with acids having odd numbers of carbons, but were not present in those grown with even-numbered substrates. This was shown directly by incubating cells, grown at the expense of adipic acid ($HO_2C \cdot [CH_2]_4 \cdot CO_2H$), with pimelic acid ($HO_2C \cdot [CH_2]_5 \cdot CO_2H$) in the presence of chloramphenicol. Glutaric acid accumulated and was identified; but in the absence of chloramphenicol, glutarate did not accumulate and pimelate was oxidized to completion (Chapman and Duggleby, 1967). Instead of using chloramphenicol, cells may be treated with ultraviolet light to prevent the synthesis of new enzymes. Thus Palleroni and Stanier (1964) incubated *Ps. fluorescens* with L-tryptophan for a period of time sufficient to induce only the enzymes for its own catabolism to anthranilate. The suspension was then irradiated to prevent further synthesis of protein and incubated with more tryptophan. The substrate was now converted almost quantitatively into anthranilate by the irradiated cells, whereas without this treatment tryptophan and anthranilate were catabolized to metabolites of the tricarboxylic acid cycle.

D. Simultaneous adaptation (sequential induction)

When a compound has been isolated from metabolism fluids and its identity has been established, further criteria of its status as an intermediate should be applied. Clearly, the rates at which the compound is formed and degraded must be compatible with the overall rate of oxidation of the growth substrate. The technique of simultaneous adaptation provides a rapid and convenient way of matching the rate of oxidation of the substrate with that of the proposed intermediate before an attempt is made to isolate the enzymes from intact cells.

When bacteria are removed from a nutrient broth culture and are placed in a medium that contains a new carbon source A, growth does not resume immediately even though the cells are able to metabolize A in due course. They must first synthesize, in sufficient amounts, those enzymes that degrade A fast enough to supply the requirements of growth processes for energy and cellular material. If the bacteria are aerobic it is probable that A will be converted into metabolites of the tricarboxylic acid cycle, and this conversion will occur through a reaction sequence that consists of many enzymic steps. When growth eventually occurs at the expense of A, the cells will then contain greatly increased amounts of enzymes that catalyse the breakdown of reaction intermediates B, C and D in the sequence: A → B → C → D → (tricarboxylic acid cycle metabolites). None of these compounds would be expected to be oxidized readily by cells from the nutrient broth culture before they were exposed to A. Accordingly, when a washed suspension of bacteria grown with A as source of carbon is incubated with A, B, C or D in a Warburg respirometer, the course of oxygen uptake would probably be as shown in Fig. 2. Compounds B, C and D would be oxidized at about the same rate as the growth substrate A; but compounds F and G, which are not members of the metabolic sequence, would either not be oxidized much faster than the stores of endogenous materials within the cells, or else a rapid uptake of oxygen would be achieved only after such time as new enzymes had been induced (curve G, Fig. 2). One feature of the design of such experiments may be mentioned. For a particular cell suspen-

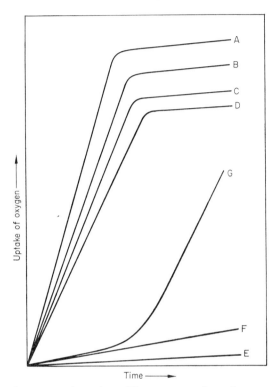

FIG. 2. Simultaneous adaptation. The consumption of oxygen is shown for various compounds incubated with a non-proliferating suspension of cells grown with A as a source of carbon. Compounds B, C and D are possible catabolites, whereas G and F may not lie on the pathway of oxidation, or alternatively may be excluded initially from the cells by permeability barriers. E denotes respiration in the absence of a substrate.

sion, the slope of curve A in Fig. 2 may be maximal because the rate of uptake of oxygen is limited by the rate at which the gas is able to diffuse to enzyme sites within the cells. Under these circumstances, as the density of the cell suspension is increased, the rate of oxidation of a poorly metabolized substrate may increase, whereas that of A cannot do so because of oxygen limitation. With a sufficiently dense suspension of cells, differences in rates of oxidation may be ill-defined, and it is therefore advisable to conduct experiments at various cell densities.

This experimental approach, which was used by Stanier (1947) for studying the bacterial degradation of benzenoid compounds, enables us to write down a feasible reaction sequence and to test the speculation by measuring initial rates of oxidation. The technique is subject to the following limitations, which were clearly defined by Stanier (1947), but which have not always been heeded. First, a compound may be a reaction intermediate and yet may not be oxidized by intact cells because it is excluded from the relevant enzymes by a permeability barrier. Second, a compound may be oxidized readily when it is not an intermediate in the postulated sequence because the enzymes for its metabolism may be constitutive. Such a possibility can readily be tested by measuring rates of oxidation from cells grown with substrates other than A as sources of carbon.

The first of these limitations may be illustrated by considering some of the evidence which was thought, in the 1940s, to indicate that the tricarboxylic acid cycle did not operate in aerobic bacteria. Let us consider the sequence—

α-Oxoglutarate $\rightarrow$ succinate $\rightarrow$ fumarate $\rightarrow$ malate $\rightarrow$ pyruvate $\rightarrow$ acetate

It was found that *Azotobacter agilis* when grown with α-oxoglutarate would readily oxidize all of these compounds. When grown with succinate, however, the progress of oxidation of all compounds except α-oxoglutarate followed curves such as those for A, B, C and D of Fig. 2, whereas α-oxoglutarate was only oxidized after a lag period, as for G of Fig. 2. When acetate was the growth substrate, only acetate was oxidized readily and the oxygen-uptake curves for succinate, fumarate and α-oxoglutarate all resembled curve G of Fig. 2. From this evidence (Karlsson and Barker, 1948) it was eminently reasonable at the time to conclude that the tricarboxylic acid cycle did not function in its entirety in *Az. agilis*. Later work, however, provided an alternative explanation of these results (Stone and Wilson, 1952). When cell-free extracts of *Azotobacter* were prepared, citrate and α-oxoglutarate were oxidized rapidly, although intact cells did not oxidize citrate at all and α-oxoglutarate was oxidized only after a lag period. Moreover, whereas acetate by itself was oxidized poorly by cell extracts, the rate was considerably increased when fumarate was added, the effect being much greater than could be accounted for by adding together the oxidation rates of the two compounds considered separately. It may therefore be concluded that the enzymes of the tricarboxylic acid cycle were present inside the cells but were inaccessible to certain metabolites placed outside them. Nevertheless it appeared that new enzymes were formed when α-oxoglutarate was presented to cells grown with succinate, because the rate of oxidation of the substrate accelerated during the course of the experiment. These enzymes may be those concerned with the "active" transport of the substrate across the cell membrane, although alternative explanations are possible.

The second limitation of the technique of simultaneous adaptation may be illustrated from the work of Wheelis *et al.* (1967) on the metabolism of benzoic acid by *Pseudomonas testosteroni*. This organism hydroxylates benzoate first at carbon 3 of the nucleus to give *m*-hydroxybenzoate and second at carbon 4 to give protocatechuate, the nucleus of which is then cleaved by a 4,5-oxygenase. In principle, *m*-hydroxybenzoate might alternatively have been converted to gentisic acid by hydroxylation at carbon 6, a reaction which is accomplished by *Pseudomonas acidovorans* when metabolizing *m*-hydroxybenzoate. However, *Ps. testosteroni* cannot hydroxylate at position 6 and therefore cannot take an alternative route for the degradation of benzoate or *m*-hydroxybenzoate by way of the gentisate pathway of metabolism. This is shown by the fact that a mutant which lacked the 4-hydroxylase failed to grow with either benzoate or *m*-hydroxybenzoate, although it grew readily with *p*-hydroxybenzoate. Nevertheless, despite the fact that they are not used for the catabolism of *m*-hydroxybenzoate, three enzymes of the gentisate pathway (gentisate oxygenase, maleylpyruvate isomerase and fumarylpyruvate hydrolase) were present in *Ps. testosteroni* and were induced to high levels on exposure to *m*-hydroxybenzoate. It is evident that without additional observations, measurements of rates of oxidation could have provided a misleading picture of the catabolism of this substrate. Compounds of either pathway were oxidized equally well, but only one route was in fact used.

Lack of specificity of the enzymes themselves may prevent a decision between possible pathways based simply upon measurements of rates of oxidation. Thus, when pseudomonads metabolize camphor, an oxygen atom is inserted into one ring of this diterpene to form a lactone, carbon 5 of the ring is hydroxylated and the hydroxyl group, which may be in either the *endo*- or *exo*-position, is oxidized to give a carbonyl group. Solely from rates of oxidation it is not possible to determine the sequence of these reactions. Either formation of a lactone or hydroxylation of the methylene group could occur first, because (+)-camphor and all of its derivatives bearing an oxygen at carbon 5 are lactonized by the same ketolactonase, whereas a similar broad range of substrate specificity is shown by the 5-methylene-hydroxylase and the 5-*exo*-dehydrogenase. Accordingly, all the intermediates that could theoretically be formed before the first carbocyclic ring-cleavage reaction takes place are oxidized with equal ease (Gunsalus *et al.*, 1965). If one of these catabolic pathways is preferred by the cells, this must be decided from other experimental approaches.

We have used the original phrase of Stanier (1947), simultaneous adaptation, to designate this technique. The name simply indicates an experimental fact, namely that when the cells have made an adjustment in the complement of their enzymes that enables them to oxidize A rapidly, they are simultaneously capable of oxidizing B, C and D. There is no implied assumption as to the way the adjustment is brought about. On the other hand, the alternative description "sequential induction" implies a mechanism of adjustment that frequently does not occur. The enzymes for degrading B, C and D are not necessarily synthesized sequentially: they may be derepressed co-ordinately and none of the three metabolites may be the responsible agent.

D. The use of cell-free extracts

The elucidation of a degradative pathway by use of cell-free bacterial extracts is assisted by the fact that the enzymes are usually both soluble and inducible so that enzymic activities of cells cultured with various sources of carbon may readily be compared. It is also an advantage if the investigator is able, in one operation, to extract from the disrupted cells all the enzymes that catalyse a number of successive reactions in a sequence. First, it is evident that the longer the segment of the reaction "chain" that remains functional after the cells have been extracted, the more the information there is to be gained by breaking the "links" at different points. Particular enzymes may be selected for inactivation by inhibitors or heat treatment; coenzymes may be removed by dialysis; or a simple fractionation of crude extracts with ammonium sulphate precipitation, or passage down a column of Sephadex, may remove one of the enzymes and leave the others to function. Second, if a whole battery of enzymes functioning in sequence can be extracted, it is easier to examine the metabolic status of a compound formed by the action of enzymes *in vitro*, or isolated from culture fluids. If the compound is indeed a catabolite in the proposed sequence, it must be formed and degraded at rates that are compatible with the overall rate of conversion of the growth substrate into its ultimate products of metabolism. It may be mentioned here that even soluble enzymes in crude extracts will not necessarily possess the same specific activities in a test tube as they did inside the intact cells. When it depends upon a particular association of enzyme subunits, catalytic activity may be rapidly abolished when the extract is diluted: some enzymes in the sequence, but not others, may be affected in this manner. Accordingly, when the specific activities of enzymes in cell extracts are compared, it is always advisable to determine the nature of the dependence of activity on protein concentration for each enzyme. It is well known that some enzymes of a sequence may be more sensitive to heating than the rest, but cooling to $0-5°C$ may cause inactivation in some cases.

The advantages of working with cell-free extracts that catalyse several successive reactions of a catabolic sequence may be seen from the investigations of Hayaishi and Stanier (1951). Fresh extracts of a *Pseudomonas fluorescens* grown with L-tryptophan converted the amino-acid into β-oxoadipate, a sequence now known to embrace at least eight enzymic reactions. It is often found, as in this case, that the multi-enzyme sequences catalysed by cell extracts are broken just before entry into the tricarboxylic acid cycle, usually because a complete enzyme system is lacking for the synthesis of a thioester of coenzyme A. Thus, before it is cleaved to give acetate and succinate, β-oxoadipate must be converted into its coenzyme A derivative by reaction with succinyl coenzyme A, a compound that, because of its instability, is not usually present in cell-free extracts. Likewise pyruvate and α-oxoglutarate are often formed as end products of the action of multi-enzyme sequences *in vitro* because their respective conversions into acetyl- and succinyl coenzyme A are catalysed by enzyme complexes that rarely survive extraction procedures. Hayaishi and Stanier (1951) found that a second break in the reaction chain occurred when their extracts were aged and the rather labile anthranilate oxygenase system was lost: anthranilic acid then accumulated from L-tryptophan. This sequence was again broken when semicarbazide was added to inhibit kynureninease by reacting with its coenzyme, pyridoxal phosphate. L-Tryptophan was then converted into L-kynurenine by these extracts.

Formerly, when a particular enzyme was seen to be strongly derepressed as a consequence of providing bacteria with a different source of carbon, it was thought reasonable to assume that this enzyme functioned in the catabolism of the new growth substrate. This assumption was based on the view that bacteria would not have survived the selective processes of evolution if they were given to synthesizing "useless" protein when conditions of growth were favourable. Gratuitous induction of enzymes has long been observed, as when non-metabolizable thiogalactosides derepressed β-galactosidase; but these systems were scarcely relevant to studies of metabolic pathways because experiments were so designed that the inducer could not serve as a source of carbon. However, we now know that when bacteria are exposed to a new carbon source they may synthesize enzymes for which they have no obvious use, along with those that are completely essential for catabolism of the growth substrate. We have referred to the derepression of high levels of enzymes of the "gentisate pathway" which occurs when *Ps. testosteroni* is exposed to *m*-hydroxybenzoate, despite the fact that the induced enzymes do not function for the degradation of this substrate. The following example provides a similar illustration and also emphasizes the fact that the isolation of a metabolite formed from a substrate by the action of a cell extract does not, of itself, establish that the compound lies on a direct catabolic pathway.

The reactions by which benzoic and *p*-hydroxybenzoic acids are degraded by ortho fissions of the benzene nucleus are shown in Fig. 3. Ornston and Stanier (1966) have purified the enzymes concerned and have shown that the metabolic routes are entirely separate and distinct. In *Pseudomonas putida* Ornston (1966) has shown that β-oxoadipate, or its coenzyme A derivative, is the derepressor of the synthesis of enzyme 4. It might be objected that benzoate cannot be converted into β-oxoadipate unless

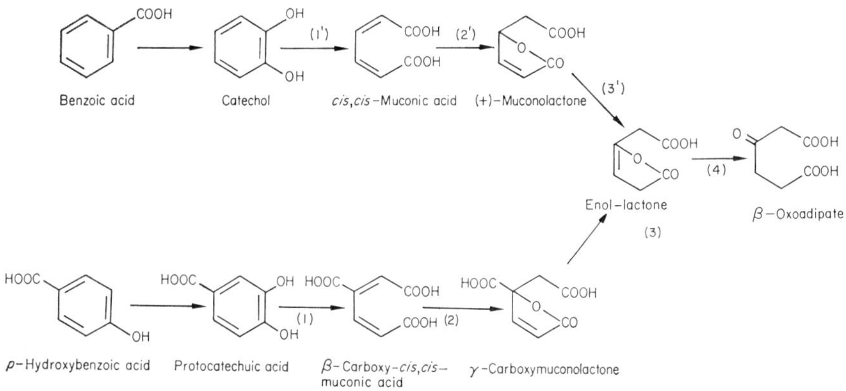

FIG. 3. Pathways of oxidation of benzoic and p-hydroxybenzoic acids involving *ortho* fission of the benzene nucleus. The numbers denote enzymes referred to in the text.

enzyme 4 is present, so that complete catabolism of the growth substrate could not occur if the synthesis of one of the enzymes must await the accumulation of the end product of the sequence. However the enzymes are not entirely absent from the bacteria before they become adapted, and when they are exposed to benzoate there is a slow but significant formation of β-oxoadipate which is sufficient to start the derepression of enzyme 4. Further, Ornston (1966) showed that in *Ps. putida* enzymes 2 and 3 are co-ordinately derepressed along with enzyme 4. This mechanism is economical when p-hydroxybenzoate is the growth substrate; but when benzoate is degraded, large amounts of non-functional enzymes 2 and 3 are, of necessity, synthesized at the same time as the one enzyme (4) that is required.

The reactions of Fig. 3 are catalysed in species of *Moraxella* although the mechanisms of derepression are different. In this case all the enzymes for the catabolism of protocatechuate through β-oxoadipate appear to constitute one co-ordinate block derepressed by protocatechuate, and all those for the catabolism of *cis-cis*-muconate constitute another block derepressed by *cis-cis*-muconate (Cánovas *et al.*, 1967). Formerly, it was believed that (+)-muconolactone was a metabolite common to both pathways in this organism, β-carboxy-*cis, cis*-muconic acid being thought to decarboxylate and lactonize in one step to give rise to this lactone. The evidence rested upon the following observations: (a) heat-treated extracts of *Moraxella* grown with p-hydroxybenzoate converted β-carboxy-*cis,cis*-muconic acid into (+)-muconolactone, and (b) untreated extracts converted (+)-muconolactone quantitatively in β-oxoadipate (Cain, 1961). The reasons why these results were obtained despite the fact that (+)-muconolactone is not an intermediate in the p-hydroxybenzoate sequence appear to be as follows. Heat treatment inactivated enzyne 4, but left sufficient amounts of enzymes 2 and 3 to catalyse the conversion of β-carboxy-cis,cis-muconate into β-oxoadipate enol-lactone. Now although the enzymes concerned with the degradation of protocatechuate are present in high concentrations in p-hydroxybenzoate-grown cells, those for catechol degradation are not entirely absent. Enzyme 3' is present in sufficient amounts to convert the β-oxoadipate enol-lactone that accumulated into $(+)$-muconolactone: this reaction is reversible and the equilibrium is strongly in favour of $(+)$-muconolactone. Accordingly, this compound accumulated when β-carboxy-cis,cis-muconate was incubated with heat-treated extracts, although it does not lie on the catabolic pathway for that compound. Furthermore, crude extracts of bacteria grown with p-hydroxybenzoate contain sufficient amounts of enzymes 3' and 4 to convert $(+)$-muconolactone into β-oxo-adipate. However, in retrospect it is evident that one important set of measurements was required before $(+)$-muconolactone could be placed on the pathway of degradation of p-hydroxybenzoate. The rates of formation and degradation of the lactone must be large enough to account for the over-all rate of conversion of β-carboxy-cis,cis-muconate into β-oxoadipate; and this is not the case. The overall conversion occurs much faster in crude extracts of p-hydroxybenzoate-grown cells than does the metabolism of $(+)$-muconolactone to β-oxoadipate. Accordingly, $(+)$-muconolactone cannot be a reaction intermediate in this pathway.

III. BIOSYNTHESIS

A. Use of radiotracers: general considerations

Radiotracers have been used to study catabolic pathways, but their most important applications have been to trace the incorporation of isotopes into cellular constituents by biosynthetic reactions. For this reason the use of radiotracers is discussed in the same Section as other methods more specifi-cally applied to biosynthesis. Since the use of these techniques in metabol-ism is almost ubiquitous, a selection of material must be made; and accord-ingly, attention will be concentrated upon work with ^{14}C using intact cells. This implies no lack of recognition of the important contributions made to our knowledge of metabolic pathways through studies with cell extracts and with other isotopes. Thus we may mention the proof that $^{15}N_2$ was fixed in ammonia by cell extracts of *Clostridium pasteurianum* (Carnahan *et al.*, 1960); or that $^{18}O_2$ was fixed in *cis,cis*-muconic acid when catechol 1,2-oxygenase initiates the degradation of the benzene nucleus (Hayaishi *et al.*, 1957; Itada, 1965).

Since the numerous chemical reactions of a living cell are interconnected to constitute a network, difficulties in tracing the fate of one labelled species of molecule or atom may be anticipated. In one type of investigation these difficulties are minimal, namely when the problem is to decide whether a compound found to be present inside cells has, or has not, been bio-synthesized by them. If it has not, other cell constituents will become label-led when the micro-organisms are grown with a ^{14}C-substrate, whereas radioactivity will not be incorporated into the compound in question. This method was used to prove that a substance, reported by several investi-gators of trace-lipid materials over several years, is a contaminant of cells and does not have a biological origin (Brown, 1968). Thus, apparently pure vitamin K from *Proteus vulgaris* and several other micro-organisms showed a weak absorption maximum at 310 nm not seen in authentic samples of vitamin K. The amounts of this compound were extremely small, but they could be separated by chromatographic fractionation (Brown and King, 1966). Material with similar spectroscopic properties was reported in extracts from the blue–green alga *Anacystis*, in lipid from livers of humans and rabbits (Florscheim and Krichesky, 1950) and in other biological materials. The origin of the compound was established (Brown, 1968) by growing *P. vulgaris* with uniformly labelled [^{14}C]-glucose and by culturing the photosynthetic *Anacystis* on $^{14}CO_2$. After repeated fractionation of the extracted lipids by chromatography, the radioactivity of the material absorbing at 310 nm fell to an insignificant value, thus proving that it was not made by the cells themselves and must have been an extraneous con-taminant. The compound was later identified as N-phenyl-2-naphthylamine which is commonly used as an antioxidant in black and dark-coloured rubber products. In the particular investigation described, it was shown that the lipids of the micro-organisms were able to extract the compound from the Neoprene tube used to transfer the culture from the fermentor to the centrifuge.

This informative study illustrates the value of radiotracers in disproving the metabolic status of a contaminant of the *cells*. On the other hand, the pitfalls of work with radiotracers is evident from the reverse situation, when a metabolic role is suggested by the appearznce of radioactivity in a com-pound whose actual origin was that of a contaminant of the added *radio-tracer*. If the compound is *not* a metabolite then it will persist, unchanged, through various biochemical transformations and will be detected as an apparent product. Before a radiotracer is used a careful examination of its purity is essential, for a study with impure starting material may be worse than no study at all.

Experiments may be interpreted with less ambiguity when they are per-formed with actively dividing bacteria than when nonproliferating suspen-sions are used. Once an amino-acid is incorporated into cellular protein it will stay there during the time that the culture remains in the exponential phase; but when cell division ceases, turnover of material begins (Mandelstam, 1958). Accordingly, conditions in cell suspensions more closely resemble those in many mammalian preparations and they favour a redistribution of isotope through the metabolic network of reactions. The difficulties of interpretation that this involves may be illustrated from a system discussed by Krebs (1964). When acetoacetate is added to slices of rat kidney cortex there is a considerable increase in the amount of glucose biosynthesized from lactate, and it might be concluded that a net conversion of acetoacetate into glucose occurs. However, there are no established reactions by which the conversion might be achieved, and an alternative explanation is more feasible, namely that acetoacetate is metabolized as a preferred fuel of respiration, so that an increased amount of lactate is "spared" for gluconeogenesis. Acetoacetate is oxidized very rapidly by kidney cortex. If this explanation is correct, the preferred oxidation of $[^{14}C]$-acetoacetate might be expected to release $^{14}CO_2$ having the same specific activity as acetoacetate carbon; and conversely, $[^{14}C]$-lactate would give rise to $[^{14}C]$-glucose. However, these results were not obtained: on the contrary, $[^{14}C]$-acetoacetate was metabolized to $[^{14}C]$-glucose, the specific activity of the CO_2 being low, whereas the radioactivity of glucose arising from $[^{14}C]$-lactate was much lower than expected.

The probable explanation of these results emerges when we consider the way in which the reactions of respiration and gluconeogenesis are interlinked. Oxaloacetate is a metabolite common to both processes. It combines with acetyl coenzyme A formed when either acetoacetate or lactate is respired, and so initiates the reactions of the tricarboxylic acid cycle; and it is converted into phosphoenolpyruvate for use in gluconeogenesis. Now it is a consequence of the steric behaviour of citrate in the aconitase system of the tricarboxylic acid cycle (Ogston, 1948) that the CO_2 released during the conversion of isocitrate to succinate must be derived exclusively from the carbon atoms of oxaloacetate. Since lactate is converted directly into oxaloacetate by fixation of CO_2 to pyruvate, its first product of oxidation, it follows that $^{14}CO_2$ will be released from $[^{14}C]$-lactate during the first "turn" of the cycle. Conversely, the $[^{14}C]$-acetyl coenzyme A from labelled acetoacetate is retained through one "turn" of the cycle before $^{14}CO_2$ is released; moreover, the $[^{14}C]$-oxaloacetate so formed can take the alternative metabolic route through phosphoenolpyruvate to glucose and in consequence ^{14}C from acetoacetate will appear in the glucose. Although these reactions explain why label from lactate appears preferentially in CO_2 and, why label from acetoacetate appears in glucose, they do not provide a mechanism for the *net* synthesis of glucose from acetoacetate. In addition to serving as a source of energy, the metabolism of acetoacetate also raises the concentration of acetyl coenzyme A. This compound is an allosteric effector of pyruvate carboxylase (Utter and Keech, 1963) and so favours the conversion of pyruvate to oxaloacetate, an obligatory intermediate in gluconeogenesis from lactate.

This example is one of many that could be cited to justify the observation of Krebs (1964): "A general asset of the isotope method is its applicability to highly complex systems such as the whole animal and intact tissue where it can supply information under physiological conditions. But there is a price to be paid. What we gain by maintaining physiological conditions we may lose in part by the difficulties of interpreting results." It might be added that the use of microbial systems enables us to take advantage of the more favourable experimental conditions of exponential growth when some of these difficulties may be avoided. Such techniques are those of "isotope competition" and "rapid sampling", which are discussed later.

One convenient procedure for identifying a [^{14}C]-labelled metabolite formed in a biochemical reaction consists of adding an excess of [^{12}C]-metabolite as a "carrier" which, on re-isolation, is shown to contain the radioactivity. Caution must be exercised when this method is applied to intact bacteria, since the carrier may not mix with metabolite formed endogenously because it encounters a permeability barrier; or because the metabolite itself, being bound to an enzyme or combined with a coenzyme, is not free to mix. Thus, in the early 1950's evidence was presented that some of the reactions of the tricarboxylic acid cycle did not operate in aerobic bacteria, and alternative reactions for oxidizing acetate were suggested, notably the so-called "Thunberg condensation"—

$$2 \text{ acetate} \rightarrow \text{succinate} + 2\text{H}.$$

If it were possible to initiate acetate oxidation in this manner, one molecule of succinate so formed could be converted by known reactions into one molecule of acetate so that a "dicarboxylic acid cycle" could operate in which one molecule of acetate is oxidized at each turn. Citrate and α-oxoglutarate would not be members of such a cycle. The experiments purporting to show that this cycle, and not the intact tricarboxylic acid, operated in bacteria were performed with nonproliferating suspensions of cells. They were allowed to oxidize acetate labelled in the methyl group with ^{14}C; unlabelled α-oxoglutarate and succinate were then added, re-isolated and examined for radioactivity. When *Micrococcus lysodeikticus* was used, both α-oxoglutarate and succinate were indeed found to be labelled on re-isolation, but the specific activities of the carbon atoms of α-oxoglutarate were lower than those of succinate. This result is not to be expected if α-oxoglutarate is the immediate precursor of succinate, as it is in the tricarboxylic acid cycle. Moreover, the specific activity of the respired CO_2

was many times greater than that of the carbon atoms of the carboxyl groups of both compounds. This, again, is not to be expected if—as is the case—CO_2 is released from these groups by the reactions of the cycle. Results with *E. coli* also argued against the tricarboxylic acid cycle and favoured a "Thunberg condensation" of acetate. Very little label from acetate was incorporated into carrier α-oxoglutarate, thereby suggesting that this compound is not an obligatory intermediate in acetate oxidation; whereas there was good incorporation into the methylene groups of succinate, as "Thunberg condensation" requires. It may be mentioned, however, that this condensation has never been convincingly demonstrated.

These isotopic experiments were shown by Swim and Krampitz (1954) to be misleading. The basic assumption that an added metabolite will mix freely with the same labelled compound inside the bacteria was shown to be invalid. It became evident that succinate and α-oxoglutarate were bound to enzymes or coenzymes inside the cells so that their ability to mix with added carriers was extremely limited. Experiments were performed with amounts of bacteria large enough to permit the extraction and chromatographic separation of endogenously formed metabolites from disrupted cells. The concentration of labelled acetate was also limited, so that the bacteria oxidized the substrate at half the normal rate; and the reaction time was kept short to ensure that the free pool of [^{14}C]-acetate was reduced to a minimum and recycling of the radiotracer was avoided. The result obtained, both with *E. coli* and *M. lysodeikticus*, were quite different from those using carriers. Label was distributed uniformly between all the endogenously formed components of the tricarboxylic acid cycle examined, including α-oxoglutarate and succinate. Moreover, the specific activities of the carbon atoms of these two compounds were those expected from the operation of the tricarboxylic acid cycle.

The isotopic techniques which use actively dividing micro-organisms rather than nonproliferating suspensions, namely "isotopic competition" and "rapid sampling" have been described in detail by Crosbie and Quayle (Volume 6B). Accordingly, our description of these methods will be brief and our main concern will be to evaluate a few of their applications.

B. Isotope competition

Let us consider the biosynthesis of a stable end-product (X) formed from glucose (G) by a sequence of reactions—

$$G \to A \to B \to C \to \to \to X$$

When [^{14}C]-glucose is metabolized X will become labelled, and so will all the intermediates A, B and C. If non-radioactive A is added, the unlabelled carbon atoms will be incorporated into B, C and X and their specific activities will be lowered. On the other hand, if unlabelled X is added, the specific activity of X will decrease, but that of A (or B or C) will not. In principle, therefore, it should be possible to determine the precursors of X and the order in which they are formed. However, this approach will only be applicable under conditions when the biosynthetic route is unidirectional and when X is a stable metabolite, so that the incorporated radioactivity will not be recycled. Such conditions may apply when X is a coenzyme whose effective functioning depends upon metabolic stability, or when it represents an amino-acid biosynthesized by bacteria in exponential phase and incorporated into protein that is stable under these conditions.

The most extensive use of this technique was that of Roberts *et al.* (1955) to whom we owe the early recognition that the tricarboxylic acid cycle functions for biosynthesis of amino-acids in *E. coli* as well as for oxidation. Bacteria were investigated in their exponential phase of growth with glucose as a source of carbon in a mineral salts medium to which was added [^{14}C]-glucose or [^{14}C]-acetate; or alternatively the culture was allowed to incorporate $^{14}CO_2$ during growth. The labelling of various amino-acids was followed by hydrolysing the protein from samples of cells and then submitting the hydrolysate to autoradiography. Some of the main findings of this group of workers may be summarized with reference to Fig. 4. In brief,

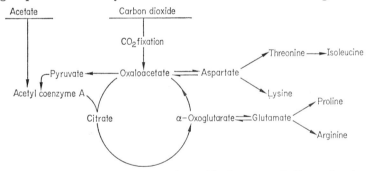

Fig. 4. Biosynthesis of various amino-acids from metabolites related to the tricarboxylic acid cycle.

the amino-acids of *E. coli* fell into two main groups, which were termed the "aspartate family" and the "glutamate family", respectively. Thus, addition of [^{12}C]-glutamate depressed the labelling of proline and arginine in the protein of bacteria incorporating ^{14}C, whereas the addition of [^{12}C]-aspartate depressed the specific activities of lysine and isoleucine. On the other hand, added [^{12}C]-threonine depressed the labelling of threonine and isoleucine, but not that of aspartate, as would be expected for a reaction sequence in which aspartate is a precursor of threonine, and threonine in turn is a precursor of isoleucine. Comparisons of the patterns of incorporation of [^{14}C]-

acetate and $^{14}CO_2$ accorded with the view that the tricarboxylic acid cycle operates to provide the protein precursors of *E. coli*. As could be predicted from Fig. 4, when [^{12}C]-glutamate was added to a culture growing with [^{12}C]-glucose and incorporating the label of [^{14}C]-acetate, there was a rapid exchange of the carbon skeleton between added glutamate and endogenously labelled α-oxoglutarate, with the result that radioactivity in the source of aspartate carbon (oxaloacetate) was diluted. That is, [^{12}C]-glutamate depressed labelling in the aspartate family of amino-acids, whereas [^{12}C]-aspartate had little effect upon labelling in the glutamate family. However, when the sole source of radioactivity was $^{14}CO_2$, addition of [^{12}C]-aspartate did depress labelling in the glutamate family; for in this case $^{14}CO_2$ was fixed into oxaloacetate, and this compound exchanged its carbon skeleton with the added aspartate before the label found its way round the cycle to glutamate.

At the time when this work was published (Roberts *et al.*, 1955) its main contribution was to emphasize the biosynthetic role of the tricarboxylic acid cycle. It was only later that the full significance of one aspect of the work was realized, namely the completeness with which additions of an amino-acid such as threonine could remove radioactivity from the [^{14}C]-threonine of cellular protein. The effect could not be ascribed entirely to dilution of the label, for in the presence of exogenous threonine the pathway from glucose to threonine was immediately and completely blocked. It is now realized that this effect of added threonine, and of other amino-acids which are the end products of biosynthetic pathways, is to be ascribed to feed-back inhibition of early enzymes in the sequence.

The work of Roberts *et al.* (1955) illuminated the *function* of a cycle of known reactions. The use and limitations of the technique to indicate the course of a previously unknown metabolic route may be illustrated from the experiments of Cox and Gibson (1966). They showed that [^{14}C]-shikimate acid was incorporated into both vitamin K_2 and ubiquinone of *E. coli*, and that chorismate was the probable precursor of these two compounds. Separate pathways from chorismate were indicated by isotope competition experiments in which 4-hydroxybenzoate abolished incorporation of [^{14}C]-shikimate into ubiquinone but not into vitamin K_2, whereas 3,4-dihydroxy-benzaldehyde prevented labelling of vitamin K_2 but not of ubiquinone. The interpretation of these results shows the limitations of the isotope competition method. There is good independent evidence that 4-hydroxybenzoate is a precursor of ubiquinone in micro-organisms (Parsons and Rudney, 1964; Frilis *et al.*, 1966) and no doubt the effect observed was due to isotope dilution. On the other hand the evidence is equally strong that 3,4-dihydroxybenzaldehyde is not a direct precursor of vitamin K_2 (Leistner *et al.*, 1967) so that its effect must be a matter for speculation at the present time.

C. Rapid sampling of incorporated radioactivity

This method possesses the advantage that the kinetics of incorporation of radioactivity into proposed reaction intermediates are determined directly. By comparison, the method of isotope dilution is indirect, insofar as the fate or point of action of the added [^{12}C]-compound may not always be known with certainty. Thus, incorporation of the isotope might be reduced directly by dilution with the added compound, or it might occur through alterations of the rates of biosynthetic enzymes catalysed by allosteric enzymes; and both of these effects might be produced after the added compound has undergone metabolic transformations. The application of rapid sampling to anabolic processes is analogous to that of simultaneous adaptation to catabolism, insofar as both techniques provide a preliminary outline of the reaction sequence under investigation. In the best applications to bacterial metabolism, such as those of H. L. Kornberg and J. R. Quayle concerned with anaplerotic reactions, experiments that employed rapid sampling have been followed by isolation of the enzymes that catalysed the proposed reactions and by measurements of reaction rates to demonstrate that the multi-enzyme sequence could occur fast enough to account for the overall metabolic rate.

The essential procedures of this technique, which have been followed by other investigators, were developed by M. Calvin and J. A. Bassham (Bassham and Calvin, 1957; Calvin and Bassham, 1962). Most of their experiments were performed with the unicellular green algae, *Chlorella pyrenoidosa* and *Scenedesmus obliquus*. When a suspension of either organism in a solution containing the necessary mineral salts was illuminated and aerated, rapid photosynthesis occurred. The air stream usually contained 1 or 4% of CO_2 in equilibrium with bicarbonate ions in solution, and on addition of $H^{14}CO_3^-$ incorporation of radiocarbon into cell constituents commenced. At various short periods after the addition, samples of culture were plunged into hot ethanol: the cells were thereby killed, photosynthesis stopped immediately and the compounds extracted from the algae were submitted to two-dimensional chromatography and autoradiography. When the algae were exposed to $H^{14}CO_3^-$ for a relatively long period, say 60 sec, many labelled compounds were identified, including hexose monophosphates, dihydroxyacetone phosphate, ribose phosphate and 3-phosphoglyceric acid; but when exposure occurred for a short time of 5 sec or less, essentially all the radioactivity appeared in 3-phosphoglyceric acid. This observation accorded with the prediction of the cycle they proposed, that the first stable intermediate expected to arise from CO_2 fixation would be 3-phosphoglyceric acid. This evidence was later re-inforced by isolating the various enzymes of the photosynthetic cycle, including ribulosediphosphate carboxylase, from algae and spinach leaves.

For the successful application of this technique, certain experimental conditions must be satisfied. The concentrations of the various reaction intermediates become adjusted to constant values when a metabolic sequence operates at a steady overall rate; and constant "pool sizes" for particular metabolites are assured only when their respective rates of formation are balanced by their rates of removal at the time when a "steady state" is attained. These conditions are achieved by a microbial culture actively dividing at a constant rate in an environment that does not alter. Radioactivity will enter the first metabolic pool of the sequence and the specific activity of the metabolite will rise until it is equal to that of the source of isotope to which the cells are exposed, assuming complete incorporation of the isotope into the molecule of the metabolite. Meanwhile, isotope will be entering the second pool, and the same specific activity will shortly be attained, although the *amount* of radioactivity will depend upon the size of the pool. It is clear that measurements of radioactivity will reveal this sequence of events, but only if pool sizes remain constant. It is also evident that a compound may serve as a reaction intermediate and yet the kinetics of its formation and removal may be such as to provide a very small metabolic pool, so that the amount of radioactivity retained in the pool may be so small that the compound may escape detection on chromatograms. On the other hand, a labelled compound that is *not* a member of the reaction sequence under consideration might appear at early times because it has been formed from such a member by a very rapid reaction. Thus, if oxaloacetate were the reaction intermediate, aspartate might be revealed by autoradiography because a rapid exchange of the carbon skeleton of oxaloacetate could occur with the aspartate which might be present in a larger metabolic pool. Quayle (Volume 6B) has described how the measurements of radioactivity for each compound on the chromatograms are plotted as *fractions* of the total radioactivity incorporated at the instant the sample was taken. Curves for the earliest compounds of the sequence will then show negative slopes at early times, declining asymptotically to values determined by the pool sizes of the compounds concerned.

The importance of re-inforcing rapid sampling experiments with studies of the isolated enzymes of a sequence may be illustrated by considering the properties of ribulose diphosphate carboxylase. This enzyme has a high Michaelis constant for CO_2, a disturbing feature for its postulated role in photosynthesis. Under natural conditions plants utilize the low concentration of CO_2 in air, and, accordingly, this carboxylation reaction would appear to operate at only a small fraction of its maximum velocity. Hatch and Slack (1966) have re-examined the radioactive products formed from $^{14}CO_2$ under steady-state conditions for photosynthesis, and at light intensities and concentrations of CO_2 as close to physiological conditions as possible. Under these conditions it did not appear that the initial carboxyla-tion reaction of photosynthesis is that catalysed by ribulose diphosphate carboxylase. Radiocarbon appeared first in a dicarboxylic acid pool, then moved to 3-phosphoglycerate and subsequently to sucrose and a glucan via the hexose phosphates. It was suggested that oxaloacetate might be the donor of CO_2 to ribulose 1,5-diphosphate rather than the bicarbonate ion or CO_2 itself. Initially, CO_2 might be fixed to pyruvate by the "malic" enzyme (1.1.1.40) or to phosphoenolpyruvate by phosphopyruvate carboxy-lase (4.1.1.31). The work of Hatch and Slack (1966) was performed with sugar-cane leaves, but it seems unlikely that the pathway they suggest is confined to this system. A further investigation of the physiological signifi-cance of ribulose diphosphate carboxylase in micro-organisms would seem desirable.

Rapid sampling experiments led Kornberg (1958) to the discovery of the glyoxylate cycle by which micro-organisms are able to synthesize C_4 dicarboxylic acids from acetate and so utilize this compound for growth as a sole source of carbon. Radioactivity from [14C]-acetate was incorporated into malate (and citrate) before succinate; and the activities of isocitrate lyase and malate synthase present in acetate-grown *Pseudomonas* were shown to be sufficient to account for the observed rates of growth. Kornberg and Gotto (1961) also showed that when pseudomonads growing with glycollate were exposed to [14C]-glycollate for brief periods, all the metabolites of the tricarboxylic acid cycle acquired radioactivity but label was incorporated most rapidly into glycine, 3-phosphoglycerate and malate. Since glyoxylate was not detected by the chromatographic procedures used, the early label-ling of glycine was taken to indicate the participation of glyoxylate in glycollate metabolism. The rapid labelling of phosphoglycerate might have suggested a metabolic pathway similar to that used by autotrophic organisms, but in this case it was shown that very little incorporation of $^{14}CO_2$ occur-red. The enzymes of the following anaplerotic sequence, now known as the "glycerate pathway", were shown to be present in cell extracts at levels adequate for the needs of exponential growth—

Glycollate → glyoxylate → tartronic semialdehyde → glycerate
→ phosphoglycerate → phosphoenolpyruvate

The enzyme tartronic semialdehyde reductase was later obtained in crystalline form from *Pseudomonas* grown with glycollate (Gotto and Korn-berg, 1961).

The researches of Quayle and his colleagues are instructive in demon-strating how rapid-sampling experiments may guide an investigator to the discovery of new enzymes, and how they may also reveal a profound change in enzyme complement when an organism is transferred to a growth medium that supplies a new source of carbon. *Pseudomonas oxalaticus* rapidly incorporated the label from [^{14}C]-oxalate into glycine and 3-phosphoglycerate (Quayle and Keech, 1960). These observations suggested that oxalate was reduced to glyoxylate which was then metabolized by the glycerate pathway; and indeed, the relevant enzymes were shown to be present in cell extracts at the concentrations required to sustain growth (Quayle *et al.*, 1961). Later work with purified enzymes (Quayle, 1963a, b) established that oxalate is converted into its thioester of coenzyme A by reaction with succinyl coenzyme A. Oxalyl coenzyme A can then undergo two reactions, namely it may be reduced by NADH to glyoxylate, which is metabolized by the reactions of the glycerate pathway to compounds used for biosynthesis; or oxalyl coenzyme A may be decarboxylated to give formyl coenzyme A. This compound, by reaction with succinate, regenerates succinyl coenzyme A and also provides formic acid which, in turn may furnish reducing power and energy needed for biosynthesis when it is oxidized to CO_2 by formate dehydrogenase. When *Ps. oxalaticus* is transferred from oxalate to formate as carbon source it is able to grow after a lag period during which a profound change occurs in the complement of its enzymes. Formate is again oxidized to CO_2, which effectively becomes the sole source of carbon for growth: that is, the bacteria change from a heterotrophic mode of growth with oxalate to an autotrophic existence when supplied with formate. This was shown by growing *Ps. oxalaticus* with formate in the presence of $H^{14}CO_2H$ or $H^{14}CO_3^-$, when most of the radioisotope was incorporated into 3-phosphoglycerate at early times (Quayle and Keech, 1959a); whereas the radioactivity of [^{14}C]-oxalate passed first into glycine when oxalate was the growth substrate. Enzyme patterns in cell extracts showed a corresponding change, from those of the glycerate pathway when growth occurred with oxalate to those of the Calvin–Bassham cycle when the bacteria grew with formate (Quayle and Keech, 1959b).

The pathway of utilization of methane by bacteria was also delineated by rapid sampling methods. Johnson and Quayle (1965) exposed cultures of *Pseudomonas methanica* to [^{14}C]-methane or [^{14}C]-methanol and found that 90% of the radioactivity was incorporated into phosphorylated compounds at the earliest times of sampling. Of this 90%, by far the largest proportion was found in glucose and fructose phosphates; only about 10% was present in 3-phosphoglycerate. The origin of these compounds was then demonstrated by Kemp and Quayle (1966), who incubated cell extracts with ribose 5-phosphate and either [^{14}C]-methanol or [^{14}C]-formaldehyde. Radioactivity was incorporated, more strongly from formaldehyde than from methanol, into the phosphate esters of fructose and allulose. On the basis of these experiments it was suggested that methane was oxidized to the level of formaldehyde and that the following reaction then occurred—

Formaldehyde + ribose 5-phosphate → allulose 6-phosphate

The isomerization of allulose 6-phosphate to fructose 6-phosphate would then provide the starting material for the series of reactions encountered in the pentose cycle, whereby rearrangements of carbon atoms in the sugar phosphate ester molecules can provide three molecules of ribose 5-phosphate and one molecule of triose phosphate from three molecules of fructose 6-phosphate. Such a cycle would convert formaldehyde (and hence methane) into triose phosphate according to the overall equation—

$$3 \text{ HCHO} + \text{ATP} \rightarrow \text{triose phosphate} + \text{ADP}$$

A final example may be given from the studies of the bacterial metabolism of tartaric acid. It has long been known that bacteria are able to utilize this substrate by first removing water and then decarboxylating the oxaloacetate so formed to give pyruvate (Barker, 1936; Shilo, 1957). However, Dagley and Trudgill (1962) found that at early times of sampling, [^{14}C]-tartrate was strongly incorporated into glycerate by *Ps. acidovorans* growing with tartrate as a sole source of carbon. Further studies with cell extracts (Dagley and Trudgill, 1963) revealed a new pathway for the metabolism of tartrate by its decarboxylation to give glycerate which, as 3-phosphoglycerate, could under-conversion to cellular constituents by known reactions. The nature of the decarboxylation reaction was established by Kohn and Jakoby (1966) who purified a protein from *Ps. acidovorans* that apparently showed two enzymic activities, namely: (1) oxidation of *meso*-tartrate to dihydroxyfumarate, requiring NAD; and (2) decarboxylation of dihydroxyfumarate, requiring NADH. Further fractionation has shown that two enzymes are responsible for these reactions (Kohn and Jacob, 1968).

D. Enzymes labelled with radiotracers

In a few, but important, instances investigation of the mode of action of an enzyme and its role in metabolism have been aided by the ability to label a strongly bound coenzyme. Thus, several biotin-containing enzymes occupy key roles in metabolism. The biosynthesis of fatty acids from acetyl coenzyme A is initiated by the biotin-enzyme acetyl coenzyme A carboxylase, while glucogenesis in many organisms is initiated by pyruvate carboxylase; and since both enzymes are allosteric, control of biosynthesis is achieved in part by regulation of these enzymic activities. Propionate, which arises from the degradation of branched-chain amino-acids and of fatty acids containing odd numbers of carbon atoms, may be carboxylated to give methylmalonyl coenzyme A and then metabolized as succinate. These various carboxylations occur in two steps. First, enzyme-bound biotin is carboxylated at the 1′-nitrogen atom (Lynen *et al.*, 1961; Knappe *et al.*, 1961)—

$$\text{Enz-biotin} + \text{HCO}_3^- + \text{ATP} \rightleftharpoons \text{Enz-biotin} \sim \text{CO}_2^- + \text{ADP} + \text{P}_i$$

Then CO_2 is transferred to the substrate which, except in the case of pyruvate carboxylase, is a coenzyme A ester—

$$Enz\text{-}biotin{\sim}CO_2^- + R\cdot CH_2\cdot CO\cdot SCoA$$
$$\rightleftharpoons R\cdot CH(CO_2^-)\cdot CO\cdot SCoA + Enz\text{-}biotin$$

Kaziro and Ochoa (1961) used $H^{14}CO_3^-$ to label crystalline pig's heart propionylcoenzyme A carboxylase which took up 1 mole $^{14}CO_2$/mole protein-bound biotin. Provided that the enzyme was held at about 0 C, it was stable enough to separate by column chromatography and could then be shown to transfer CO_2 quantitatively to propionyl coenzyme A yielding [^{14}C]methylmalonyl coenzyme A. This procedure has been used to study other biotin-enzymes. Thus, Knappe et al. (1962) incubated β-methylcrotonyl coenzyme A carboxylase from *Achromobacter* with ATP and $H^{14}CO_3^-$ and isolated the enzyme-biotin${\sim}CO_2^-$ complex by passage through a Sephadex column. After brief treatment with trypsin and methylation with diazomethane they obtained a stabilized carbomethoxybiotinyl peptide from which 1'-N-carbomethoxybiotin was liberated by the action of biotinidase. This compound was proved to be identical with that isolated by Lynen et al. (1961) when the site of carboxylation of biotin was established. A somewhat different approach was that of Allen et al. (1963) who grew *Propionibacterium shermanii* in a medium containing [2'-^{14}C]-biotin and isolated [^{14}C]-transcarboxylase from the bacteria. The labelled enzyme was used to catalyse a transcarboxylation from methylmalonyl coenzyme A to pyruvate, and it was shown that no loss of ^{14}C from the enzyme occurred and no label appeared in the oxaloacetate which was formed in the reaction. From this observation it was concluded that biotin does not function in this reaction by transfer of the ureido carbon of the enzyme-bound biotin, as other workers had suggested. The preparation of this same enzyme to a high degree of purity was also greatly assisted by growing the bacteria in a medium containing tritiated biotin, whereby the protein became labelled and could therefore be located in separation procedures (Wood et al., 1963).

The original culture of *Methanobacillus omelianskii* (*Methanobacterium omelianskii*) (Barker, 1956) oxidized ethanol to acetate during growth and employed CO_2 as the final electron acceptor, reducing it to methane. This culture has now been resolved into two distinct organisms, a methanogenic organism (*Methanobacterium* strain M.o.H.) that oxidizes H_2 and reduces CO_2 to methane, and an organism (S) that oxidizes ethanol to acetic acid with the formation of H_2 (Bryant et al., 1967). Although the experiments to be described were performed with the symbiotic culture, Bryant et al. (1968) have shown that the methane-forming system is complete in strain M.o.H. and that its formation or functioning is not dependent upon association with the S organism. Extracts of *Methanobacillus omelianski* formed methane from CO_2 and H_2 in the presence of ATP; and methyl cobalamin and $5N$-methyltetrahydrofolate have been implicated in the transfer of C-1 units to the B_{12}-containing enzyme which catalyses the last reaction of the sequence, and which Wolfe *et al.* (1966) have formulated—

$$\text{Enzyme} - \text{factor III} - CH_3 + XH_2 \rightarrow X + CH_4 + \text{enzyme} - \text{factor III}$$

This enzyme system is very labile, and resisted all attempts at the purification that was necessary before its nature and mode of action could be investigated. Finally Wood and Wolfe (1966) devised an ingenious method by which the enzyme was converted to an inactive form sufficiently stable to be taken through separation procedures and was at the same time labelled with radiocarbon so that its passage through these procedures could be followed. The purified protein was then converted back to the enzymically active form. The method was based upon the following reactions of the coenzyme, factor III, which is firmly bound to the enzyme—

$$\underset{\text{(active)}}{\overset{\diagdown\cdots\diagup}{\underset{\diagup|\diagdown}{Co\cdot\text{enzyme}}}} + CH_3CH_2CH_2I \rightarrow \underset{\text{(inactive)}}{\overset{\overset{\textstyle CH_2CH_2CH_3}{\diagdown|\diagup}}{\underset{\diagup|\diagdown}{Co\cdot\text{enzyme}}}}$$

$$\underset{\text{(inactive)}}{\overset{\overset{\textstyle CH_2CH_2CH_3}{\diagdown|\diagup}}{\underset{\diagup|\diagdown}{Co\cdot\text{enzyme}}}} + H_2 \xrightarrow{\text{light}} \underset{\text{(active)}}{\overset{\diagdown\cdots\diagup}{\underset{\diagup|\diagdown}{Co\cdot\text{enzyme}}}} + CH_3CH_2CH_3$$

Propyl iodide combined with the B_{12} moiety of the enzyme to give the stable, inactive form which became labelled when [1-^{14}C]propyl iodide was used. After the protein had been purified by ammonium sulphate fractionation and chromatography, the propyl group was liberated as propane and active enzyme was regenerated by photolysis under hydrogen. The spectral and chromatographic properties of the B_{12} coenzyme, factor III, were also examined after it had been released from the protein by treatment first with ethanol and then with phenol.

E. The use of nutritionally exacting micro-organisms

Many micro-organisms found in Nature are unable to grow unless certain essential growth factors are provided, owing to a metabolic lesion compared with competent organisms. Such growth factors are of two main types: substances such as amino-acids that are incorporated into main cell constituents; and those that serve an ultimate catalytic function, such as members of the vitamin B group. The use of natural auxotrophs has not only aided the discovery, assay and isolation of compounds in the second of these two categories, but has also helped to elucidate the chemical structures of coenzymes and provided information about their functions. Three outstanding contributions may be mentioned.

First, the elucidation of the chemical structure and biological function of α-lipoic acid stemmed from the convergence of three independent lines of research with micro-organisms. Gunsalus, O'Kane and their colleagues discovered that a new coenzyme-like factor was required for the oxidation of pyruvate by *Strep. faecalis* and they developed a convenient assay (O'Kane and Gunsalus, 1948; Gunsalus *et al.*, 1952a, b). Meanwhile Snell and his colleagues found that acetate stimulated the early growth of several lactobacilli and could be replaced by small amounts of yeast extract (Guirard *et al.*, 1964a, b) and Stockstad *et al.*, (1949) pursued the isolation of a factor present in liver that Kidder and Dewey (1949) showed to be required for the growth of the ciliate *Tetrahymena gelsii* W. Since it was found, in due course, that the three factors were largely interchangeable in their biological effects, one compound common to all three appeared to be responsible for activity. Attention was concentrated upon its extraction from liver, and from 10 tons of acid-hydrolysed liver residue, 30 mg of crystalline α-lipoic acid were obtained (Reed *et al.*, 1943). This material provided sufficient information about the chemistry of the compound to enable its synthesis to be accomplished (Hornberger *et al.*, 1953).

A second example of the use of natural auxotrophs to determine both the function and chemical structure of a coenzyme may be taken from the work of Gunsalus, Umbreit and their colleagues. They found that when *Strep. faecalis* was grown in media deficient in pyridoxine, ability to decarboxylate tyrosine was impaired (Bellamy and Gunsalus, 1944). This loss of activity was not restored by adding pyridoxine to the reaction mixture: a little stimulation was given by pyridoxal, but strong decarboxylase activity was observed when ATP and pyridoxal were added together (Gunsalus *et al.*, 1944). This work led to the realization that the cofactor required for decarboxylations and other reactions of amino-acids is pyridoxal phosphorylated on the hydroxymethyl group at position 5 (Umbreit and Gunsalus, 1949).

Third, natural auxotrophs provided valuable information pertaining to the chemical structure and biological function of coenzyme A. Certain bacteria, for example, cannot synthesize pantothenic acid but they are able to convert it into coenzyme A to satisfy their metabolic requirements. These biosynthetic steps involve phosphorylation and extension of the molecule by addition of a β-mercaptoethylamine residue to give pantetheine 4'-phosphate, from which coenzyme A is synthesized after combination with ATP and further phosphorylation. Other bacteria cannot perform this synthesis from pantothenate, but they are able to utilize preformed pantetheine. A survey of the nutritional requirements of such organisms indicated the units from which the chemical structure of coenzyme A was derived, at a time when this problem had not been resolved; and it also suggested methods of biological assay for the coenzyme and for the compounds involved in its synthesis. Further, the biological function of the coenzyme was indicated by the experiments of Novelli and Lipmann (1950) who obtained yeast deficient in coenzyme A after growth in a medium that lacked pantothenic acid. This deficiency was paralleled by impairment of ability of intact cells to oxidize acetate, and of cell-free extracts to synthesize citrate from oxaloacetate and acetyl phosphtte. The very important conclusion was reached that these results indicated the "involvement of coenzyme A in acetate activation for citrate synthesis" (Novelli and Lipmann, 1950).

At the present time, metabolic investigations no longer depend upon the availability of suitable natural auxotrophs, since mutants of interest can be selected, by means of penicillin for example (Lederberg and Zinder, 1948), after wild-type organisms have been exposed to radiation or chemical mutagens. The biological functions of cofactors can then be investigated by methods that are similar to those employed with natural auxotrophs in the classical experiments we have described. Thus, the function of ubiquinone in mitochondria has been the subject of extensive research, but its role in bacterial electron-transport systems is less clearly understood. Cox *et al.* (1968) adopted a new approach, in which metabolic reactions that might involve ubiquinone were compared, as between normal cells of *E. coli* K12 and those of a mutant that had lost its ability to make ubiquinone. They found clear evidence that ubiquinone was involved in the oxidation of malate by a membranous small-particle fraction obtained from disrupted cells. Such particles from the normal strain oxidized malate twice as fast as those from the ubiquinone-deficient mutant.

F. The use of induced auxotrophs in determining biosynthetic pathways

The principles employed in this method are well known and will only be briefly considered. We shall use present knowledge of the routes of biosynthesis of branched-chain amino-acids and of aromatic amino-acids mainly for the purpose of illustrating two themes: first, that, as always, the complexities of metabolism require that experimental findings to be interpreted with caution; and second, that the elucidation of biosynthetic pathways proceeds from an outline of the steps involved, through a more detailed knowledge of their chemistry, to a study of isolated enzymes and the nature of their regulation in the cell.

Let us consider a reaction sequence by which wild-type bacteria synthesize an amino-acid (X) from a source of carbon, say glucose G, with compounds A, B and C as intermediates in a reaction sequence—

$$G \rightarrow A \overset{(1)}{\rightarrow} B \overset{(2)}{\rightarrow} C \rightarrow \rightarrow X$$

Any mutant that lacks the ability to synthesize enzyme (1) will not grow with either G or A as sole sources of carbon unless sufficient of X is added to the medium to satisfy its requirements for growth. However, B or C may replace X; and another mutant that lacks enzyme (2) may grow if either C or X is supplied, but not when A or B is added. Clearly, if a series of mutants is obtained, all requiring X, it is then possible to suggest a route of biosynthesis from glucose. Further, the mapping of a pathway is assisted by the fact that when a mutant lacking enzyme (1) grows with glucose supplemented by X, then compound A will accumulate in the growth medium and may be isolated and identified. Such an accumulation might, in principle, entail further metabolic consequences. Thus, when the pathways of biosynthesis of isoleucine and valine (Fig. 5) were first investigated by Bonner *et al.*

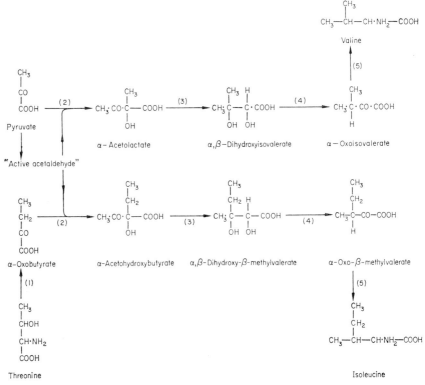

Fig. 5. Biosynthesis of valine and isoleucine. The numbers denote enzymes referred to in the text.

(1943) mutants of the mould *Neurospora crassa* were isolated that required *both* valine and isoleucine for growth. Since genetic analysis showed that a particular mutant differed from its wild-type by deletion of a single gene, this appeared at first to be a variance with the accepted theory that one gene controlled the synthesis of one enzyme. It was therefore suggested that the double requirement arose from the fact that a metabolite of one pathway accumulated and competed with its homologue for an enzyme of the second pathway, which accordingly became blocked. This suggestion was fruitful insofar as it led to the isolation and identification of α,β-dihydroxyisovalerate and α,β-dihydroxy-β-methylvalerate both of which accumulated (Sjolander *et al.*, 1954), although the explanation for the observed double block became unnecessary when it was realized that both compounds are formed and metabolized by the same enzymes (3 and 4 of Fig. 5). Thus, for enzyme 3 Umberger *et al.* (1960) found that extracts of *E. coli* and *A. aerogenes* reduced and isomerized both α-acetohydroxybutyrate and α-acetolactate. The α,β-dihydroxyacid dehydratase, enzyme V, has since been purified 120 fold from spinach leaves without any fractionation of activities between the valine and isoleucine intermediates (Satyanarayana and Radhakrishnan, 1962). The substrate specificity of this enzyme isolated from micro-organisms appears to have been less extensively studied. However, the fact that mutants blocked at various steps beyond pyruvate or α-oxobutyrate require *both* isoleucine and valine, or the appropriate precursors, leaves no doubt that the same enzymes (2, 3 and 4) serve to catalyse the respective reactions of both biosynthetic pathways.

Once the chemical reactions of Fig. 5 had been clarified by mutant methodology, studies of the individual enzymes provided results of great significance for our understanding of the mechanisms by which biosynthetic sequences in general are regulated. Enzyme 2 (Fig. 5) was shown to be inhibited by valine (Halpern and Umbarger, 1959) and enzyme 1 by isoleucine (Umbarger, 1961) so that each enzyme was seen to be subject to inhibition by the end product of the corresponding biosynthetic sequence. In this and other properties these enzymes differed from two others that were inducible rather than constitutive and that functioned in catabolism by catalysing the same respective chemical transformations as did enzymes 1 and 2.

One of the most extensive applications of mutant methodology, and one particularly fruitful in revealing new metabolites, has been that used to elucidate the pathways of biosynthesis of aromatic compounds. We may regard the progress made in this area as having taken place in two phases, each of which began with the recognition of a metabolite of central importance for biosynthesis. The first of these compounds was shikimic acid, a compound found in a few plants, but formerly regarded as having no meta-

10

bolic significance until it was shown by Davis (1950, 1951) to satisfy the multiple growth requirements of "aromatic polyauxotrophs". Shikimic acid was able to replace tyrosine, phenylalanine, tryptophan, p-aminobenzoic acid and p-hydroxybenzoic acid, a mixture of all of which compounds was required by some of these mutants. Certain of these strains were found to excrete a precursor of shikimate, designated compound X and later identified as 3-dehydroshikimic acid (formerly named 5-dehydroshikimic acid; Salamon and Davis, 1953). Similar studies with mutants showed that the precursor of compound X was 5-dehydroquinic acid (Weiss *et al.*, 1953). Once the chemical intermediates had been assigned to their places on the biosynthetic route, attention was directed to the properties of the enzymes that convert 5-dehydroquinate into 3-dehydroshikimate (Mitsuhashi and Davis, 1954a) and thence into shikimate (Yaniv and Gilvarg, 1955). Evidence was forthcoming for each one of the reactions leading to the formation of shikimate (Fig. 6) when once the enzyme that catalyses the synthesis of

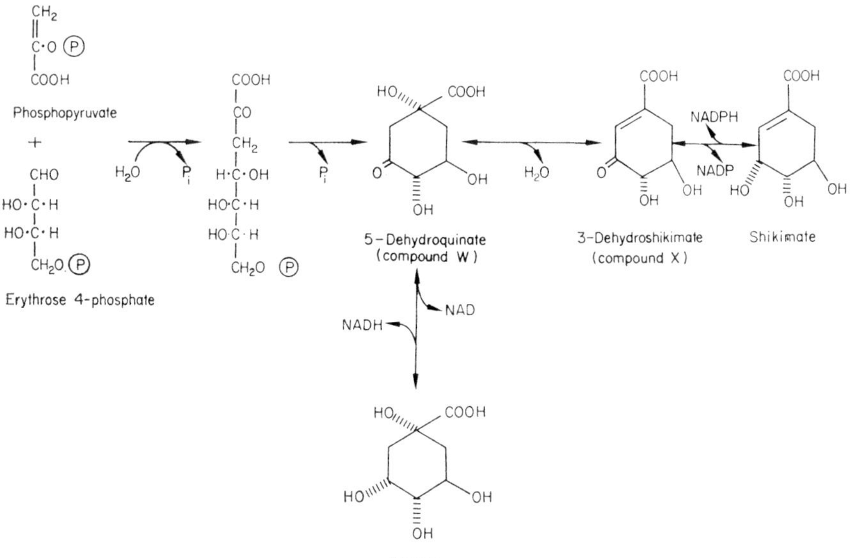

FIG. 6. Biosynthesis of shikimic acid.

2-keto-3-deoxy-D-*arabino*-heptulosonic acid 7-phosphate from erythrose 4-phosphate and phosphopyruvate was isolated and purified 60-fold (Hurwitz and Weissbach, 1959; Srinivasan and Sprinson, 1959). Srinivasan *et al.* (1959) prepared cell-free extracts that formed 5-dehydroquinate from these two starting materials, and they showed that sedoheptulose 1,7-diphosphate, which is also converted enzymically into 5-dehydroquinate

Kalan *et al.*, 1956), is not an obligatory intermediate in the synthesis from erythrose 4-phosphate and phosphopyruvate.

This phase of the work on aromatic biosynthesis provided four examples of experimental findings that called for particularly cautious interpretation. They concern: (1) a growth requirement that was removed by a compound that was not a precursor; (2) an obligatory intermediate in synthesis that could not satisfy a growth requirement; (3) a compound that accumulated in cultures on account of a metabolic lesion, but was not a biosynthetic intermediate; and (4) a precursor that gave rise to a growth requirement when added to the culture.

The reasons for these findings, and the systems that provided them, were, respectively, as follows. (1) The requirements of certain aromatic polyauxo-trophs of *A. aerogenes* could be satisfied by quinic acid which, although not a biosynthetic intermediate, was converted into 5-dehydroquinate by an inducible dehydrogenase and could, in fact, serve as a sole source of carbon for this organism (Mitushashi and Davis, 1954b). This enzyme is not induced in *E. coli* and accordingly its mutants that are blocked before 5-dehydroquinate do not respond to quinate. (2) Davis and Mingioli (1953) found that certain mutants of *Salmonella* and *A. aerogenes* accumulated compounds which they designated Z_1 and Z_2 (Fig. 7). Weiss and Mingioli (1956) identified Z_2 as 3-phosphoshikimic acid (formerly 5-phosphoshikimic acid) but found that this compound did not relieve the growth requirements. The most probable reason for this finding is that Z_2, like many other phos-phorylated compounds, cannot gain access to the interior of a bacterial cell when added to a growth medium. (3) Compound Z_1 did not relieve growth requirements because it was not an aromatic precursor. It was formed in cultures by dephosphorylation of a true precursor that was identified as 5-enoylpyruvylshikimate 3-phosphate (Levin and Sprinson, 1960; 1964). (4) 3-Dehydroshikimate inhibits competitively the utilization of shikimate. Accordingly, in a mutant with metabolic lesions both before and after dehydroshikimate—so that this compound was no longer an effective metabolite—increasing concentrations of dehydroshikimate relative to shikimate induced growth requirements for tyrosine, then for tyrosine plus phenylalanine and so on (Davis, 1952a, b).

The second phase of development in this field was marked by the recognition of chorismic acid as the branch-point from which a family of aromatic compounds is synthesized by way of shikimate and its derivatives. However it may be mentioned that prephenic acid, which is a precursor of tyrosine and phenylalanine and lies beyond chorismate (Fig. 7), had been isolated and identified several years previously by Weiss *et al.* (1954). This compound was accumulated by a mutant of *E. coli* requiring phenylalanine, and extracts of the same auxotroph were shown to contain an NAD-dependent

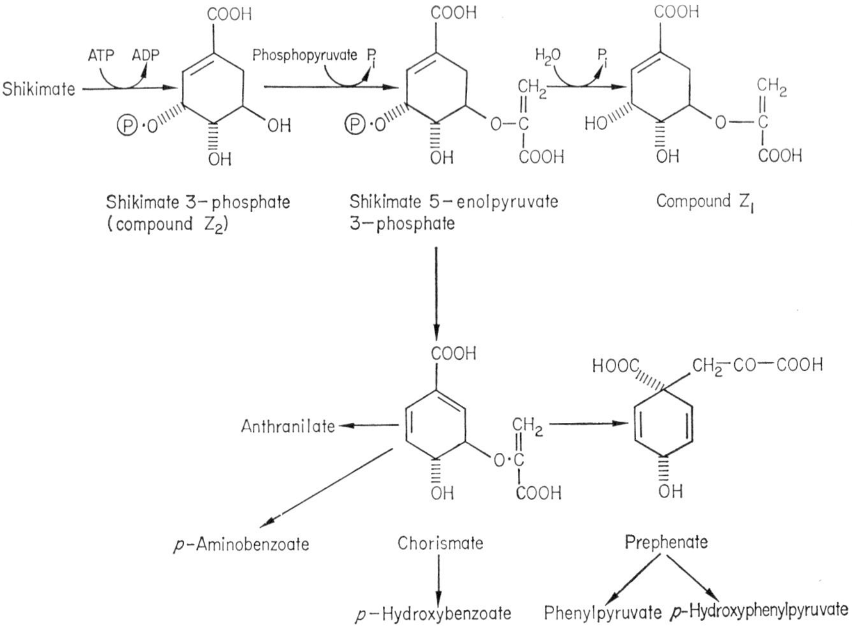

FIG. 7. The roles of chorismic and prephenic acids in the biosynthesis of aromatic compounds.

enzyme that converted prephenic acid into p-hydroxyphenylpyruvic acid (Schwink and Adams, 1959). The discovery of chorismate arose from a combination of work with cell-free extracts and mutants. Gibson and Gibson (1962) used an auxotroph of *A. aerogenes* that required tryptophan because of a lesion immediately beyond anthranilic acid, and they produced further mutations which precluded the enzymic formation of prephenate, phenylalanine and tyrosine. As a consequence of these metabolic blocks, cell-free extracts of the polyauxotroph converted shikimic acid largely into anthranilic acid when incubated with glutamine and ATP. When glutamine was omitted, a new labile ether-extractable compound was formed; it could be converted by cell-free extracts from other sources into recognized products of aromatic biosynthetic sequences. Washed suspensions of the multiply blocked auxotroph of *A. aerogenes* also accumulated this intermediate, which was isolated as its barium salt (Gibson, 1964). The structure of the compound, now named chorismic acid (Gibson and Gibson, 1964), was determined conclusively by Gibson and Jackson (1963) using n.m.r. spectroscopy. The establishment of chorismate as a central metabolite has raised many questions regarding the enzymology of later steps in aromatic biosynthesis which are receiving attention at the present time.

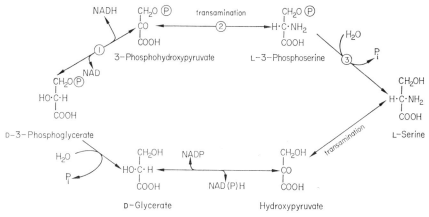

FIG. 8. Possible routes of biosynthesis of serine. The upper pathway operates in *E. coli.* Numbers denote enzymes referred to in the text.

G. Assessment of the function of a metabolic pathway

Metabolites of the central sequences of metabolism, such as the tri-carboxylic acid cycle and glycolysis, serve as intermediates for many reaction pathways, both biosynthetic and degradative. As a result of this inter-linking of sequences, the situation may arise when it is possible to write down several feasible alternative schemes for converting one metabolite into another by means of enzymes which the organism is known to contain. The question then arises as to which of these pathways is actually employed in a given situation. Sometimes it is possible to show that although one of the enzymes may be present, its concentration is insufficient to account for the observed overall rate of conversion. However, a decision on this basis is not always possible; for determinations of enzyme levels may simply indicate that, in principle, alternative pathways may be used: as indeed may be the case in fact. In such cases microbial systems offer certain unique advantages, since the use of auxotrophs or studies of enzyme regulation may furnish additional evidence from which a decision may be made. We may illustrate from two investigations, concerned with the biosynthesis of serine and phosphopyruvate, respectively.

Two pathways have been suggested for the biosynthesis of serine in mammals (Sallach, 1956; Ichihara and Greenberg, 1957; Willis and Sallach, 1962) (Fig. 8). It might be considered that a micro-organism employs both pathways, but as Umbarger and Umbarger (1962) have pointed out, this is unlikely for *E. coli* and *Salmonella typhimurium*. These organisms probably use only one pathway of biosynthesis of serine from a single carbon source such as glucose, because serine auxotrophy frequently arises from a single

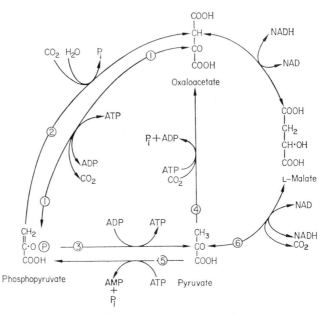

FIG. 9. Metabolic relationships between pyruvate, phosphopyruvate and oxalo-acetate. The enzymes are denoted as follows: (1) phosphopyruvate carboxykinase (enzymes from different species require GTP, ITP instead of ATP); (2) phospho-pyruvate carboxylase; (3) pyruvate kinase; (4) pyruvate carboxylase; (5) phospho-pyruvate synthase; (6) "malic" enzyme (E.C. 1.1.1.38).

mutational step. Further, Umbarger and Umbarger (1962) examined two serine auxotrophs of *Salm. typhimurium* and found that their requirement was due, respectively, to a lack of enzymes 1 and 3 (Fig. 8). The conclusion that this organism exclusively uses the pathway in which these two enzymes function was strongly supported by the observation that L-serine inhibits enzyme 1, the first in the biosynthetic sequence, and also blocks the conversion of both glucose and D-3-phosphoglycerate into serine by extracts of the bacteria. The amino-acid did not prevent the metabolism of 3-phospho-hydroxypyruvate or 3-phosphoserine to serine by these extracts. These findings are to be expected if this sequence functions for serine biosynthesis and is regulated by feed-back control.

    Phosphopyruvate is the starting material for several important biosyn-thetic sequences, including those for hexoses, pentoses and aromatic amino-acids. When micro-organisms grow with glucose, phosphopyruvate is formed directly from the carbon source by the reactions of the glycolytic sequence; but since pyruvate kinase (e.c. 2.7.1.40) is essentially irreversible under physiological conditions, phosphopyruvate cannot be formed directly from pyruvate by the action of this enzyme. Accordingly, other reactions must be called into play when growth substrates are utilized which are catabolized to pyruvate, acetate and other tricarboxylic acid cycle metabolites. Possible routes of synthesis of phosphopyruvate from pyruvate, two of which involve prior fixation of CO_2 to give oxaloacetate, are shown in Fig. 9. These reactions may also serve the anaplerotic function of replenishing the cycle with oxaloacetate; for this compound must be furnished continually when metabolites of the cycle are removed for the biosynthesis of cellular constituents during growth.

The existence of this network of reactions (Fig. 9) raises the question as to which of them serve for the synthesis of phosphopyruvate or oxaloacetate in particular organisms. Yeast (Losada *et al.*, 1964), *Arthrobacter globiformis* (Bridgeland and Jones, 1967) and *Pseudomonas citronellolis* (Seubert and Remberger, 1961) can synthesize oxaloacetate from pyruvate by means of enzyme 4, although the pyruvate carboxylase from the last-named microorganism differs from that from other species in not requiring acetyl coenzyme A for activity. However, Enterobacteriaceae do not contain this enzyme (Kornberg, 1965) and they must use other means for synthesizing oxaloacetate and phosphopyruvate. It appears that when these organisms are plentifully supplied with phosphopyruvate, as when glucose serves as carbon source, oxaloacetate is formed by enzyme 2, namely phosphopyruvate carboxylase. This was proved by Theodore and Englesberg (1964) who obtained mutants of *S. typhimurium* that could not grow with glucose because this enzyme was lacking. Cánovas and Kornberg (1965) showed that bacterial phosphopyruvate carboxylase required acetyl coenzyme A as an allosteric effector and in this respect differed from the enzyme (E.C. 4.1.1.31) that catalyses the same reaction in plants.

In contrast to these conditions of growth, Enterobacteriaceae may utilize a carbon source which is catabolized to pyruvate by a pathway that does not include phosphopyruvate. In such cases they synthesize the phosphopyruvate they need by means of pyruvate synthase (5), an enzyme which can operate in the reverse direction from pyruvate kinase (3) because free energy is released through the formation of AMP and orthophosphate, rather than ADP, as products (Cooper and Kornberg, 1967). When pyruvate is the source of carbon, therefore, *E. coli* synthesizes the oxaloacetate required for growth by the concerted action of enzymes 5 and 2. It is interesting to note that two other enzymes might, but apparently do not, function for the synthesis of oxaloacetate and phosphopyruvate. When sufficient reducing power is available, "malic" enzyme (6; 1.1.1.38) can fix CO_2 to pyruvate, giving malate and hence oxaloacetate; and this compound may be decarboxylated and phosphorylated by enzyme 1 to give phosphopyruvate. Both of these enzymes are elaborated by *E. coli*, but are not used for the purpose discussed. An indication of the function of enzyme 1 is given by studies of the metabolic impairments suffered by mutants of *E. coli* that lack this enzyme. These auxotrophs were able to grow with glucose or pyruvate but could not grow with tricarboxylic acid cycle compounds as sole sources of carbon (Hsie and Rickenberg, 1966). Further, when the wild-type organisms from which the mutants arose were grown with succinate, the amounts of phosphopyruvate carboxykinase (1) that they contained were about ten times greater than when they grew with glucose. It therefore appears that the function of enzyme 1 is to furnish phosphopyruvate from oxaloacetate when this is in abundant supply, as it would be when succinate, fumarate, malate or α-oxoglutarate—but *not* pyruvate—serve as carbon sources for growth. The diversity, and hence the fascination of microbes is shown by the fact that *Arthrobacter globiformis* synthesizes oxaloacetate from pyruvate by means of enzyme 4, which *E. coli* does not possess; and it converts the oxaloacetate so formed into phosphopyruvate by means of phosphopyruvate carboxykinase, an enzyme that *E. coli* elaborates but does not use for pyruvate → phosphopyruvate conversions (Bridgeland and Jones, 1967).

ACKNOWLEDGMENT

Our work on bacterial metabolism is assisted by grants GB5656 of the National Science Foundation and A107656 of the U.S. Public Health Service.

REFERENCES

Allen, S. H. G., Stjernholm, R., and Wood, H. G. (1963). *J. biol. Chem.*, **238**, PC2889–2892.
Barker, H. A. (1936). *Proc. K. ned. Akad. Wet.*, **39**, 674–683.
Barker, H. A. (1956). "Bacterial Fermentations", pp. 1–27. John Wiley & Sons, New York.
Bassham, J. A., and Calvin, M. (1957). "The Path of Carbon in Photosynthesis". Prentice-Hall, Englewood Cliffs, N.J.
Behrman, E. J., and Stanier, R. Y. (1957). *J. biol. Chem.*, **228**, 923–945.
Bellamy, W. D., and Gunsalus, I. C. (1944). *J. Bact.*, **48**, 191–199.
Bonner, D. M., Tatum, E. L., and Beadle, G. W. (1943). *Arch. Biochem.*, **3**, 71–91.
Bridgeland, E. S., and Jones, K. M. (1967). *Biochem. J.*, **104**, 9P–10P.
Brown, B. S. (1968). *Chemistry in Britain*, **3**, 524–526.
Brown, B. S., and King, H. K. (1966). *Biochem. J.*, **100**, 58P.
Bryant, M. P., Wolin, E. A., Wolin, M. J., and Wolfe, R. S. (1967). *Arch. Mikrobiol.*, **59**, 20–31.
Bryant, M. P., McBride, B. C., and Wolfe, R. S. (1968). *J. Bact.*, **95**, 1118–1123.
Cain, R. B. (1961). *Biochem. J.*, **79**, 298–312.
Callely, A. G., and Dagley, S. (1959). *Biochim. biophys. Acta*, **35**, 256–257.
Calvin, M., and Bassham, J. A. (1962). "The Photosynthesis of Carbon Compounds". Benjamin, New York.

Cánovas, J. L., and Kornberg, H. L. (1965). *Biochim. biophys. Acta*, **96**, 169–172.
Cánovas, J. L., Ornston, L. N., and Stanier, R. Y. (1967). *Science, N.Y.*, **156**, 1695–1699.
Carnahan, J. E., Mortenson, L. E., Mower, H. F., and Castle, J. E. (1960). *Biochim. biophys. Acta*, **44**, 520–535.
Chapman, P. J., and Duggleby, R. G. (1967). *Biochem. J.*, **103**, 7C–9C.
Cooper, R. A., and Kornberg, H. L. (1967). *Biochem. J.*, **105**, 49C–50C.
Cox, G. B., and Gibson, F. (1966). *Biochem. J.*, **100**, 1–6.
Cox, G. B., Snoswell, A. M., and Gibson, F. (1968). *Biochim. biophys. Acta.* **153**, 1–12.
Dagley, S., and Patel, M. D. (1955). *Biochim. biophys. Acta*, **16**, 418–423.
Dagley, S., and Patel, M. D. (1957). *Biochem. J.*, **66**, 227–233.
Dagley, S., and Trudgill, P. W. (1962). *Biochem. J.*, **84**, 95P.
Dagley, S., and Trudgill, P. W. (1963). *Biochem. J.*, **89**, 22–31.
Dagley, S., and Walker, J. R. L. (1956). *Biochim. biophys. Acta*, **21**, 441–447.
Dagley, S., Fewster, M. E., and Happold, F. C. (1952). *J. Bact.*, **63**, 327–336.
Dagley, S., Chapman, P. J., and Gibson, D. T. (1965). *Biochem. J.*, **97**, 643–650.
Davis, B. D. (1950). *Experientia*, **6**, 41–50.
Davis, B. D. (1951). *J. biol. Chem.*, **191**, 315–325.
Davis, B. D. (1952a). *J. Bact.*, **64**, 729–748.
Davis, B. D. (1952b). *J. Bact.*, **64**, 749–763.
Davis, B. D., and Mingioli, E. S. (1953). *J. Bact.*, **66**, 129–136.
DeLey, J., and Stouthamer, A. J. (1959). *Biochim. biophys. Acta*, **34**, 171–183.
Dixon, G. H., Kornberg, H. L., and Lund, P. (1960). *Biochim. biophys. Acta*, **41**, 217–233.
Drysdale, G. R., and Lardy, H. A. (1953). *J. biol. Chem.*, **202**, 119–136.
Evans, W. C. (1947). *Biochem. J.*, **41**, 373–382.
Florscheim, W. H., and Krichesky, B. (1950). *Proc. Soc. exp. Biol. Med.*, **75**, 693–695.
Fox, C. F., Robinson, W. S., Haselkorn, R., and Weiss, S. B. (1964). *J. biol. Chem.*, **239**, 186–195.
Friis, P., Daves, G. D., Jr., and Folkers, K. (1966). *J. Am. chem. Soc.*, **88**, 4754–4756.
Gale, E. F. (1940). *Biochem. J.*, **34**, 392–413.
Gibson, F. (1964). *Biochem. J.*, **90**, 256–261.
Gibson, M. I., and Gibson, F. (1962). *Biochim. biophys. Acta*, **65**, 160–163.
Gibson, M. I., and Gibson, F. (1964). *Biochem. J.*, **90**, 248–256.
Gibson, F., and Jackman, L. M. (1963). *Nature, Lond.*, **198**, 388–389.
Giles, N. H., Partridge, C. W. H., Ahmed, S. I., and Case, M. E. (1967). *Proc. natn. Acad. Sci. U.S.A.*, **58**, 1930–1937.
Gotto, A. M., and Kornberg, H. L. (1961). *Biochem. J.*, **81**, 273–284.
Guirard, B. M., Snell, E. E., and Williams, R. J. (1946a). *Arch. Biochem.*, **9**, 361–379.
Guirard, B. M., Snell, E. E., and Williams, R. J. (1946b). *Arch. Biochem.*, **9**, 381–386.
Gunsalus, I. C., Bellamy, W. D., and Umbreit, W. W. (1944). *J. biol. Chem.*, **155**, 685–686.
Gunsalus, I. C., Dolin, M. I., and Struglia, L. (1952a). *J. biol. Chem.*, **194**, 849–857.
Gunsalus, I. C., Struglia, L., and O'Kane, D. J. (1952b). *J. biol. Chem.*, **194**, 859–869.

Gunsalus, I. C., Conrad, H. E., Trudgill, P. W., and Jacobson, L. A. (1965). *Israel J. med. Sci.*, 1, 1099–1119.

Halpern, Y. S., and Umbarger, H. E. (1959). *J. biol. Chem.*, 234, 3067–3071.

Hartman, S. C., Levenberg, B., and Buchanan, J. M. (1956). *J. biol. Chem.*, 221, 1057–1070.

Hatch, M. D., and Slack, C. R. (1966). *Biochem. J.*, 101, 103–111.

Hayaishi, O., and Stanier, R. Y. (1951). *J. Bact.*, 62, 691–709.

Hayaishi, O., Katagiri, M., and Rothberg, S. (1957). *J. biol. Chem.*, 229, 905–920.

Henderson, M. E. K. (1957). *J. gen. Microbiol.*, 16, 686–695.

Henderson, M. E. K., and Farmer, V. C. (1955). *J. gen. Microbiol.*, 12, 37–46.

Hopper, D. J. (1967). Ph.D. Thesis, University of Hull.

Hornberger, C. S., Jr., Heitmiller, R. F., Gunsalus, I. C., Schnakenberg, G. H. F., and Reed, L. J. (1953). *J. Am. chem. Soc.*, 75, 1273–1277.

Hsie, A. W., and Rickenberg, H. V. (1966). *Biochem. Biophys. Res. Commun.*, 25, 676–683.

Hurlbert, R. E., and Jakoby, W. B. (1965). *J. biol. Chem.*, 240, 2772–2777.

Hurwitz, J., and Weissbach, A. (1959). *J. biol. Chem.*, 234, 710–712.

Ichihara, A., and Greenberg, D. M. (1957). *J. biol. Chem.*, 224, 331–340.

Ichihara, A., Adachi, K., Hosokawa, K., and Takeda, Y. (1962). *J. biol. Chem.*, 237, 2296–2302.

Itada, N. (1965). *Biochem. Biophys. Res. Commun.*, 20, 149–153.

Jensen, S. L., Cohen-Bazire, G., Nakayama, T. O. M., and Stanier, R. Y. (1958). *Biochim. biophys. Acta*, 29, 477–498.

Johnson, P. A., and Quayle, J. R. (1965). *Biochem. J.*, 95, 859–867.

Kalan, E. B., Davis., B. D., Srinivasan, P. R. and Sprinson, D. B. (1956). *J. biol. Chem.*, 223, 907–912.

Karlsson, J. L., and Barker, H. A. (1948). *J. biol. Chem.*, 175, 913–921.

Kaziro, Y., and Ochoa, S. (1961). *J. biol. Chem.*, 236, 3131–3136.

Kemp, M. B., and Quayle, J. R. (1966). *Biochem. J.*, 99, 41–48.

Kennedy, E. P., and Lehninger, A. L. (1949). *J. biol. Chem.*, 179, 957–972.

Kidder, G. W., and Dewey, V. C. (1949). *Arch. Biochem.*, 20, 433–443.

Kilby, B. A. (1951). *Biochem. J.*, 49, 671–674.

Kluyver, A. J.,and van Zijp, J. C. M. (1951). *Antonie van Leeuwenhoek*, 17, 315–324.

Knappe, J., Ringelmann, E., and Lynen, F. (1961). *Biochem. Z.*, 335, 168–176.

Knappe, J., Biederbick, K., and Brümmer, W. (1962). *Angew. Chem.*, 74, 432.

Kohn, L. D., and Jakoby, W. B. (1966). *Biochem. Biophys. Res. Commun.*, 22, 33–37.

Kohn, L. D. and Jacoby, W. B. (1968) *J. Biol. Chem.*, 243, 2472.

Kornberg, H. L. (1958). *Biochem. J.*, 68, 535–542.

Kornberg, H. L. (1965). *Symp. Soc. gen. Microbiol.*, 15, 8–31.

Kornberg, H. L., and Gotto, A. M. (1961). *Biochem. J.*, 78, 69–82.

Krebs, H. A. (1964). *Proceedings of the Robert A. Welch Foundation Conferences on Chemical Research*, 8, 101–129.

Lack, L. (1959). *Biochim. biophys. Acta*, 34, 117–123.

Lederberg, J., and Zinder, N. J. (1948). *J. Am. chem. Soc.*, 70, 4267–4268.

Leistner, E., Schmitt, J. H., and Zenk, M. H. (1967). *Biochem. Biophys. Res. Commun.*, 28, 845–850.

Leloir, L. F., and Muñoz, J. M. (1939). *Biochem. J.*, 33, 734–746.

Levin, J. G., and Sprinson, D. B. (1960). *Biochem. Biophys. Res. Commun.*, 3, 157–163.

Levin, J. G., and Sprinson, D. B. (1964). *J. biol. Chem.*, 239, 1142–1150.

Lewis, G. N. (1926). "The Anatomy of Science". Yale.

Losada, M., Cánovas, J. L., and Ruiz-Amil, M. (1964). *Biochem. Z.*, **340**, 60–74.

Lynen, F., Knappe, J., Lorch, E., Jütting, G., Ringelmann, E., and Lachance, J. P. (1961). *Biochem. Z.*, **335**, 123–167.

Mandelstam, J. (1958). *Biochem. J.*, **69**, 110–119.

Mitsuhashi, S., and Davis, B. D. (1954a). *Biochim. biophys. Acta*, **15**, 54–61.

Mitsuhashi, S., and Davis, B. D. (1954b). *Biochim. biophys. Acta*, **15**, 268–280.

Morris, D. R., and Pardee, A. B. (1966). *J. biol. Chem.*, **241**, 3129–3135.

Novelli, G. D., and Lipmann, F. (1950). *J. biol. Chem.*, **182**, 213–228.

Nozaki, M., Kojima, Y., Nakazawa, T., Fujisawa, H., Ono, K., Kotani, S., and Hayaishi, O. (1966). *In* "Biological and Chemical Aspects of Oxygenases" (Ed. K. Bloch and O. Hayaishi), pp. 347–367. Maruzen, Tokyo.

Ogston, A. G. (1948). *Nature, Lond.*, **162**, 963.

O'Kane, D. J., and Gunsalus, I. C. (1948). *J. Bact.*, **56**, 499–505.

Ornston, L. N. (1966). *J. biol. Chem.*, **241**, 3800–3810.

Ornston, L. N., and Stanier, R. Y. (1966). *J. biol. Chem.*, **241**, 3776–3786.

Palleroni, N. J., and Stanier, R. Y. (1964). *J. gen. Microbiol.*, **35**, 319–334.

Parsons, W. W., and Rudney, H. (1964). *Proc. natn. Acad. Sci. U.S.A.*, **51**, 444–450.

Peters, R. A. (1952). *Proc. R. Soc.*, B **139**, 143–170.

Quayle, J. R. (1963a). *Biochem. J.*, **87**, 368–373.

Quayle, J. R. (1963b). *Biochem. J.*, **89**, 492–503.

Quayle, J. R., and Keech, D. B. (1959a). *Biochem. J.*, **72**, 623–630.

Quayle, J. R., and Keech, D. B. (1959b). *Biochem. J.*, **72**, 631–637.

Quayle, J. R., and Keech, D. B. (1960). *Biochem. J.*, **75**, 515–523.

Quayle, J. R., Keech, D. B., and Taylor, G. A. (1961). *Biochem. J.*, **78**, 225–236.

Raina, A., and Cohen, S. S. (1966). *Proc. natn. Acad. Sci. U.S.A.*, **55**, 1587–1593.

Reed, L. J., Gunsalus, I. C., Schnakenberg, C. H. F., Soper, Q. F., Boaz, H. E., Kern, S. F., and Parke, T. V. (1953). *J. Am. chem. Soc.*, **75**, 1267–1270.

Ribbons, D. W., and Evans, W. C. (1960). *Biochem. J.*, **76**, 310–317.

Roberts, R. B., Abelson, P. H., Cowie, D. B., Bolton, E. T. and Britten, R. J. (1955). "Studies of Biosynthesis in *Escherichia coli*". Carnegie Institution of Washington Publication No. 607.

Salamon, I. I., and Davis, B. D. (1953). *J. Am. chem. Soc.*, **75**, 5567–5571.

Sallach, H. J. (1956). *J. biol. Chem.*, **223**, 1101–1108.

Satyanarayana, T., and Radhakrishnan, A. N. (1962). *Biochim. biophys. Acta*, **56**, 197–199.

Schwink, I., and Adams, E. (1959). *Biochim. biophys. Acta*, **36**, 102–117.

Seubert, W., and Remberger, V. (1961). *Biochem. Z.*, **334**, 401–414.

Shilo, M. (1957). *J. gen. Microbiol.*, **16**, 472–481.

Shive, W., Ackermann, W. W., Gordon, M., Getzendaner, M. E., and Eakin, R. E. (1947). *J. Am. chem. Soc.*, **69**, 725–726.

Sjolander, J. R., Folkers, K., Adelberg, E. A., and Tatum, E. L. (1954). *J. Am. chem. Soc.*, **76**, 1085–1087.

Smith, J., and Kornberg, H. L. (1967). *J. gen. Microbiol.*, **47**, 175–180.

Srinivasan, P. R., and Sprinson, D. B. (1959). *J. biol. Chem.*, **234**, 716–722.

Srinivasan, P. R., Katagiri, M. and Sprinson, D. B. (1959). *J. biol. Chem.*, **234**, 713–715.

Stadtman, E. R., Cohen, G. N., LeBras, G., and de Robichon-Szulmajster, H. (1961). *J. biol. Chem.*, **236**, 2033–2038.

Stanier, R. Y. (1947). *J. Bact.*, **54**, 339–348.
Stephenson, M. (1930). "Bacterial Metabolism", 1st Edn. Longmans, London.
Stephenson, M. (1949). "Bacterial Metabolism", 3rd Edn. Longmans, London.
Stokstad, E. L. R., Hoffmann, C. E., Regan, M. A., Fordham, D., and Jukes, T. H. (1949). *Arch. Biochem.*, **20**, 75–82.
Stone, R. W., and Wilson, P. W. (1952). *J. Bact.*, **63**, 605–617.
Stoolmiller, A. C., and Abeles, R. H. (1966). *J. biol. Chem.*, **241**, 5764–5771.
Strominger, J. L. (1962). *In* "The Bacteria" (Ed. I. C. Gunsalus and R. Y. Stanier), Vol. 3, pp. 413–470. Academic Press, New York.
Sugiyama, K., Yano, K., Tanaka, H., Komagato, K., and Arima, K. (1958). *J. gen. appl. Microbiol.*, *Tokyo*, **4**, 223–240.
Swim, H. E., and Krampitz, L. O. (1954). *J. Bact.*, **67**, 419–425.
Theodore, T. S., and Englesberg, E. (1964). *J. Bact.*, **88**, 946–955.
Thijsse, G. J. E. (1964). *Biochim. biophys. Acta*, **84**, 195–197.
Tomisek, A. J., Kelly, H. J., and Skipper, H. E. (1956). *Arch. Biochem.*, **64**, 437–455.
Umbarger, H. E. (1961). *Cold Spring Harb. Symp. quant. Biol.*, **26**, 301–312.
Umbarger, H. E., and Umbarger, M. A. (1962). *Biochim. biophys. Acta*, **62**, 193–195.
Umbarger, H. E., Brown, B., and Eyring, E. J. (1960). *J. biol. Chem.*, **235**, 1425–1432.
Umbreit, W. W. and Gunsalus, I. C. (1949). *J. biol. Chem.*, **179**, 279–281.
Utter, M. F. and Keech, D. B. (1963). *J. biol. Chem.* ,**238**, 2603–2608.
Watson, J. D. (1965). "Molecular Biology of the Gene". Benjamin, New York.
Webley, D. M., Duff, R. B., and Farmer, V. C. (1955). *J. gen. Microbiol.*, **13**, 361–369.
Weimberg, R., and Doudoroff, M. (1955). *J. biol. Chem.*, **217**, 607–624.
Weiss, U., and Mingioli, E. S. (1956). *J. Am. chem. Soc.*, **78**, 2894, 2898.
Weiss, U., Davis, B. D., and Mingioli, E. S. (1953). *J. Am. chem. Soc.*, **75**, 5572–5576.
Weiss, U., Gilvarg, C., Mingioli, E. S., and Davis, B. D. (1954). *Science, N.Y.*, **119**, 774–775.
Wheelis, M. L., Palleroni, N. J., and Stanier, R. Y. (1967). *Arch. Mikrobiol.*, **59**, 302–314.
Willis, J. E., and Sallach, H. J. (1962). *J. biol. Chem.*, **237**, 910–915.
Wolfe, R. S., Woiln E. A., Wolin, M. J., Allam, A. M., and Wood, J. M. (1966). *Devs ind. Microbiol.*, **7**, 162–169.
Wood, H. G., and Werkman, C. H. (1936). *Biochem. J.*, **30**, 48–53.
Wood, H. G., Allen, S. H. G., Stjernholm, R., and Jacobson, B. (1963). *J. biol. Chem.*, **238**, 547–556.
Wood, J. M., and Wolfe, R. S. (1966). *Biochemistry, N.Y.*, **5**, 3598–3603.
Yaniv, H., and Gilvarg, C. (1955). *J. biol. Chen.*, **213**, 787–795.

CHAPTER V

Methods for Studying Enzyme Regulation

PATRICIA H. CLARKE

Department of Biochemistry, University College, London

I. INTRODUCTION

The study of enzyme regulation in micro-organisms has generated ideas which have become an accepted part of biology as a whole. Current knowledge of gene action and of protein synthesis owes much to early studies on adaptation and induced enzyme synthesis in bacteria. Many investigations are in progress to determine how far the theories developed from the study of control mechanisms in bacteria can be applied to enzyme regulation and cellular differentiation in higher organisms. Even among bacteria there is such variety of behaviour that it still remains to be established whether the results obtained from studying a relatively small number of control systems will be found to apply to all. Attempts are being made to discover in what way the mechanisms controlling synthesis of enzyme proteins apply to the regulation of synthesis of cell walls, cell membranes and other cell structures. Regulation of sporulation and of chromosomal replication and cell division are also under active investigation.

The methods used to study enzyme regulation include many different techniques. The core of any investigation is the development of reliable and sensitive enzyme assays using the techniques of the biochemist. The strains of micro-organisms used may be classic stock cultures or fresh isolates often obtained from enrichment cultures. Growth methods range from simple experiments in batch or continuous culture to those involving rapid changes in the growth media sometimes using radioactively labelled materials. The isolation of mutants and use of various methods of genetic recombination are of great importance. These techniques are described in detail elsewhere and this article is concerned with the design of experiments rather than with the details of their execution. Each system presents its own special problems and interest and from considering a number of different regulatory systems it has been possible to develop general theories of enzyme regulation.

This article will be restricted to the regulation of bacterial enzyme synthesis and, since it is difficult if not impossible to prove that an enzyme is not subject to regulation of some kind, it was necessary to impose a further self regulation and to limit the number of enzymes considered. This is therefore not a comprehensive survey of the subject. The enzyme systems discussed were chosen partly in order to illustrate the different methods used to study regulatory mechanisms and partly because they had been of particular interest to the author. References to many other enzyme systems will be found in the general reviews cited in the text.

A. Adaptation

The concept of adaptation to environment has been particularly fruitful with regard to the multitudinous activities of micro-organisms. Observations on the differences in enzymic activities of various moulds and bacteria grown in different chemical environments began to appear towards the end of the last century. By 1900 it had been shown that a glucose-grown yeast suspension fermented glucose immediately, but only fermented galactose after a lag period of several hours. This enzymic adaptation did not require growth of the culture. It was also observed that colonies of the bacterium now known as *Escherichia coli mutabile* growing on lactose endo-agar (see this Series, Volume 3A for media) appeared colourless, because they did not produce acid from the fermentation of lactose, but after a few days red papillae of lactose-fermenting bacteria appeared. When the lactose-fermenting bacteria were picked off and cultured, it was found that they retained their lactose-fermenting ability through subsequent generations. The adaptation of the yeast culture to galactose fermentation was an example of a solely phenotypic phenomenon and all the cells of the culture were able to acquire the property without a genetic change. On the other hand, the adaptation of *E. coli mutabile* involved first of all a genetic change producing mutant bacteria which, under appropriate conditions, could replace the original non-lactose-fermenting population. Many years were to elapse before the distinction between the two types of phenomena was clearly understood.

Karstrom (1938) studied the relationship between fermentative ability and the presence of the sugar substrates in the growth medium. He suggested that enzymes could be classified into "constitutive enzymes" which were always present and "adaptive enzymes" which were formed only in response to the substrate compound in the growth environment. Many studies were made on adaptive enzymes using washed suspensions of bacteria to avoid changes occurring in the microbial population. Evidence was produced to show that adaptive enzymes could be formed without any increase in the number of micro-organisms present, (e.g., formic hydro-genlyase, (Stephenson and Stickland, 1933); tetrathionase, (Knox and Pollock, 1944). Other experiments on adaptation were carried out by "training" micro-organisms through a large number of subcultures to grow on new substrates, and these were essentially experiments in mutation and selection.

The confusion resulting from the indiscriminate use of the term adaptation led Monod and Cohn (1952) to propose that phenotypic adaptive enzyme synthesis should be known as "induced biosynthesis of enzymes" and that the specific substance which brought about this synthesis should be known as the "enzyme inducer". The proof that enzyme induction depended on the *de novo* synthesis of enzyme protein (Hogness, *et al.*, 1955; Rotman and Spiegelman, 1954) meant that this system could be used to study both the events occurring during protein synthesis and the way in which protein synthesis was regulated. The finding that analogues of lactose could act as non-substrate inducers for β-galactosidase (Monod *et al.*, 1951) not only showed that enzyme induction could be dissociated from enzyme activity but also allowed the investigation of enzyme synthesis under conditions in which the inducer was not necessary for the growth of the bacterium. This was termed gratuitous induction.

B. End-product repression of enzyme synthesis

Specific repression of enzyme synthesis was first described by Monod and Cohen-Bazire (1953) who showed that tryptophan synthesis was selectively repressed by the addition of tryptophan or certain of its analogues to the growth medium. It was soon shown that repression of the synthesis of biosynthetic enzymes by their end-products is a general regulatory mechanism. Vogel (1957) and Gorini and Maas (1957) described repression by arginine of the enzymes involved in its biosynthetic pathway and Yates and Pardee (1956) described repression of the enzymes of the pyrimidine biosynthetic pathway. The significance of end-product repression in the regulation of biosynthetic pathways has been reviewed by Statdman (1963) and Cohen (1965).

Repression is not confined to biosynthetic enzymes. The alkaline phosphatase of *E. coli* is repressed by inorganic phosphate. Urease production by *Proteus rettgeri* is induced by urea and repressed by ammonia (Magana-Plaza and Ruiz-Herrera, 1967) and the nitrate reductase of *Chlorella* is induced by nitrate and repressed by ammonia (Morris and Syrett, 1963).

C. The glucose effect and repression by carbon compounds

The addition of glucose to media has long been known to produce marked changes in enzyme activity. Glucose represses the synthesis of many inducible enzymes including β-galactosidase of *E. coli* (Cohn and Monod, 1953). If a culture is grown in a medium containing both glucose and lactose the synthesis of β-galactosidase is repressed until the glucose has all been used. This results in diphasic or diauxic growth.

Neidhart and Magasanik (1956, 1957) pointed out the similarity between glucose repression of enzyme synthesis and end-product repression and suggested that glucose exerted its effect through its metabolic products. One or more of the intermediary metabolites produced from the breakdown of glucose might be expected to accumulate and could repress the synthesis of enzymes whose activity would lead to an accumulation of what would be essentially the same products. Magasanik (1961) suggested the term "catabolite repression". It was suggested that specific metabolites were responsible for the repression of individual enzymes.

D. Enzyme variation and growth conditions

1. *Growth phase*

In any medium considerable variation in the specific activities of enzymes may occur during the growth of the culture. It is common to harvest cultures in the stationary phase for metabolic studies although it is likely that biosynthetic enzymes are more active in cultures still in the exponential growth phase.

In some media, synthesis of one or more enzymes may be essential to initiate growth. This will mean that synthesis of these enzymes precedes any significant increase in cell mass. It is commonly observed that there is a growth lag if a culture is transferred to a medium containing a different carbon source requiring an inducible enzyme for an early step in its metabolism. However, a growth lag in a medium containing a different source may be due to the time needed to synthesize a specific permease rather than a metabolic enzyme.

2. *Complex and minimal media*

It is clear that in minimal media, containing inorganic salts and a single carbon source for growth, a greater variety of enzymes are required than in a complex medium containing a mixture of amino-acids, sugars and growth factors. Transfer of a culture from a complex to a minimal medium often results in a growth lag which can be related to the synthesis of an increased battery of enzymes. Transfer of a culture from a minimal to a complex medium is also accompanied by a transition period during which there is severe repression of synthesis of certain enzymes. When the new metabolic balance has become established the culture will be found to grow at a different rate. Growth is most rapid in complex media. In minimal media the mean generation time is related to the carbon compound used as growth substrate. Many studies have been made on the events occurring during the "shift-down" from complex to minimal medium and also during the corresponding "shift-up". Almost immediately on "shift-down" there is a decrease in the overall rate of protein synthesis and a decrease in the rate of RNA synthesis followed by a slowing down of DNA synthesis (Neidhardt, 1966). The subject was discussed in detail by Maaløe and Kjeldgaard (1966). The relation between growth rates, cell division and chromosomal replication was discussed by Lark (1966).

3. *Physico-chemical factors*

The growth of strict aerobes may be limited by oxygen availability and this may be reflected in changes in respiratory and other enzymes (Smith,

1961; Lascelles, 1962). More complex interactions are found with facultative aerobes which are capable of growth in both aerobic and anaerobic
environments. This is not a simple matter of using alternative enzyme
reactions. The specific activities of key enzymes may be quite different in
aerobically grown cultures from those of anaerobic cultures (Wimpenny,
1969). Metabolic pathways for assimilation of carbon compounds may also
change when the energy supplying reactions are switched from oxidation to
fermentation. pH changes in the medium have been found to have marked
effects on enzyme production. Gale (1943) reported that many enzymes were
produced in increased amounts if the cultures were grown in media maintained at a pH value away from the optimum pH for enzyme activity. It
was suggested that some enzymes, only produced in acid media, carry out
reactions which tend to neutralize the acids produced by the metabolic
activities of the culture. When fermentation products are assayed during
growth the succession of compounds produced is related to the pH changes
which occur.

Growth at different temperatures may be associated with changes in
enzyme specific activities. Some enzymes are formed preferentially at
particular temperatures. There may be differences in the temperature
stability of the enzymes or of their regulatory systems. For example, temperature sensitive mutants of *E. coli* have been described which produce a
thermolabile alkaline phosphatase and others in which the enzyme is
repressible at lower temperatures but constitutive at temperatures above
37 °C (Gallant and Stapleton, 1963).

Little information is available about the effect of ionic strength and
atmospheric pressure on enzyme regulation. Most investigators have been
concerned to measure the conditions which allow or inhibit growth. In
general, high salt concentrations inhibit enzymes extracted from non-
halophilic bacteria whereas many enzymes from halophiles have optimal
activity at these concentrations (Larsen, 1962).

II. CURRENT THEORIES OF ENZYME REGULATION

A. End-product inhibition

One type of control of the functioning of biosynthetic pathways is exerted
by inhibition of the first enzyme of the pathway by the end-product. An
increase in the concentration of the end-product therefore results in immediate slowing down of the entire pathway. Feedback inhibition by the end-
product can be thought of as the fine control of the functioning of the pathway. It is characteristic of end-product inhibition that there is little or no
chemical similarity between the end-product inhibitor and the substrate

of the enzyme, e.g., histidine inhibits the enzyme phosphoribosyl-ATP-pyrophosphorylase which is the first enzyme of the histidine pathway (Ames et al., 1961). The chemical dissimilarity of substrate and inhibitor, and the unusual properties of some of these enzymes, led Monod et al. (1963) to put forward the theory of allosteric interaction. They suggested that all enzymes subject to regulation by this type of inhibition had at least two binding sites, one for the substrate and one for the allosteric inhibitor. It was suggested that when the allosteric inhibitor was bound to the enzyme the conformation of the enzyme protein altered in such a way that its affinity for the substrate molecule was reduced. Gerhart and Schachman (1965) found that aspartic transcarbamylase of E. coli had binding sites for the substrate aspartate, and also for the end-product inhibitor of the pyrimidine biosynthetic pathway, cytidine triphosphate. The substrate and allosteric binding sites of aspartic transcarbamylase are carried on different protein subunits. The role of enzyme subunits in allosteric interactions was discussed by Monod et al. (1965) and has been reviewed by Cohen (1965, 1968), Gutfreund and Knowles (1967) and Haber and Koshland (1967).

End-product inhibition is a very straightforward and direct method of control of a linear biosynthetic pathway. However, an enzyme may carry out a reaction which is common to a number of different pathways. Inhibition of such an enzyme by one of its products could result in a reduction of the concentration of the common intermediate below that required to synthesize another metabolic product. Several systems have been found which overcome difficulties of this kind.

If an enzyme reaction is required for the biosynthesis of two different products there may be isoenzymes for the biosynthesis of the common intermediates, each regulated by one of the products e.g., in the biosynthesis of the aspartate family of amino-acids one aspartokinase of E. coli is inhibited by lysine and another by threonine. A number of different sites of feedback inhibition may occur and the first enzyme after each branch point may also be subject to feedback inhibition by the final product (Stadtman et al., 1961; Stadtman, 1963).

In some cases the inhibition is exerted by the combined effects of more than one of the products. Such concerted feedback inhibition was described by Datta and Gest (1964) for the aspartokinase of Rhodopseudomonas capsulatus which is inhibited by a combination of threonine and lysine. Jensen and Nester (1965) found that the biosynthesis of the aromatic amino-acids by Bacillus subtilis was regulated by feedback inhibition by prephenic acid and chorismic acid, which are the last of the common intermediates before the pathway branches first for tryptophan synthesis and then for phenylalanine and tryosine synthesis. The variety of combinations in which feedback inhibition operates in different bacteria was discussed by Datta and Gest (1964) and has also been reviewed by Cohen (1965, 1968).

The idea that end-product inhibition is exerted through allosteric interaction producing conformational changes in the enzyme protein is of very great importance in attempting to understand the molecular basis of induction and repression. In examining the total regulatory system it is often found that the end-product of a pathway produces both end-product inhibition of the first enzyme of the pathway and also repression of the synthesis of all the enzymes of the pathway. In carrying out experiments on the regulation of enzyme synthesis it is necessary to bear in mind that growth or enzyme activity may be affected by feedback inhibition as well as by repression of synthesis.

B. The operon theory of induction and repression

1. *The lac operon*

In 1961 Jacob and Monod outlined a theory of enzyme regulation which took into account both induction by substrate and repression by product. Their evidence was based mainly on experiments with β-galactosidase of *E. coli* but was able to account for the experimental results obtained with other systems. This paper contained several predictions which have since been substantiated and the main conclusions are widely accepted. It was suggested that there are two kinds of genes; structural genes, determining the amino-acid sequence of enzymes, and regulator genes whose function is to regulate the expression of the corresponding structural genes. The wild type *E. coli* is inducible for β-galactosidase but mutants had been isolated which produced enzyme in the absence of inducer. For this system the regulator gene was denoted as i^+ (inducible) in the wild type and i^- (non-inducible) in the constitutive mutant. When diploids were made containing both gene types, i^+/i^-, the strain was inducible which indicated that i^+ was dominant to i^-. Lactose utilization in *E. coli* requires the enzyme β-galactosidase, and a specific galactoside permease. Induction of these two proteins in the wild-type strain also resulted in the production of another enzyme, thiogalactoside transacetylase. Genetic experiments showed that the genes determining these three proteins were closely linked on the bacterial chromosome. The wild-type strain was phenotypically inducible for β-galactosidase (z gene), permease (y gene) and transacetylase (a gene) and had the genetic structure $i^+z^+y^+a^+$. When inducer was added to the wild-type strain the three proteins were co-ordinately induced and the same ratio of activities was found in the i^- constitutive strain so that it appeared that the synthesis of these proteins was regulated as a single unit. In a diploid i^+z^-/i^-z^+ strain β-galactosidase

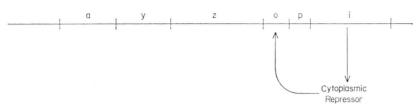

FIG. 1. *lac* operon repressed. The regulator gene *i* produces the cytoplasmic repressor protein which combines with the operator *o* and prevents the expression of the *lac* structural genes z, β-galactosidase; y, β-galactoside permease and a, thiogalactoside transacetylase. An inducer, e.g., isopropyl-β-D-thiogalactoside combines with the cytoplasmic repressor and releases it from the operator. Transcription of the polycistronic mRNA starts from the promotor p.

was inducible so that the *i* gene was active even when carried on a separate chromosomal segment. The i^+ character was therefore dominant in the *trans* position. Another class of constitutive mutants was isolated which behaved in a different way. The mutations mapped very close to the z gene and the mutants were constitutive if the mutation was carried on the same chromosomal segment but not if it was on a separate segment. These were termed o^c mutations. The strain was constitutive if it had the genetic structure $o^c z^+$ and diploids which were $o^c z^+/o^+ z^-$ were constitutive but diploids which were $o^c z^-/o^+ z^+$ were inducible. The o^c character was therefore dominant only in the *cis* position to the z gene. These genetic findings were important to the development of the operon theory.

It was suggested that the *i* gene produced a substance, the cytoplasmic repressor, which combined with the segment of the chromosome defined as the operator or *o* gene. The operator was thought to be required for the expression of the three structural genes z, y and a. These three linked genes under the control of a single operator were termed an operon or genetic unit of regulation. (see Fig. 1).

In developing this theory it was postulated that the first step in gene expression was the synthesis of a messenger RNA (mRNA) complementary to the DNA sequence of the structural genes. This process was termed *transcription*. Subsequent steps in the synthesis of the specific proteins required the sequence of bases in the mRNA to be translated into the sequence of amino-acids in the protein and this process was termed *translation*. The operator in an uninduced wild-type strain was normally blocked by the cytoplasmic repressor produced by the *i* gene but the cytoplasmic repressor could also combine with an inducer and when this occurred it was released from the operator and mRNA synthesis could take place. The only difference envisaged in the control of enzyme synthesis by end-product repression was that the regulator gene produced an inactive cytoplasmic repressor which was only able to combine with the operator if it had first combined with the low molecular weight co-repressor molecule.

During translation, protein synthesis takes place by the sequential addition of amino-acids to a polypeptide chain which remains bound to a ribosome until completed. A number of ribosomes are able to associate with a single mRNA forming a polysome so that a number of polypeptide chains are synthesized in succession. The ribosome is thought to move along the mRNA as the polypeptide chain is being formed. Each amino-acid is defined or coded by a triplet of bases in the mRNA (Crick *et al.*, 1961). Starting at the N-terminal end, the amino-acids are linked together in turn by peptide bonds. Before this stage each amino-acid is activated by a specific enzyme which also links it to a molecule of transfer RNA (tRNA). The tRNA molecules are of relatively small size (about 80 nucleotides) and there is at least one species of tRNA for each amino-acid. The tRNA functions as an adaptor molecule and carries a triplet sequence which acts as an anticodon to the triplet code on the messenger RNA defining the amino-acid at a particular place in the sequence.

The Jacob-Monod theory stated that the product of the regulator gene prevented transcription. It was considered that this explained the results better than action at some later step in protein synthesis. The operator was thought to be required for the initiation of transcription so that if it was blocked by the regulator gene product no protein synthesis could occur. If an operator was blocked in this way all the genes controlled by that operator would be repressed. This was a general theory and it has been subject to very critical examination to find out how far it could be applied directly or in a modified form to all enzyme regulation systems. It has in this way stimulated both experimentation and speculation. Discussion has centred round the existence and function of regulator genes, the chemical identity of regulator gene products, the existence of operons in other systems and their relation to regulator genes. At various times it has been suggested that destruction of mRNA is important in regulation of protein synthesis, that regulation occurs at translation and not transcription, or perhaps at both stages, and that regulation of synthesis of a protein is connected with its folding into the correct conformation for activity.

The chemical nature of the *i* gene product was in doubt for some time. Early experiments suggested that it could be a type of RNA (Pardee and Prestidge, 1959) but the specific binding properties required of the molecule were best fulfilled by a protein. Indirect experiments with a temperature sensitive regulator mutant (Horiuchi *et al.*, 1961) and experiments on the kinetics of the induction and repression of β-galactosidase (Sadler and Novick, 1965) were consistent with the properties to be expected of a protein. The isolation and identification of i^- mutations which could be suppressed by the type of suppressor mutations known to act at the translation stage made it almost certain that the i gene product was a protein (Bourgeois et al., 1965; Müller-Hill (1965). This was followed by the isolation by Gilbert and Müller-Hill (1966) of a protein which fulfilled the requirements for the *lac* cytoplasmic repressor and the isolation by Ptashne (1967) of the repressor for λ phage.

Gilbert and Müller-Hill (1966) isolated a mutant with a higher affinity for the inducer isopropyl-β-D-thiogalactoside (IPTG) than the wild type and when the repressor proteins were isolated it was found that the K_m for IPTG was $1\cdot3 \times 10^{-6}$M for the wild type and 6×10^{-7}M for the mutant. Gilbert and Müller-Hill (1967) found that the *lac* repressor had a high affinity for the DNA of the *lac* region and it was confirmed by Riggs, Newby and Bourgeois (1970) that compounds which were inducers *in vivo* also affected repression-operator interaction *in vitro*.

Striking evidence in favour of the operon as a regulatory unit was obtained by the isolation of mutants of *E. coli* in which the synthesis of the lactose enzymes had become controlled by adenine. A large deletion extended from the lactose operon to the operon for the biosynthesis of purines (Jacob et al., 1965). In these mutants the deletion extended into the z gene but they were still able to make β-galactoside permease and acetylase. The synthesis of these proteins was no longer regulated by induction by β-galactosides but was subject to repression by adenine. The deletion of a large segment of chromosome had therefore resulted in the formation of a new operon in which adenine repressed the lactose enzymes.

The operator was originally considered to be able to combine with the cytoplasmic repressor and also to be the site for initiation of mRNA transcription. However, a number of mutants were isolated by Scaife and Beckwith (1966) which had a greatly reduced maximum rate of synthesis of β-galactosidase and in which the o and i genes were unaltered. This new controlling element was termed the promotor (Jacob et al., 1964) and mapped between the i and o genes. It is thought to be the site of initiation of transcription by acting as the binding site for RNA polymerase (Ippen et al., 1968). Shapiro et al. (1969) devised a method for isolating the DNA of the *lac* operon in a pure form by using two specialized transducing bacteriophages carrying the *lac* operon inserted into their DNA in opposite directions. The *lac* operon DNA prepared by this method contained an intact z gene, the o and p regions with parts of the i and y genes and it was calculated that the o-p region consisted at the most of 410 base pairs.

2. Enzyme regulation systems

(a) *Evidence for operons.* Ames and Martin (1964) reviewed the evidence for the existence of operons for other enzyme systems. For the *gal* operon, Buttin (1963) found that the structural genes for the galactose enzymes of *E. coli* were closely linked. Mutations in an unlinked regulator gene produced constitutive mutants and the R^+ gene was shown to be active in the *trans* position to the structural genes. These mutants behaved like the *lac i$^-$* constitutive mutants. Other constitutive mutants, were isolated in which the constitutivity character could be co-transduced with the structural genes. These mutations were dominant in the *cis* position only, and were thought to be O^c mutations. The *gal* operon is considered to be also under negative control (Saedler *et al.*, 1968).

Genetic mapping has shown that in *E. coli*, and *Salmonella typhimurium*, genes for related enzymes may occur in closely linked clusters on the bacterial chromosome. Synthesis of the enzymes may be co-ordinately regulated. Very elegant studies by Ames and Garry (1959) and Hartman *et al.* (1960) showed that the histidine genes are closely linked, and regulated co-ordinately. The genes for the ten enzymes of this unbranched pathway form a very large operon and the mechanism of its regulation has been intensively studied. More than a thousand mutants have been mapped in this gene region (Ames and Hartman (1963)). Mutants which behaved as operator mutants were mapped at the extreme end of the structural genes beyond, or within *his G* which determines the first enzyme of the pathway (Ames *et al.*, 1963; Roth *et al.*, 1966a). Other regulator mutants were isolated and mapped and it was concluded that regulation of histidine biosynthesis could be altered by mutation in one of at least four genes, none of which appeared to be a regulator gene of the *lac i* type. It was suggested that the effective co-repressor in this sytem is histidyl-tRNA and Roth *et al.* (1966) discuss a number of possible ways in which it could act.

The genes for the tryptophan pathway are thought to form a single operon in *E. coli* and an operator region has been identified near the first of the five genes (Imamoto *et al.*, 1966). A single regulator gene was found unlinked to the operon (Cohen and Jacob, 1959; Ito and Crawford, 1965). In *S. typhimurium* the tryptophan genes are arranged in a similar operon, but Margolin and Bauerle (1966) found that while this forms a single unit of regulation, it is composed of two subunits with respect to expression so that it consists of an operon with a single operator but two promotors. Ramakrishnan and Adelberg (1965) found that the closely linked genes for the isoleucine-valine pathway were not all repressed in the same way and suggested that there were at least two operator sites.

The genes for some other biosynthetic enzymes in *E. coli* are known to be unlinked in spite of having some common regulation. The arginine enzymes are scattered around the chromosome. Baumberg *et al.* (1965) suggested that there was a common repressor and that each gene, or small gene cluster, had its own recognition site. Jacoby and Gorini (1969) showed that although arginine represses its biosynthetic enzymes in *E. coli* K 12 and slightly stimulates their biosynthesis in *E. coli B*, the regulator *arg R* gene is allelic in the two strains. They suggest that each cluster of *arginine* structural genes has an operator with an affinity for the repressor produced by the *arg R* gene.

The methionine genes are also scattered, but like the histidine system, there are several regulator genes and methionyl-tRNA may be involved in repression (Lawrence *et al.*, 1968).

(b) *Transcription and translation.* The Jacob-Monod model for regulation of gene expression envisaged the product of the regulator gene acting on the operator and preventing transcription of the mRNA. Most of the alternative theories of enzyme regulation have centred about control at the translation level. There have been several variations on the idea that the mRNA remained bound to the DNA of the gene unless translation was initiated or, in some variations, completed. Suggestions were made that inducers (or repressors) were concerned with the correct folding of the enzyme protein (e.g., Cline and Bock, 1966; Cohen, 1966). Rather too much emphasis was laid on the similarity of inducer and substrate as support for this type of interaction. Whatever the mechanism, it is not unreasonable to suppose that an enzyme should be regulated by an inducer molecule either the same or closely related to the substrate. Stent (1964) saw mRNA synthesis as dependent on all the components necessary to complete translation and suggested that the regulator genes produced enzymes which were capable of removing the terminal nucleotides from certain rare species of tRNA.

Cline and Bock (1966) pointed out that it has usually been assumed that end-product inhibition and repression of enzyme synthesis were two different and unrelated processes. They suggested that the sensitive site in regulation could be the nascent polypeptide chain linked to tRNA. In some cases this could be the allosteric regulatory subunit of the enzyme sensitive to end-product inhibition and in other cases it would be a catalytically active subunit. The configuration of the nascent peptide could be such that it would block further synthesis of itself, but this conformation could be modified by interaction with other polypeptides such as regulator gene proteins of the *i* type. Maas and McFall (1964) had suggested that the operator could produce a specific protein which regulated transcription through allosteric interaction with inducers, co-repressors, DNA and possibly *i* gene products. If the operator were within the structural gene for the first enzyme, this would then implicate that enzyme in regulation of transcription of its own mRNA. In the regulation model put forward by Cline and Bock (1966) two (or more) proteins or nascent polypeptide chains are thought to interact at the site of protein synthesis. The interaction was considered to be dependent on the conformation of the protein molecules which could be modified by allosteric interaction with inducers or co-repressors. This interaction would result in stopping both protein synthesis and mRNA transcription by immobilizing the ribosomes.

The isolation of polarity mutations in several systems drew attention to the relation between transcription and translation. In the histidine operon, for example, mutation in one of the structural genes was shown to result in a decrease in the amounts of the enzymes coded by genes on the side of the mutation furthest from the operator. (Ames and Hartman, 1963). Polarity mutations were shown to be due to the presence of nonsense codons which could be counteracted by the appropriate suppressor genes. Martin (1963) had shown that the histidine operon produced a giant messenger RNA and it was clear that the polarity mutations affected the rates of translation of the different cistrons.

It is now thought that translation of mRNA follows rapidly on the heels of transcription. For the tryptophan operon the transcription of the polycistronic messenger after derepression takes 8 min. A tightly packed cluster of ribosomes (100–200) is believed to translate each molecule following closely behind the RNA polymerase down the nascent chain. Imamoto *et al.* (1966) found that some of the polar mutations resulted not only in a decrease in the distal enzymes but also a decrease in the lengths of mRNA molecules. Morse and Yanofsky (1969) suggest that the untranslatable parts of the mRNA molecule of polar mutants are not covered with ribosomes and are exposed to attack by endonucleases. The mRNA molecules are normally degraded by exonucleases in the same direction as transcription and translation (5′→3′). (Morikawa and Imamoto, 1969; Morse *et al.*, 1969).

(c) *Positive control.* Most enzyme regulation theories have included the negative type of control put forward by Jacob and Monod (1961) for the *lac* operon in which a regulator gene protein prevents gene expression. A totally different system was suggested for the regulation of the arabinose enzymes in *E. coli*. Three linked structural genes for the arabinose enzymes and an unlinked permease gene, were found to be controlled by a single regulator gene. In this system the product of the regulator gene *ara C* is necessary for the expression of the structural genes. Mutants which are *ara C⁻* cannot be induced and the *ara C⁻* mutations are recessive to *ara C⁺*, inducible, and *ara Cᶜ*, constitutive (Sheppard and Englesberg, 1966, 1967).

Englesberg *et al.* (1969) put forward a modified scheme of positive control for this system which envisaged that the initial product of the *ara C* gene was a repressor P 1 in equilibrium with the activator P 2. The repressor P 1 combines with the operator *ara o* and is removed by the inducer arabinose which shifts the equilibrium to produce more of the activator P 2 which combines with the initiator *ara I* and thereby stimulates the expression of the arabinose structural genes.

Jones-Mortimer (1968) found that mutations in the *cys B* and *cys E* genes affected the synthesis of all the cysteine biosynthetic enzymes and concluded that O-acetylserine synthesized by the enzyme controlled by *cys E* combined with the product of gene *cys B* to exert positive control of the expression of the structural genes.

Henning *et al.* (1966) have suggested that the pyruvate dehydrogenase complex may be subject to a form of positive control in which one of the enzymes regulates its own synthesis. Properties of regulatory mutants of the maltose (Schwartz, 1967) and rhamnose (Power, 1967) enzyme systems have indicated that they may also be subject to positive control.

III. ENZYME MEASUREMENTS

The choice of methods for enzyme assays depends on the enzymes being studied and the information required. For experiments involving a large number of assays it is an advantage to have a chromogenic substrate which will allow a simple and rapid assay. It may also be useful to devise methods for assaying, or at least detecting, the enzyme in bacterial colonies and during preparative procedures, e.g., on paper or starch or polyacrylamide gels. For extremely sensitive assays radioactive methods have been found to be suitable. Fluorescent substrates have been used for sensitive assays and also for examining enzyme synthesis by single cells. Immunological methods have been widely used to compare mutant proteins.

If whole cells can be used for the enzyme assays it is often possible to devise very simple and speedy methods. However, the cells may not be freely permeable to the substrates, especially if substrates with attached chromogens are employed, but it may be possible to increase permeability by adding surface active agents or solvents which partially disrupt the cell membrane. The variations in specific activity in experiments with induced enzymes are very great and it may be necessary to check that a treatment which increases substrate permeability sufficiently at low levels of enzyme activity, is also suitable for samples with very high specific activity. More complete methods of cell disruption may be required, e.g., ultrasonication, Hughes press, French press, Mickle shaker etc. details of which are given by Hughes *et al.* (Vol. 5B this Series).

A. Experimental methods

Brief examples will be given of the types of methods employed for assaying a few of the enzymes which have been widely used for studying enzyme regulation. Many other examples of the methods used for looking at particular enzymes and for studying metabolic pathways will be found in Sections V and VI. The original papers should be consulted for complete experimental details. Permease methods are discussed in Sections VII and methods devised for mutant isolation in Section VIII.

1. *β-Galactosidase*

β-Galactosidase activity has been measured by most workers by following the rate of hydrolysis of *o*-nitrophenyl-*β*-D-galactoside (ONPG). The cells of *E. coli* are not very permeable to ONPG and permeability is increased by shaking with toluene.

There are variations of detail in the methods used for treating samples for assays. Moses and Prevost (1966) took 0·2 ml samples of cultures and mixed with 20 µl of chloramphenicol (1 mg/ml) to arrest enzyme synthesis. One drop of toluene was added and after vigorous agitation for 20 sec with a vortex mixer the *β*-galactosidase activity was measured at 37°C with ONPG as substrate. Detailed methods are also given by the following authors: Lederberg (1950); Pardee (1957); Paigen (1963); Loomis and Magasanik (1964) and Beggs and Rogers (1966). Dobrogosz (1966) defined a unit of activity as that amount of enzyme that hydrolyses 1 µmole ONPG per h at 30°C in the presence of 2×10^{-3}M ONPG, $1 \cdot 24 \times 10^{-4}$M glutathione and 0·05M sodium phosphate buffer, (pH 7·5). ONPG has also been used to detect *β*-galactosidase in bacterial colonies and on paper or gels. Indicator media have been used to distinguish colonies producing *β*-galactosidase by acid production from lactose (see Section VIII).

2. *Alkaline phosphatase*

Alkaline phosphatase in *E. coli* and other bacteria has usually been assayed with *p*-nitrophenyl phosphate as substrate without pretreatment of the cells to increase permeability (Garen and Levinthal, 1960; Torriani, 1960; Neumann and Vreedendaal, 1967). Other phosphate esters may be used, e.g., *α*-naphthyl phosphate (Seal *et al.*, 1966) or indoxyl phosphate Tsou and Su, 1965). The chromogenic phosphate esters have also been used to detect the enzyme in bacterial colonies and on paper or gels.

3. Penicillinase

Methods for measuring or detecting penicillinase activity have been reviewed by Hamilton-Miller *et al.* (1963) and Citri and Pollock (1966). Many different methods are available for measuring the activity of the enzyme. Sensitive microbiological methods are based on the assay of residual penicillin by a penicillin-sensitive organism. Colour changes in pH indicators, resulting from the formation of penicilloic acid, have been used for detecting penicillinase in bacterial colonies. Assays have been based on titration of the carboxyl group. Several methods have employed iodometric estimation of penicilloic acid (e.g., Perret, 1954; Novick, 1962). Penicillinases have been found to attack several substituted penicillins, with different side-chains, and also a number of substituted cephalosporins. The wide substrate range has been used to compare penicillinases from different bacterial strains (Pollock, 1965a; Richmond, 1965). Immunological comparisons have been made of penicillinases from different organisms and also those obtained by mutations (Pollock, 1965b).

4. Amidase

The aliphatic amidase of *P. aeruginosa* has been assayed by estimating the ammonia released by hydrolysis (Kelly and Clarke, 1962) or by acyl-hydroxamate formation (Brammar and Clarke, 1964). Ester hydrolysis was measured by a titrimetric method (McFarlane *et al.*, 1965). All the methods were suitable for using with whole cells. The enzyme was detected on starch gels or paper either by hydroxamate formation or by a Nessler reaction for the ammonia released by hydrolysis. The range of substrate and inducer specificities made it possible to select mutants with altered enzyme or regulation properties (Brown and Clarke, 1966; Brammar *et al.*, 1967).

B. Samples for enzyme assay

If assays are being carried out on samples from growing cultures it is often convenient to store them in ice in order to carry out a number of assays at the same time. If the enzyme is being synthesized rapidly it is advisable to add chloramphenicol to give a final concentration of 100 μg/ml, at the time of sampling to prevent further enzyme synthesis. Many enzymes remain stable for many hours under these conditions but the enzyme stability may vary with the growth conditions of the culture. The specific activity of samples from carbon-starved batch cultures, or from carbon-limited continuous cultures, may fall off markedly when stored at 0°C. Samples from cultures in the logarithmic or stationary phase of batch culture grown with an excess of the growth substrate in the medium are likely to be much more stable. If samples have to be kept some time before assay it may be most convenient to store them in the frozen state.

C. Automated enzyme assays

It may be worth setting up automated enzyme assays for regulation studies in which a large number of assays are required. Automated enzyme analysis would be particularly useful for continuous assays where the enzyme level is expected to exhibit periodicity. All the simpler spectrophotometric assays can be readily adapted to automation. The Technicon system (Technicon Instruments Co. Ltd., Hanworth Lane, Chertsey, Surrey) is very widely used and can either be applied to discrete samples or used with a continuous flow system. Enzyme samples are fed into a stream of buffer, diluted as required, and mixed with substrates and reactants. The assay mixture is fed through an incubation vessel and then further reagents may be led in before the assay samples reach the measuring device. This is usually a recording spectrophotometer. The apparatus is designed on a module basis and can be adapted to fit individual methods. The system can also be adapted for multiple enzyme analysis so that variations in several enzymes can be followed at the same time. The principles of automated enzyme analysis are described fully by Roodyn (1968). see also Ferrari and Marten (this Series, Vol. 6B).

IV. ENZYME MEASUREMENTS WITH BACTERIAL SUSPENSIONS

A. Preparation of cell suspensions

It is convenient to consider methods using resting cell suspensions separately from those using growing cultures, not because they are fundamentally different but because they are frequently used for rather different types of investigation. Washed cell suspensions have usually been prepared from cultures harvested from the stationary phase (frequently equated with overnight growth), the bacteria are washed and resuspended in an appropriate solution. Similar experiments have been carried out with preparations made from bacteria harvested from exponential growth, from continuous culture or from cultures allowed to become starved by exhausting the carbon or nitrogen source in the medium (or any other essential nutrient). For many purposes it may be unnecessary to go through the procedure of washing and resuspending the bacteria in buffer or fresh medium, but this is a useful way of concentrating the material if the enzyme activity is low.

The simplest approach to the study of enzyme regulation is to compare the enzyme activities of suspensions prepared from cultures grown under different conditions. Such investigations have included the effects of possible inducers and repressors, carbon and nitrogen sources, growth factors and the less specific effects of temperature pH etc. This has been a standard procedure in investigating metabolic pathways. When mutants have been available this type of direct enzyme analysis has yielded a great deal of information and it has formed a preliminary stage in almost all investigations. When the enzyme assays are particularly difficult it may be the only type of enzyme comparison which can be used. If it is sufficient to establish that an enzyme, or group of enzymes, is regulated in a particular way by environmental conditions, then these measurements of enzyme activities of cell suspensions may be all that it required. Co-ordinate regulation of enzyme synthesis is usually established by direct comparison of the activities of the group of enzymes when the cultural conditions for the organism (and its mutants) are subjected to experimental variation. This method is of general application and no examples will be given here but many instances of its use may be found in later sections.

B. Enzyme synthesis by cell suspensions

Washed suspensions, or other cell preparations, have also been used for experiments on rates of enzyme synthesis. Although most workers now use spectrophotometric methods of enzyme assay, the classical technique in this field has been that of manometry. The high Q_{O_2} (or Q_{CO_2}) values of microbial systems have made this an attractive method for microbiologists since a great deal of information can be obtained with a very little material using relatively simple and cheap apparatus. In all such experiments it is assumed that the culture is "non-growing". This state is seldom defined but usually means that if measurements were to be made there would be no significant increase in cell numbers. Before the nature of enzyme induction was understood the idea of using a "non-growing" culture was highly regarded. The nitrogen for the synthesis of new enzyme can be accounted for by the turnover of protein which is greater than that in actively growing cultures (Willetts, 1967). It is sometimes useful to use starved cells in these experiments to ensure that catabolite repression is minimal. This can be achieved either by harvesting from a carbon-limited medium or by pre-incubating the washed suspension in the absence of growth substrates.

Manometric methods with washed cell suspensions were used by Cain (1958) and Cartwright and Cain (1959) to investigate the microbial metabolism of nitro-aromatic compounds. Washed suspensions of *Nocardia erythropolis*, grown on *p*-nitrobenzoate, took up oxygen immediately on the addition of *p*-nitrobenzoate while those grown in broth or a glucose-asparagine medium showed lags of up to 2 h before the oxygen uptake exceeded the endogenous value. Shilo and Stanier (1957) found similar lags in the oxidation of the tartrate isomers by pseudomonads, but in this case the induction lag involved both the synthesis of the specific dehydrases and the specific tartrate permeases. Similar observations have been made on many other oxidative enzymes but although this method is now much less widely used, it can contribute to a more detailed investigation of enzyme regulation.

The amount of information which can be obtained from experiments with washed suspensions is usually limited. The rate of enzyme synthesis is very much lower than in actively growing cultures (Mandelstam, 1961) and it is difficult to analyse the metabolic events going on in the cells. There are however some systems in which these methods can yield results which are less easy to obtain by other means. Clarke and Brammar (1964) used carbon-starved cells, without harvesting from the medium, to examine the effect of the amide analogue repressor, cyanoacetamide, on the induction of amidase in *Pseudomonas aeruginosa*. Values were obtained for the rates of enzyme induction at different concentrations of the non-substrate inducer, N-acetylacetamide, in the presence and absence of cyanoacetamide. Plots of the reciprocal of the rates of induction against the reciprocal of the inducer concentrations were similar to Lineweaver-Burke competitive enzyme inhibition graphs. A value was obtained for K_{Ind} for N-acetylacetamide of about 1 mM and an "inhibitor constant" for cyanoacetamide of 50 μM. Similar results were obtained with acetamide as inducer with a K_{Ind} of 7 μM and the same value of "inhibitor constant" for cyanoacetamide (Brammar, 1965; Clarke, 1970).

V. ENZYME SYNTHESIS DURING GROWTH

A. Comparative measurements

With growing cultures it is possible to measure the differential rates of enzyme synthesis with respect to the growth and total protein synthesis of a culture. This is of particular value in the study of induced enzymes when the addition of inducer results in a large increase in enzyme activity over a short period of time. If non-substrate inducers are available the inducer concentration can be kept constant during the experimental period. When the investigation has been concerned with the comparison of a large number of different mutant strains, or with enzyme synthesis in a variety of different media, relatively simple experimental design has been employed. The cultures have been allowed to grow in the presence of inducer through one or two generations and the enzyme activities have been measured at the end of this time. Dubnau and Pollock (1965) compared penicillinase synthesis of mutants of *Bacillus licheniformis* in the presence and absence of added inducer. Overnight cultures were diluted ten-fold with fresh medium and incubated until they reached a standard cell density. The cultures were then divided into two parts one of which received a standard amount of inducer (Cephalosporin), and incubated for a further $1\frac{1}{2}$ h when the penicillinase activities were determined. The experiments gave values for the "induction ratio" (specific activity of induced culture/specific activity of uninduced culture) of the mutants under standard conditions and were used to discriminate between the different phenotypes. Brammar *et al.* (1967) used similar methods to compare mutants of *Pseudomonas aeruginosa*.

B. Gratuitous enzyme induction

Substrate inducers are of limited value for kinetic studies since they are destroyed as the enzymes are induced. The introduction of non-substrate inducers and the concept of gratuitous induction made it possible to examine enzyme induction at a constant inducer concentration. Jacob and Monod (1961) compared a number of galactosides as inducers and substrates of β-galactosidase and galactoside transacetylase. Isopropyl-β-D thiogalactoside (IPTG) was found the most effective non-substrate inducer and this compound or methyl-β-D-thiogalactoside (TMG) has been extensively used for studying regulation of the *E. coli* lactose system. After a very short lag, the differential rate of enzyme synthesis is linear for several generations. The differential rate is related to the concentration of the non-substrate inducer and increases with concentration until the system reaches saturation. Most workers have used 5×10^{-4}M IPTG in induction experiments. β-Galactosidase, β-galactoside permease and transacetylase were co-ordinately induced both by substrate and non-substrate inducers and this was part of the evidence that they were regulated as a single operon.

The galactose enzymes were studied in the same way by Buttin (1963). Of a number of galactose analogues only fucose was an effective non-substrate inducer. It was not utilized as a carbon source for growth and the differential rate of enzyme synthesis was linear for at least an hour. It was found that growth in the presence of fucose co-ordinately induced the synthesis of galactokinase, epimerase and transferase. A specific galactose permease was induced at the same time but while the structural genes for the three enzymes were closely linked and co-transduced the permease gene was found to be located at some distance on the bacterial chromosome.

Some of the mono-N-substituted aliphatic amides were found to be non-substrate inducers for the amidase produced by *P. aeruginosa* (Kelly and Clarke, 1962) and of these N-acetylacetamide at 10^{-2}M was used to measure gratuitous enzyme induction in cultures growing on different carbon sources, as well as with non-growing suspensions. Other amides were found to compete with the inducing amides and to prevent amidase

11

induction. It was shown that at least one of these amide analogue repressors, cyanoacetamide, had no effect on the entry of acetamide and N-acetylacetamide into the cells (Brammar *et al.*, 1966). In exponentally growing cultures thioacetamide and cyanoacetamide acted as competitive repressors for the induction of amidase by N-acetylacetamide or acetamide (Brammar and Clarke, 1964).

Müller-Hill *et al.* (1964) found that in a similar way 2-nitrophenyl-β-D-fucoside (ONPF) was a specific competitive repressor of induction of the proteins of the *lac* operon of *E. coli* by TMG. The conclusion that the interaction was with the cytoplasmic repressor produced by the *i* gene, was supported by the effects of ONPF on β-galactosidase synthesis by constitutive mutants. In *i⁻* mutants which were not affected by TMG there was no repression by ONPF, but in mutants with defective but partially functional *i⁻* gene products, TMG induced further β-galactosidase synthesis and ONPF decreased the amount below that in the absence of added inducer.

Buttin (1963) found that TMG and IPTG repressed the induction of the galactose group of enzymes by fucose and McBrien and Moses (1966) showed that the extent of the repression depended on the relative concentration of fucose and IPTG. In this system also, the analogue repression is probably due to competition at the inducer-binding site of the cytoplasmic repressor.

C. Early events in induction

Detailed kinetic studies showed that there was a lag of a few minutes after the addition of inducer before β-galactosidase synthesis reached constant and linear rate. The events during this first period have been investigated in several ways. Nakada and Magasanik (1964) exposed exponentially growing cells of *E. coli* to inducer (IPTG) for 3 min only. At this time no β-galactosidase had been synthesized. The inducer was then removed and they showed that β-galactosidase was synthesized for about 10 min in the inducer-free medium. If the pyrimidine analogue 5-fluorouracil was added at the beginning of the experiment there was no synthesis of β-galactosidase, but it had no effect on enzyme synthesis if it was added after the induction period when the cells were already synthesizing the enzyme. The 3 min induction period was therefore thought to be due to the time taken to synthesize the specific messenger RNA for β-galactosidase synthesis. Alper and Tompkins (1965) looked at the order of induction and deinduction of the enzymes of the lactose operon and found that β-galactosidase began to appear about 3 min after the addition of inducer (IPTG) and transacetylase 2 min later. On removal of inducer by dilution transacetylase was synthesized for about 2 min longer than β-galactosidase.

Képès (1967) also examined the times at which β-galactosidase and transacetylase appeared and concluded that transcription and translation were both sequential. Synthesis of the enzymes was measured during periods of about 10 min after adding IPTG. The lag before transacetylase appeared was decreased in a deletion mutant and the results were compatible with the hypothesis that the polycistronic messenger was sequentially translated from the operator end. Burstein *et al.* (1965) compared the induction lags for β-galactosidase synthesis using IPTG and lactose as inducers. While, as had been found previously, there was a lag of about 3 min with IPTG as inducer, the lag with lactose was about 10 min and it was concluded that lactose was not itself an inducer of the enzyme but was converted in the bacterial cell into the effective inducer molecule. When the *lac* repressor was isolated it was found that it had a very high affinity for IPTG but not for lactose, which supported the conclusions made from these kinetic experiments. (Gilbert and Müller-Hill, 1966; Riggs *et al.*, 1970).

The early events in the induction of histidase in *Bacillus subtilis* were examined by Hartwell and Magasanik (1963). The authors pointed out that a sensitive and simple assay had to be developed to detect the small amounts of enzyme present at this time. They were unable to find a non-substrate inducer for the enzyme in this organism so they grew the cells on glutamic acid which, although a product of the histidase pathway, has no repressing activity. In this medium the enzyme was not required by the culture and histidine itself could be regarded as a gratuitous inducer. Histidase appeared 5 min after the addition of inducer to the culture. When actinomycin was added at the same time as inducer no histidase was synthesized but if it was added after 5 min histidase was formed initially at the same rate as in the culture without actinomycin, but the rate decreased with time. On the assumption that the actinomycin prevented the further synthesis of messenger RNA it was calculated that the half-life of the histidase mRNA was 2·4 min. Leive (1965) made *E. coli* permeable to actinomycin by brief treatment with EDTA and concluded that the synthesis of the β-galactosidase mRNA required 2·5 min of the 4 min interval between adding inducer and detecting enzyme synthesis.

The experiments of Hartwell and Magasanik (1963) and Nakada and Magasanik (1964) suggested that mRNA was freely formed during the induction period before enzyme synthesis could be detected. From this it followed that transcription preceded, and could be separated from, the process of translation. In experiments with β-galactosidase Nakada and Magasanik (1964) added 50 μg/ml chloramphenicol to inhibit protein synthesis and found that this did not prevent induction and that β-galacto-sidase was formed after the chloramphenicol was removed. Mehdi an Yudkin (1967) pointed out that this amount of chloramphenicol was insufficient to block protein synthesis completely. They carried out similar experiments but used the catabolite-insensitive strain of *E. coli* LA-12G isolated by Loomis and Magasanik (1965). When 500 μg/ml chloramphen-icol was added during the induction period there was no subsequent forma-tion of β-galactosidase. They suggested that transcription of mRNA is normally linked to translation and movement of the ribosomes along the nascent m-RNA.

D. The Kinetics of enzyme repression

Cultures of *E. coli* grown in media with limiting phosphate were found to have very high alkaline phosphatase activities. Torriani (1960) examined the kinetics of synthesis and repression of this enzyme in exponential cultures. In a glucose minimal salt medium with 0·2 mM phosphate the culture grew at a rate of one doubling an hour until the phosphate con-centration in the medium had fallen to a minimal value. The growth rate then fell rapidly to about a fifth of the earlier rate and at this time the alka-line phosphatase began to be synthesized. The differential rate of enzyme was high and remained linear for about 3 h. When inorganic phosphate was added to the culture the original growth rate was resumed and the synthesis of alkaline phosphatase was completely repressed. The rapid response of the culture in repression of synthesis of alkaline phosphatase on the addition of phosphate was therefore similar to the rapid induction of an enzyme such as β-galactosidase after the addition of an inducer. However, repression and derepression of alkaline phosphatase in these experiments was accompanied by changes in the growth rate of the culture.

The kinetics of derepression of alkaline phosphatase in *B. subtilis* have been studied by Moses (1967). Cultures growing exponentially were resus-pended in phosphate-free medium. The alkaline phophatase activity was measured on samples treated with chloramphenicol to prevent further enzyme synthesis and it was found that enzyme activity appeared about 10 min after removal of phosphate from the culture. Enzyme-forming potential appeared after about 6 min and during this time total RNA synthesis was diminished. When inorganic phosphate was added back to the phosphate-free medium the overall RNA synthesis increased and the synthesis of alkaline phosphatase fell off rapidly during the following 6 min. Enzyme-forming potential was equated with specific messenger RNA synthesis in the experiments of Nakada and Magasanik (1964) with β-galactosidase and these experiments with the alkaline phosphatase of *B. subtilis* were also designed to shed light on the molecular events occurring early in regulation. When actinomycin was added RNA synthesis was initially inhibited and alkaline phosphatase synthesis ceased after a few minutes as the enzyme-forming potential decayed. In the presence of chloramphenicol the amount of enzyme-forming potential which developed in the cells was about the same as in the controls without chloramphenicol during the same period. These experiments were interpreted, as were those of Nakada and Magasanik (1964), to mean that the synthesis of mRNA was independent of enzyme synthesis and that regulation of alkaline phosphatase by repression was effected at the level of transcription only. The concentration of chloramphenicol used in these experiments was 15 μg/ml and it is possible, as suggested by Mehdi and Yudkin (1967) for β-galactosidase, that some small amount of protein synthesis had taken place during the period of incubation with chloramphenicol when the enzyme-forming potential had developed.

From studies on the kinetics of synthesis of the polycistronic mRNA of the tryptophan operon Morikawa and Imamoto (1969) concluded that it took 8 min to complete transcription and that translation and degradation of *trp* mRNA started before transcription was completed. The *trp* genes can be attached to prophage ϕ80. The amount of *trp* mRNA was determined by pulse-labelling with ^{3}H-uridine and measuring the amount of RNA/DNA hybrid formed with ϕ80 prophage DNA carrying part or all of the *trp* operon (Imamoto *et al.*, 1966; Morse and Yanofsky, 1969).

E. Catabolite repression

The existence of catabolite repression was first inferred from experiments in which the presence of glucose or other compounds in the growth medium had been shown to decrease the activity of certain bacterial enzymes. Mandelstam (1961) showed that many metabolizable carbon compounds were also able to repress induction of β-galactosidase in non-growing suspensions of *Escherichia coli*. Most investigators have worked with exponential cultures and investigations have been designed to determine the site of action of the catabolite repressor, the chemical identity of the repressing molecule and the relationship between induction and repression.

A simple method of comparing the catabolite repressor action of carbon compounds is to use each of them as carbon source for growth and to measure the differential rate of enzyme synthesis of induced enzymes. The carbon source allowing the highest rate of enzyme synthesis is then usually employed as the standard medium for testing catabolite repression. On this criterion glycerol was found to be a less effective catabolite repressor for β-galactosidase than glucose (Moses and Prevost, 1966) and pyruvate a much less effective catabolite repressor for amidase than succinate (Brammar et al., 1967).

The search for a specific catabolite repressor for β-galactosidase has implicated at one time or another almost all the known metabolites of glucose as well as coenzymes such as ATP and the pyridine nucleotides. The observations of Cohn and Horibata (1959) that β-galactosidase synthesis during aerobic growth in a glucose medium could be derepressed by making the culture anaerobic, suggested that repression might be associated with a high growth rate and a high rate of energy production. Okinaka and Dobrogosz (1967) showed that cultures which had been derepressed by being made anaerobic could be repressed again by adding nitrate to the culture. The changes in glucose metabolism during the switching on and off of repression of β-galactosidase were followed by measuring the release of $^{14}CO_2$ during growth of the cultures on specifically labelled glucose. They concluded that catabolite repression was closely associated with oxidative decarboxylation of pyruvate. This association of catabolite repression with a fast growth rate and rapidly metabolized substrates has been observed with many other enzyme systems.

Experiments carried out by Mandelstam (1962) had indicated that catabolite repression could not be reversed by adding inducer. In a more detailed kinetic study Clark and Marr (1964) concluded that there were two stages of catabolite repression and that one stage could be reversed by adding more inducer and the other was not reversible by inducer. Another way of approaching the problem was suggested by some experiments of Paigen (1966). Cultures of E. coli were transferred from a medium containing glycerol to a medium containing a β-galactosidase inducer, and either glucose or glycerol as the carbon source. The synthesis of β-galactosidase began within a few minutes in the glycerol medium but there was a lag before the enzyme was induced in the glucose medium. The lag did not occur if non-induced cultures were grown on glucose and then transferred to the medium containing glucose and inducer. Since the bacteria eventually became induced to form β-galactosidase this was termed transient repression by glucose. Moses and Prevost (1966) showed that glucose repression could be partially reversed if a sufficient amount of a powerful inducer such sa IPTG were added to the culture.

A mutant insensitive to catabolite repression by glucose was isolated by Loomis and Magasanik (1965) and the mutation was found not to be linked to the lac opcron but to map near the tryptophan genes. Loomis and Magasanik (1967) suggested that the wild type produced another cytoplasmic repressor which combined with a genetic region contiguous with the lac operon This mutation was not specific for β-galactosidase since it affected the repression of other enzymes as well.

Silverstone *et al.* (1969) showed that mutants in the promotor region were insensitive to catabolite repression and suggested that catabolite repression affected transcription by interfering with the binding of RNA polymerase. Such a mechanism would require some specificity of RNA polymerases such as that reported for the enzymes occurring during bacteriophage infection (Burgess *et al.*, 1969) and sporulation (Losick *et al.*, 1970). A low molecular weight metabolite could combine with one of the RNA polymerase subunits to induce transcription or to prevent transcription. Perlman and Pastan (1968) reported that cyclic adenosine 3′,5′-monophosphate (cyclic AMP) stimulated β-galactosidase synthesis in inducible and constitutive strains and overcame transient repression by glucose but had no effect on a mutant with a deletion in the promotor region. Other workers have suggested that catabolite repression affects translation (Yudkin and Moses, 1969) and Yudkin (1969) suggests that transcriptional and translational control may vary in different strains. The extensive literature on catabolite repression was reviewed by Paigen and Williams (1970).

F. Continuous culture

The growth of bacteria in continuous culture (see Tempest *et al.*, this Series, Vol. 2) can be used to examine many aspects of enzyme regulation. The cell density in chemostat culture can be kept constant by limiting the carbon source for growth or by limiting the supply of an essential nutrient. Gorini (1958) grew an arginine-requiring mutant of *E. coli* in continuous culture with limiting arginine and measured the level of ornithine transcarbamylase activity. At very low arginine concentrations the arginine was rapidly utilized for growth and the level of ornithine transcarbamylase remained constant. It was concluded that at these concentrations the control on arginine biosynthesis was exerted by feedback inhibition. As the arginine concentration was increased the synthesis of ornithine transcarbamylase was increasingly repressed. This experiment demonstrated the different roles played in enzyme regulation by the "fine control" of feedback inhibition and the "coarse control" of enzyme repression. Gorini (1960) also showed that at a fixed arginine concentration the extent of repression was dependent on the flow rate of the medium. Under these conditions repression by arginine was relieved by ornithine and the greater the repression the more ornithine was required to relieve it.

By altering the flow rate of the medium and by using different growth substrates it is possible to produce wide variations in the internal environment of cells growing in continuous culture. Many observations have been made on the amount of growth, cell chemical composition and product formation, but there have been very few attempts to make direct studies on enzyme regulation. McFall and Mandelstam (1963) studied catabolite repression of three enzymes of *E. coli*, β-galactosidase, serine deaminase and tryptophanase in continuous culture in glycerol medium with growth limited by low magnesium concentration. In these experiments the cultures were first grown in flask culture in the presence of inducers and were then washed, transferred to the continuous culture apparatus and supplied with the glycerol magnesium-limiting medium. The extent of repression of synthesis of the three enzymes was followed as the cultures adjusted to the steady state. In another experiment the serine deaminase and tryptophanase activities were measured in cultures growing in continuous culture following the addition of pyruvate and an increase in the flow rate of the incoming medium.

When more than one carbon compound is provided for growth in continuous culture some interesting problems of regulation can arise. Boddy *et al.* (1967) grew cultures of *P. aeruginosa* in the steady state at various dilution rates on succinate as the carbon source. The incoming medium was then changed to one containing succinate plus acetamide and measurements were made on amidase synthesis. At low flow rates amidase was synthesized very rapidly after only a very short lag. At higher flow rates this lag increased, and at the highest flow rates there was almost no increase in amidase activity 4 h after the inducer had been added to the medium. In a further series of experiments it was shown that not only could induction and repression of amidase synthesis be studied in the transition period during which the culture had been disturbed by alterations in the incoming medium but induction and repression could also be studied in the steady state at different flow rates.

Clarke *et al.* (1968) grew the wild-type *P. aeruginosa* 8602 in a succinate plus acetamide medium and found that there was a sharp peak of maximum amidase activity at a dilution rate of about 0.35 h^{-1}. It was thought that the two parts of the curve, as the amidase activity fell off, at the lower and higher dilution rates, could be due to the effects of induction and catabolite repression respectively. Constitutive mutants had maximal amidase activity at low dilution rates and the enzyme activities then fell off as the dilution rate increased. Semi-constitutive mutants gave curves intermediate between that of the wild type and a related fully constitutive mutant. Mutants with altered catabolite repressibility gave curves which fell off less steeply at the higher dilution rates which lent support to the view that catabolite repression was responsible for the falling off in enzyme synthesis as the flow rate, and hence the growth rate of the culture, was increased. In these experiments it was concluded that the specific activity of this enzyme in continuous culture in steady state conditions was determined by the balance between induction and catabolite repression and that catabolite repression was directly related to the growth rate of the culture.

The differences between the constitutive mutants, semi-constitutive mutants, mutants with altered catabolite repressibility and the wild type, were very clearly shown by their different regulatory response.

Hamlin *et al.* (1967) examined the regulation of glucose and citrate enzymes in *P. aeruginosa* 2F32 in continuous culture. This organism exhibits an unusual growth diauxie in that when inoculated into a glucose plus citrate medium the citrate is utilized in preference to glucose until the citrate has almost all been utilized. In continuous culture it was shown that the extent of induction of glucose enzymes in the presence of a constant citrate concentration was directly related to the concentration of exogenous glucose. In a nitrogen-limiting medium, at a constant citrate concentration, there was no significant induction of eight different enzymes concerned with glucose metabolism when the glucose concentration was less than a third of that of the citrate. Induction could be effected either by increase in the glucose concentration or by reducing the citrate concentration. Ng and Dawes (1967) concluded that these enzymes were under dual control with glucose serving as an inducer and citrate as a precursor of a repressor.

Continuous culture can be a very powerful tool for the study of enzyme regulation during growth. It is particularly suitable for looking at the interactions of regulatory mechanisms. As soon as the steady state is disturbed in any way for any one enzyme system it will have repercussions on many other systems. Fluctuation in enzyme activity also produces fluctuations in concentrations of intracellular metabolites. Goodwin (1963, 1966) suggested that oscillations in enzyme synthesis could occur in systems controlled by feedback mechanisms and would be found in continuous culture. Oscillations in extracellular pyruvate concentrations have been described by Sikyta and Slezak (1965) for *E. coli* growing in continuous culture on lactate. Oscillations were found in amidase activity of *P. aeruginosa* by Boddy *et al.* (1967) and in β-galactosidase activity in *E. coli* by Goodwin (1969).

VI. THE REGULATION OF METABOLIC PATHWAYS

A. Catabolic pathways

When investigations were made on the intermediate steps in catabolic pathways it was frequently found that the necessary enzymes were only present if the substrate had been included in the growth medium. It soon became clear therefore, that to study the sequence of steps in a metabolic pathway was to become involved in problems of regulation. This could however work both ways. If the metabolic route was not already known, the simplest method of finding out about it might be to see which of the possible enzymes were induced by the substrate being investigated. Regu-

lation of catabolic pathways has been studied in many bacteria and it is
now possible to see that very elegant regulatory mechanisms have evolved
which allow wide flexibility, in potential growth substrates and metabolic
pathways, and yet maintain an efficient and balanced economy in enzyme
synthesis.

The methods used at various times to study the oxidation of aromatic
compounds by pseudomonads reflect the evolution of enzyme methodology
and ideas on regulatory mechanisms. Stanier (1947, 1950) used mainly
manometric methods and was greatly assisted by finding that most of the
enzymes were inducible. He was able to establish the main reactions in the
oxidation of tryptophan and benzoic acid derivatives and concluded that
the synthesis of these enzymes was regulated by sequential induction. By
this it was meant that in a pathway $A \rightarrow B \rightarrow C \rightarrow D$, the first substrate A
induced the first enzyme thereby producing B, and B induced the second
enzyme and so on. The regulation of these pathways was re-examined by
Ornston and Stanier (1964), Palleroni and Stanier (1964), Mandelstam and
Jacoby (1965), Stevenson and Mandelstam (1965), Hegeman (1966a),
Ornston (1966) and Ornston and Stanier (1966).

Hegeman (1966a) showed that the first five enzymes of the mandelate
pathway were co-ordinately regulated. These enzymes carry out the
reactions D-mandelic acid→L-mandelic acid→benzoylformic acid→benz-
aldehyde→benzoic acid. (There are two benzaldehyde dehydrogenases.)
The first three compounds were shown to be equipotent inducers of all
five enzymes. Enzymes acting at later stages in the pathway, beyond benzoate, were not induced co-ordinately with the mandelate enzymes.
Hegeman (1966a) used exponential cultures, disrupted the cells by sonica-
tion and stored the cell extracts in ice until assays could be made. All the
enzymes were assayed by spectrophotometric measurements. Three of
these methods were adapted to give very sensitive radioassays for measuring
the basal enzyme levels. From the results obtained, Hegeman (1966a) was
able to conclude that, the synthesis of these enzymes was normally severely
repressed. The basal enzyme level could not be measured at all by the
standard spectrophotometric assays. The rates of synthesis of two of these
enzymes was increased 2000-fold in the presence of DL-mandelate.
Hegeman (1966b, c) isolated mutants which were defective for some of
these enzymes and also mutants which synthesized all five enzymes
constitutively. He concluded that the five enzymes formed a single regulation group. (see Fig. 2).

Mandelstam and Jacoby (1965) obtained similar results with *Pseudomonas
putida* and showed that benzoate repressed the synthesis of the mandelate
group of enzymes. Benzoate is further metabolized to catechol, β-keto-
adipate and succinate. The synthesis of the mandelate group of enzymes

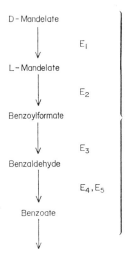

FIG. 2. Pathway for oxidation of mandelate to benzoate. The same enzymes oxidize p-hydroxymandelate to p-hydroxybenzoate. The enzymes are co-ordinately regulated as a single regulation group in *Pseudomonas putida* (after Hegeman, 1966a).

was also repressed by catechol and succinate and the repression could be largely overcome by the addition of mandelate as inducer. They suggested that the pathway was regulated by induction and by multi-sensitive end-product repression. In these experiments glucose was used as the carbon source since it did not appear to repress synthesis of the enzymes. Stevenson and Mandelstam (1965) found that p-hydroxymandelate oxidation was regulated in the same way. p-Hydroxymandelate was metabolized to p-hydroxybenzoate by the mandelate enzymes with the corresponding hydroxy compounds acting as substrates and end-product repressors.

Benzoate induced the synthesis of benzoate oxidase and the synthesis of this single enzyme was repressed by catechol, succinate and acetate. The next group of enzymes were induced in the presence of catechol and at least one of these was found to be repressed by succinate. These enzymes appeared to form another regulation group. The repression of enzyme synthesis was not due to inhibition of permease activity since the bacteria were freely permeable to the compounds tested. The experiments of Mandelstam and Jacoby (1965) and Stevenson and Mandelstam (1965) were carried out with cultures growing in a glucose minimal medium and after about one generation samples were removed for enzyme assay. Oxygen uptake by whole cells was determined by manometric methods and some enzymes were assayed in cell free extracts.

The regulation of the later group of enzymes was studied in more detail by Ornston (1966). The details of the pathways for the conversion of proto-catechuate (from hydroxybenzoate) and catechol (from benzoate) to the common intermediate β-ketoadipate were completed by the isolation of two new intermediates (Ornston and Stanier, 1966). Regulation was studied by examining which enzymes were subject to co-ordinate induction and by identifying the inducers, using the wild-type strain and mutants blocked in one of the enzymes. The wild-type strain was not permeable to most of the intermediates and the investigation was helped by finding some mutants with increased permeability. In *Pseudomonas putida* catechol oxygenase was found to be induced, not by catechol, but by its product *cis, cis,* muconate, which was also the inducer for the next two enzymes. These two enzymes, but not catechol oxygenase, were co-ordinately induced so that there were two separate regulation units. Further metabolism depended on the induction of the next enzyme by its product β-ketoadipate, but at the same time and co-ordinately, it induced two earlier enzymes belonging to the hydroxybenzoate-protocatechuate pathway. These enzymes were required for growth on the hydroxyaromatic compounds but were produced gratuitously when the organism was growing on mandelate or benzoate. The regulation of these pathways is summarized in Fig. 3.

Palleroni and Stanier (1964) found similar complex regulatory relationships for the enzymes of tryptophan catabolism. The first two enzymes of this pathway were also induced by their product, kynurenine. The tryptophan products are converted to catechol in fluorescent pseudomonads so that this pathway converges with the pathway for benzoate and mandelate. The regulation of these pathways is therefore achieved by induction of the first group of co-ordinately regulated enzymes followed by the sequential induction of the next group which in some cases is a single enzyme. At the convergence points, and where there are intermediates which can serve independently as growth substrates, a new induction sequence begins.

The evolution of a different regulatory pattern for these pathways was described in *Moraxella calcoacetica* by Cánovas and Stanier (1967). The metabolic pathways are chemically identical but the enzyme regulation is very different. There is a much higher degree of co-ordinate regulation in *Moraxella* and the absence of sequential induction at the point of convergence of the catechol and protocatechuate pathways has been solved by the separate regulation of isoenzymes for the final steps. This diversity of regulation of synthesis of enzymes of convergent catabolic pathways bears some resemblance to the diversity of feedback inhibition patterns which have been found for the branched pathways for the biosynthesis of amino-acids (Datta and Gest, 1964).

Of the many other catabolic pathways which have been studied it is

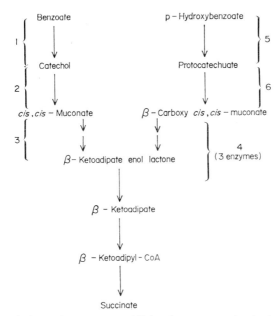

FIG. 3. Regulation of enzymes oxidizing benzoate and p-hydroxybenzoate in *Pseudomonas putida*. The probable inducers for the different regulation groups of enzymes are as follows: Group 1, Benzoate; Groups 2 and 3, *cis, cis*-Muconate; Group 4, β-Ketoadipate; Group 5, β-Hydroxybenzoate; Group 6, Protocatechuate (after Cánovas and Stanier, 1967).

interesting to note that the inducer of the enzymes of the histidine catabolic pathway in *P. aeruginosa* and in other bacterial species was found to be urocanate which is the product of the first enzyme. The first two enzymes of the pathway were very sensitive to catabolite repression and were co-ordinately repressed (Lessie and Neidhardt, 1967).

B. Biosynthetic pathways

The means used to establish the details of biosynthetic pathways differed in several respects from those used to establish catabolic pathways. While it was commonly found that a growth substrate would induce a high specific activity of some or all of the enzymes of a catabolic pathway there was no such simple method of making use of regulatory mechanisms to identify enzyme reactions and sequences in the biosynthetic pathways. In most cases mutants were isolated with requirements for amino-acids, or other essential cellular constituents, and the particular metabolic block identified. Cross-feeding of mutants helped to locate the metabolic blocks and with a sufficiently wide range of mutants available the pathways could

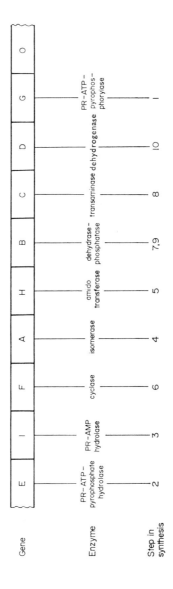

Fig. 4   Histidine operon. Genes and enzymes (after Roth et al., 1966a).

be defined with reasonable certainty and confirmed by studying the reactions of cell-free extracts. Not until the outlines of many of the bio-chemical pathways for amino-acid biosynthesis had been established did it become clear that the synthesis of many biosynthetic enzymes was regulated as a unit.

Ames *et al.* (1960) showed that four of the enzymes required for histidine biosynthesis by *Salmonella typhimurium* were co-ordinately repressed by histidine. Hartman *et al.* (1960) found that the histidine-requiring mutants could be arranged in several classes according to the genetic grouping, the enzymes produced and the metabolic intermediates accumulated and that the genes for the entire pathway could be co-transduced and were therefore closely linked. A total of ten enzymes are now known to be required for this pathway and the structural genes form the gene cluster of the histidine operon (Roth *et al.*, 1966b) (Fig. 4).

Ames *et al.* (1960) found that growth on formylhistidine allowed a much higher level of enzyme activity in the mutants. Formylhistidine was very slowly hydrolysed to histidine so that a state of histidine starvation was produced leading to derepression of the enzymes. Derepression of the mutants was also achieved by growth on histidinol, instead of histidine, and the wild type was derepressed by growth in minimal media containing 1,2,4-thiazole-3-alanine which produces "false feedback" inhibition of the first enzyme of the pathway. Derepression was always co-ordinate for all the wild-type enzymes and for the enzymes which the mutants were still able to produce. The specific activity varied from a repressed level of 1 up to 75 for some of the derepressed mutants (Ames *et al.*, 1963).

Regulatory mutants were isolated in which the histidine operon was not fully repressed so that they produced fairly high levels of the histidine biosynthetic enzymes. All the mutants could be further derepressed when they were grown on limiting histidine so that it appeared that their regula-tion was impaired and not completely freed from histidine control. They were classified into four genetic groups located at different sites on the chromosome. (Roth *et al.*, 1966a). The *his O* class was located near the *his G* structural gene and was thought to be similar to the operator consti-tuitive mutants of other systems. The *his S* class were mutants for the structural gene for histidyl-tRNA synthetase and mutants of the *his R* class had only about half the normal amount of histidyl-tRNA. No definite role was assigned to the *his T* gene. The histidine permease gene (*his P*) was located elsewhere (Shifrin *et al.*, 1966). From these results it was concluded that histidyl-tRNA played an essential part in the regulation of the histidine operon. The interpretation that it acted as the corepressor for a cytoplasmic repressor of the Jacob-Monod model (possibly produced by *his T*) was thought to be less likely than some form of control involving translation. A system in which the folding of the first enzyme, produced by gene G was the point at which a transcription/translation control operates was discarded for several reasons discussed by Roth *et al.*(1966b). The feedback insensitive mutants and feedback supersensitive mutants, derepress normally; feedback inhibitors do not repress, and non-metabolizable repressors do not produce feedback inhibition; histidine is the feedback inhibitor and histidyl-tRNA appears to be the repressor and nonsense mutations in gene *his G* are subject to normal repression.

Regulation of methionine biosynthesis has also been found to be complex. Lawrence *et al.* (1968) have found that mutants of *E. coli* which have become less sensitive to methionine repression also fall into several classes and that at least three genes are involved in regulation. (See also Section VIII).

C. Central metabolic pathways

The idea that enzymes could be rigidly divided into inducible and constitutive, led to very productive experimentation with enzymes whose activities could be varied 100- or 1000-fold. It was tacitly assumed that most of the enzymes of the central metabolic pathways were not subject to regulation of this kind. More exact enzyme measurements and critical analysis of metabolic pathways has shown variation in the activities of many of these enzymes under different growth conditions although of a much less dramatic order.

In most aerobic bacteria it is now established that the terminal steps in catabolism can be carried out by the reactions of the tricarboxylic acid cycle. Complex molecules such as proteins and polysaccharides are first split into their monomeric units. Metabolic pathways for the breakdown of amino-acids, sugars, fatty acids, aromatic compounds etc. then converge by producing such compounds as pyruvate or acetyl-coenzyme A or intermediates of the tricarboxylic acid cycle such as succinate or α-oxoglutarate. In addition to its catabolic role, the tricarboxylic acid cycle also serves as a starting point for many biosyntheses. It has therefore a particularly important part to play in metabolism under almost all growth conditions. Kornberg (1966a) has pointed out that when bacteria are grown on C_2 and C_3 compounds, the utilization of intermediates of the tricarboxylic acid cycle for biosynthesis makes it imperative for additional reactions to occur which allow the net synthesis of C_4 compounds and thus the replenishment of the tricarboxylic acid pool.

Growth of *E. coli* and pseudomonads on acetate as carbon source involves the reactions of the tricarboxylic acid cycle and two additional reactions requiring the enzymes isocitrate lyase and malate synthase (Kornberg, 1966b). A molecule of acetyl-CoA is condensed with oxaloacetate by the

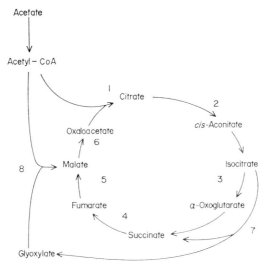

FIG. 5. Reactions of the Tricarboxylic Acid and Glyoxylate Cycles. The enzymes are numbered as follows: 1, Citrate synthase; 2, Aconitase; 3, Isocitrate dehydrogenase; 4, Succinate dehydrogenase; 5, Fumarase; 6, Malate dehydrogenase; 7, Isocitrate lyase; 8, Malate synthase.

enzyme citrate synthase to form citrate, which is then isomerized to isocitrate. Isocitrate lyase converts isocitrate to a molecule of succinate and a molecule of glyoxylate. Another molecule of acetyl-CoA is condensed with the glyoxylate by the action of malate synthase. These two reactions thus bypass part of the tricarboxylic acid cycle and allow for the net synthesis of a molecule of succinate from two molecules of acetate (see Fig. 5). When *Pseudomonas ovalis* Chester was grown on various carbon sources it was found that the specific activity of isocitrate lyase was highest for acetate-grown cultures. (Kornberg *et al.*, 1958). In *E. coli* the specific activities of both isocitrate lyase and malate synthase were ten-fold greater in cultures grown on acetate than on succinate, malate or lactate. There was also an increase in the specific activity of citrate synthase in acetate-grown cultures.

A possible interpretation of these results was that isocitrate lyase was induced by acetate, but Kornberg (1963) showed that isocitrate lyase activity was not increased by the addition of acetate to *E. coli* growing on a number of different carbon sources. Isocitrate lyase was formed when acetate was added to cultures growing on glutamate, but this did not occur with mutants lacking citrate synthase. This suggested that acetate could be acting by removing a repressing metabolite. Further evidence was obtained by examining mutants of *E. coli* with other enzyme defects (Kornberg,

1966b). Pyruvate was able to repress isocitrate lyase synthesis in mutants lacking part of the pyruvate dehydrogenase complex, and also in mutants lacking phosphoenolypyruvate carboxylase. Mutants lacking both phosphoenolpyruvate carboxylase and phosphoenolpyruvate synthase, and therefore unable to convert pyruvate to phosphoenolpyruvate, were not repressed by pyruvate, but were repressed by glucose from which phosphoenolpyruvate was produced by the reactions of the Embden-Meyerhof pathway. It was concluded that isocitrate lyase synthesis was regulated by repression by phosphoenolpyruvate or a closely related compound. Thus a combination of studies on the specific activities of isocitrate lyase in cultures of *E. coli* (and other species of bacteria) grown on different carbon sources, measurements of the kinetics of enzyme synthesis and repression, and of growth inhibition of wild-type and mutant strains, was able to define the regulation of the synthesis of this enzyme (Kornberg, 1966b). It is of interest that fine control of the operation of the glyoxylate cycle also appears to involve phosphoenolpyruvate which is an allosteric inhibitor of isocitrate lyase activity (Ashworth and Kornberg, 1963).

Control of isocitrate lyase synthesis by an intermediate such as phosphoenolpyruvate means that compounds other than acetate may be metabolized in such a way that the level of the intracellular repressor falls sufficiently to allow gratuitous enzyme synthesis. This occurs when *E. coli* (Ashworth and Kornberg, 1964) and *P. aeruginosa* (Skinner and Clarke, 1968) are grown on propionate. An acetate-negative mutant of *P. aeruginosa* with a very low citrate synthase activity was found to have about a third of the isocitrate lyase activity of the wild type when grown on succinate. In this case the defect in citrate synthase activity may have allowed the internal concentration of the metabolic repressor to reduce the isocitrate lyase activity below the level normally produced on succinate.

When organisms are grown in complex media and amino-acids are already available, the role of the tricarboxylic acid cycle may be entirely catabolic. Gray *et al.* (1966) compared the amounts of the tricarboxylic acid enzymes produced by *E. coli* grown under various nutritional conditions and in the presence or absence of oxygen. The bacteria were grown under very carefully controlled conditions of pH and aeration and the cultures were harvested in the exponential growth phase so that very exact enzyme comparisons could be made on bacteria provided with different growth problems. In a minimal salt medium with glucose as the carbon source the ratios of the specific activities of the enzymes of aerobically and anaerobically grown bacteria varied between two-fold for fumarase up to 20-fold for malic dehydrogenase and aconitase. The differences in the specific activities of these enzymes in aerobic and anaerobic growth conditions was not so marked if pyruvate or gluconate replaced glucose as the carbon source. The effect of glucose in reducing the enzyme activities under anaerobic conditions was even greater when the bacteria were grown in complex media. It was concluded that in a complex medium the tricarboxylic acid cycle functions in a purely catabolic role in terminal respiration and this function could be induced or repressed by aerobic or anaerobic conditions.

At a high glucose concentration in minimal medium, energy production from the reactions of the Embden-Meyerhof pathway would be high, even under aerobic conditions, so that the role of the tricarboxylic acid cycle would be mainly biosynthetic. It was suggested that the enzymes were regulated in three separate groups: (a) those metabolizing tricarboxylic acids, (b) those metabolizing 5-carbon dicarboxylic acids and (c) those metabolizing 4-carbon dicarboxylic acids. This most important enzymes for biosynthesis were thought to be those of group (a) leading up to the production of α-oxoglutarate and glutamic acid.

Hanson and Cox (1967) examined the effect of different nutritional conditions on the regulation of some of the tricarboxylic acid enzymes in *E. coli* and species of *Bacillus*. For some of the experiments with *B. licheniformis* and *B. subtilis* they used freshly germinated spores which do not contain detectable amounts of the tricarboxylic acid cycle enzymes. The cultures were grown up to a standard cell density under the test conditions. In a glucose minimal medium, when the tricarboxylic acid cycle was providing the precursors for biosynthesis of amino-acids, there was severe repression of aconitase when α-oxoglutarate, glutamate, arginine or proline was added to the medium. The specific activities of isocitric dehydrogenase, succinic dehydrogenase, malic dehydrogenase and fumarase were not affected. Succinate and malate had no effect on the synthesis of aconitase. They concluded that the actual co-repressor of aconitase synthesis was either α-oxoglutarate or glutamate. Isocitrate dehydrogenase is also necessary for α-oxoglutarate synthesis but was not repressed by glutamate or amino-acids giving rise to glutamate. Some of the experiments were carried out in continuous culture with limited nitrogen. Under these conditions the nitrogen supplied was efficiently used up for protein synthesis and it was again found that α-oxoglutarate and glutamate produced severe repression of aconitase. From these results it appeared that the regulation of aconitase is independent of that of isocitric dehydrogenase, succinic dehydrogenase and fumarase. However, the specific activities of all the tricarboxylic acid cycle enzymes tested was lower in media containing glucose or glycerol than in media containing acetate as the carbon source. This suggested a dual regulatory control with compounds such as glucose repressing the catabolic functioning of the cycle and α-oxoglutarate repressing the biosynthetic function. In *E. coli* Hanson and Cox (1967) found that glutamate repressed the synthesis of aconitase, isocitrate dehydrogenase and fumarase but not malate dehydrogenase, so that the regulation pattern differed from that of the *Bacilli*.

In *P. aeruginosa* glucose is metabolized mainly by the Entner-Doudoroff pathway and the specific activities of these enzymes is markedly higher in glucose-grown cultures. Hamlin *et al.* (1967) found that the specific activity of glucose-6-phosphate dehydrogenase was 30 times higher in glucose-grown cells than in citrate-grown cells. It is interesting to note that in the same experiment the aconitase specific activity of citrate-grown cells was twice that of glucose-grown cells. The presence of peptone repressed the synthesis of aconitase and isocitric dehydrogenase. As was discussed previously, these two enzymes are particularly important when the tricarboxylic acid cycle is required for biosynthetic purposes. The inducible nature of the glucose enzymes was confirmed by experiments in continuous culture, and it was also shown that repression of the glucose enzymes by citrate could be overcome by increasing the glucose concentration.

Regulation of the central metabolic pathways especially with respect to the balance of catabolism and biosynthesis and the interlocking of separate pathways, has been relatively neglected in micro-organisms. The main reason for this is that much more spectacular enzyme differences can be measured for enzymes which are not invariably required by the organism than for those involved in reactions essential for metabolic integration and balanced cell growth. These central metabolic enzymes are likely to be under much more rigorous control, and to understand them it may be necessary to employ more exacting conditions of metabolic disturbance and mutants whose defects have been carefully tailored to the particular metabolic problems.

VII. PERMEABILITY

The existence of a permease for galactosides was postulated in order to explain the anomalous kinetics of β-galactosidase synthesis at low inducer concentrations. Cohen and Monod (1957) reviewed the evidence for β-galactoside permease and defined permeases as stereospecific permeation systems, functionally specialized and distinct from metabolic enzymes. They suggested that the entry of most organic molecules into bacterial cells probably required specific transport systems of this kind and examined the evidence then available for such systems. A permeability barrier for a particular compound can be demonstrated when the enzyme activity of cell extracts is found to be higher than that of whole cells (although in some cases this could be due to *in vivo* enzyme inhibition). A mutant of *E. coli* had been described by Doudoroff *et al.* (1949) which grew well on maltose but could only metabolize glucose very slowly. This was a typical example of crypticity to a substrate due to impermeability. It was known that in some systems adaptation to a substrate required protein synthesis, even though the metabolic enzymes were already present in whole cells, and from such experiments it was concluded that adaptation could involve the synthesis of stereospecific permeases. Adaptations of this kind were cited as evidence for specific permeases for the acids of the tricarboxylic acid cycle (Barrett and Kallio, 1953; Kogut and Podoski, 1953; Clarke and Meadow, 1959) and for the tartrate isomers (Shilo and Stanier, 1957). Since many experiments on enzyme regulation are carried out with intact cells, and often with actively growing cultures, it is essential to know as much as possible about the permeation systems present. In studying the rates of enzyme induction and repression and the effects of analogues it is particularly important to be able to distinguish between events which occur within the cell and those which are due to the properties of the permease.

Képès and Cohen (1962) reviewed in detail the experimental findings which had accumulated on permease systems for sugars, amino-acids, inorganic ions and various organic compounds such as the tricarboxylic acids. They pointed out that permeability systems provided important regulatory mechanisms. The rate-limiting step for lactose utilization was β-galactoside permease so that as lactose entered the cell it would be rapidly metabolized without superfluous accumulation of glucose and galactose. Yet, with a low external lactose concentration, the action of the permease would be to increase the internal concentration of lactose to a sufficient level to allow enzyme induction. The constitutive amino-acid permeases on the other hand, allowed immediate feedback inhibition and repression by exogenous amino-acids.

The experimental results necessary to demonstrate a permease were listed by Képès and Cohen (1962) as follows: (1) accumulation of a natural substrate above the external concentration; (2) accumulation of a non-metabolizable analogue; (3) specific crypticity as opposed to normal utilization; (4) specific crypticity for a substrate analogue known to compete with metabolic enzymes *in vitro*. Since these conditions can only be fully satisfied if there are non-metabolizable analogues for the system and if mutants are available which either lack metabolic enzymes or lack the specific permease it is not surprising that there are few systems for which the requirements have been completely fulfilled.

A method widely used to study permease activity was to measure the rate of uptake by incubating a bacterial suspension with a radioactively labelled compound and removing samples at intervals for radioactivity assays after rapid filtration on millipore filters. Although this technique was most satisfactory when used with non-metabolizable substrates it was also used with some success for compounds which could be metabolized by the bacteria. Similar results for the kinetics of accumulation were obtained with many different substrates. Sugars and their derivatives, and certain amino-acids were taken up rapidly by cell suspensions of *E. coli* (induced if necessary) and the accumulation plateaued out after 5–10 min (Képès and Cohen, 1962). Uptake of radioactively labelled amides by *P. aeruginosa* followed a similar pattern (Brammar et al., 1966). Many, although not all, of these permease systems were inhibited by metabolic inhibitors such as dinitrophenol or sodium azide. These results suggested that the process of accumulation was energy requiring. In the experiments on rates of accumulation and maximum steady state levels of the test compound, some of the effects of inhibitors could have been due to an increase in the exit rate rather than a decrease in the rate of intake. Models for permease mechanisms based on the β-galactoside permease which include a consideration of exit as well as entrance systems were discussed by Képès and Cohen (1962) and by Koch (1964). These were derived from purely kinetic data.

The substrate specificity of β-galactoside permease distinguished it from other sugar permeases and also from β-galactosidase. However, both β-galactosidase and the permease were co-ordinately induced by the same compounds, and genetic studies showed that the permease gene (y) was closely linked to the β-galactosidase gene (z). When it was found that thiogalactoside transacetylase was regulated together with β-galactosidase and the permease, and that its gene formed part of the *lac* operon, it was thought that this enzyme might play some part in permeation. The properties of the enzyme were not consistent with it acting as part of the permease, and permease-negative mutants were isolated which produced normal amounts of thiogalactoside transacetylase. This galactoside permease is unique in that the gene is closely linked with the gene for β-galactosidase, so that the permease gene and the gene for the first enzyme for metabolizing lactose are within the same operon. The genes for all other inducible or constitutive permeases which have been mapped so far are unlinked to the genes for related metabolic enzymes.

Horecker et al. (1960) found that galactose accumulation was constituitive although the rate of galactose exit appeared to be increased by growth in the presence of galactose. Some of the earlier results on permeation may have to be revised in the light of the findings that there are four separate permease systems for galactose and galactosides. (Ganesan and Rotman, 1966). All four permeases are able to transport galactose to some extent. The β-galactoside permease which is the product of the y gene is induced by lactose, melibiose and thiogalactosides such as TMG and IPTG and transports lactose, galactose and the thiogalactosides. Prestidge and Pardee (1965) suggested that it should be referred to as TMG-permease I. They found a second permease (TMG permease II) capable of transporting TMG but not lactose. TMG permease II was induced by galactinol or melibiose, but not by lactose or IPTG. Leder and Perry (1967) were re-examining the effect of galactose on β-galactosidase induction, since it had been claimed at various times that galactose was the catabolite co-repressor molecule, and found that galactose stimulated β-galactosidase induction by TMG. They used galactokinase-less mutants so that the internal galactose concentration remained high, and found that the permease induced was probably TMG permease since it was also induced by melibiose, and galactinol but not by TMG, IPTG or lactose. Pardee and Prestidge (1965) found TMG permease II in *E. coli* strains B, ML and K12, although in K12 it was thermolabile and was induced at 25°C but not at 37°C.

Ganesan and Rotman (1966) found that several strains of *E. coli* produced a permease which accumulated both galactose and methyl-β-D-galactoside (MG). This accumulation was thought to be due to MG permease which also transports fucose. Mutants were obtained lacking MG permease and the gene was found to map near the *his* region. The accumulation of MG could be measured only in z^- strains since it is a substrate for β-galactosidase. The parent strains were semi-constitutive for MG permease but the activity was increased ten-fold by fucose. Regulator mutants for MG permease were obtained which were wholly constitutive and the regulator gene was found to be distinct from the R genes for the *lac* and *gal* operons. The R$^+$MG permease character was co-transduced with *gal* by phage λ. Wu (1967) found that a galactokinase-less mutant which was also defective for MG permease was inducible for the *gal* operon. One effect of galactokinase mutations is to render the *gal* operon phenotypically constitutive because of the generation of galactose within the cell from UDP-galactose. The defect in MG permease in these strains resulted in a restoration to inducibility so that it appears that MG permease is necessary to retain galactose within the cells.

One strain of *E. coli* K12, with a deletion of the *lac* region, was found by Ganesan and Rotman (1966) to accumulate only galactose at 37°C. TMG and MG were not accumulated. The accumulation was partially constitutive and was increased about four-fold by fucose. In this strain galactose accumulation was entirely due to the activity of the specific galactose permease.

The main characteristics of the four galactose and galactoside permeases are as follows: TMG permease I, the product of the *y* gene of the *lac* operon, induced by β-galactosides and β-thiogalactosides, transports lactose, thiogalactosides and galactose; TMG permease II, induced by galactinol, melibiose and galactose, transports TMG and galactose; MG permease, the product of the P-MG gene, induced by fucose and galactose, transports methyl-β-D-galactoside, fucose and galactose; galactose permease, induced by fucose and galactose, is specific for the transport of galactose.

Kolber and Stein (1966) attempted to identify the β-galactoside permease of *E. coli* by a double-labelling technique. The proteins of induced or non-induced cultures were labelled by incubating with either ^{3}H or ^{14}C phenylalanine. The extracts of induced and non-induced cultures were mixed and the proteins separated by fractionation on Sephadex. IPTG was used to induce the *lac* proteins and it was found that induced cultures of the wild type $z^+y^+a^+$ had three areas of differential labelling of protein but only two were found for a $z^+y^-a^+$ mutant so that the missing area presumably corresponded to the y gene product.

Fox and Kennedy (1965) were able to identify a membrane protein (M protein) from *E. coli* ML 30 which appeared to be an essential component of the β-galactoside transport system. Permease activity was inhibited by N-ethylmaleimide (NEM) but the permease was protected by pre-treatment with a permease substrate such as thiodigalactoside. The M protein in a cell-free extract was also protected from reaction with NEM by thiodigalactoside. In the assay developed for the M protein the measurements were based on the difference in uptake of ^{3}H labelled NEM by samples incubated in the presence and absence of saturation amounts of thiodigalactoside. Fox, Carter and Kennedy (1967) showed that the M protein was produced by i^-y^+ constitutive strains and by induced, but not non-induced, i^+y^+ strains and by none of the y^- *E. coli* ML and K12 strains. Some of the y^- strains gave temperature-sensitive lac^+ revertants. When intact cells of one of these mutants were heated at 42°C they rapidly lost the ability to take up ONPG and TMG, but this heat inactivation could be prevented by thiodigalactoside. The M protein in extracts of this mutant was also inactivated by heating at 42°C while the M protein from the wild type was almost unaffected. It seems clear that the M protein is associated with the y gene β-galactoside permease, TMG permease I.

A totally different approach to permease studies was suggested by the report of Nossal and Heppel (1966) that there was a selective release of enzymes and membrane proteins from cells of *E. coli* subjected to osmotic shock. Kundig *et al.* (1966) found that the ability of *E. coli* to concentrate methyl-β-thiogalactoside and methyl-α-glucoside was substantially reduced by the osmotic shock treatment. The ability to take up these sugars could be restored by adding a heat stable protein (HPr) which was released from the cells by the osmotic shock treatment. The uptake was shown to be specific since TMG was taken up only by cells induced by IPTG, or by cells induced by IPTG and then subjected to the cold-shock treatment to which the heat stable protein (HPr) had been restored. It was suggested that the transport system consisted of two enzymes which, together with the heat-stable protein, carried out the following reactions.

$$\text{Phosphoenolpyruvate} + \text{HPr} \underset{\longleftarrow}{\overset{\text{Enzyme I}}{\rightleftharpoons}} \text{Pyruvate} + \text{Phospho-HPr}$$

$$\text{Phospho-HPr} + \text{sugar} \overset{\text{Enzyme II}}{\longrightarrow} \text{Sugar-6-phosphate} + \text{HPr}$$

Enzyme II determined the specificity of the transport system and was membrane-bound while Enzyme I and HPr were in the soluble fraction of cell extracts. In this model for transport of sugars Enzyme I and HPr are thought to be the same for a number of different sugars. Tanaka and Lin (1967) found two pleiotropic mutants of *A. aerogenes* which had multiple defects for growth on carbohydrates. One of these lacked Enzyme I and the other lacked HPr. Both mutants reverted to full utilization of all sugars.

Simoni *et al.* (1967) reported that a single mutation in *Salmonella typhimurium* resulted in an inability to grow on nine carbohydrates and a loss of Enzyme I. Reversion to growth on any one of the sugars restored the ability to grow on the others in all except a very few cases. Transductants selected for their ability to grow on one sugar were also able to grow on all the other eight sugars. The rate of uptake of the sugar substrates by the mutant, lacking Enzyme I was negligible, but it was possible to show some uptake of two non-metabolizable substrates. Methyl-α-D-glucoside, which is thought to be transported by the constitutive glucose permease, was taken up by the mutant, although the rate of uptake by the parent and mutant strains differed 50-fold. Uptake of methyl-β-D-galactoside was increased by growth on galactose, and was thought to involve the MG-permease. The slight growth of the mutant on glucose after previous growth on galactose, or in the presence of fucose, suggested that glucose could be transported to a limited extent by the MG permease. The transport of sugars in the mutant lacking Enzyme I was thought to be by facilitated diffusion catalysed by the specific Enzyme II, whereas the complete transport system involved phosphorylation by the transferase system. Fox and Kennedy (1968) had suggested that the M protein might act either in facilitated diffusion or in energy dependent transport resulting in β-galactoside accumulation.

The osmotic shock method has been valuable for studying other permease systems. Pardee (1966) isolated a sulphate-binding protein from a *S. typhimurium* mutant lacking the first enzymes for sulphate utilization. The mutant was grown under derepressing conditions and the sulphate-binding protein was isolated from the supernatant after osmotic shock treatment. The protein has a molecular weight of 32,000 and one sulphate ion was bound to each protein molecule. Piperno and Oxender (1966) isolated an amino-acid binding protein released from *E. coli* K12 after shock treatment. The lyophilized supernatant was dialysed against labelled amino-acids and a protein was isolated which had a dissociation constant for binding leucine or isoleucine which was identical with that for the uptake of these amino-acids by whole cells.

Most amino-acid permeases are constitutive (Kepes and Cohen, 1962) but the tryptophan permease in *E. coli* is inducible. Using mutants unable to synthesize tryptophan, and also lacking tryptophanase, Burrous and DeMoss (1963) found that fully induced cells achieved maximal accumulation of tryptophan in about 1 min at 37°C. Histidine permease is constitutive and permease-less mutants of *S. typhimurium* were isolated as mutants resistant to growth inhibition by the α-hydrazine analogue of histidine which inhibits arginine synthesis (Shifrin *et al.*, 1966). The histidine analogue is transported by the histidine permease and growth inhibition was prevented by adding histidine at the same time as the growth inhibitor. The *his P* gene was co-transduced with *pur F*. The *his T* regulator gene is also linked to *pur F* but on the opposite side. The permease gene has therefore a separate location from the *his* operon and the four histidine regulator genes (Section VIII).

Permease investigations have been pursued by several more or less independent methods, but the recent combination of genetic analysis with studies on substrate and inducer specificity and with studies on isolated transport proteins is likely to bring about considerable advances in our understanding of permeation mechanisms.

VIII. SELECTION OF MUTANTS WITH ALTERED REGULATION

A. Inducible systems

Methods for the isolation of regulatory mutants are based on the same general principles as those for the isolation of any other type of mutant. The culture is treated with a suitable mutagen, an enrichment technique is used if available and a method devised for selecting and identifying the required mutant type on agar plates. For many inducible enzyme systems, mutants have been isolated which synthesize enzyme in the absence of inducer, and similarly mutants have been isolated which synthesize enzymes which are normally under severe repression in the wild type. The genetic defect which results in a constitutive or irrespressible phenotype, can only be identified by subsequent genetic analysis. Collins *et al.* (1965) suggested a standard nomenclature for the various regulatory phenotypes based on the amount of enzyme produced in the presence or absence of inducers with respect to the amount produced by a non-induced and fully induced wild type. The original paper should be consulted for details of the scheme proposed for classification and nomenclature of regulatory mutants. The mutants most commonly described for inducible systems fall into the classes defined by Collins *et al.* (1965) as (a) magno-constitutive, fully constitutive mutants synthesizing enzyme at the same rate as the fully induced wild type and not affected by the presence of inducer or, (b) semi-constitutive, producing a significant amount of enzyme in the absence of inducer, but capable of being induced to the wild-type level when inducer is present. The mutations which results in an altered phenotype for enzyme regulation may be in regulator genes, or in the structural gene for the enzyme, or in a structural gene for a different enzyme. A single mutation may have a pleiotropic effect on regulation. Most mutations which result in the total absence of enzymes are in the structural genes for the enzymes, but this phenotype may also result from mutations in a regulator gene.

The regulator *i* gene for the *lac* operon is close enough to the structural *lac* genes to be co-transduced (Jacob and Monod, 1961). Co-transduction of regulator and structural genes has also been found for amidase (Brammar *et al.*, 1967). The regulator *C* gene, which appears to produce an activator rather than a repressor, is co-transduced with the *ara* structural genes (Englesberg *et al.*, 1965) and also regulates the unlinked permease gene. The regulator gene for the *gal* operon is not linked to the structural genes (Buttin, 1963).

There are a few general methods which have been used to isolated regulatory mutants. Horiuchi *et al.* (1962) isolated mutants of *E. coli* which produced β-galactosidase constitutively by growing the wild-type strain in continuous culture with a low concentration of lactose as the sole carbon source for growth. Since lactose is not effective as an inducer at low concentrations, the constitutive mutants had a selective advantage. This method was used by Hegeman (1966c) to isolate mutants of *P. putida* which were constitutive for the enzymes of the mandelate pathway. Another general method used by Cohen-Bazire and Joliot (1953) to isolate constitutive lactose mutants was that of alternate subculture in glucose and lactose medium. Constitutive mutants had a temporary growth advantage immediately on transfer to the lactose medium, and could be sufficiently enriched to be isolated on plates. Buttin (1963) and Adhya and Echols (1966) used alternate subculture on glucose and galactose to obtain mutants producing the galactose enzymes constitutively.

Lin *et al.* (1962) suggested a general method for obtaining mutants which would be constitutive for enzymes required to metabolize carbo-hydrates. They grew *Aerobacter aerogenes*, after mutagenesis and enrich-ment, on a complex medium without added carbohydrate. When the colonies had developed they were sprayed with a solution containing the substrate and chloramphenicol. After 30 min further incubation, they were sprayed with a tetrazolium solution and the colonies containing constitutive cells immediately turned red. This method does not seem to have been widely used.

The most successful methods have been those which exploited the speci-fic properties of the enzyme system. Buttin (1963) obtained constitutive *gal* mutants by growing *E. coli* on a medium containing galactose as the carbon source in the presence of TMG. This is a specific repressor of induction of the galactose enzymes so that only the constitutive mutants were able to grow. Englesberg *et al.* (1965) isolated mutants which were constitutive for the arabinose enzymes by selection on a medium containing arabinose together with fucose which acts as a specific repressor of the arabinose enzymes, Müller-Hill (1965) isolated constitutive *lac* mutants on a medium which contained melibiose as the carbon source in the presence of 2-nitrofucoside which specifically repressed the induction of the lactose enzymes. Melibiose is not a substrate for β-galactoside, but is an inducer and is transported into the cells by the β-galactoside permease of the y gene. It could therefore only be used as a carbon source in the presence of 2-nitrofucoside if the permease, and therefore β-galactosidase, were produced constitutively.

If non-inducing substrates are available this provides a method for isolating constitutive mutants. Neolactose is a substrate but not an inducer of β-galactosidase and has been used to select constitutive mutants (Pardee, 1962). Jayaraman *et al.* (1966) used the non-inducing substrate 2-nitro-phenol-α-1-arabinoside to select *lac* constitutve mutants. When inducible and constitutive *lac* strains were grown on a non-inducing medium, it was possible to identify the constitutive strains by spraying with the chromo-genic substrate *o*-nitrophenyl-β-D-galactoside. The constitutive colonies rapidly developed a yellow colour by the release of the nitrophenol. Form-amide is a poor substrate for the aliphatic amide of *P. aeruginosa* and is only a very weak inducer. Brammar *et al* (1967) used formamide as the nitrogen source and succinate as the carbon source, to isolate amidase constitutive mutants. This technique also produced other regulatory mutants with altered inducibility characteristics which unlike the wild type, were readily induced by formamide.

Mutants of *B. licheniformis* producing penicillinase constitutively were isolated on plates containing Andrade indicator (Dubnau and Pollock, 1965). After growth, the plates were flooded with penicillin and the constitutive mutants attacked penicillin immediately and were identified by the pink zones produced around the colonies. The catabolism of sugars by E. coli results in acid production and this has been the basis of methods for identifying mutants lacking one of the enzymes required to metabolize carbohydrates. The media used include eosin-methylene blue (EMB) agar, (Lederberg, 1947), bromthymol blue agar (Korman and Berman, 1958) and tetrazolium agar (Signer et al., 1965). These media have been widely used to obtain mutants which are unable to metabolize lactose, galactose and other sugars.

Simoni et al. (1967) adapted this method to obtain permeability mutants of S. typhimurium. Melibiose negative mutants were isolated on EMB plates and one was obtained which had a pleiotropic defect for transport of melibiose and eight other carbohydrates. Galactokinase-less mutants have been isolated which are constitutive for the gal operon and this has been thought to be due to induction by internal galactose (Wu and Kalckar, 1966).

Mutants have been isolated for several enzymes systems which are constitutive at low temperatures but inducible at higher temperatures and these are considered to be due to the production of thermolabile cytoplasmic repressor proteins (Sadler and Novick, 1965; Dubnau and Pollock, 1965). Altered cytoplasmic repressors are also inferred from the properties of constitutive regulator mutants with altered behaviour to analogue repression (Jayaraman etal., 1966; Brammar et al., 1967).

Loomis and Magasanik (1965, 1967) isolated a mutant in which β-galactosidase synthesis was insensitive to catabolite repression by glucose. The mutant was isolated by selection on a medium containing N-acetyl-lactosamine as the nitrogen source in the presence of glucose. The mutant was grown on minimal medium containing 1% glucose and 0·2% lactose, treated with toluene vapour for 5 min and layered with a solution of 10^{-2} M o-nitrophenyl-β-D-galactoside and the colonies became yellow within 3 min whereas wild-type colonies on this medium remained colourless for more than an hour (Loomis and Magasanik, 1967).

B. Repressible systems

Mutants which have become derepressed for biosynthetic enzymes have usually been isolated as mutants resistant to growth inhibition by analogues. Histidine regulatory mutants were selected as resistant to growth inhibition by 1,2,4-triazole-3-alanine (TRA) which acts as a false corepressor of the histidine operon (Roth et al., 1966a). The wild type S. typhimurium growing on minimal medium has almost fully repressed levels of the histidine enzymes so that TRA does not affect growth, but if there is a partial block in the histidine pathway they produce high enzyme levels and growth is inhibited by TRA. The partial block required for making *S. typhimurium* sensitive to TRA inhibition was obtained by using "leaky" histidine-requiring mutants. The wild type could be phenotypically derepressed by growth in the presence of 3-amino-1,2,4-triazole which is an inhibitor of imidazole glycerol phosphate dehydrase, and was then sensitive to TRA inhibition so that resistant mutants could also be selected by this method. Another histidine analogue 2-methyl histidine was used in a similar way to obtain resistant mutants which were derepressed for the histidine operon. The mutants obtained, could be put in four genetically distinct classes: *hisO* at one end of the histidine operon; *hisS*, the structural gene for histidyl-tRNA synthetase; *hisR*, with low levels of the histidine tRNA; *hisT* for which the gene function was not known (Roth *et al.*, 1966a).

Selection of the histidine regulatory mutants was assisted by finding that bacteria with derepressed levels of the histidine enzymes formed wrinkled colonies on media containing 2% glucose. This morphological difference could be used to distinguish them from other TRA resistant mutants which had defective histidine permeases, or mutations resulting in a dehydrase which was not inhibited by the triazole compound (Roth *et al.*, 1966a).

Mutants which were derepressed for the tryptophan enzymes were isolated by Cohen and Jacob (1959) as mutants resistant to growth inhibition by 5-methyltryptophan. Similar mutants were isolated by Ito and Crawford (1965) and in both series of experiments it was found that the regulator mutation was not associated with the genes for the biosynthetic enzymes. It was concluded that there was a regulator gene which mapped near the threonine locus. Another class of mutants resistant to 5-methyl-tryptophan were isolated by Somerville and Yanofsky (1965). They selected for a mutation linked to the *trp* operon by first selecting for resistance to 5-methyltryptophan and then using the colonies which developed as hosts for a transducing phage. The phage lysate was used to transduce a *try A* mutant. By selecting on minimal medium containing 5-methyltrypto-phan only those transductants were selected which had acquired a trans-ducing fragment in which the resistance was linked to the *try* operon.

Regulatory mutants for the arginine enzymes have been isolated as canavanine-resistant mutants. These enzymes are controlled in *E. coli* strain K by repression by arginine but in *E. coli* B arginine has a slight inductive effect but the *arg R* genes are allelic in the two strains (Gorini *et al.*, 1961; Jacoby and Gorini, 1969; Maas, 1961). Jacoby and Gorini (1967) also isolated arginine regulator mutants of *E. coli* B from conditional streptomycin dependent mutants of one of the arginine enzymes.

Mutants with altered regulation of the methionine pathway of *S. typhi-murium* were isolated by Lawrence *et al.* (1968). These were selected for resistance to growth inhibition by the methionine analogues α-methyl methionine, ethionine and norleucine. Most of the mutants excreted methionine thus indicating an impaired regulation of synthesis. Three distinct gene loci were identified and the mutants could also be differentiated on the basis of the specificity of their resistance to grow inhibition by the analogues. It was thought that one class of mutants were resistant to feedback inhibition by α-methyl methionine and that the other two classes could be analagous to the regulatory mutants of the histidine operon. The methionine genes, like the arginine genes, are scattered around the chromosome with partial clustering.

Mutants of *E. coli* have been isolated which produce alkaline phosphatase constitutively, i.e., in medium containing a concentration of inorganic phosphate which represses the enzyme in the wild type. Torriani and Rothman (1961) used β-glycerol phosphate as the sole carbon source in the presence of a repressing concentration of potassium phosphate. Alkaline phosphatase was required for the hydrolysis of β-glycerol phosphate, so that only those mutants able to produce the enzyme in the presence of inorganic phosphate were able to grow. Colonies of constitutive bacteria were distinguished from the wild type on plates by spraying with *p*-phenyl phosphate. The colonies of constitutive mutants turned yellow within a few seconds. Mutations in one of two regulator genes can lead to constitutive synthesis of alkaline phosphatase (Echols *et al.*, 1961; Garen and Echols, 1962).

IX. GENERAL APPLICATIONS

Information about enzyme regulation may be of practical value for enzyme extraction and purification. If the specific activity of the starting material is increased the subsequent purification may be made considerably easier. Regulatory mutants are very useful for this purpose. It may be possible to select mutants which produce a high activity of an enzyme normally repressed in the wild type. For inducible systems, it is often more convenient to use a constitutive mutant than to grow the wild type in the presence of inducer.

If suitable genetic methods are available it may be possible to construct strains containing multiple copies of structural genes. Strains of *E. coli* are known in which both the chromosome and extra-chromosomal elements carry structural genes for particular enzymes (e.g., β-galactosidase $z^+/F'z^+$, Jacob and Monod, 1961). Another genetic method which was used by Müller-Hill *et al.* (1968) to increase the yield of the *lac* cytoplasmic repressor was to incorporate the *i* gene into the genome of an inducible but defective bacteriophage. When the bacteria carrying the prophage were induced the product of the *i* gene was also synthesized.

An increase in enzyme yield can also be achieved by choosing a medium in which catabolite repression is minimal. It may be better to choose a compound which gives less than the maximum amount of growth if it allows a higher specific activity to be reached. For some systems it may be worth growing the bacteria in continuous rather than in batch culture. Each enzyme system has its own problems but for several enzymes it has been possible to devise conditions in which a single enzyme forms 1–5% of the total cell protein.

Most of the detailed information on enzyme regulation has been derived from examining the regulation of single enzymes or of groups of enzymes belonging to a single catabolic or biosynthetic pathway. This made it possible to focus on a single regulatory unit. One of the most useful tools in such investigations was the non-substrate inducer. By using non-substrate inducers, the gratuitous synthesis of an enzyme could be isolated to a large extent from the general metabolism. The factors controlling the synthesis of an enzyme produced under gratuitous conditions could then be examined without having to take too much account of the other events going on in the cell at the same time. Now that the general outlines of enzyme regulation have been established it is becoming increasingly interesting to examine enzyme regulation under non-gratuitous conditions. Studies on the regulations of the enzymes of the tricarboxylic acid cycle, and similar enzymes of central metabolic pathways, are particularly important in attempting to see how different regulatory units fits together during bacterial growth.

There are many problems in enzyme regulation still to be solved. Most of the information has been obtained by a detailed study of relatively few systems. An extension of the methods already developed to the study of the regulation of other metabolic enzymes, and the use of a wider variety of bacterial species could produce new and valuable ideas. Nevertheless, the concentration of effort on studying enzymes in organisms for which genetic information was available has been of the greatest importance. In selecting new species for study it is worth considering first whether genetic analysis is possible.

REFERENCES

Adhya, S., and Echols, H. (1966). *J. Bact.*, **92**, 601–608.
Alper, D. H., and Tomkins, G. M. (1965). *Proc. natl. Acad. Sci. U.S.A.*, **53**, 797–803.
Ames, B. N., and Garry, B. (1959). *Proc. natl. Acad. Sci. U.S.A.*, **51**, 1291–1299.
Ames, B. N., Garry, B., and Herzenberg, L. A. (1960). *J. gen. Microbiol.*, **22**, 369–378.
Ames, B. N., and Hartman, P. E. (1963). *Cold Spring Harb. Symp. quant. Biol.*, **28**, 349–356.

Ames, B. N., Hartman, P. E., and Jacob, F. (1963). *J. molec. Biol.*, **7**, 23–42.
Ames, B. N., and Martin, R. G. (1964). *A. Rev. Biochem.*, **33**, 235–258.
Ames, B. N., Martin, R. G., and Garry, B. J. (1961). *J. biol. Chem.*, **236**, 2019–2026.
Ashworth, J. M., and Kornberg, H. L. (1963). *Biochim. biophys. Acta*, **73**, 519–522.
Ashworth, J. M., and Kornberg, H. L. (1964). *Biochim. biophys. Acta*, **89**, 383–384.
Baidya, T. K. N., Webb, F. C., and Lilly, M. D. (1967). *Biotech. Bioeng.*, **9**, 195–204.
Barrett, J. T., and Kallio, R. E. (1953). *J. Bact.*, **66**, 517–525.
Baumberg, S., Bacon, D. F., and Vogel, H. J. (1965). *Proc. natl. Acad. Sci. U.S.A.*, **53**, 1029–1032.
Beckwith, J. R. (1964). *J. molec. Biol.*, **8**, 427–430.
Beggs, W. H., and Rogers, P. (1966). *J. Bact.*, **91**, 1869–1874.
Berberich, M. A., Kovach, J. S., and Goldberger, R. F. (1967). *Proc. natl. Acad. Sci. U.S.A.*, **57**, 1857–1863.
Boddy, A., Clarke, P. H., Houldsworth, M. A., and Lilly, M. D. (1967). *J. gen. Microbiol.*, **48**, 137–145.
Bourgeois, S., Cohen, M., and Orgel, L. E. (1965). *J. molec. Biol.*, **14**, 300–302.
Brammar, W. J., and Clarke, P. H. (1964). *J. gen. Microbiol.*, **37**, 307–319.
Brammar, W. J., Clarke, P. H., and Skinner, A. J. (1967). *J. gen. Microbiol.*, **47**, 87–102.
Brammar, W. J., McFarlane, N. D., and Clarke, P. H. (1966). *J. gen. Microbiol.*, **44**, 303–309.
Brown, P., and Clarke, P. H. (1967). *J. gen. Microbiol.*, **46**, x.
Burrous, S. E., and DeMoss, R. D. (1963). *Biochim. biophys. Acta*, **73**, 623–637.
Burnstein, C., Cohn, M., Képès, A., and Monod, J. (1965). *Biochim. biophys. Acta*, **95**, 634–639.
Buttin, G. (1963). *J. molec. Biol.*, **7**, 164–182.
Cain, R. B. (1958). *J. gen. Microbiol.*, **19**, 1–14.
Cánovas, J. L., and Stanier, R. Y. (1967). *European. J. Biochem.*, **1**, 289–300.
Capecchi, M. R. (1967). *Proc. natl. Acad. Sci. U.S.A.*, **58**, 1144–1151.
Cartwright, N. J., and Cain, R. B. (1959). *Biochem. J.*, **71**, 248–261.
Citri, N., and Pollock, M. R. (1966). *Adv. Enzym.*, **28**, 237–323.
Clark, D. J., and Marr, A. G. (1964). *Biochim. biophys. Acta*, **92**, 85–94.
Clarke, P. H. (1970). *Adv. Microb. Physiol.*, **4**, 179–222.
Clarke, P. H., and Brammar, W. J. (1964). *Nature, Lond.*, **203**, 1153–1155.
Clarke, P. H., Houldsworth, M., and Lilly, M. D. (1968). *J. gen. Microbiol.*, **51**, 225–234.
Clarke, P. H., and Meadow, P. M. (1959). *J. gen. Microbiol.*, **20**, 144–155.
Cline, A. L., and Bock, R. M. (1966). *Cold Spring Harb. Symp. quant. Biol.*, **31**, 321–333.
Cohen, G. N. (1965). *A. Rev. Microbiol.*, **19**, 105–126.
Cohen, G. N. (1968). "The Regulation of Cell Metabolism". Holt, Rinehart and Winston Inc., New York.
Cohen, G. N., and Jacob, F. (1959). *C.r. hebd. Séanc. Acad. Sci. Paris*, **248**, 3490–3492.
Cohen, G. N., and Monod, J. (1957). *Bact. Rev.*, **21**, 169–194.
Cohen, N. R. (1966). *Biol. Rev.*, **41**, 503–560.
Cohen-Bazire, G., and Joliot, M. (1953). *Annls. Inst. Pasteur. Paris*, **84**, 937–945.
Cohn, M., and Horibata, K. (1959). *J. Bact.*, **78**, 624–635.
Cohn, M., and Monod, J. (1953). *Symp. Soc. gen. Microbiol.*, **7**, 132–149.

Collins, J. F., Mandelstam, J., Pollock, M. R., Richmond, M. H., and Sneath, P. H. A. (1965). *Nature, Lond.*, **208**, 841–843.
Crick, F. H. C., Barrett, L., Brenner, S., and Watts-Tobin, R. J. (1961). *Nature, Lond.*, **192**, 1227–1232.
Datta, P., and Gest, H. (1964). *Proc. natl. Acad. Sci. U.S.A.*, **52**, 1004–1009.
Dobrogosz, W. J. (1966). *J. Bact.*, **91**, 2263–2269.
Doskočil, J., Pačeo, V., and Šorm, F. (1967). *Biochim. biophys. Acta*, **145**, 771–779.
Doudoroff, M., Hassid, W. Z., Putman, E. W., Potter, A. L., and Lederberg, J. (1949). *J. biol. Chem.*, **179**, 921–934.
Dubnau, D. A., and Pollock, M. R. (1965). *J. gen. Microbiol.*, **41**, 7–21.
Echols, H., Garen, A., Garen, S., and Torriani, A. (1961). *J. molec. Biol.*, **3**, 425–438.
Englesberg, E., Irr, J., Power, J., and Lee, N. (1965). *J. Bact.*, **90**, 946–957.
Englesberg, E., Sheppard, D., Squires, C., and Meronk, F. (1969). *J. mol. Biol.*, **43**, 281–298.
Fox, C. F., Carter, J. R., and Kennedy, E. P. (1967). *Proc. natl. Acad. Sci. U.S.A.*, **57**, 698–765.
Fox, C. F., and Kennedy, E. P. (1965). *Proc. natl. Acad. Sci. U.S.A.*, **54**, 891–899.
Gale, E. F. (1943). *Bact. Rev.*, **7**, 139–173.
Gale, E. F. (1946). *Adv. Enzymol.*, **6**, 1–32.
Gallant, J., and Stapleton, R. (1963). *Proc. natl. Acad. Sci. U.S.A.*, **50**, 348–355.
Ganesan, A. K., and Rotman, B. (1966). *J. molec. Biol.*, **16**, 42–50.
Garen, A., and Echols, H. (1962). *Proc. natl. Acad. Sci. U.S.A.*, **48**, 1398–1402.
Garen, A., and Levinthal, C. (1960). *Biochim. biophys. Acta*, **38**, 470–483.
Gerhart, J. C., and Schachman, H. K. (1965). *Biochemistry*, **4**, 1054–1062.
Gilbert, W., and Müller-Hill, B. (1966). *Proc. natl. Acad. Sci. U.S.A.*, **56**, 1891–1898.
Gilbert, W., and Müller-Hill, B. (1967). *Proc. natl. Acad. Sci. U.S.A.*, **58**, 2415–2421.
Goodwin, B. C. (1963). "Temporal Organization in Cells". Academic Press, London.
Goodwin, B. C. (1966). *Nature, Lond.*, **209**, 479–481.
Goodwin, B. C. (1969). *Eur. J. Biochem.*, **10**, 515–522.
Gorini, L. (1958). *Bull. Soc. Chim. biol.*, **40**, 1939–1952.
Gorini, L. (1960). *Proc. natl. Acad. Sci. U.S.A.*, **46**, 682–690.
Gorini, L., Gunderson, W., and Burger, M. (1961). *Cold Spring Harb. Symp. quant. Biol.*, **26**, 173–182.
Gorini, L., and Maas, W. K. (1957). *Biochim. biophys. Acta*, **25**, 208–209.
Gray, C. T., Wimpenny, J. W. T., and Mossman, M. R. (1966). *Biochim. biophys. Acta*, **117**, 22–32.
Gutfreund, H., and Knowles, J. R. (1967). *Essays in Biochem.*, **3**, 25–72. Academic Press, London.
Haber, J. E., and Koshland, D. E. (1967). *Proc. natl. Acad. Sci. U.S.A.*, **58**, 2087–2093.
Hamilton-Miller, J. M. T., Smith, J. T. and Knox, R. (1963). *J. Pharm. Pharmacol.*, **15**, 81–91.
Hamlin, B. T., Ng. F. M-W., and Dawes, E. A. (1967). Microbiol Physiology and Continuous Culture. Third International Symposium, H.M.S.O., London, 211–231.
Hanson, R. S., and Cox, D. P. (1967). *J. Bact.*, **93**, 1777–1787.
Harte, M. J., and Webb, F. C. (1967). *Biotech. Bioeng.*, **9**, 205–221.
Hartman, P. E., Loper, J. C., and Šerman, D. (1960). *J. gen. Microbiol.*, **22**, 323–353.

Hartwell, L. H., and Magasanik, B. (1963). *J. molec. Biol.*, **7**, 401–420.
Hayashi, S., and Lin, E. C. C. (1965). *J. molec. Biol.*, **14**, 515–521.
Hegeman, G. D. (1966a). *J. Bact.*, **91**, 1140–1154.
Hegeman, G. D. (1966b). *J. Bact.*, **91**, 1155–1160.
Hegeman, G. D. (1966c). *J. Bact.*, **91**, 1161–1167.
Henning, U., Dennert, G., Hertel, R., and Shipp, W. S. (1966). *Cold Spring Harb. Symp. quant. Biol.*, **31**, 227–234.
Hogness, D. S., Cohn, H., and Monod, J. (1955). *Biochim. biophys. Acta.*, **16**, 99–116.
Horecker, B. L., Thomas, J., and Monod, J. (1960). *J. biol. Chem.*, **235**, 1580–1585.
Horiuchi, T., Horiuchi, S., and Novick, A. (1961). *J. molec. Biol.*, **3**, 703–704.
Horiuchi, T., Tomizawa, J., and Novick, A. (1962). *Biochim. biophys. Acta*, **55**, 152–163.
Imamoto, F., Ito, J., and Yanofsky, C. (1966). *Cold. Spring Harb. Symp. quant. Biol.*, **31**, 235–249.
Ippen, K., Miller, J. H., Scaife, J., and Beckwith, J. (1968). *Nature, Lond.*, **217**, 825–827.
Ito, J., and Crawford, I. P. (1965). *Genetics*, **52**, 1303–1316.
Jacob, F., and Monod, J. (1961). *J. molec. Biol.*, **3**, 318–356.
Jacob, F., Ullman, A., and Monod, J. (1964). *C.r. hebd. Séanc. Acad. Sci., Paris*, **258**, 3125–3128.
Jacob, F., Ullmann, A., and Monod, J. (1965). *J. molec. Biol.*, **13**, 704–719.
Jacoby, G. A., and Gorini, L. (1967). *J. molec. Biol.*, **24**, 41–50.
Jacoby, G. A., and Gorini, L. (1969). *J. molec., Biol.*, **39**, 73–87.
Jayaraman, K., Müller-Hill, B., and Rickenberg, H. V. (1966). *J. molec. Biol.*, **18**, 339–343.
Jensen, R. A., and Nester, E. W. (1965). *J. molec. Biol.*, **12**, 468–481.
Karstrom, H. (1938). *Ergebn. Enzymforsch.*, **7**, 350.
Kelly, M., and Clarke, P. H. (1962). *J. gen. Microbiol.*, **27**, 305–316.
Kemp, M. B., and Quayle, J. R. (1966). *Biochem. J.*, **99**, 41–48.
Képès, A. (1967). *Biochim. biophys. Acta*, **138**, 107–123.
Képès, A., and Cohen, G. N. (1962). *In* "The Bacteria" (Ed. I. C. Gunsalus and R. Y. Stanier), Vol. 4, pp. 179–221. Academic Press, New York.
Knox, R., and Pollock, M. R. (1944). *Biochem. J.*, **38**, 299–304.
Koch, A. L. (1964). *Biochim. biophys. Acta*, **79**, 177–200.
Kogut, M., and Podoski, E. P. (1953). *Biochem. J.*, **55**, 800–811.
Kolber, A. R., and Stein, W. D. (1966). *Nature, Lond.*, **209**, 691–694.
Korman, R., and Berman, D. T. (1958). *J. Bact.*, **76**, 454–455.
Kornberg, H. L. (1963). *Biochim. biophys. Acta*, **73**, 517–519.
Kornberg, H. L. (1966a). *In* "Essays in Biochemistry", Vol. 2, pp. 1–31. Academic Press, London.
Kornberg, H. L. (1966b). *Biochem. J.*, **99**, 1–11.
Kornberg, H. L., Gotto, A. M., and Lund, P. (1958). *Nature, Lond.*, **182**, 1430–1431.
Kundig, W., Kundig, F. D., Anderson, B., and Roseman, S. (1966). *J. biol. Chem.*, **241**, 3243–3246.
Lark, K. G. (1966). *Bact. Rev.*, **30**, 3–32.
Larsen, H. (1962). *In* "The Bacteria" (Ed. I. D. Gunsalus and R. Y. Stanier), Vol. 4, pp. 297–342. Academic Press, New York.

Lascelles, J. (1962). *In* "The Bacteria" (Ed. I. C. Gunsalus and R. Y. Stanier), Vol. 3, pp. 335–372. Academic Press, New York.

Lawrence, D. A., Smith, D. A., and Rowbury, R. J. (1968). *Genetics*, **58**, 473–492.

Lederberg, J. (1947). *Genetics*, **32**, 505–525.

Lederberg, J. (1950). *J. Bact.*, **60**, 381–392.

Leive, L. (1965). *Biochem. Biophys. Res. Comm.*, **20**, 321–327.

Lessie, T. G., and Neidhardt, F. C. (1967). *J. Bact.*, **93**, 1800–1810.

Lin, E. C. C., Lerner, S. A., and Jorgensen, S. E. (1962). *Biochim. Biophys. Acta*, **60**, 422–424.

Loomis, W. F. Jr., and Magasanik, B. (1964). *J. molec. Biol.*, **8**, 417–426.

Loomis, W. F. Jr., and Magasanik, B. (1965). *Biochem. Biophys. Res. Commun.* **20**, 230–234.

Loomis, W. F. Jr., and Magasanik, B. (1966). *J. Bact.*, **92**, 170–177.

Loomis, W. F., and Magasanik, B. (1967). *J. molec. Biol.*, **23**, 487–494.

Loomis, W. F., and Magasanik, B. (1967). *J. Bact.*, **93**, 1397–1401.

Maaløe, O., and Kjeldgaard, N. O. (1966). "Control of Macromolecular Synthesis". W. A. Benjamin Inc., New York.

Maas, W. K. (1961). *Cold Spring Harb. Symp. quant. Biol.*, **26**, 183–191.

Maas, W. K., and McFall, E. (1964). *A. Rev. Microbiol.*, **18**, 95–110.

Magana-Plaza, I., and Ruiz-Herrera, J. (1967). *J. Bact.*, **93**, 1294–1301.

Magasanik, B. (1961). *Cold Spring Harb. Symp. quant. Biol.*, **26**, 249–256.

Mandelstam, J. (1961). *Biochem. J.*, **79**, 489–496.

Mandelstam, J. (1962). *Biochem. J.*, **82**, 489–493.

Mandelstam, J., and Jacoby, G. A. (1965). *Biochem. J.*, **94**, 569–577.

Margolin, P., and Bauerle, R. H. (1966). *Cold Spring Harb. Symp. quant. Biol.*, **31**, 311–320.

Martin, R. G. (1963). *J. biol. Chem.*, **238**, 257–268.

Martin, R. G., Whitfield, H. J., Jr., Berkowitz, D. B., and Voll, M. J. (1966). *Cold Spring Harb. Symp. quant. Biol.*, **31**, 215–220.

McBrien, D. C. H., and Moses, V. (1966). *J. Bact.*, **91**, 1391–1392.

McFall, E., and Mandelstam, J. (1963). *Biochem. J.*, **89**, 391–398.

McFarlane, N. D., Brammar, W. J., and Clarke, P. H. (1965). *Biochem. J.*, **95**, 24C–25C.

Mehdi, Q., and Yudkin, M. D. (1967). *Biochim. biophys. Acta*, **149**, 288–290.

Monod, J., Changeux, J.-P., and Jacob, F. (1963). *J. molec. Biol.*, **6**, 306–329.

Monod, J., and Cohen-Bazire, G. (1953). *C.r. hebd. Séanc. Acad. Sci., Paris*, **236**, 530–532.

Monod, J., Cohen-Bazire, G., and Cohn, N. (1951). *Biochim. biophys. Acta*, **7**, 585–599.

Monod, J., and Cohn, M. (1952). *Adv. Enzym.*, **13**, 67–119.

Monod, J., Wyman, J., and Changeux, J-P. (1965). *J. molec. Biol.*, **12**, 88–118.

Morikawa, N., and Imamoto, F. (1969). *Nature, Lond.*, **223**, 37–40.

Morris, I., and Syrett, P. J. (1965). *J. gen. Microbiol.*, **38**, 21–28.

Morse, D. E., Mostellar, R., Baker, R. F., and Yanofsky, C. (1969). *Nature, Lond.*, **223**, 40–43.

Moses, V. (1967). *Biochem. J.*, **103**, 650–659.

Moses, V., and Prevost, C. (1966). *Biochem. J.*, **100**, 336–353.

Müller-Hill, B. (1965). *J. molec. Biol.*, **15**, 374–376.

Müller-Hill, B., Rickenberg, H. V., and Wallenfels, K. (1964). *J. molec. Biol.*, **10**, 303–318.

Nakada, D., and Magasanik, B. (1964). *J. molec. Biol.*, **8**, 105–127.
Neidhardt, F. C. (1966). *Bact. Rev.*, **30**, 701–719.
Neidhardt, F. C., and Magasanik, B. (1956). *Nature, Lond.*, **178**, 801–802.
Neidhardt, F. C., and Magasanik, B. (1957). *J. Bact.*, **73**, 253–263.
Neumann, H., and Vreedendaal, M. van. (1967). *Clinica. Chim. Acta*, **17**, 183–187.
Newton, W. A., Beckwith, J. R., Zipser, D., and Brenner, S. (1965). *J. molec. Biol.*, **14**, 290–296.
Ng, F. M-W., and Dawes, E. A. (1967). *Biochem. J.*, **104**, 48P.
Nossal, N. G., and Heppel, L. A. (1966). *J. biol. Chem.*, **241**, 3055–3062.
Novick, R. P. (1962). *Biochem. J.*, **83**, 229–235.
Okinaka, R. T., and Dobrogosz, W. J. (1967). *J. Bact.*, **93**, 1644–1650.
Ornston, L. N. (1966). *J. biol. Chem.*, **241**, 3800–3810.
Ornston, L. N., and Stanier, R. Y. (1964). *Nature, Lond.*, **204**, 1279–1283.
Ornston, L. N., and Stanier, R. Y. (1966). *J. biol. Chem.*, **241**, 3776–3786.
Paigen, K. (1963). *Biochim. biophys. Acta*, **77**, 318–328.
Paigen, K. (1966). *J. Bact.*, **92**, 1394–1403.
Paigen, K., and Williams, B. (1970). *Adv. Microbiol. Physiol.*, **4**, 252–324.
Paigen, K., Williams, B., and McGinnis, J. (1967). *J. Bact.*, **94**, 493–494.
Palleroni, N. J., and Stanier, R. Y. (1964). *J. gen. Microbiol.*, **35**, 319–334.
Palmer, J., and Moses, V. (1967). *Biochem. J.*, **103**, 358–366.
Pardee, A. B. (1957). *J. Bact.*, **73**, 376–385.
Pardee, A. B. (1962). *In* "The Bacteria" (Ed. I. C. Gunsalus and R. Y. Stanier), Vol. 3, pp. 577–630. Academic Press, New York.
Pardee, A. B. (1966). *J. biol. Chem.*, **241**, 5886–5892.
Pardee, A. B., and Prestidge, L. S. (1959). *Biochim. biophys. Acta*, **36**, 545–547.
Pastan, I., and Perlman, R. L. (1968). *Proc. natl. Acad. Sci. U.S.A.*, **61**, 1336–1342.
Perret, C. J. (1954). *Nature, Lond.*, **174**, 1012–1013.
Perlman, R. L., and Pastan, I. (1968). *J. biol. Chem.*, **243**, 5420–5427.
Piperno, J. R., and Oxender, D. L. (1966). *J. biol. Chem.*, **241**, 5732–5743.
Pollock, M. R. (1965a). *Biochem. J.*, **94**, 666–675.
Pollock, M. R. (1965b). *Federation of European Biochemical Societies*. 2nd Meeting. 221–222.
Power, J. (1967). *Genetics*, **55**, 557–568.
Prestidge, L. S., and Pardee, A. B. (1965). *Biochim. biophys. Acta*, **100**, 591–593.
Prevost, C., and Moses, V. (1967). *Biochem. J.*, **103**, 349–357.
Ptashne, M. (1967). *Proc. natl. Acad. Sci. U.S.A.*, **57**, 306–313.
Ramakrishnan, T., and Adelberg, E. A. (1965). *J. Bact.*, **89**, 654–664.
Richmond, M. H. (1965). *Biochem. J.*, **94**, 584–593.
Riggs, A. D., Newby, R. F., and Bourgeois, S. (1970). *J. molec. Biol.*, **51**, 303–314.
Roodyn, D. B. (1968). "Automation in Analytical Chemistry". Proceedings Technicon Symposium. Mediad Press, New York.
Roth, J. R., Antón, M. J., and Hartman, P. E. (1966). *J. molec. Biol.*, **22**, 305–323.
Roth, J. R., Silbert, D. F., Fink, G. R., Voll, M. J., Antón, D., Hartman, P. E., and Ames, B. N. (1966b). *Cold Spring Harb. Symp. quant. Biol.*, **31**, 383–392.
Rotman, B., and Spiegelman, S. (1954). *J. Bact.*, **68**, 419–429.
Sadler, J. R., and Novick, A. (1965). *J. molec. Biol.*, **12**, 305–327.
Saedler, H., Gullon, A., Fiethen, L., and Starlinger, P. (1968). *Mol. gen. Gen.*, **102**, 79–88.
Scaife, J., and Beckwith, J. R. (1966). *Cold Spring Harb. Symp. quant. Biol.*, **31**, 403–408.

Schwartz, M. (1967). *Ann. Inst. Pasteur*, **112**, 673–700.
Seal, U. S., Mellinger, G. T., and Doe, R. P. (1966). *Clin. Chem.*, **12**, 620–631.
Shapiro, J., Machattie, L., Eron, L., Ihler, G., Ippen, K., and Beckwith, J. (1969). *Nature, Lond.*, **224**, 768–774.
Sheppard, D., and Englesberg, E. (1966). *Cold. Spring Harb. Symp. quant. Biol.*, **31**, 345–347.
Sheppard, D. E., and Englesberg, E. (1967). *J. molec. Biol.*, **25**, 443–454.
Shifrin, S., Ames, B. N., and Ferroluzzi-Ames, G. (1966). *J. biol. Chem.*, **241**, 3424–3429.
Shilo, M., and Stanier, R. Y. (1957). *J. gen. Microbiol.*, **16**, 482–490.
Signer, E. R., Beckwith, J. R., and Brenner, S. (1965). *J. molec. Biol.*, **14**, 153–166.
Sikyta, B., and Slezak, J. (1965). *Biochim. biophys. Acta*, **100**, 311–313.
Silverstone, A. E., Magasanik, B., Reznikoff, W. S., Miller, J. H., and Beckwith, J. R. (1969). *Nature, Lond.*, **221**, 1012–1014.
Simoni, R. D., Levinthal, M., Kundig, F. G., Kundig, W., Anderson, B., Hartman, P. E., and Roseman, S. (1967). *Proc. natl. Acad. Sci. U.S.A.*, **58**, 1963–1970.
Skinner, A. J., and Clarke, P. H. (1968). *J. gen. Microbiol.*, **50**, 183–194.
Smith, L. (1961). *In* "The Bacteria" (Ed. I. C. Gunsalus and R. Y. Stanier), Vol. 2, pp. 365–396. Academic Press. New York.
Somerville, R. L., and Yanofsky, C. (1965). *J. molec. Biol.*, **11**, 747–759.
Stadtman, E. R. (1963). *Bact. Rev.*, **27**, 170–181.
Stadtman, E. R., Cohen, G. N., LeBras, G., and de Robichon-Szulmajster, H. (1961). *J. biol. Chem.*, **236**, 2033–2038.
Stanier, R. Y. (1947). *J. Bact.*, **54**, 339–348.
Stanier, R. Y. (1950). *Bact. Rev.*, **14**, 179–191.
Stent, G. S. (1964). *Science*, **144**, 816–820.
Stephenson, H., and Stickland, L. H. (1933). *Biochem. J.*, **27**, 1528–1532.
Stevenson, I. L., and Mandelstam, J. (1965). *Biochem. J.*, **96**, 354–362.
Tanaka, S., and Lin, E. C. C. (1967). *Proc. natl. Acad. Sci., U.S.A.*, **57**, 913–919.
Torriani, A. (1960). *Biochim. biophys. Acta*, **38**, 460–479.
Torriani, A., and Rothman, F. (1961). *J. Bact.*, **81**, 835–836.
Tsou, K. C., and Su, H. C. F. (1965). *Anal. Biochem.*, **11**, 54–65.
Vogel, H. J. (1957). "The Chemical Basis of Heredity" (Eds. W. D. McElroy and B. Glass), pp. 267–289. The Johns Hopkins Press, Baltimore, Md., U.S.A.
Walker, N. E., and Campbell, L. L. (1963). *J. Bact.*, **86**, 1202–1210.
Willetts, N. S. (1967). *Biochem. J.*, **103**, 453–466.
Wimpenny, J. W. T. (1969). *Symp. Soc. gen. Microbiol.*, **19**, 161–197.
Wu, H. C., and Kalckar, H. M. (1966). *Proc. natl. Acad. Sci. U.S.A.*, **55**, 622–629.
Yates, R. A., and Pardee, A. B. (1956). *J. biol. Chem.*, **221**, 757–770.
Yudkin, M. (1969). *Biochem. J.*, **114**, 307–311.
Yudkin, M., and Moses, V. (1969). *Biochem. J.*, **113**, 432–427.
Zubay, G., Lederman, M., and DeVries, J. K. (1967). *Proc. natl. Acad. Sci. U.S.A.*, **58**, 1669–1675.

CHAPTER VI

Methods for Studying Bacterial Spores

G. W. GOULD

Unilever Research Laboratory, Colworth Welwyn, Sharnbrook, Bedford, England

I. INTRODUCTION

Bacterial spores have excited the interest of researchers for six principal reasons. Firstly, spores are exceptionally resistant to heat and other physical and chemical agents even though they contain enzymes, nucleic acids, membranes, and other structures basically similar to other living cells. An understanding of the mechanisms of resistance remains a challenging problem and is receiving much study. Secondly, spores are exceedingly dormant and long-lived, and dormancy in bacterial spores and in other organisms is so far little understood. Thirdly, the dormancy and resistance of spores disappears during germination by reactions that are so rapid as probably to be unique, and to be aptly termed "trigger reactions". The changes underlying germination trigger reactions are not yet known. Fourthly, germinated spores outgrow to form new vegetative cells. Outgrowth comprises a sequence of changes as one type of cell, the just-germinated spore, develops into what is really a distinct form, the vegetative cell. Description of the outgrowth sequence, and studies in the way it is controlled by the cell, are important areas of developmental biology. Fifthly, to complete the growth cycle, the vegetative cell must resporulate. Sporulation in bacteria has proved to be an excellent model system for studying the control of cellular differentiation, for during sporulation the vegetative genome is essentially suppressed and the spore genome, controlling synthesis of numerous new proteins and other easily recognised products and structures, is expressed within a very short period of time. In synchronous cultures this differentiation process can be studied with precision. Finally, there are, of course, good practical reasons for studying spores. Spores tend to be the "last-ditch" survivors of almost any process that one designs for killing micro-organisms, be it sterilization of foods by heat, of surgical instruments by chemicals, or of spacecraft by ionizing radiations. The experimentalist, therefore, hopes that research may sufficiently reveal the secrets of resistance, dormancy, germination, out-growth, and sporulation so that, eventually, as yet unexpected methods of controlling spores may become available.

Spores are characteristically formed by *Bacillus* and *Clostridium* species, but also by *Sporosarcina*, and spores of thermophilic *Actinomyces* and cysts of *Azotobacter* have features in common with spores of the *Bacillaceae*. Nevertheless, the bulk of research has been carried out using spores of *Bacillus* species, simply because they have proved to be easy to grow and work with, and using spores of food poisoning *Clostridium* species because of their practical importance to the food industry and public health laboratory. It is likely that spores of different micro-organisms have so much in common that the concentration of effort that has occurred on spores of one genus (and indeed, on just one strain of *Bacillus cereus*) will not prove unwise.

An idealized growth cycle typical of spore-forming bacteria in general, indicating the resistant and dormant phases and the terminology in common usage is shown in Fig. 1. The most recent reviews concerning spores were by Murrell (1961; 1967), Sussman and Halvorson (1966), Halvorson *et al.* (1966), Kornberg *et al.* (1968), Mandelstam (1969) and by the authors of various chapters in "*The Bacterial Spore*" (1969). The symposia on spores should also be consulted; "*Spores*" (1957), "*Spores II*" (1961), "*Spores III*" (1965), "*Spores I V*" (1969), and the symposium papers in *J. appl. Bact.*, **33** (1970) on "*Bacterial Spores: Properties, Problems and Uses*".

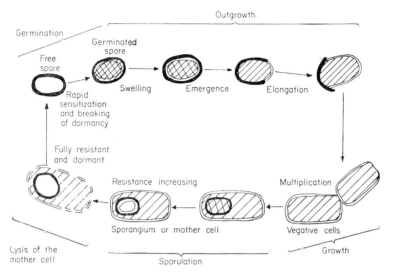

Fig. 1. Cycle of growth, sporulation, germination, and outgrowth of a typical sporeforming bacterium.

II. SPORULATION

A. Production of spores

1. *Media and Environment*

The use of standard sporulation media is important in many spore studies because the sporulation environment partly determines the subsequent resistance, activation, and germination response of the spores (Lechowich and Ordal, 1962; Levinson and Hyatt, 1964; Roberts and Ingram, 1966). The commonly used spores of *B. cereus* T are most often grown in the liquid medium of Stewart and Halvorson (1953) at 30°C in well aerated fermentors or in shaken flask cultures. Medium G contains—

Medium G (Stewart and Halvorson, 1953)

Glucose	4 g
K_2HPO_4	1 g
$(NH_4)_2SO_4$	6 g
Yeast extract (Difco)	2 g
$MnSO_4.H_2O$	0·1 g
$MgSO_4$	0·8 g
$ZnSO_4$	10 mg
$CuSO_4.5H_2O$	10 mg
$CaCl_2$	10 mg
$FeSO_4.7H_2O$	1 mg
Distilled water	1 litre

pH 7·2

TABLE I

Sporulation of *Bacillus coagulans* NCTC 3991

Medium	Ref.	Viable count (per ml) after 40 h[a] Total	Spore[b]	Microscopical appearance
SCM medium	d	$6 \cdot 9 \times 10^8$	$6 \cdot 1 \times 10^8$	100% free spores
B. *megaterium* medium	e	$4 \cdot 0 \times 10^8$	$3 \cdot 3 \times 10^8$	100% free spores
B. *coagulans* medium	f	$1 \cdot 5 \times 10^8$	$1 \cdot 2 \times 10^8$	85% free spores
G medium	g	$7 \cdot 6 \times 10^7$	$5 \cdot 7 \times 10^7$	90% free spores
Nutrient broth[c]		$1 \cdot 4 \times 10^8$	$8 \cdot 5 \times 10^7$	75% free spores plus spores in mother cells
B. *licheniformis* medium	h	$2 \cdot 9 \times 10^8$	$6 \cdot 7 \times 10^7$	25% free spores plus vegetative cells
Heart infusion broth[c]		$2 \cdot 3 \times 10_2$	$2 \cdot 3 \times 10^5$	10% free spores plus vegetative cells
B. *megaterium* (modified) medium	i	$5 \cdot 7 \times 10^5$	$1 \cdot 8 \times 10^5$	No free spores many vegetative cells
Lemco-glucose-broth[c]		$5 \cdot 8 \times 10^8$	$1 \cdot 6 \times 10^4$	Few free spores many vegetative cells
Yeast-glucose broth[c]		$6 \cdot 0 \times 10^4$	$1 \cdot 3 \times 10^3$	Few free spores many vegetative cells
"All-purpose" tryptone	j	$1 \cdot 5 \times 10^8$	$9 \cdot 1 \times 10^2$	Vegetative cells

a. Cultures (100 ml) were grown in 250 ml conical flasks on a rotary shaker at 37°C.
b. Spore count is the number of organisms surviving heating for 30 min. at 70°C.
c. Nutrient broth consisted of (per litre) peptone (Evans), 5 g; NaCl, 5 g; Lab Lemco (Oxide), 5 g; pH 7·2. Heart infusion broth was a Difco product. Lemco glucose broth contained (per litre) peptone (Evans), 10 g; Lab Lemco (Oxoid), 10 g; glucose 10 g; pH 7·0. Yeast glucose broth contained (per litre) yeast extract (Difco) 5 g; peptone (Evans), 5 g; $Na_2HPO_4.12H_2O$, 5 g; Lab Lemco (Oxiod), 5 g; glucose, 5 g; pH 7·2.
d. Doi and Igarishi (1964a).
e. Millet and Aubert (1960).
f. Ohye and Murrell (1962).
g. Stewart and Halvorson (1953).
h. Bernlohr and Novelli (1963).
i. Tamir and Gilvarg (1966).
j. Evans and Niven (1951).

Dow-Corning (Box 592, Midland, Michigan) antifoam A is a suitable foam controller. With 5% inoculum and adequate aeration sporulation and lysis of the mother cells can be complete in about 18 h. Nakata (1963, 1964) described a synthetic ("CGDS") medium based on medium G (see Table 2). Many *Bacillus* species will sporulate readily in medium G, and also in many ordinary laboratory media provided the glucose concentration is not above about 0·5% w/v and adequate Mn^{++} is present. For example *Bacillus coagulans* NCTC 3991 sporulates well in the first six media listed in Table I, though vegetative cell-free crops are produced in only the first four. It is clear that rich media allowing good vegetative growth (for instance, the last one in Table I) do not necessarily support rapid and complete sporulation. Many specially-formulated liquid media supporting sporulation of particular strains and species have been described; e.g., *Bacillus subtilis* (Doi and Igarishi, 1964a), *Bacillus licheniformis* (Bernlohr and Novelli, 1963), *Bacillus coagulans* (Ohye and Murrell, 1962), *Bacillus megaterium* (Millet and Aubert, 1960; Tamir and Gilvarg, 1966). *B. subtilis* Marburg, now widely used for sporulation studies, sporulates with good synchrony (Schaeffer *et al*, 1963) at 37°C when aerated in the following medium—

Medium

Nutrient broth (Difco)	8 g
$MgSO_4.7H_2O$	0·25 g
KCl	1 g
Distilled water	1 litre

pH 7·0–7·2

after autoclaving, sterile additions are made of—

$Ca(NO_3)_2$	1 mM
$MnCl_2$	10 μM
$FeSO_4$	1 μM

The corresponding solid medium contains agar (Difco; 17 g/litre; Schaeffer *et al.*, 1963). The effect of varying N- and C-source, C-concentration and temperature on sporulation of *B. subtilis* Marburg, has been studied in detail (Schaeffer *et al.*, 1965).

Cultures on solid media support good sporulation. High yields can be obtained by using large polypropylene or enamelled trays as culture vessels. *B. subtilis* SJ2 spores, used for study of germination and amino-acid-handling enzymes by Hermier (1962) and Hermier and Rousseau (1967) can be grown on the surface of the following medium in Roux bottles at 30°C—

Medium

Lab-Lemco	10 g
Yeast extract (Difco)	2 g
$MnSO_4.H_2O$	40 mg
Agar	25 g
Distilled water	1 litre

pH 7·0

Potato-based media make good general purpose sporulation agars, for instance *B. cereus* PX, used for study of lytic enzymes (Gould *et al.* 1966), and most strains of *B. cereus, subtilis, megaterium, coagulans,* and *licheni-formis* (Gould and Ordal, 1968) will sporulate well at 30°C on medium containing—

Medium

Potato extract (Difco)	4 g
Yeast extract (Difco)	4 g
Glucose	2·5 g
Agar	15 g
Distilled water	1 litre

pH 7·2

Spores for heat-resistance work are often grown on media fortified with cations to ensure maximal resistance. For instance, spores of *B. subtilis* A with high heat resistance are formed at 45°C on the fortified nutrient agar (FNA) of Edwards *et al.* (1965) which contains—

Medium (Edwards et al., *1965)*

Beef extract (Difco)	3 g
Peptone (Difco)	5 g
NaCl	8 g
Glucose	0·1 g
$CaCl_2 . 2H_2O$	0.08 g
$MnCl_2$	5 mg
Modified Gb minerals solution	100 ml
Agar	20 g
Distilled water	1 litre

Modified Gb minerals solution (Pelcher et al., *1963)*

$(NH_4)_2SO_4$	20 g
$MgSO_4$	20 g
$MnSO_4 . H_2O$	0·5 g
$ZnSO_4 . 7H_2O$	0·5 g
$CuSO_4 . 5H_2O$	0·5 g
$FeSO_4 \cdot 7H_2O$	0·005 g
Distilled water	1 litre

The most often used spores of *Bacillus stearothermophilus,* National Canners Association strain 1518 (ATCC 7953), can be produced readily at 52°C on the surface of fortified nutrient agar (Finley and Fields, 1962) prepared as follows—

Fortified nutrient agar (Finley and Fields, 1962)

Nutrient agar (Difco)	15 g
Plain agar (Difco)	5 g
Glucose	0·5 g
$MnSO_4 . H_2O$	30 mg
Distilled water	1 litre

The additional agar aids water retention during extended incubation times at the high temperature: for the same reason incubation is best carried out in Roux bottles or in partly sealed plates or trays. Table II lists a number of defined media which will support sporulation of some *Bacillus* species. Studies on defined media and the non-defined supplements needed to support growth and sporulation of insect larva pathogens such as *Bacillus popilliae* and crystal formation by *Bacillus thuringiensis* have been reported (Singer *et al.*, 1966).

Spores of the peculiar motile coccus *Sporosarina ureae* can be grown readily provided the temperature of incubation is not above about 22°C, for instance on the potato-based agar described above (Gould and Ordal, 1968) or a modified G medium agar (MacDonald and MacDonald, 1962)—

Modified G Medium (*MacDonald and MacDonald*, 1962)

Yeast extract	2 g
Peptone	3 g
Glucose	4 g
Malt extract	3 g
K_2HPO_4	1 g
$(NH_4)_2SO_4$	4 g
$CaCl_2$	0·1 g
$MgSO_4$	0·8 g
$MnSO_4 \cdot H_2O$	0·1 g
$ZnSO_4$	10 mg
$CuSO_4 \cdot 5H_2O$	10 mg
$FeSO_4 . 7H_2O$	1 mg
Agar	30 g
Distilled water	1 litre

The spore-like cysts of *Azotobacter vinlandii* can be produced at 33°C on Burk's nitrogen-free salts medium solidified with 1·5% agar (Wilson and Knight, 1952) and containing 0·3% butanol (Socolofsky and Wyss, 1961) or 0·05% sucrose as carbon sources. Higher levels of sucrose (0·5%) support sporulation if calcium and iron are omitted from the medium (Layne and Johnson, 1964). Fixed nitrogen generally suppresses sporulation.

Spores of *Clostridium* species are generally less readily prepared than those of *Bacillus* species, and complex amino-acid mixtures are usually necessary for good sporulation (Perkins, 1965); these may be supplied by meat infusions, or by various combinations of peptones. Typical particle-free media are as follows; for Putrefractive Anaerobe (PA) 3679 (Brown *et al.*, 1957) growing at 37°C—

Medium (*Brown* et al., 1957)

Trypticase (BBL)	30 g
$(NH_4)_2SO_4$	10 g
Sodium thioglycollate	1 g
Distilled water	1 litre

pH 7·2

TABLE II

Defined media for sporulation

Organism	B. cereus var lacticola ATCC 4342	B. megaterium	B. subtilis Marburg	B. licheniformis A 5	B. cereus T	Cl. botulinum 62 A	Cl. botulinum Type E
Reference	h	i, j,	k	l	m, n	o	p
Temperature	28°, 37°C	30°C	29°C	37°C	30°C	30°C	30°C
Initial pH value	6·7	6·8	7.1	7·2[a]	6·3	7·0	7·4
Medium constituents (per litre)							
Glucose	5·0g	1·0g	1·8g	3·6g[b]	2·0g	5·0g[b]	
Sucrose							5·0g
Citric acid				0·31g			
Ammonium lactate				5·4g[b]			
NH₄NO₃				96 mg			
NH₄Cl		2·0g	0·54g				
(NH₄)₂SO₄					2·0g		
L-Glutamic acid	10g		1·5g		1·84g		
Glycine	0·1g						
Amino-acid mixture					g	c	e
Growth factor mixture						d	f
H₃PO₄				0·45g			
Na₂HPO₄.12H₂O		6·0g					
K₂HPO₄	0·5g				} 0·1M	1·0g	0·5g
KH₂PO4	0·5g	3·0g	68mg		} 0·1M	1·0g	0·5g
Na₂SO₄	0·11g	0·11g					
NaHCO₃							2·2g
NaCl	10mg	3·0g		0·4g		2mg	0·68g
CaCl₂		0·15g	0·11g		80mg	2mg	20 mg
CaHPO₄	2ml (satd. soln)						
MgSO₄.7H₂O	0·2g			1·0g	0·2g	40mg	20mg
MgCl₂.6H₂O		0·1g	8·3mg				
MnSO₄.4H₂O	10mg			6mg	50mg	10mg	3·1mg
MnCl₂.4H₂O		10mg	20mg				
FeSO₄.(NH₄)₂SO₄.6H₂O				25mg			
FeSO₄.7H₂O	10 mg				5mg	2 mg	9·6mg
FeCl₃			0·06mg				
ZnSO₄.7H₂O	13mg				5mg		1·6mg
CuSO₄.5H₂O					5mg		0·9mg
(NH₄)₂MoO₄							0·5mg
Na₂B₄O₇.10H₂O							2·8mg
Sodium thioglycollate							2·0g

The highly sporogenic variant PA 3679h sporulates well at 35°C under N_2 in a medium (Uehara *et al.*, 1965) containing—

Medium (*Uehara* et al., 1965)

Trypticase (BBL)	60 g
Glucose	1 g
Distilled water	1 litre

pH 7·0

Agitation of these media is not necessary, but best synchrony is obtained using a modified active culture technique as detailed in Table III.

Clostridium thermosaccharolyticum spores are usually produced in pea infusion media (100 g peas/1 water) containing polypeptone (BBL; 10 g/l) and buffered at pH 7·0 with Tris (hydroxymethyl amino methane)-HCl; 0·05 M (Perkins, 1955).

Fall in pH value during culture of acid-producing clostridia certainly

---

Notes to Table II

a. pH-Value adjusted with KOH

b. Ingredients sterilized separately.

c. Amino-acid mixture (final concentration, mM); L-alanine, 4·5; L-arginine, 67; L-cysteine, 7·0; L-glutamic acid, 0·7; glycine, 1·6; L-histidine, 1·3; L-isoleucine, 3·8; L-leucine, 11·5; L-lysine, 8·2; L-methionine, 4·0; L-phenylalanine, 6·0; L-proline, 4·3; L-serine, 9·5; L-threonine, 8·4; L-tryptophan, 0·25; L-tyrosine, 1·4; DL-valine, 17·0.

d. Growth factor mixture (final concentration, μg/litre); biotin, 0·5; thiamine, 400; *p*-amino-benzoic acid, 10.

e. Amino-acid mixture (final concentration, mg/litre); L-alanine, 315; L-arginine, 258; L-aspartic acid, 99; L-glutamic acid, 83; L-histidine, 197; L-proline, 61; glycine, 135; L-valine, 250; L-isoleucine, 180; L-leucine, 204; L-lysine.HCl, 308; L-phenylalanine, 165; L-tyrosine, 164; L-threonine, 189; L-tryptophan, 175; L-serine, 108; taurine, 42; L-ornithine.HCl, 74; L-methionine, 44; L-cystine, 104; L-cysteine, 260; L-glutamine, 136; L-asparagine, 81; DL-α-aminobutyric acid, 55.

f. Growth factor mixture (final concentration, mg/litre); thiamine.HCl, 0·5; riboflavin, 0·5; pyridoxine.HCl, 0·25; pyridoxal.HCl, 0·25; niacin, 5·0; DL-calcium pantothenate, 1·0; biotin, 0·05; folic acid, 0·25; vit. B12, 0·1; choline chloride, 0·2; inositol, 0·016. The medium also contained Tween 80 (12·5 mg/l) and phenol red (20 mg/l).

g. Amino-acid mixture; glutamic acid (listed in Table) and (mg/litre) L-leucine, 800; L-valine, 300; L-threonine, 168; L-methionine, 70; L-histidine, 50.

h. Beskid and Lundgren (1961)

i. Millet and Aubert (1960).

j. Bach and Gilvarg (1966).

k. Donnellan, *et al.* (1964).

l. Bernlohr and Novelli (1963).

m. Nakata (1963).

n. Nakata (1964)

o. Perkins and Tsuji (1962).

p. Snudden and Lechowich (1966).

hinders sporulation. Incorporation of 1% (w/v) sterile calcium carbonate into medium containing—

Medium	
Glucose	30 g
Yeast extract	8 g
Distilled water	1 litre
initial pH 7·0–7·4	

allows good sporulation of *Clostridium pasteurianum* (Bowen and Smith, 1955). *Clostridium bifermentans* sporulates well in nutrient broth supplemented with glucose (2·5 g/l) and incubated anaerobically at 37°C for 72 h (Gibbs, 1964).

Spores of *Clostridium perfringens* (*welchii*) are generally grown in Ellner's (1956) medium consisting of—

Ellner's Medium (Ellner, 1956)	
"Polypeptone" (BBL) or other peptone	10 g
Yeast extract	3 g
Starch	3 g
$MgSO_4$	0·1 g
KH_2PO_4	1·5 g
$Na_2HPO_4 . 7H_2O$	50 g
Distilled water	1 litre
pH 7·8	

The medium is steamed first to ensure anaerobiosis, then a heavy vegetative inoculum is introduced to give about 5×10^5 cells/ml and incubated at 37°C for 24 h; 138 strains sporulated well in this system. A comparative study with seven strains (Groom and Strong, 1966) showed Ellner's procedure to support better sporulation of *Cl. perfringens* than SEC broth (Angelotti *et al.*, 1962), a cooked meat medium and a medium held in a dialysis-sac apparatus (Schneider, *et al.*, 1963). Dialysis cultures have the advantage of keeping cells free from insoluble medium components; advanced dialysis culture vessels have been described by Gerhardt and Gallup (1963). Duncan and Strong (1968) showed that spores produced in Ellner's medium were atypical, having low heat resistance, and formulated the following medium which supported good sporulation and produced spores of greater heat-resistance—

Medium (Duncan and Strong, 1968)	
Yeast extract	4 g
Proteose peptone	15 g
Soluble starch	4 g
Sodium thioglycollate	1 g
$Na_2HPO_4 . 7H_2O$	10 g
Distilled water	1 litre

TABLE III

Sequence of operations in the active-culture technique for preparation of spores of putrefactive anaerobe 3679h (Uehara et al. (1965))

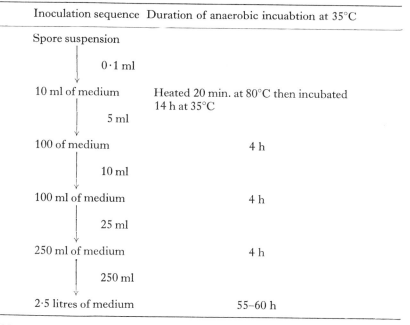

Inoculation sequence	Duration of anaerobic incuabtion at 35°C
Spore suspension	
0·1 ml	
10 ml of medium	Heated 20 min. at 80°C then incubated 14 h at 35°C
5 ml	
100 of medium	4 h
10 ml	
100 ml of medium	4 h
25 ml	
250 ml of medium	4 h
250 ml	
2·5 litres of medium	55–60 h

Clostridium botulinum Type A sporulates well at 30°C in a simple polypeptone (BBL; 50 g/l; pH 7·0) medium (Tsuji and Perkins, 1962) or in—

Medium (Wagenaar and Dack, 1958; Schmidt and Nank, 1960)

Trypticase (BBL)	50 g
Peptone (Difco)	5 g
Distilled water	1 litre

pH 7·0

held in filled bottles or in lengths of Pyrex tube fitted with serum caps to facilitate inoculation (Tsuji and Perkins, 1962). A completely defined medium supporting sporulation of *Cl. botulinum* Type A is given in Table II. *Cl. botulinum* Type B strains also sporulate well in this medium (Schmidt and Nank, 1960). The predominantly saccharolytic Type E strains sporulate better in media containing sugars, for instance—

Medium

Trypticase (BBL)	50 g
Peptone (Difco)	5 g
Distilled water	1 litre

pH 7·0

to which is added, after autoclaving and prior to inoculation, sterile concentrated solutions of glucose and sodium thioglycollate to give final levels (per litre) of 4 and 2 g (Schmidt, *et al.*, 1962). Cysteine (1 g) may be used in place of the thioglycollate (Strasdine, 1966). Different type E strains vary markedly in their sporulation in different media (Roberts, 1965). A defined medium has been described (Table II, column 7). Spores of other clostridia can usually be produced in particulate cooked-meat medium (e.g., *Clostridium aerofoetidum, histolyticum, sporogenes*; Perkins, 1965; Roberts *et al.*, 1966) in trypticase-peptone broths like those described above, sometimes with supplements (e.g., ammonium sulphate, 10 g/litre and yeast extract 2 g/litre for *Clostridium sordellii*), or on blood agar (*Clostridium caloritolerans*) or other agar media in anaerobic jars or incubators. Roberts (1967) found a cooked-meat medium based on Hartley's digest broth to be the most often effective medium to support the sporulation of clostridial strains.

2. *Harvesting, cleaning, and storing spores*

The normal procedure is to recover spores from the medium by centrifugation and then to wash them with cold sterile distilled water at least six times. For species in which lysis of sporangia occurs, this simple procedure may produce pure clean spores particularly if the top layer of the pellet is discarded after each centrifugation (Long and Williams, 1958), however, further cleaning is generally necessary. Incubation of the suspension with trypsin (100 μg/ml; e.g., *Cl. botulinum*; Grecz *et al.*, 1962), papain (1 mg/ml; e.g., *B. coagulans* and *stearothermophilus*; Warth *et al.*, 1963) or lysozyme (200 μg/ml; e.g., *Cl. botulinum*; PA 3679, Brown *et al.*, 1957; *B. popilliae*, St. Julian *et al.*, 1967) may remove any remaining vegetative debris, sometimes aided by ultrasonication (e.g., *B. popilliae* and *Cl. botulinum*).

Two-phase treatment (Sacks and Alderton, 1961) involves shaking the suspension with mixtures of polyethylene glycol ("Carbowax 4000"; Union Carbide Co.) and potassium phosphate buffer (3 M; pH 7·1). Typical systems contain 11·18 g glycol + 34·1 ml buffer, or 10·56 g glycol + 33·9 ml buffer, made to 100 ml with the suspension. Free spores of various *Bacillus* species enter the upper layers of the resulting two phase systems, from where they can be recovered free from debris by centrifugation. Density gradient centrifugation will separate spores from vegetative debris and from germinated spores, and also separate spores of different density in a single spore suspension (Lewis *et al.*, 1965; Tamir and Gilvarg, 1966). When the metal content of spores is of interest it is advisable to remove surface-absorbed cations by an acid wash (e.g. 0·03 N HCl) at 0–2°C (Murrell and Warth, 1965).

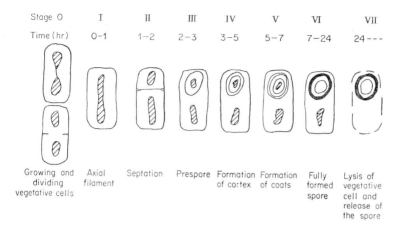

Fig. 2. Cytological stages in the sporulation of *Bacillus subtilis* Marburg. (Adapted from Schaeffer *et al.*, 1963.)

Cleaned spores of most organisms store satisfactorily at 0°–2°C or frozen in water, although slow changes (e.g., in ease of germination) occur with time. Organisms which are not easily freed of vegetative debris or traces of absorbed culture constituents may tend to germinate spontaneously (e.g., *Cl. botulinum* Type E spores as generally prepared) during storage unless freeze-dried. Freeze-drying avoids the major storage-changes and is therefore to be preferred for storing spores for any long-term study.

B. Methods of study

1. *Definition and recognition of stages*

The place of sporulation in the growth cycle is indicated in Fig. 1. Sporulation can be divided into a number of stages which occur in definite sequence which has been best described for *B. subtilis* Marburg and is shown in Fig. 2. The stages are based on changes seen in electron micrographs of thin sections of sporulating cells (Schaeffer *et al.*, 1963), but the following simple staining method (Gordon and Murrell, 1967) can be used for rapidly detecting septation, the beginning of stage II, in large cells like those of *B. cereus, B. megaterium,* nd *B. coagulans.* The sporulating cell suspension is simply mounted in an equal volume of aqueous crystal violet (0·03% w/v). The invaginated membranes immediately take up the stain allowing the stage and synchrony of sporulation to be determined. In some species septation can be detected using Nomarski interference contrast microscopy (Hitchins *et al.*, 1968).

2. Synchronous sporulation

Accurate chemical and cytological study of sporulation depends on attainment of a high degree of synchrony of the sporulation stages in a culture. This is usually obtained by some form of the so-called "active culture" technique (Halvorson, 1957). With *B. cereus* T this involves using an initial heavy inoculum of about 10^6 cells/ml followed by three $3\frac{1}{2}$ to 4-hourly subcultures using 10% inocula into prewarmed medium (G) at 28°C. Finally the sporulation culture is similarly inoculated and left to complete sporulation. A similar procedure induces good synchrony of sporulation in *Clostridium roseum* cultures. Table 3 shows a modified active culture technique for use with PA 3679 (Uehara *et al.*, 1965).

3. Endotrophic sporulation

A culture may be grown until its cells have become "committed" to sporulation, then centrifuged, and the washed cells resuspended in water or some solution. Although now free of complete medium, the cells may continue to form spores; this process is termed "endotrophic" sporulation. By adding various substances to the aqueous endotrophic culture, one can study the effects of the substances on sporulation or on spore properties more or less in isolation. For example Pelcher *et al.*, (1963) and Black and Gerhardt (1963) studied the effects of additives including Ca^{++} on viability, dipicolinic acid and calcium content and heat resistance of *B. cereus* T spores. Foerster and Foster (1966b) allowed *B. megaterium* QM B1551 and *B. cereus* T spores to form endotrophically in solutions of calcium, strontium, and barium chlorides and obtained spores enriched in the respective metal. Vinter and Slepecky (1965) incorporated the phenylalanine antimetabolite β-2-thienylalanine in the endotrophic sporulation medium and studied the resulting changes in spore heat resistance. It is important not to use cell suspensions in excess of about 10^7/ml for endotrophic sporulation studies, otherwise sporulation really takes place in an environment of cell autolysate.

"Committed" cells of *B. cereus* T may be recognized by their granular appearance under the microscope. The time of committment of other sporeformers can be quickly worked out by trial and error.

4. Microcycle sporogenesis

The first cell to emerge from a germinated spore can be made to resporulate without the intervention of vegetative cell division. Such "microcycle" sporogenesis in *B. cereus* NCIB 8122 is induced by replacing the outgrowing cells from the outgrowth medium into water or saline (Vinter and Slepecky, 1965); rapid replacement can be achieved by filtration or centrifugation. Nutritional requirements for microcycle sporogenesis and associated metabolism can be studied by incorporating nutrients or meta-bolic inhibitors in the replacement solution. *B. megaterium* required only acetate and a small amount of a tricarboxylic acid cycle intermediate for completion of microcycle sporogenesis (Holmes and Levinson, 1967).

5. *Changes in macromolecules and new syntheses*

Developmental changes in macromolecules occurring during sporula-tion can be studied once a good synchronous sporulation system has been developed (above).

The nucleotide pool of sporulating cells can be extracted by shaking cells (10 g wet weight) with 5% trichloroacetic acid (150 ml) for 5 min. then sonicating for 10 min at 0°C (Lietzmann and Bernlohr, 1965). ^{32}P-labelled cells and pulse labelling can be used in association with chromatography on methylated albumin-kieselguhr columns to follow changes in RNA content and distribution of particle sizes (Doi and Igar-ishi, 1964a, b). Pulse labelling with [^{14}C]- uracil allows accurate measure-ment of the rate of RNA synthesis and, with sucrose gradient centrifuga-tion, shows up changes in rate of synthesis of different particles (Szulmajster, 1964; Sykes this series; Eaton this series). Balassa (1966) compared several methods for analysing spore RNA. DNA can be extracted from sporulating cells and spores and measured by the diphenylamine method (Burton, 1956); it is necessary to use two perchloric acid extrac-tions at 70°C to achieve maximal yield (Holmes and Levinson, 1967). Alternatively, RNA and DNA can be extracted by disrupting spore suspen-sions in absolute ethanol by shaking with an equal weight of Ballotini beads (size 12; Jencons Scientific Ltd., Hemel Hempstead, Herts) (Young and Fitz-James, 1959). Szulmajster (1964) measured the death rates of spores due to disintegration of atoms of ^{32}P incorporated at different times during sporulation to follow the synthesis of spore DNA (^{32}P-suicide technique; Stent and Fuerst, 1955). The technique involves allowing sporulation to commence in a medium containing about 20 μg P/ml (specific activity about 60 mC/mgP). At intervals, incorporation of the isotope is essentially halted by adding to aliquots of culture at 30-fold excess of unlabelled phosphate. Each aliquot is then allowed to complete the sporulation process. Samples of each aliquot are stored at -20°C and viable counts performed daily. A plot is made of the number of survivors: $1 - e^{\lambda t}$ (where t is time in days and λ is the fraction of P atoms disintegrating per day). The slope of the suicide curve is a function of the specific activity of the ^{32}P incor-porated into DNA during the exposure period and not subsequently diluted out by the unlabelled phosphate. Protein synthesis is best measured by following the rate of incorporation of [^{14}C]-phenylalanine or [^{14}C]-methionine from the medium (Szulmajster, 1964); the reaction is stopped by adding an equal volume of perchloric acid (0·6N) and the acid-insoluble precipitate collected for radioactive counting by membrane filtration.

Synthesis of murein structures in sporulating cells can be measured by following incorporation of [^{14}C]-diaminopimelic acid (DAP). Decarboxylation of DAP to form lysine is minimized by adding excess of [^{12}C]-lysine to the medium (Vinter, 1963). In a similar manner, accumulation of calcium and sulphur during sporulation is best measured using ^{45}CaCl$_2$ (Vinter, 1960; Young and Fitz-James, 1962) and [^{35}S]-cysteine (Vinter, 1960). The ratio of thiol groups to disulphide bonds cannot be so confidently measured, but rough estimations can be obtained by amperometric titration (Gould and Ordal, 1968) or by measuring fluorescence quenching of the thiol reagent fluorescein mercuric acetate (Blankenship and Pallansch, 1966). Synthesis of dipicolinic acid (DPA) during sporulation (Young and Fitz-James, 1962; Vinter, 1962a) can be followed using colorimetric or UV-absorption methods (see Section III C 2).

6. Sporulation-linked changes

Detection of changes in levels of acetate, pyruvate, lactate, and acetoin and other organic acids which occur during sporulation of B. cereus T in a modified G medium was described by Nakata (1963) and Nakata and Halvorson (1960). The two most obvious classes of substances which are excreted by some sporulating cells are extracellular proteolytic enzyme (B. subtilis, Schaeffer, 1967; B. licheniformis, Bernlohr, 1964; but not B. megaterium, Millet and Aubert, 1964) and antibiotics. The proteases are easily detected by incubating culture supernatants (e.g., 1 ml, 37°C, 30 min.) with casein, Azocasein or Azocoll (Calbiochem) (5 mg). Trichloracetic acid (1 ml, 10% w/v) is added and the resulting protein precipitate is filtered off. Proteolysis of the casein is detected by measuring extinction of the filtrates at 280 nm. Proteolysis of the azo-coupled proteins is detected by adding NaOH (0·5 ml, N) and measuring extinction of the filtrates at 440 nm (Michel, 1966; Levisohn and Aronson, 1967). It is advantageous to use the azo-coupled proteins when the culture supernatants are intensely U.V.—absorbing at 280 nm. Millet (1969) described the separation and assay of the two extracellular sporulation proteases of B. subtilis Marburg, a "metal protease" active at neutral pH, and a "serine protease" active in alkali.

Interest has been shown recently in antibiotic production by B. subtilis Marburg, and its mutants see Section (IIC). Antibiotic production by different strains is recognized by inoculating nutrient agar plates, heavily seeded with Staphylococcus aureus, with drops of the B. subtilis culture under investigation: the plates are examined for zones of inhibition after 15 h incubation at 37°C (Schaeffer, 1967). Production of lytic enzymes by sporulating cultures can be detected by spotting cultures onto plates containing autoclaved cells of *Micrococcus lysodeikticus* (1 mg dry weight/ ml). Zones of lysis are visible after 48 h incubation at 37°C.

During sporulation, resistance of the newly forming spore increases, but resistance to all agents does not occur simultaneously. Resistance to octanol (0·2%, 10 min. at 37°C), for instance, increases markedly at the end of stage IV during sporulation of *B. subtilis* Marburg, whereas heat-resistance rises sharply at the end of stage V (Schaeffer *et al.*, 1963). Increase in resistance of sporulating cells of *B. cereus* NCIB 8122 to ionizing radiation precedes increase in heat resistance (Vinter, 1962a).

7. *Use of inhibitors*

Valuable information can be gained by identifying inhibitors of sporulation and studying their mechanisms of action. Suitable methods of screening for sporulation inhibitors have been described, for instance to investigate the effects of pyridine mono- and dicarboxylic acid (Gollakota and Halvorson, 1960) and organic acids and their esters (Gollakota and Halvorson, 1963) on sporulation and DPA synthesis by *B. cereus* T. An "active culture" is first prepared by four subcultures (as in Table III). This culture is divided into aliquots to which are added the various potential inhibitors at different concentrations and at different times during the sporulation sequence (Fig. 2). Samples are then withdrawn and examined by phase-contrast microscopy, by microscopy of stained smears or by viable counts following heating (70°C, 30 min.) to kill non-spore forms. In these studies the state of sporulation affected was defined by the accompanying pH changes in the cultures. 8-Azaguanine inhibits sporulation of *B. cereus* T only if added before transition to presporulation (equivalent to about stage I in Fig. 2); use of purine bases and nucleosides to overcome the inhibition has been described (Doi and Igarishi, 1964b). *β*-Phenethyl alcohol can be used to inhibit sporulation through its action on cell membranes; at 0·35% it inhibits development of the spore septum and forespore membranes in sporulating cells of *B. cereus* ATCC 4342 (Remsen, *et al.*, 1966).

Of the antibiotics used, chloramphenicol (100 µg/ml) (Vinter, 1964; Ryter and Szulmajster, 1965) has little effect on sporulation if added late in the sequence (*B. cereus* NCIB 8122, Vinter, 1964; *B. subtilis* Marburg *et al.*, 1965), but blocks formation of the coat layers (stage V, Fig. 2) if added before this event (Ryter and Szulmajster, 1965). Penicillin (1000 units/ml) was used by Vinter (1964) to interfere specifically with synthesis of murein during sporulation and produced cortex-deficient spores of *B. cereus* NCIB 8122. Murrell and Warth (1965) used celbenin (about 100µg/ ml; Beecham Research Laboratories, Betchworth, Surrey) similarly with

B. cereus T to form relatively heat-sensitive spores. Cycloserine (100μg/ml) can also be used to interfere with murein synthesis by inhibiting D-alanyl-D-alanine synthetase and alanine racemase during sporulation of *B. cereus* T (Murrell and Warth, 1965). Vinter (1962b) found sporulating cells of *B. cereus* and *B. megaterium* to bind chlortetracycline. Chlortetracycline, oxytetracycline and tetracycline (5 μg/ml) will stop calcium incorporation and synthesis of dipicolinic acid by sporulating cells (Vinter, 1962b). Actinomycin D (0·5 μg/ml) can be used to inhibit sporulation, presumably by arresting m-RNA synthesis, if added early in the sequence (*B. licheniformis* A-5, Leitzmann and Bernlohr, 1965; *B. subtilis* Marburg, Szulmajster, 1964).

C. Sporulation mutants

Genetic control of sporulation has been mostly studied using the Marburg strain of *B. subtilis*, shown to be transformable by Spizizen (1958). Spores of the Marburg strain grown on nutrient agar (Schaeffer and Michel, 1968) or potato dextrose agar (Difco; Northrop and Slepecky, 1967) contain melanin pigments which cause wild-type sporulating colonies to turn brown. Asporogenous mutants can easily be recognized by the lack of pigmentation of their colonies (Schaeffer and Ionesco, 1960; Schaeffer *et al.*, 1965). The asporogenous mutants obtained are blocked at different stages of the sporulation sequence (Fig. 2) and also show mutations in sporulation—linked characters like antibiotic, protease and lysin production (Section III A 6). Other phenotypic traits studied in asporogenous mutants of *B. subtilis* Marburg, include formation of extracellular RNAase, DNAase and amylase, and the ability to be made competent for genetic transformation (Schaeffer, 1967; Schaeffer *et al.*, 1965).

UV-irradiation (10^{-3} survivors) is a satisfactory means of inducing sporulation mutations. A large proportion of mutants exhibiting abnormal sporulation can also be obtained by heating dry spores of *B. subtilis* Marburg *in vacuo* at 90°–100°C for 9–12 h. Under these conditions only few spores are killed although the mutation rate is exceptionally high (Northrop and Slepecky, 1967).

III. THE SPORE

A. Measurement of resistance

1. *Chemicals and enzymes*

Resistance of spores to soluble chemicals and enzymes can be measured by contacting spores with various concentrations of the agents for different times in water or buffers, removing samples, and counting survivors by

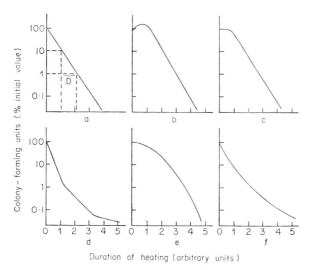

Duration of heating (arbitrary units)

FIG. 3. Variations in form of heat: survivor curves as determined by counting colony-forming units surviving different times at constant temperature.

conventional methods. Quenching agents for various chemicals (Sykes, 1965) may be required to stop carried-over reagent inhibiting outgrowth in the counting medium if the reagent is not out-diluted. If chemical agents are tested in organic media, which may be desirable in assessing usefulness of germicides, it must be accepted that germination may occur so that the resistance of *germinated* spores is really measured. Germination is less likely to occur during testing of vapour-phase sterilizing agents. Apart from the necessity of guarding against (or allowing for) germination, resistance studies on spores and vegetative cells can be treated similarly and inactivation curves and "D-values" sometimes worked out as for heat sterilization (below) (Rubbo and Gardner, 1965). The detailed literature was most recently reviewed by Sykes (1965), Rubbo and Gardner (1965), Hugo (1967), Bean (1967).

2. Heat resistance

The theory and practice of heat resistance measurement has been dealt with in several recent reviews and books, Goldblith, Joslyn and Nickerson (1961), Cheftel and Thomas (1965), Stumbo (1965), Roberts and Hitchins (1969). The most accurate and informative methods involve heating small volumes (e.g., 0·02–1·0 ml) of spore suspensions in sealed thin-walled glass ampoules or sealed capillary tubes (Stern and Proctor, 1954) *completely immersed* in accurately thermostatted water or oil baths. An alternative method which avoids large warm-up time effects and can be used for temperatures below the boiling point of water is to preheat a large stirred volume of menstruum, then add the spores in a relatively small volume of liquid so as scarcely to change the temperature, at zero time. A disadvantage of this method is that any spores in liquid splashed and perhaps dried on the vessel walls will receive protection from heat-killing (Stumbo, 1965). Whichever method is used samples, ampoules or capillaries are removed and rapidly cooled at intervals and survivors counted by plating, most probable number, or other techniques. Survivor curves may then be plotted on semi-log paper, and are ideally straight lines (Fig. 3a). Departures from linearity, however, may occur for many reasons. Clumping may cause irregularities in survivor curves. Activation of spores (see Section V) may cause a rise in viable count during the early course of heating, reflecting an increase in the numbers of spores able to germinate and form colonies (Fig. 3b). If heat activation and heat inactivation balance, or warm-up time is long, then curves with a shoulder (Fig. 3c) may be obtained. Suspensions containing organisms of different heat resistance or organisms protected to different extents in a heterogeneous environment (fat globules, dry regions etc.) will typically give curves with well marked changes in slope (Fig. 3d). The fact that the heat-resistance of spores can change *during* heating, by cation exchange reactions (Alderton and Snell, 1963; Alderton *et al.*, 1964), means that curves of constantly changing slope can be expected (Fig. 3e and f), particularly in low pH environments (convex) and under conditions where low-cation (e.g., acid-treated) spores are heated in high calcium media (concave). For example, Alderton and Snell (1969) reduced the heat resistance of *B. stearothermophilus* spores in strained beef liver several hundred-fold by treatment for 1 h at pH3 and 70°C prior to adjusting the pH-value to 5·9. Spores which have survived severe heating often grow to form colonies less readily than unheated or heat-activated spores. Special media containing starch (Stumbo, 1965) or calcium dipicolinate (see section V B 3) may allow increased recovery. Addition of lysozyme (2 μg/ml) to the plating medium allows best recovery of heated spores of *Cl. perfringens* ATCC 3624 (Cassien and Sebald, 1969), so that the otherwise heat-sensitive spores appear heat-resistant when related in lysozyme-containing medium.

The slope of the survivor curve at any one temperature is usually signified as the D-value or decimal reduction time (Katzin *et al.*, 1943; see Fig. 3a), i.e., the time taken (min.) for the survivor (= colony) count to fall by one log cycle *at the specified temperature.*

The relative heat resistance of a spore suspension at different temperatures can be expressed as the z-value. This is the change in temperature necessary to change the D-value by one log cycle. In food processing, where the Farenheit scale is generally used, z is therefore taken as numeri-

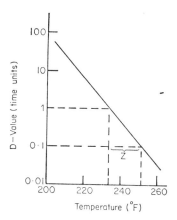

F IG. 4. Estimation of z-value by plotting D-values obtained at different temperatures.

cally equal to the increase in °F necessary to cause a 90% reduction in D-value (Fig. 4). The plot is usually termed the thermal destruction curve, and is generally a straight line over the medium temperature region but may depart from linearity in the region of interest in high temperature short time sterilization (Edwards *et al.*, 1965; Wang *et al.*, 1964) and is affected by components of the heating menstruum (Busta, 1967).

The F-value is a term used to describe the total heat involved in a process, which may include considerable heating up and cooling down times. F is numerically equal to the equivalent *time (min.) at* 250°F (unless otherwise stated) of the complete process with respect to a particular organism. Derivations of these terms are given in standard texts (Stumbo, 1965).

Other methods of investigating heat-resistance are less informative than the construction of survivor curves at various temperatures described above, but may be more rapidly performed and be more appropriate to practical situations. For instance, thermal death time methods which involve sealing samples (usually 1 ml) in glass ampoules or distributing spores in small cans containing the menstruum under investigation. The ampoules or cans are then heated for various times in accurately thermostatted oil baths or autoclaves. Each sample is then transferred to growth medium, or simply incubated if the sample medium, or can menstruum, will support growth. If many replicates are used, these methods give results which are most relevant to actual commercial canning practice.

The methods described above are of less value in determining resistance of spores at ultra high temperatures (UHT), where heating times may be of only seconds or fractions of a second duration. It becomes important to keep warm-up times as short as possible. Small unsealed (cotton wool plugged) tubes containing small volumes of suspension can be rapidly heated and cooled under pressure in special autoclaves (Schmidt, 1950). Meaningful practical results can be obtained using commercial UHT and steam injection devices (Edwards *et al.*, 1965). The thermoresistomer (Stumbo, 1948) is a special apparatus designed to allow rapid warm-up and cool-down of small samples (0·01–0·02 ml) in fluted aluminium cups. Heating and cooling is effected automatically by steam, and, following heating, samples are automatically dropped into tubes of medium or of diluent. Heating times of 6 seconds or more suffer from $<5\%$ error, and heating times are reproducible to within about 0·03 seconds (Stumbo, 1965). Accurate shorter exposures are best obtained in tubular-flow reactors in which spores are injected into a hot flowing stream of liquid. In such a reactor, thermal equilibrium can be obtained in $<0·0006$ seconds with exposure times down to 0·2 seconds or so (Wang *et al.*, 1964).

Methods for isolating single spores which can be subjected to heat individually, were described by Holdom and Johnstone (1967) and Johnstone (this series).

3. *Radiation resistance*

Measurement of radiation resistance of spores is essentially simpler than measurement of heat resistance for two reasons. Firstly, no allowance need be taken for warm-up time, and secondly only total dose need generally be considered since changes in dose rate have little effect on the kill. Samples of spores may therefore be irradiated with ionizing radiations, like X-rays and ^{60}Co γ-rays, at a number of discrete doses, in glass ampoules, and "dose : survivor" curves constructed as for heat resistance. For less penetrating ionizing radiation (e.g., linear accelerator β-radiation), depth of sample must be kept small to avoid absorption, and for ultra-violet radiation open dishes with $<0·5$ cm depth of well stirred sample are preferable.

Woese (1958, 1959) discussed the types of survivor curves obtained when spores are subjected to ionizing radiation. Donnellan and Morowitz (1957) described methods for irradiating dry spores and for evaluating the survivor curves. Absence or presence of oxygen affects sensitivity of vegetative bacteria and, less markedly, of wet and dry spores to ionizing radiation (Tallentire and Davies, 1961). The gas phase of samples should always, therefore, be controlled, most simply by making anoxic (i.e., oxygen-free) by bubbling or de-gassing with N_2, under which conditions resistance is greater than when samples are bubbled with air or held in O_2.

B. Disruption of spores

Methods depending on shearing or cavitation are relatively ineffective for disrupting spores. For instance, ultrasonication which will rapidly remove exosporia (Berger and Marr, 1960) may only cause partial disruption of spores after treatments as long as 6 h (Mastroeni et al., 1967). Single treatments with pressure units like the French pressure cell (McCormick and Halvorson, 1964) or the Ribi unit (Ribi et al., 1959) used at 30,000 p.s.i. will remove exosporia from B. cereus T spores (Gerhardt and Ribi, 1964; and see Section C4 below), whereas repeated passage at 50,000 p.s.i. is necessary to appreciably breach the spore coat.

In contrast, spores are very easily broken by methods based on abrasion or ballistic disintegration. For instance, small quantities can be disrupted by shaking, for 5 min. or so in each cup of a Mickle tissue homogeniser, 7 ml of suspension containing not more than 20 mg dry wt spores per ml plus 4 g Ballotini glass beads size 12 (Jencons Scientific Ltd., Hemel Hempstead, Herts.) (Strange and Dark, 1957). About 50 ml suspension can be broken similarly by shaking in a CO_2-cooled Braun disintegrator with glass beads (0·1–0·12 mm) or about 9 ml in a cooled Nossal disintegrator (18 ml capsule) containing, 4 g glass beads (0·1–0·14 mm) (Sierra, 1963). High speed blenders can be used to treat larger amounts (Simmons and Costilow, 1962). Even with efficient cooling, however, autolytic changes occur during disintegration. These can be minimised by incorporating EDTA (1·5% w/v at pH 9·5; Warth, 1965) during disruption, or by heat-killing the spores prior to disruption (Warth et al., 1963). An acid environment (< pH 3·5) allows breakage of the spore coats to proceed more rapidly than breakage of the core region so that core-enriched preparations may be obtained (Hitchins and Gould, 1964).

Spore pastes frozen in methanol : solid CO_2 or in liquid N_2 can be disrupted by grinding in a mortar with 2 volumes of 0·1 mm glass beads (Doi and Igarishi, 1964a) or 1 volume of alumina (Bishop and Doi, 1966).

Rupture of dry spores may be achieved by grinding spores for about 6 h with an equal volume of 325 mesh alumina, cooled by adding solid CO_2 (Lawrence and Halvorson, 1954). More rapid dry rupture is caused by shaking dry spores (10 mg) at 5°C with 30 mg NaCl crystals (50– to 100–mesh) and a 55 mg steel ball in a dental amalgamator for 3 min. (Sacks and Bailey, 1963; Sacks et al., 1964).

Spores have been disrupted chemically to form part-purified coat fractions by heating (120°C) in HCl (0·1N) for 2 h (Hunnell and Ordal, 1961). Sodium hypochlorite (about 0·025–0·1% w/v) will dissolve spores but leave coat layers intact (Rode and Williams, 1966).

Spores of some species can be sufficiently lysed by lysozyme to allow leakage of large molecules like DNA. For example, spores of B. stearother-

mophilus were partly lysed by first incubating in 2-mercaptoethanol (10% v/v) plus urea (8M) at pH 8, 60°–65°C for 15 min, followed by addition of *N*-ethylmaleimide to 0·15M and a further incubation of 1 h. The spores were then washed prior to incubating in lysozyme (2 mg/ml in 0·15M NaCl+0·1M EDTA, pH 8·0) at 37°C for 16 h (Tabatabai and Walker, 1967). A similar technique was used by Tansoka and Sakakibara (1968) to extract transforming DNA from spores of *B. subtilis*.

C. Chemical analyses

1. *Calcium and other metals*

The high calcium content of normal spores, commonly about 2% of the dry weight, and its role in resistance has prompted much study of spore cations. Samples for cation analysis are usually prepared by a wet ashing procedure (Slepecky and Foster, 1959); spores (50 mg dry weight) are heated over a flame in a micro-Kjeldahl flask with 2 ml concentrated H_2SO_4, 1 ml concentrated HNO_4 and 5 ml double-distilled water. When white fumes appear the mixture is cooled, 0·6 ml H_2O_2 (30%) added, and the digestion repeated. Further digestion with additions of 1 ml HNO_4 are made until the solution is clear. It is then made to volume (say 10 ml) and analysed for metal content (Ca, Mg, Mn, Fe, K, Na) by any standard chemical (Lundgren and Cooney, 1962; Levinson and Hyatt, 1964) or flame photometric method (Lechowich and Ordal, 1962; Herbert *et al.*, this series).

Uptake of Ca during sporulation and exchange reactions of Ca in spores or spore fractions with exogenous cations is most easily studied using [45]Ca-labelled spores. Production of these spores and studies of cation exchange were described by Rode and Foster (1966). The initial work on cation exchange properties of spores was described by Alderton and Snell (1963) and Alderton *et al.* (1964). Methods for studying the state of Ca and Mn in intact spores using electron paramagnetic resonance was described by Windle and Sacks (1963).

The location of mineral matter in spores can be studied by micro-incineration and visualization of the mineral deposits by light (Knaysi, 1961, 1965) or electron microscopy (Thomas, 1964).

2. *Dipicolinic acid*

The most widely used method for estimation of the dipicolinic acid (DPA) content of spores is that devised by Jannsen, Lund and Anderson (1958), based on formation of the coloured Fe(II)DPA complex. The spores (4–20 mg equiv. dry wt.) in 5 ml water are first autoclaved (15 lb for 60 min.) and cooled, then acetic acid (0·1 ml N) or trichloroacetic acid (0·1 ml

10% w/v; Lechowich and Ordal, 1962) is added. One hour at room temperature is allowed to ensure complete extraction of the DPA; the cells are then removed by centrifuging. To 4 ml of the supernatant is added reagent (1 ml) consisting of freshly prepared $Fe(NH_4)_2(SO_4)_2.6H_2O$ (1% w/v) and ascorbic acid (1% w/v) in sodium acetate buffer (0·5 M; pH 5·5). The extinction is read at 440 nm within one hour. Suitable standards contain 50, 100, and 150 μg DPA.

Practically all the ultraviolet absorbance of spore extracts is attributable to DPA so that absorbance at 270 nm, which is about the absorption peak of calcium DPA, gives a good measure of DPA (Martin and Foster, 1958). Lewis (1967) described a procedure for specific extraction of DPA from spores and a particularly sensitive method for its estimation by spectrometry of the calcium chelate.

Ultraviolet absorption of DPA in whole spores and in other environments has been compared (Holsinger et al., 1967), and methods have been described for measuring ultraviolet absorption spectra of DPA complexes in dried spores (Bailey et al., 1965).

3. Enzymes

Methods used for studying spore enzymes are too numerous to describe in detail, Table IV therefore simply lists some of the enzyme activities which have been most studied in spores or in sporulating cells and gives references to the methodology employed. Methods for studying DNA and RNA synthesis by sporulating cells were considered before (Section IIB 5).

4. Exosporium

The exposporium of B. cereus spores can be isolated by passing the cells (up to 50 mg wet wt/ml) once through a refrigerated "Ribi" press (Ribi et al., 1959). Further purification by centrifugation at 400 g for 50 min. through a linear gradient of glycerol was described by Gerhardt and Ribi (1964), together with chemical analysis (Matz and Gerhardt, 1964).

5. Spore coats

Preparations of coats may be obtained by disrupting spores by any of the methods described above (section IIIB I), and washing the coat fragments by centrifuging in water. Coats so prepared are free of much of the cortex due to its autolysis during the breakage process. Autolysis can be minimised and more of the cortex retained in the debris by breaking spores in the presence of sodium ethylenediaminetetraacetate (1% w/v) at

TABLE IV

Spore enzymes: methods of preparation and detection

Enzyme system	Organism	Remarks	References
Purine nucleoside phosphorylases	*B. cereus* T	Active on inosine deoxyinosine, guanosine, deoxyguanosine but not adenosine	a, b
Adenylate kinase	*B. subtilis*		q′
Purine ribosidase	*B. cereus*	Adenosine and inosine	c, d
Pyrimidine ribosidase	*B. cereus* T	Uridine	e
Purine deaminase	*B. cereus*	Adenosine	d
Pyrimidine deaminase	*B. cereus* T	Cytidine	e
DNA polymerase	*B. subtilis* SB133		f
	B. megaterium QM B1551		o′
RNA polymerase	*B. megaterium* QM B1551		o′
Protein synthetic system	*B. megaterium* QM B1551		p′
L-Alanine dehydrogenase	*B. cereus* T	Active on L-alanine L-α-aminobutyric acid and L-cysteine	g, h i, j
	B. subtilis SJ2		k, 1
L-Valine dehydrogenase	*B. subtilis* SJ2		k
L-Leucine dehydrogenase	*B. subtilis* SJ2		1
Transaminases	*B. subtilis* ATCC 6633	Glutamic-oxaloacetic	m
	B. subtilis	α-Oxoglutaric-L-aspartic, L- or D-alanine	n
	B. megaterium QMB 1551	Glutamic-aspartic	o
NADH$_2$-oxidase	*B. cereus* T	Stimulated by DPA	p
	B. subtilis Marburg		q
	Cl. botulinum 62A (ATCC 7948)		r, s
Catalase	*B. cereus* T		t, u, v
NADH$_2$-cytochrome *c* reductase	*B. cereus* T	Stimulated by DPA	w
	B. subtilis Marburg		q
Diaphorase	*B. cereus* T		w
	B. subtilis and *B. megaterium*		x
	Cl. botulinum 62A		r
Pyrophosphatase	*B. megaterium* *B. subtilis*	Mn^{2+}-activated	y

TABLE IV (*continued*)

Enzyme system	Organism	Remarks	References
Esterases and lipases	*B. subtilis* Marburg		a′, b
	B. coagulans ATCC 8038		c′
	B. cereus		c′
Enzymes of glucose catabolism	*B. cerus* T		d′
	B. subtilis	Anaerobic oxidation inhibited by DPA	e′
	Cl. botulinum 62A ATCC 7498		r
Glucose dehydrogenase	*B. cereus* T	Modification of heat resistance	f′, g′
Fructose 1,6-diphosphate aldolase	*B. cereus* T		r′
Tricarboxylic acid cycle enzymes	*B. subtilis* Marburg		q
Enzymes catalysing breakdown of arginine	*B. licheniformis* A–5		h′
Lytic enzymes	*B. cereus* PX		i′, j′
	B. subtilis Marburg		k′
Enzymes catalysing synthesis of DPA	*B. megaterium*		l′
	B. cereus T		m′
Proteases	*B. megaterium* QMB 1551	Mn^{2+}-activated	n′
	B. subtilis Marburg		b′

a. Krask and Fulk (1959).
b. Gardner and Kornberg (1967).
c. Lawrence (1955).
d. Powell and Hunter (1956).
e. Lawrence and Tsan (1962).
f. Falaschi and Kornberg (1966).
g. O'Connor and Halvorson (1960).
h. O'Connor and Halvorson (1961a).
i. O'Connor and Halvorson (1961b).
j. McCormick and Halvorson (1964).
k. Hermier (1962).
l. Hermier (1965).
m. Rowley and Newcomb (1964).
n. Falcone and Caraco (1958).
o. Levinson and Sevag (1954).
p. Doi and Halvorson (1961).
q. Szulmajster (1964).
r. Simmons and Costilow (1962)
s. Green and Sadoff (1965).
t. Lawrence and Halvorson (1954).
u. Sadoff (1961).
v. Norris and Baillie (1964).

w. Halvorson, *et al.* (1958).
x. Spencer and Powell (1952).
y. Levinson, *et al.* (1958).
z. Tono and Kornberg (1967).
a′ Sierra (1963).
b′ Sierra (1967b).
c′ Roberts and Rosenkrantz (1966).
d′ Goldman and Blumenthal (1966).
e′ Hachisuka, *et al.* (1965).
f′ Bach and Sadoff (1962).
g′ Sadoff *et al.* (1965).
h′ Ramaley and Bernlohr (1966).
i′ Strange and Dark (1957).
j′ Gould *et al* (1966).
k′ Schaeffer (1967).
l′ Bach and Gilvarg (1966).
m′ Aronson *et al.* (1967).
n′ Levinson and Hyatt (1955).
o′ Chambon *et al.* (1968)
p′ Deutscher *et al.* (1968)
q′ Spudich and Kornberg (1969)
r′ Sadoff *et al.* (1969)

pH 9–10 (Strange and Dark, 1957) or by heating the spores to inactivate lytic enzymes prior to breakage. Cortex murein can mostly be removed from coats by incubation with lysozyme (100 μg/ml). Lysozyme is only weakly active in media of low ionic strength, but ammonium acetate buffer (0·05M; pH 7·2) can be used if the presence of inorganic ions is undesirable (Warth et al., 1963); the cortical membrane of some species is lysozyme-resistant. Kondo and Foster (1967) described methods for fractionating spore coats of B. megaterium into components with different structures and chemical compositions. Lysozyme-treated coats (see above; extinction about 0·8 at 560 nm) are first extracted with NaOH (60 mM; 50°C for 1 h). The supernatant is neutralized with HCl, concentrated by rotary evaporation and dialyzed to yield the "alkali-soluble fraction". The sediment undissolved in NaOH is suspended (150 mg) in distilled water (15 ml) in a 20 ml beaker (3·5 cm dia., 4·5 cm height) and sonicated (Branson Sonifier; Branson Instruments, Inc., Danbury, Conn. U.S.A.; power setting 3 for 5 min.). The faintly opalescent supernatant is concentrated in vacuo, and precipitates as the "paracrystal fraction". The residue is incubated for 25 h at 50° in tris (hydroxymethylaminomethane): HCl buffer (pH 8·0; 0·01 M; 40 ml) containing Pronase (10 mg; California Biochemical Corp., Los Angeles, Calif.). The resulting sediment is washed and is the "resistant residue". Alkali (100 mM NaOH; 15 min; 2°C) extracts a coat protein from spores previously treated with mercapto-ethanol (10% v/v; 37°C; 1 h; in 8M urea; pH 3) (Gould, Stubbs and King, 1970). Alkaline thioglycollate was found to solubilize 80% of coat protein without altering coat morphology (Aronson and Fitz-James, 1968); dithiothreitol plus sodium lamyl sulphate at pH 10·5 stripped most of the coat off spores grown in the presence of sulphite. Analytical methods for amino-acids, phosphorus, and amino sugars in coat fractions have been described (Strange and Dark, 1956; Salton and Marshall, 1959; Warth et al., 1963; Herbert et al., this Series, Volume 5B).

Spore coats contain a disulphide-rich protein layer. Estimation of disulphide content was described by Vinter (1960). The ratio of disulphide to thiol content can be found by fluorescence quenching of fluorescein mercuric acetate (Blankenship and Pallansch, 1966) or by amperometric titration with silver nitrate (Gould and Ordal, 1968). Methods have been described for the X-ray diffraction analysis of spore coats (Kadota et al., 1965).

6. Spore cortex

Pure preparations of spore cortex have not been obtained but it has been shown that the cortex is dissolved by lysozyme and by autolytic spore enzymes (Warth et al., 1963). Partly-degraded cortex material can there-

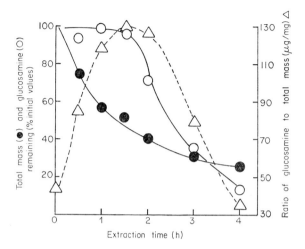

FIG. 5. Preparation of murein-enriched fraction of *B. cereus* PX spore integuments by formamide extraction at 160°C. (W. L. King, unpublished data).

fore be prepared by autolysis, and the soluble autolysate analysed (Warth, 1965). It proves to consist largely of muropeptides, suggesting that murein in the cortex is the site of origin of "spore germination exudate" (Strange and Powell, 1954). Whether calcium and DPA and other spore components are situated in the cortex in the intact spore is not certain. A murein-enriched fraction can be prepared from spores of *B. cereus* (c. 10 g) by first autoclaving spores at 15 lb for 30 min then disrupting them by shaking with glass beads, and centrifuging and washing the deposit once with formamide before extracting the washed debris with formamide (100 ml) at 160°C for 90–120 min. The murein content of the residue rises to about 60% (≡ about 13% glucosamine by weight) as shown in Fig. 5. Further extraction leads to loss of murein components.

7. *Parasporal bodies*

Parasporal bodies most studied have been the toxic crystals formed during sporulation of insect-pathogenic *Bacillus* species (for reviews see Rogoff, 1966). *Bacillus thuringiensis* crystals can be separated from spores efficiently by a two-phase system based on that described by Sacks and Alderton (1961). Typically about 250 mg of toxic crystals containing about 0·06% spores may be obtained from 10 g spore crystal paste (Goodman *et al.*, 1967). Foam separation of spores can be achieved by shaking suspension (70 mg wet wt/ml) and separating from foam on Whatman No. 1 filter paper. Spores in the foam can be further cleaned by floating the foam onto a large volume of water. Addition of a drop of octanol allows spores in the foam to be resuspended in water (Pendleton and Morrison, 1966). Crystals in the bulk of the liquid can be concentrated by mixing 35 ml with 30 ml 1% Na_2SO_4 and 35 ml CCl_4, homogenizing and leaving for 15 min. The aqueous phase then contains >98% crystals, with an overall yield of about 35% (Bateson, 1965; Pendleton and Morrison, 1966). Laboratory media supporting good sporulation and crystal formation by B. thuringiensis have been described (Singer et al., 1966).

The sequence of changes during sporulation and crystal formation in B. cereus var. alesti was described by Young and Fitz-James (1959) who also described changes in extractability of the crystals in alkaline thioglycollate which probably accompanied formation of disulphide cross-links during maturation of the crystal. The first studies of crystal structure and alkali-solubility in B. thuringiensis was by Hannay and Fitz-James (1955); study of crystal structure in B. cereus var. alesti was described by Norris and Watson (1960). Methods for hydrolysis and analysis of crystal amino-acids have been reported (Hannay and Fitz-James, 1955; Angus, 1956) and electrophoretic methods for detecting the protein subunits have been described (Angus, 1956; Krywienczyk and Angus, 1960; Monro, 1961, Cooksey, 1968).

Experiments first defining clearly the toxic nature of the crystal of an insect pathogen were described by Angus (1954) who more recently described methods studying the mode of action of the toxin in larvae (Angus, 1964; Fast and Angus, 1965).

Assay methods for commercial B. thuringiensis insecticide preparations which have been described (Splittstoerser and McEwan, 1961; Burgerjon, 1962; Burges, 1964) are still not thought to be completely satisfactory.

D. Antigenic studies

Whole spore antigens used have generally consisted of spores which have been exhaustively cleaned (Norris and Wolf, 1961), for instance as described in section II A 2, and sometimes additionally autoclaved (120°C for 15 min.) to guard against germination and formation of vegetative forms in vivo (Walker and Batty, 1965). Norris (1962) revived the preparation and use of spore antigens and listed methods which have been used to clean spores. Methods range from chemical treatments; e.g., incubation of spores in NaOH (75 g/litre) plus sodium hypochlorite (1·5% available chlorine), which seems unnecessarily severe, to incubation in lysozyme (100–1000 µg/ml in 0·1 M buffer pH 5–8, 37° for >1 h). The latter treatment is much preferred so long as vegetative debris is lysozyme-sensitive. Soluble antigens may be prepared using disruption techniques described in section III B; antisera have been used for immunoelectrophoretic detection of spore- and vegetative cell-specific antigens (Waites, 1968). Heat-stable spore antigens have been identified with heat-stable spore enzymes in some instances (Norris and Baillie, 1964; Baillie and Norris, 1964; Green and Sadoff, 1965).

Walker and Batty (1965) prepared and used fluorochrome-labelled spore and vegetative antisera to follow changes in surface antigens during sporulation and germination. Use of ferritin-labelled antibodies in conjunction with electron microscopy is described in this series.

E. Water content and permeability

Ross and Billing (1957) described use of phase contrast and interference microscopy and immersion refractometry to determine the refractive index of spores and estimate their water content. Black and Gerhardt (1962) developed a technique for measuring water content and permeability of spores more directly. Essentially they took 3 g packs of water-wet centrifuged spores, and resuspended them in different solutions or tritiated water, centrifuged again and measured dilution of the solution or label. Having used a high molecular weight dextran (unable to penetrate spores) to measure inter-spore space in the pack, the volume of the spores permeable to different solutes could be worked out (Black and Gerhardt, 1961).

Methods for investigating density and surface structure of spores by gas displacement and gas adsorption were described by Berlin et al. (1963). Neihof et al. (1967) measured adsorption and desorption of water and nitrogen by spores to investigate permeability and water binding and changes in spore structures during drying.

F. Electron microscopy

The sporulation and germination processes are best visualized by electron microscopy of thin sections of cells fixed by techniques based on those of Kellenberger et al. (1958). For instance, samples may be taken and immediately mixed with OsO_4 (1% w/v) at pH 7·2 and incubated for about 18 h at near 4°C (Freer and Levinson, 1967) prior to washing dehydrating in alcohol or acetone series, and embedding in an epoxy, resin (Ohye and Murrell, 1962). Hamilton and Stubbs (1967) used glutaraldehyde + OsO_4 to fix outgrowing cells of B. cereus and B. polymyxa. Cell pellets were resuspended in glutaraldehyde (5% w/v) in sodium phosphate buffer (0·1 M; pH 7·3) for 90 min. at 4°C, washed once in the buffer, then resuspended in OsO_4 solution for 120 min. at 4° before extensive washing. The OsO_4 solution contained sodium barbiturate: acetic acid buffer (0·14 M; pH 9·0), 5 ml; HCl (0·1 M), 7 ml; $CaCl_2$ (2M),

0·12 ml; OsO$_4$ (2% w/v), 13 ml. The most useful reagents for staining sections to increase contrast have been uranyl acetate (4% w/v in methanol) and lead citrate (about 1·5%, aqueous at pH 12·0) (Fitz-James, 1960; Rousseau et al., 1966). Extended exposure to lead shows up details of exosporium structure not otherwise visualized (Moberly, et al., 1966). Negative staining with phosphotungstic acid also demonstrates exosporium structure (Gerhardt and Ribi, 1964) and the substructure of unsectioned filaments attached to spores of various Clostridium species (Hodgkiss et al. 1967; Yolton et al., 1968). These filaments are most easily seen in shadowed preparations of whole spores and in carbon replicas. Franklin and Bradley (1957) described carbon replica methods for studying topography of spores of Bacillus and Clostridium species.

Fully-formed dormant spores are usually only well fixed by extended treatment times or, most easily, by use of KMnO$_4$ (e.g., 2% w/v; 90 min. at ambient temperature). Resistance to fixation probably reflects the lack of available functional groups in dormant spores or their impermeability to fixatives and embedding resins, for Rode et al., (1962) showed that successful fixation methods (like KMnO$_4$) actually altered spore properties, for instance by extracting dipicolinic acid. It is important to interpret micrographs of dormant spores in the knowledge that major spore components (probably principally Ca and DPA) may have been removed. Freeze-etch techniques which reveal detailed surface structure of spores were described by Holt and Leadbetter (1969).

Sections can be ashed in order to reveal the distribution of mineral matter within them. Bearing in mind the possibility of loss through leaching, the technique offers the best approach yet to discovering the location of calcium in dormant spores (Thomas, 1964). Walker et al., (1967) used ferritin-labelled antibodies to locate spore and vegetative antigens in spores and spore fractions, and also described methods for cytochemical detection of enzymes with esterase activity in sporulating cells.

IV. ACTIVATION OF SPORES

A. Heat and other physical agents

Curran and Evans (1945) first clearly recognised that some spore suspensions germinated more rapidly and more completely following sublethal heating. Thus activation itself cannot be measured, but only the result of activation. This may be seen as an increase in viable count on a particular medium ("activation for viable count") or as an increase in rate of germination of a spore suspension ("activation for germination");

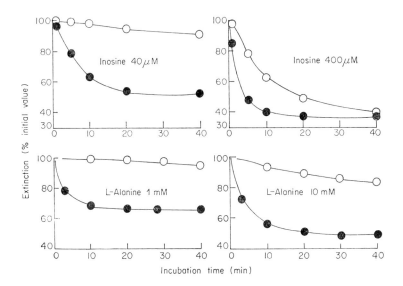

F<small>IG</small>. 6. Activation of spores of *B. cereus* T for germination. Spores were either left unactivated or activated by heating at 70°C for 30 min. just prior to measuring their germination in high and low levels of L-alanine and inosine in sodium phosphate buffer (80 mM; pH 8·0) at 30°C. Unheated spores, ○; heat activated spores, ●.

it is important to realize that these two phenomena do not invariably accompany each other.

It is not possible to generalise regarding the amount of heat necessary to optimally activate spores since this varies greatly with different organisms and spore crops. For example, aqueous suspensions of spores of *B. cereus* T are optimally activated for germination by heating at about 70°C for 30 min (Fig. 6) whilst spores of *B. stearothermophilus* may be activated for viable count even during heating at more than 110°C. Activation for viable count thus often results in a rise in the early part of survivor curves (Fig. 3).

Activation is not an all-or-nothing phenomenon. For instance, spores of *B. cereus* T will germinate at a rapid rate in inosine whether activated or not; unactivated spores, however, will require a *higher concentration* of the germinant for a given rate of germination (Fig. 6). Furthermore, the magnitude of this effect differs with the germinant. For instance, unactivated *B. cereus* T spores germinate extremely slowly in even 10 mM L-alanine, whereas activated spores germinate rapidly in much lower concentrations (Fig. 6). Activation may also increase the range of germinants active on a spore, thereby making its germination requirements less exacting. All these changes can therefore be used to measure the extent of activation caused by a particular treatment. Kinetics of heat activation were studied by Busta and Ordal (1964), Lewis et al. (1965) and McCormick (1965).

Activated spores become partly deactivated on storage. Incubation in well-aerated water quickly deactivates spores of B. cereus (Keynan et al., 1965). Extended storage of spores, however, mimics activation in that germination requirements become less exacting.

Spores of some species can be activated by ionizing radiation. Doses and germination responses were given by Gould and Ordal (1968). Even spores γ-irradiated sufficiently to render them non-viable (i.e., by colony count) may still be able to go through the changes typical of germination, so that activation for germination can be studied quite distinctly from viability.

Lyophilised spores of B. megaterium can be activated and eventually germinated by exposure to air saturated with water vapour (Hyatt et al., 1966) presumably because of some physical change in water-dependent spore structures which is so far little understood.

B. Chemical agents

Spores of some organisms can be activated by low pH values and deactivated by high pH values in the presence of calcium. The cycle of activation-deactivation can be repeated a number of times. Suitable treatments for B. stearothermophilus were pH 1·5, 80 min., 25°C (first activation); pH 9·7, 20 mM Ca^{++}, 16 h, 18° then 3·5 h, 80° (deactivation); pH 1·5, 21 h, 18° (second activation) (Lewis et al., 1965). Methods were described for activating B. cereus T spores by treatment at low pH values (Keynan et al., 1964; Keynan et al., 1965) and Cl. bifermentans spores by treatment at high pH values (Gibbs, 1967).

Spores of B. coagulans were activated by incubation in chloral hydrate in water or ethylene glycol (Lewis et al., 1965). Dimethyl sulphoxide and dimethyl formamide (90% v/v, 1 min.) (Widdowson, 1967) activated spores of B. pantothenticus. Methods for activating spores with calcium dipicolinate (40 mM; pH 7·0; about 70 min. at 10°C) were described by Lee and Ordal (1963). Generally effective chemical activating agents are those which alter tertiary structure of macromolecules. For instance, methods were described for activating spores with reagents which rupture disulphide bonds (Keynan et al., 1964), and the presence of urea (4–6M) increases the germination rate of B. cereus spores (Z. J. Ordal, personal communication).

V. GERMINATION OF SPORES

A. Definition

The term "germination" applied to a bacterial spore describes a rapid and irreversible process whereby the spore loses its typical dormant and resistant properties. The resulting cell is in contrast, typically metabolically active, heat-labile, non-refractile, and stainable, and yet is readily distinct from a vegetative bacterium (Campbell, 1957; Keynan and Halvorson, 1965). The further development of the germinated spore, which results in formation of a new vegetative cell is termed outgrowth and is dealt with in section VI.

B. Media and methods of initiating germination

1. *General requirements*

Spores have been found to have very specific requirements for germination which are much less complex than their requirements for outgrowth and for growth of vegetative cells. A substance which initiates germination is usually termed a "germinant". A difficulty in simply reporting germinants for different spores lies in the fact that germination of a population of spores may be very rapid in one germinant, slower in another and barely measurable in another. Where one draws the line becomes rather subjective. Nevertheless certain germination systems which have been well documented can usefully be described.

Firstly, an ionic strength equivalent to about 80 mM sodium phosphate is often optimal (Fleming and Ordal, 1964): other buffer systems can be used but a requirement of Na^+ by many spores should be satisfied. Optimum pH value for germination of *B. cereus* T spores is near pH 8 in a number of germinants but the optimum varies much with the species and germinant (Thorley and Wolf, 1961; Levinson, 1961). Optimum temperature for *B. cereus* T spore germination is 28°C. Determinations of optima for other *Bacillus* and *Clostridium* species have been described (Mol, 1957; Hyatt and Levinson, 1962; Knaysi, 1964).

2. *Metabolizable germinants*

Some amino-acids, ribosides, sugars, and related compounds which have most often been found germinative for spores of different species are listed in Table V. Concentrations are not given in the table because the effective concentration depends on so many factors like the extent of activation (see Fig. 6), sporulation medium, method of preparation and storage of the spore crops. Rather, the reader should be aware of the variety of factors involved and refer to the key references given for details and for earlier work. Furthermore, the apparent germinant requirements

TABLE V

Metabolizable germinants for various spores

Organism	Germinants	Remarks	References
B. cereus T and PX and other strains, *B. anthracis*	L-Alanine, or sometimes less effectively L-cysteine L-α-aminobutyric acid or other amino-acids or adenosine or inosine	Most rapid germination is caused by amino-acid + riboside together	a, b c
B. subtilis (Marburg and SJ2) *thuringiensis, coagulans, polymyxa licheniformis circulans, sphaericus, stearothermophilus* and other species	L-Alanine, or sometimes (less effectively) L-valine, L-leucine and other amino-acids	Often additional stimulation by glucose. Study of analogues of alanine using *B. subtilis* (Marburg)	c, d e, f g h
B. megaterium QMB 1551, "Texas" and other strains	Alanine, inosine, alanine + inosine		i, c
	Glucose (and other sugars) and other C-sources		c, j
	Various N-sources		i
B. megaterium ATCC 9885	L-leucine (+ other compounds)	Germination followed by lysis	c
B. macerans (some strains)	Adenine, 2,6-diaminopurine	But not germinated by adenosine or inosine	k
Cl. sporogenes PA 3679 h	L-Arginine + glucose	50 mM + 10 mM + 0·05% w/v sodium thioglycollate	l
	L-Alanine	Further stimulated by L-arginine + L-phenylalanine	m n
Cl. sporogenes PA 3679, *chauvei, perfringens, botulinum* (62A and 115B)	Glucose	2% w/v, incubated anaerobically	o
	Glucose + various carcinogens	0·2% w/v glucose	p
Cl. acetobutylicum, roseum, butylicum	L-Alanine + L-arginine + L-phenylalanine		q
Cl. bifermentans CN 1617 *Cl. septicum*	L-alanine + L-phenylalanine (or L-leucine) + lactate + Na+		r, s t
Cl. tetani	L-Methionine + L-lactate + nicotinamide + Na+	All essential aerobically but not anaerobically. Spores + vegetative debris	u
Cl. tyrobutyrium	Acetate + NH_4^+	Further stimulated by L-aspartic acid, CO_2 and Cl^-	v

are influenced by cleanliness of a spore crop. Incompletely cleaned spores may be contaminated with trace amounts of germinants, and this is particularly true of spores of many *Clostridium* species, which are not easily freed of all remnants of the old sporangium.

3. *Chelates*

Brown (1956) first discovered that ethylenediaminetetraacetate (EDTA) could germinate spores of *Cl. sporogenes* PA 3679. Suspensions of spores of strain h could be 99% germinated by incubation at 37°C in 5·5 mM EDTA in water between pH 5·5 and pH 9·0. Higher concentrations of EDTA (e.g., 100 mM) were not germinative for PA 3679 strain h, but were germinative for the NCA (National Canners Association) strain. Riemann (1963) described methods for detailed study of EDTA-germination.

Study of chelate germination led to the discovery that calcium dipicolinate (CaDPA) would initiate germination of spores of many species (Riemann and Ordal, 1961). CaDPA-germination is best attained by mixing equimolar $CaCl_2$ and DPA and immediately adding it to spores in phosphate-free buffer (e.g., 10mM Tris HCl at pH 8·0) at 37°C. CaDPA solutions must not be stored because precipitation and consequent loss of activity rapidly occurs from 40 mM solutions, even during germination experiments. The precipitation can be usefully delayed by adding aminoacids (10 mM) or gelatin (0·2% w/v) to the germination mixtures (Riemann, 1961).

An agar medium containing CaDPA was described (Busta and Ordal, 1964; Edwards *et al.*, 1965) which supported good recovery of *B. subtilis* A spores, particularly following heat-damage. It consisted of fortified nutrient agar (FNA) made up over-strength (see p. 332) to which is added solutions of $CaCl_2$ and Na_2DPA *immediately* before pouring the plates to give final concentrations of 50 mM and 40 mM respectively in norma strength medium (Suitable stock solutions are 2M $CaCl_2$ and 0·5M Na_2DPA; the latter is made by adding stoichiometric amounts of NaOH

Notes to Table V

a. Hills (1949a).	l. Kan, *et al.* (1958).
b. Hills (1949b).	m. Uehara, *et al* (1965).
c. Foerster and Foster (1966a).	n. Uehara and Frank (1965).
d. Hills (1950).	o. Wynne, *et al* (1954).
e. Wolf and Thorley (1957).	p. Hachisuka *et al.* (1959).
f. Wolf and Mahmoud (1957)	q. Hitzman *et al.* (1957).
g. Hermier (1962).	r. Gibbs (1964).
h. Woese, *et al* (1958).	s. Gibbs (1967a).
i. Levinson and Hyatt (1962).	t. Gibbs (1967b).
j. Hyatt and Levinson (1964).	u. Shoesmith and Holland (1968).
k. Sacks (1967).	v. Bergere (1969).

to DPA). The plates are swirled only once to mix, then left immobile to set otherwise separation of calcium dipicolinate may occur.

4. *Surfactants*

Numerous cationic surface active chemicals which will initiate germination of most spores were listed by Rode and Foster (1960b, 1961) and methods of study described. The most active germinant in this class is *n*-dodecylamine (laurylamine). It is relatively insoluble, but germinates spores at concentrations as low as 10 to 100 μM, and can most easily be used as a $\frac{1}{5}$th saturated solution in dilute buffer (e.g., 10 mM sodium phosphate, pH 8·0) incubated at 42°C. Germination begins even more rapidly at 60° or 70°C, but also quickly reaches a plateau. Strong buffers inhibit surfactant germination. Germinated spores die if left in contact with the surfactant, but can be kept viable if cephalin (0·17%) is quickly added as a quenching agent.

5. *Germination with enzymes*

The *B. subtilis* protease subtilisin will cause germination (Sierra, 1967a) when incubated with spores of some species optimally at 37°–40°C in buffer (100 mM sodium or potassium phosphate or sodium borate; Tris HCl was slightly inhibitory). *B. subtilis* Marburg was particularly sensitive. The mode of action of subtilisin may be to attack the spore coat protein or to autodegrade the enzyme protein to form L-alanine, for subtilisin-germination can be inhibited by D-alanine (Gould and King, 1966) which specifically inhibits L-alanine-initiated germination.

Lysozyme (as little as 2 μg/ml) will cause germination-like changes followed by lysis in spores of *B. megaterium* ATCC 9885 within 10 min. at 37°C (Suzuki and Rode, 1967) and will also germinate heated spores of some *Cl. perfringens* (Cassier and Sebald, 1969). Other spores are similarly affected by lysozyme only following treatment of the spores with reagents which rupture disulphide bonds, optimally at pH 3 (Gould and Hitchins, 1963). For instance, spores may be sensitized to lysozyme by incubation at 37°C in 1–10% w/v (depending on species) 2-mercaptoethanol, thioglycollic acid or performic acid at pH 3 in 8M urea for 1 h. More severe treatments (e.g. 70°C, 10% thioglycollic acid 1 h) invariably kill spores, though still sensitizing them to the enzyme. After removing the disulphide breakers by centrifuging three times in water, the spores are held in NaOH (0·1)N for 15 min at 4°C and washed again, and can then be "germinated" by incubation at 37°C in lysozyme (100 μg/ml) in sodium phosphate buffer (100 mM; pH 8·0). On continued incubation in lysozyme the spores lose viability. Viability can be retained by rapidly transferring samples to a growth medium.

Spores treated with disulphide-breaking reagents also become sensitive to lysis by H_2O_2 (King and Gould, 1969). Some treated spores lose heat-resistance but γ-radiation-resistance is retained (Hitchins et al., 1966; Rowley and Levinson, 1967).

A B. cereus spore enzyme will substitute for lysozyme in the above reactions. First described by Strange and Dark (1957), crude preparations can be made at 4°C by disrupting B. cereus PX spores (20 mg dry wt/ml in 7 ml water containing 0·1 mM dithiothreitol) by shaking with glass beads (4g Ballotini size 12) in Mickle or Braun (multiply quantities by 7) disintegrators (about 5 min). Debris is removed by centrifugation at 70,000 g for 20 min. and the enzyme precipitated from the supernatant with $(NH_4)_2SO_4$ (60% saturated), dissolved in water and reprecipitated with sodium phosphate-citrate buffer (0·1 M; pH 3·4) and finally dissolved in water with the pH value raised just sufficiently to effect solution. Incorporation of diethiothreitol (0·1 mM) in all reagents prevents inactivation of the enzyme by air oxidation. The enzyme causes germination-like changes in spores of B. cereus and B. subtilis, which have been sensitized with disulphide-breakers, optimally at 37°C in sodium phosphate buffer (100 mM; pH 8·0) containing dithiothreitol (0·1 mM) (Gould and Hitchins, 1965; Gould et al., 1966).

6. *Mechanical germination*

The term "mechanical germination" was invented by Rode and Foster (1960a) to describe the germination which can be initiated by abrading or cracking spores, for instance by shaking about 13 mg (dry weight) of spores in 7 ml water with 4 g ground glass (particles of subspore to 44 μm size) in a Mickle tissue disintegrator for about 10 min. at 4°C. Pressure exerted on a coverslip with a microscope nosepiece can be used to cause germination-like phase-darkening of spores in a wet mount (Lewis et al., 1960), and even emulsification of a drop of spore suspension with a wire loop will cause this change in a proportion of the spores (Knaysi and Curran, 1961). Spores may also be germinated by hydrostatic pressures above a few hundred atmospheres (Clouston and Wills, 1969; Sale et al., 1970) and, depending on the temperature and pressure, this form of germination may be stimulated by L-alanine and other metabolizable germinants (Gould and Sale, 1970).

C. **Methods of study**

1. *Viable counts*

The heat-resistance of individual spores decreases rapidly during germination. The extent of germination in a spore population can therefore be estimated by heating samples sufficiently to kill the germinated, but not the ungerminated spores, and counting the survivors by conventional viable count techniques. Adequate heating of the sample is essential when the proportions of ungerminated survivors is low, for instance, by complete immersion in sealed ampoules in a water bath, as described in section IIIA2. For most mesophiles e.g., *B. cereus* T, heating at 70°C for 30 min. is adequate, and for heat-resistant thermophiles like *B. stearothermophilus* 90°C for 30 min. but it is not possible to generalize. Some organisms (e.g., *Cl. botulinum* type E strains, some *Cl. welchii* and others) form relatively heat-sensitive spores, so that heating at 60°C for 30 min. should not be exceeded without danger of killing ungerminated spores. In such instances germinated forms can be killed by chemical agents in place of heat. Exposure to ethanol (50% v/v) at 25° for 1 h can be used to kill vegetative *Cl. botulinum* type E without seriously reducing viability of spores (Johnstone *et al.*, 1964). Phenol (1% w/v) has been used similarly with *Bacillus* species (Fernalius, 1960). Germination of *B. megaterium* QM B1551 spores can be arrested by $HgCl_2$ (2 mM) and surviving spores counted on Thioglycollate Medium (Baltimore Biological Laboratories, Baltimore, 18, Maryland) (Levinson and Hyatt, 1966). When the germination rate is high, some method of rapid sampling is essential, otherwise significant germination will occur during handling and warm-up time of heat-treated samples. Rapid sampling and warm-up can be attained by pipetting small samples (c. 1 ml) into large volumes (c. 9 ml) of preheated water (or chemical reagent).

2. *Optical density methods*

Some of the disadvantages and time-consuming steps in viable count procedures can be overcome by using absorptiometric methods to follow germination. The optical density (OD) of a spore suspension falls during germination, so that OD changes can be used to monitor germination within the range of about 5 to 95% with perhaps 2% or so accuracy. The usual technique is to preincubate samples of medium or buffers + germinants + inhibitors etc. in optical cuvettes or absorptiometer tubes to allow temperature equilibration, then add pre-warmed spores at zero time to give an initial OD of 0·3 to 0·4. Filters with peak transmission at 580 or 600 nm are commonly used, but any visible light wavelength is suitable. Tubes may then be removed from water bath, or preferably dry heating block, to absorptiometer at intervals as short as 30 sec or so. One may simply plot OD versus time, or normalize the data so that the total OD fall is unity and plot $\log \log \dfrac{OD_i - OD_f}{OD_i - OD_t}$ versus log time (Fig 7, where OD_t

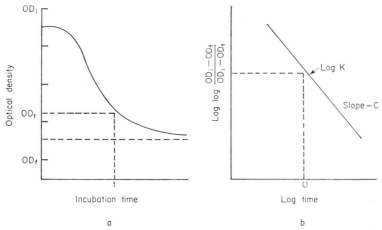

FIG. 7. Optical density changes during germination of a spore suspension (a) as experimentally determined, and (b) plotted according to McCormick (1965) in order to facilitate determination of constants.

is the optical density at time t, and OD_i and OD_f are respectively the initial and final optical densities), when the negative slope of the straight line portion of the curve gives the germination rate constant, c (Vary and McCormick, 1965). McCormick (1965) developed the following germination equation—

$$OD_t = OD_i \left(1 - (1-\alpha) e^{-Kt}\right)$$

in which the constant α is the ratio of OD_i to OD_f; i.e., a measure of the total OD fall under the particular experimental conditions; c is the slope, influenced mainly by temperature; and K is the intercept of lag; with α, it is a function of germinant or inhibitor concentration and the activation treatment of the spores.

3. *Microscopical methods*

Ungerminated spores appear bright, and germinated spores dark when viewed by dark (positive) phase-contrast optics (Pulvertaft and Haynes, 1951). Differential microscopic counts therefore allow the percentage germination in a suspension to be quickly assessed, for instance by counting about 200–300 individual cells. This method has an advantage over OD methods in that germination can be estimated in media containing solid particles (e.g., inoculated foodstuffs). Also, germination of individual spores, rather than of large populations can be studied so that lag and germination times of single spores can be measured ("microlag" and "microgermination"; Vary and Halvorson, 1965). The method has the disadvantage that in a rapidly germinating suspension the sampling and counting time is inordinately long. Methods which can be used to arrest germination of spores of some species so that counts can be performed later and with less urgency, include adding samples of germinating suspensions to equal volumes of saturated NaCl solution (Mol, 1957), or to 2 mM $HgCl_2$ (Levinson and Hyatt, 1965).

Whilst ungerminated spores are stained only with difficulty germinated spores and vegetative cells readily take up simple stains. In place of phase contrast changes, one can therefore use stainability as a criterion of germination simply by estimating the ratio of unstained to stained spores. The most useful stain for this purpose is methylene blue (0·5% w/v) used for about 1 min.

Onset of heat sensitivity, stainability, and phase-darkening occur concurrently for practical purposes, though a sequence of changes can be defined using rapid sampling methods (Levinson and Hyatt, 1965).

4. Mass and volume changes

During germination spores shed up to about 30% of their dry weight. The exudate consists principally of calcium, dipicolinic acid, and muropeptides, which can be detected by the methods described in Section IIIC, and smaller amounts of amino-acids and peptides. The weight loss can be measured directly by determining the dry weight of cells in samples at intervals. In a medium which can support outgrowth new syntheses follow germination so that a rapid weight increase occurs after the initial decrease. Spore volume increases by about 20% during germination and by a further 100% or more prior to emergence of the new vegetative cell. Volume changes are most easily measured by determining the packed cell volume of samples using microhaematocrit devices (Hitchins *et al.*, 1963) or by using the Coulter Counter (Parker and Barnes, 1967).

Permeability of spores increases during germination. Methods are described in Section IIIE.

D. Dormancy

1. Superdormant spores

Unlike heat or radiation survivor curves, germination curves invariably plateau due to superdormant individuals in the population. Completely dormant spores will be essentially undetectable, and therefore scored as dead when studied by conventional methods. Superdormant spores are most readily demonstrated by allowing germination to occur in one medium, then heating to kill germinated spores, centrifuging, and replacing the cells into fresh medium. Spores remaining ungerminated in the first medium can then be detected germinating slowly in the second medium. Clearly the more dormant the spores, the more difficult they become to count. Spores exhibiting exceptionally delayed germination can best be detected by most-probable-number techniques, in which a germinated suspension (as above) is heated to kill the germinated spores then diluted and dispensed in a large number of tubes of fresh medium so that the superdormant survivors are distributed at a mean number of about 2 spores per tube. The tubes can then be incubated for days or months if necessary to detect late germinating spores (Foster and Wynne, 1948b).

Ungerminated spores can be separated from germinated spores by density gradient centrifugation in solutions of sucrose (45–75% w/v; about 2000 g; 1 h), special lead chelates (Lewis, Snell and Alderton, 1965), or Urografin (E. R. Squibb & Sons Ltd., Regal House, Twickenham, Middlesex) (Tamir and Gilvarg, 1966). Urografin is supplied as a 76% w/v solution, and best used as an exponential gradient from 46 to about 10%; 25,000 g 30 mm. Superdormant spores can be separated from their germinated neighbours in this manner unless present in very low numbers ($<0.1\%$ of the population).

2. Fractional germination

Fractional germination is a special case of dormancy in which different (large) fractions of a spore population respond differently to different germinants. The combined germinants therefore germinate a greater *proportion* of the population than each germinant alone. Examples are given by Foster and his colleagues (Rode and Foster, 1962; Foerster and Foster, 1966a).

E. Inhibitors of germination

Germination can be inhibited by numerous substances at high concentrations, but specific inhibitors which act at realistic ("physiological") levels are relatively few (Gould, 1964). Table 6 lists some of the most well known germination inhibitors. Concentrations are not given because inhibitory levels generally depend upon the nature and concentration of germinant used. Further details can be found in the references cited.

VI. OUTGROWTH

A. Definition

Outgrowth refers to that part of the growth cycle (Fig. 1) following germination and terminating in the formation of the first mature vege-

G. W. GOULD

TABLE VI

Inhibitors of spore germination

Inhibitor	Germinant	Remarks	References
D-Alanine	L-Alanine	D : L ratio > 0·03 inhibiting for most spores	a, b c
Glycine, L-methionine and other amino-acids D-serine, D-threonine	L-Alanine	High levels needed to inhibit (e.g., > 50 mM) B. megaterium	d e
Variety of alanine analogues	L-Alanine	Structure-activity relationships B. subtilis	f
Ethyl pyruvate	L-Alanine	B. licheniformis	g
Bis-1 : 3-β-ethylhexyl-5-methyl-5-amino-hexahydropyrimidine	L-Alanine	Inhibits pyruvate metabolism B. cereus T	h
Octyl alcohol	Glucose Yeast extract L-Alanine + adenosine	About 0·1% inhibitory B. subtilis B. cereus T	i, j
Ethanol	Glucose	About 10% (v/v) inhibitory	i
2,4-Dinitrophenol	L-Leucine, L-valine, L-alanine	Partial inhibition by 10 mM B. megaterium	e
Fluoride	Glucose	B. coagulans	k
Azide	Various germinants	B. megaterium	e
Atebrin	L-Alanine Inosine Glucose	B. subtilis B. coagulans	l k
p-Chloromercuri-benzoate	L-Alanine	B. subtilis B. megaterium	l e
Iodacetate	Glucose	B. coagulans	k
Heavy metals	Various germinants	B. cereus T B. megaterium	e, m n, o
2,3-Dimercapto-propanol	L-Alanine L-valine	Good inhibition by 1 mM B. megaterium	e
Diisopropyl fluorophosphate	Subtilo-peptidases	Does not inhibit L-alanine-initiated germination	p
Guanosine	Inosine	B. megaterium	q
Unsaturated fatty acids and oxidation products	Complex medium	Cl. botulinum Cl. pasteurianum B. subtilis B. stearothermophilus	r, s

TABLE VI (*continued*)

Inhibitor	Germinant	Remarks	References
Oxygen	L-Alanine-deficient medium	*Cl. sporogenes.* No inhibition in L-alanine-rich medium.	t
	Various defined and complex media	*Cl. botulinum. Cl. roseum Cl. acetobutylicum, Cl. butylicum*	u
β-Phenethyl alcohol alcohol	L-Alanine + inosine and others	*B. megaterium B. cereus* and others. Reversible inhibition of germination. Also inhibits sporulation	v, w x
Chlorpromazine	L-Alanine	*B. subtilis*	y
Chelating agents (including oxine and EDTA)	Various germinants	*B. coagulans* *B. subtilis* *B. megaterium* *B. cereus* T Generally reversible inhibition	z, a′ b′, e
Dipicolinic acid	Various germinants	*B. megaterium*	e
	Calcium dipicolinate	*B. megaterium*	c′
p-Chloro-m-cresol	Broth. Reversible with Tween 80	*B. subtilis*	d′

a. Hills (1949a, b).
b. Hills (1950).
c. Uchara and Frank (1965).
d. Caraco, *et al.* (1958).
e. Hyatt and Levinson (1962).
f. Woese, *et al.* (1958).
g. Halmann and Keynan (1962).
h. Halvorson and Church (1957).
i. Curran and Knaysi (1961).
j. Gollakota and Halvorson (1963).
k. Amaha and Nakahara (1959).
l. Falcone and Caraco (1958).
m. Murty and Halvorson (1957).
n. Levinson and Hyatt (1965).
o. Hyatt and Levinson (1957).

p. Sierra (1967a).
q. Murrell (1961).
r. Foster and Wynne (1948a).
s. Roth and Halvorson (1952).
t. Urehara and Frank (1965).
u. Hitzman *et al.* (1957).
v. Slepecky and Celkis (1964).
w. Remsen, *et al.* (1966).
x. Slepecky (1963).
y. Galdiero (1967).
z. Powell, (1950).
a′ Powell (1951).
b′ Murty and Halvorson (1957).
c′ Jaye and Ordal (1966).
d′ Parker and Bradley (1968).

tative cell (Strange and Hunter, 1969). It therefore includes swelling of the germinated spore, emergence of the new vegetative cell from the spore coats and its subsequent elongation, and is essentially a period of synthesis.

B. Media and environment

Requirements for outgrowth are generally more complex than for germination. Reasonable synchrony in outgrowth may therefore be achieved by activating and then germinating spores in a specific germination medium (section VB), and then initiating outgrowth by transferring them to the more complex outgrowth medium. For example, *B. cereus* spores can be germinated in L-alanine + adenosine or inosine in buffer, then transferred to Trypticase Soy broth at 30°C. Samples taken and rapidly cooled and washed in buffer at intervals during the ensuing outgrowth are stable for some hours (Goldman and Blumenthal, 1961).

Defined media for outgrowth of *B. megaterium* were studied by Hyatt and Levinson (1957, 1959) who showed that although not essential for germination, phosphate (about 1 mM per 10^8 spores/ml) and a source of sulphur (about 0·1 mM) became necessary during outgrowth—along with nitrogen, carbon, and energy sources (Levinson and Hyatt, 1962; Hyatt and Levinson, 1964).

Amino-acids and growth factors required for outgrowth of *B. coagulans* and *B. stearothermophilus* were described by O'Brien and Campbell (1957) and for *B. subtilis* by Woese (1959). Good synchronous outgrowth of *B. cereus* T spores occurs in the defined CDGS medium of Nakata (1964) (Table II), see Kobayashi *et al.* (1965). In general, defined media for growth of vegetative cells are satisfactory for outgrowth. Halvorson *et al.* (1966) reviewed recent progress in studies of outgrowth.

C. Methods of study

1. Optical density and microscopical methods

The rate of outgrowth of a spore suspension can most easily be measured by following the rise in OD following the fall during germination as described in section VC2. Good mixing, and aeration for aerobes, is much more essential than in germination studies. Increases in mass and volume during outgrowth can be followed by weighing centrifuged samples and measuring cell volumes as for germination. The stage of growth reached during outgrowth can most easily be visualized by phase-contrast microscopy. A simple technique is to dry a droplet of activated spore suspension on a coverslip, then place it onto a pad of agar medium (about 1 mm depth) on a microscope slide (< 1 mm depth) on a warm stage or in an incubator. Periodic examination with a phase contrast microscope allows the germination and outgrowth of individual spores to be followed, and the effects of inhibitors or nutrients in the medium to be assessed (Gould, 1964).

2. *Respiration*

The respiration of ungerminated spores is undetectable, yet respiration commences immediately on germination and increases in rate during outgrowth in a well-defined manner (Levinson and Hyatt, 1962). It is therefore an excellent guide to the progress of outgrowth, as measured by conventional Warburg manometry.

3. *Synthesis of new molecules*

Interest has centred around protein, RNA, and DNA synthesis, which commence sequentially during outgrowth. The stepwise appearance of different enzyme activities can be followed in synchronously outgrowing cells of *B. cereus* T up to about five divisions (Kobayashi *et al.*, 1965; Steinberg and Halvorson, 1968). Methods for measuring DNA and RNA in outgrowing cells, and pulse-labelling to measure synthetic and turnover rates are similar to those used with vegetative cells, see section II B5; Balassa and Contessc (1966), Vinter (1966), Doi and Igarishi (1964), Mendelson and Gross (1967), Kobayashi *et al.* (1965).

Methods for measuring synthesis and re-utilization of murein components during outgrowth and the effect of antibiotics were described by Vinter (1965a, b).

REFERENCES

Alderton, G., and Snell, N. (1963). *Biochem. Biophys. Res. Commun.*, **10**, 139–143.
Alderton, G., and Snell, N. (1969). *Science*, **163**, 1212–1213.
Alderton, G., Thompson, P. T., and Snell, N. (1964). *Science*, **143**, 141–143.
Amaha, M., and Nakahara, T. (1959). *Nature, Lond.*, **184**, 1255–1256.
Angelotti, R., Hall, H. E., Foter, M. J., and Lewis, K. H. (1962). *Appl. Microbiol.*, **10**, 193–199.
Angus, T. A. (1954). *Nature, Lond.*, **173**, 545–546.
Angus, T. A. (1956). *Can. J. Microbiol.*, **2**, 416–426.
Angus, T. A. (1964). *J. Insect Path.*, **6**, 254–257.
Aronson, A. I., and Fitz-James, P. C. (1968). *J. Molec. Biol.*, **33**, 199–212.
Aronson, A. I., Henderson, E., and Tincher, A. (1967). *Biochem. Biophys. Res. Commun.*, **26**, 454–460.
Bach, J. A., and Sadoff, H. L. (1962). *J. Bact.*, **83**, 699–707.
Bailey, G. F., Karp, S., and Sacks, L. E. (1965). *J. Bact.*, **89**, 984–987.
Baillie, A., and Norris, J. R. (1964). *J. Bact.*, **87**, 1221–1226.
Balassa, G. (1966). *Annls Inst. Pasteur, Paris*, **110**, 17–24.
Balassa, G., and Contesse, G. (1966). *Annls Inst. Pasteur, Paris*, **110**, 25–48.
Bateson, T. B. (1965). *Nature, Lond.*, **205**, 622.
Bean, H. S. (1967). *J. appl. Bact.*, **30**, 6–16.
Berger, J. A., and Marr, A. G. (1960). *J. gen. Microbiol.*, **22**, 147–157.
Bergere, J.-L. (1969). *Annls Inst. Pasteur, Paris*, **117**, 179–195.
Berlin, E., Curran, H. R., and Pallansch, M. J. (1963). *J. Bact.*, **86**, 1030–1036.

Bernlohr, R. W. (1964). *J. biol. Chem.*, **239**, 538–543.
Bernlohr, R. W., and Novelli, G. D. (1960). *Archs Biochem. Biophys.*, **87**, 232–238.
Bernlohr, R. W., and Novelli, G. D. (1963). *Arch. Biochem. Biophys.*, **103**, 94–104.
Beskid, G., and Lundgren, D. G. (1961). *Can. J. Microbiol.*, **7**, 543–551.
Bishop, H. L., and Doi R. H. (1966). *J. Bact.*, **91**, 695–701.
Black, S. H., and Gerhardt, P. (1961). *J. Bact.*, **82**, 743–749.
Black, S. H., and Gerhardt, P. (1962). *J. Bact.*, **83**, 960–967.
Black, S. H., and Gerhardt, P. (1963). *Ann. N.Y. Acad. Sci.*, **102**, 755–762.
Blankenship, L. C., and Pallansch, M. J. (1966). *J. Bact.*, **92**, 1615–1617.
Bowen, J. F., and Smith, E. S. (1955). *Fd. Res.*, **20**, 655–658.
Brown, W. L. (1956). Thesis, University of Illinois.
Brown, W. L., Ordal, Z. J., and Halvorson, H. O. (1957). *Appl. Microbiol.*, **5**, 156–159.
Burgerjon, A. (1962). *Annls Epiphyt.*, **13**, 59–72.
Burges, H. D. (1964). *Wld. Crops*, **2**, 8.
Burt, M. M., and Ley, F. J. (1963). *J. appl. Bact.*, **26**, 484–489.
Burton, K. (1956). *Biochem. J.*, **62**, 315–323.
Busta, F. F. (1967). *Appl. Micriobiol.*, **15**, 640–645.
Busta, F. F., and Ordal, Z. J. (1964). *Appl. Microbiol.*, **12**, 106–110.
Busta, F. F., and Ordal, Z. J. (1964). *J. Fd. Sci.*, **29**, 1–9.
Campbell, L. L. (1957. *In* "Spores", pp. 33–37.
Caraco, A., Falcone, G., and Salvatore, G. (1958). *G. Microbiol.*, **5**, 127–132.
Cassier, M., and Sebald, M. (1969). *Annls Inst. Pasteur, Paris*, **117**, 312–324.
Chambon, P., DuPraw, E. J., and Kornberg, A. (1968). *J. biol. Chem.*, **243**, 5101–5109.
Cheftel, H., and Thomas, G. (1965). *In* "Principles and Methods for Establishing Thermal Processes for Canned Foods". Israel Programme for Scientific Translations Ltd., Jerusalem.
Clouston, J. G., and Wills, P. H. (1969). *J. Bact.*, **97**, 684–690.
Cokksey, K. E. (1968). *Biochem. J.*, **106**, 445–454.
Curran, H. R., and Evans, F. R. (1945). *J. Bact.*, **49**, 335–346.
Curran, H. R., and Knaysi, G. (1961). *J. Bact.*, **82**, 793–797.
Deutscher, M., Chambon, P., and Kornberg, A. (1968). *J. biol. Chem.*, **243**, 5117–5125.
Doi, R. H., and Halvorson, H. O. (1961). *J. Bact.*, **81**, 642–648.
Doi, R. H., and Igarishi, R. T. (1964a). *J. Bact.*, **87**, 323–328.
Doi, R. H., and Igarishi, R. T. (1964b). *Proc. natn. Acad. Sci. U.S.A.*, **52**, 755–762.
Donnellan, J. E., and Morowitz, H. J. (1957). *Radiat. Res.*, **7**, 71–78.
Donnellan, J. E., Nags, E. H., and Levinson, H. S. (1964). *J. Bact.*, **87**, 332–336.
Duncan, C. L., and Strong, D. H. (1968). *Appl. Microbiol.*, **16**, 82–89.
Edwards, J. L., Busta, F. F., and Speck, M. L. (1965). *Appl. Microbiol.*, **13**, 851–857.
Ellner, P. D. (1956). *J. Bact.*, **71**, 495–496.
Evans, J. B., and Niven, C. F. (1951). *J. Bact.*, **62**, 599–603.
Falaschi, A., and Kornberg, A. (1966). *J. biol. Chem.*, **241**, 1478–1482.
Falcone, G., and Caraco, A. (1958). *G. Microbiol.*, **5**, 80–86.
Fast, P. G., and Angus, T. A. (1965). *J. Insect Path.*, **7**, 29–32.
Fernelius, A. L. (1960). *J. Bact.*, **79**, 755–756.
Finley, N., and Fields, M. L. (1962). *Appl. Microbiol.*, **10**, 231–236.

Fitz-James, P. C. (1960). *J. biophys. biochem. Cytol.*, **8**, 507–528.
Fleming, H. P., and Ordal, Z. J. (1964). *J. Bact.*, **88**, 1529–1537.
Foerster, H. F., and Foster, J. W. (1966a). *J. Bact.*, **91**, 1168–1177.
Foerster, H. F., and Foster, J. W. (1966b). *J. Bact.*, **91**, 1333–1345.
Foster, J. W., and Wynne, E. S. (1948a). *J. Bact.*, **55**, 495–501.
Foster, J. W., and Wynne, E. S. (1948b). *J. Bact.*, **55**, 623–625.
Franklin, J. C., and Bradley, D.E. (1957), *J. Appl. Bact.*, **20**, 467–472.
Freer, J. H., and Levinson, H. S. (1967). *J. Bact.*, **94**, 441–457.
Galdiero, G. (1967). *Farmacista*, **22**, 85–87.
Gardner, R., and Kornberg, A. (1967). *J. biol. Chem.*, **242**, 2383–2388.
Gerhardt, P., and Gallup, D. M. (1963). *J. Bact.*, **86**, 919–929.
Gerhardt, P., and Ribi, E. (1964). *J. Bact.*, **88**, 1774–1789.
Gibbs. P. A. (1964). *J. gen. Microbiol.*, **37**, 41–48.
Gibbs, P. A. (1967a). *J. gen. Microbiol.*, **46**, 285–291.
Gibbs, P. A. (1967b). *J. appl. Bact.*, **30**, iv.
Goldblith, S. A., Joslyn, M. A., and Nickerson, J. T. R. (1961). "An Anthology of Food Science", Vol. I. "Introduction to Thermal Processing of Foods". Avi Publishing Co., Westport, Connecticut, U.S.A.
Goldman, M., and Blumenthal, H. J. (1961). *Can. J. Microbiol.*, **7**, 677–679.
Goldman, M., and Blumenthal, H. J. (1964). *J. Bact.*, **87**, 377–386.
Gollakota, K. G., and Halvorson, H. O. (1960). *J. Bact.*, **79**, 1–8.
Gollakota, K. G., and Halvorson, H. O. (1963). *J. Bact.*, **85**, 1386–1393.
Goodman, N. S., Gottfiried, R. J., and Rogoff, M. H. (1967). *J. Bact.*, **94**, 485.
Gordon, R. A., and Murrell, W. G. (1967). *J. Bact.*, **93**, 495–496.
Gould, G. W. (1964). *In* 4th Symp. Fd Microbiol. (Ed., N. Molin), pp. 17–24. Almqvist and Wiksell, Stockholm.
Gould, G. W., and Hitchins, A. D. (1963). *J. gen. Microbiol.*, **33**, 413–423.
Gould, G. W., and Hitchins, A. D. (1965). *In* "Spores III", pp. 213–221.
Gould, G. W., Hitchins, A. D., and King. W. L. (1966). *J. gen. Microbiol.*, **44**, 293–302.
Gould, G. W., and King, W. L. (1966). *Nature, Lond.*, **211**, 1431–1432.
Gould, G. W., and Ordal, Z. J. (1968). *J. gen. Microbiol.*, **50**, 77–84.
Gould, G. W., Stubbs, J. M., and King, W. L. (1970). *J. gen. Microbiol.*, *In press*.
Gould, G. W., and Sale, A. J. (1970). *J. gen. Microbiol.*, *In press*.
Grecz, N., Anellis, A., and Schneider, M. D. (1962). *J. Bact.*, **84**, 552–558.
Green, J. H., and Sadoff, H. L. (1965). *J. Bact.*, **89**, 1499–1505.
Groom, R. A., and Strong, D. H. (1966). *J. appl. Bact.*, **29**, 308–318.
Hachisuka, Y., Tochikubo, K., and Murachi, T. (1965). *Nature, Lond.*, **207**, 220–221.
Hachisuka, Y., Wynne, E. S., Galyen, L. J., and Jenkins, L. L. (1959). *Bact. Proc.*, 40.
Halmann, M., and Keynan, A. (1962). *J. Bact.*, **84**, 1187–1193.
Halvorson, H. O. (1957). *J. appl. Bact.*, **20**, 305–314.
Halvorson, H. O., and Church, B. D. (1957). *J. appl. Bact.*, **20**, 359–372.
Halvorson, H. O., Doi, R. H., and Church, B. D. (1958). *Proc. natn. Acad. Sci. U.S.A.*, **44**, 1171–1180.
Halvorson, H. O., Vary, J. C., and Steinberg, W. (1966). *A. Rev. Microbiol.*, **20**, 169–188.
Hamilton, W. A., and Stubbs, J. M. (1967). *J. gen. Microbiol.*, **47**, 121–129.
Hannay, C. L., and Fitz-James, P. C. (1955). *Can. J. Microbiol.*, **1**, 694–710.

Hermier, J. (1962a). *Annls Inst. Pasteur, Paris*, **102**, 629–643.
Hermier, J. (1962b). *C. r. hebd. Séanc. Acad. Sci., Paris*, **254**, 2865–2867.
Hermier, J. (1965). *Annls Biol. anim. Biochim. Biophys.*, **5**, 483–496.
Hermier, J., and Rousseau, M. (1967). *Annls Inst. Pasteur, Paris*, **113**, 327–340.
Hills, G. M. (1949a). *Biochem. J.*, **45**, 353–362.
Hills, G. M. (1949b). *Biochem. J.*, **45**, 363–370.
Hills, G. M. (1950). *J. gen. Microbiol.*, **4**, 38–47.
Hitchins, A. D., and Gould, G. W. (1964). *Nature. London.*, **203**, 895–896.
Hitchins, A. D., Gould, G. W., and Hurst, A. (1963). *J. gen. Microbiol.*, **30**, 445–453.
Hitchins, A. D., Kahn, A. J., and Slepecky, R. A. (1968). *J. Bact.*, **96**, 1811.
Hitchins, A. D., King, W. L., and Gould, G. W. (1966). *J. appl. Bact.*, **29**, 505–511.
Hitzman, D. O., Halvorson, H. O., and Ukita, T. (1957). *J. Bact.*, **74**, 1–7.
Hodgkiss, W., Ordal, Z. J., and Cann, D. C. (1967). *J. gen. Microbiol.*, **47**, 213–225.
Holdom, R. S., and Johnstone, K. I. (1967). *J. gen. Microbiol.*, **46**, 315–319.
Holmes, P. K., and Levinson, H. S. (1967). *J. Bact.*, **94**, 434–440.
Holsinger, V. H., Blankenship, L. C., and Pallansch, M. J. (1967). *Archs Biochem. Biophys.*, **119**, 282–287.
Holt, S. C., and Leadbetter, E. R. (1969). *Bact. Revs.*, **33**, 346–378.
Hugo, W. B. (1967). *J. appl. Bact.*, **30**, 17–50.
Hunnell, J. W., and Ordal, Z. J. (1961). *In* "Spores II", pp. 101–112.
Hyatt, M. T., Holmes, P. K., and Levinson, H. S. (1966). *Biochem. Biophys. Res. Commun.*, **24**, 701–704.
Hyatt, M. T., and Levinson, H. S. (1957). *J. Bact.*, **74**, 87–93.
Hyatt, M. T., and Levinson, H. S. (1959). *J. Bact.*, **77**, 487–496.
Hyatt, M. T., and Levinson, H. S. (1962). *J. Bact.*, **83**, 1231–1237.
Hyatt, M. T., and Levinson, H. S. (1964). *J. Bact.*, **88**, 1403–1415.
Jannsen, F. W., Lund, A. J., and Anderson, L. E. (1958). *Science*, **127**, 26–27.
Jaye, M., and Ordal, Z. J. (1966). *Can. J. Microbiol.*, **12**, 199–201.
Johnstone, R., Harmon, S., and Kautter, D. (1964). *J. Bact.*, **88**, 1521–1522.
Kadota, H., Iijima, K., and Uchida, A. (1965). *Agric. Biol. Chem.*, **29**, 870–875.
Kan, B., Goldblith, S. A., and Proctor, B. E. (1958). *Fd. Res.*, **23**, 41–50.
Katzin, L. I., Sandholzer, L. A., and Strong, M. E. (1943). *J. Bact.*, **45**, 265–272.
Kellenberger, E., Ryter, A., and Sechaud, J. (1958). *J. biophys. biochem. Cytol.*, **4**, 671–678.
Keynan, A., and Halvorson, H. O. (1965). *In* "Spores III", pp. 174–179.
Keynan, A., Halvorson, H. O., and Hastings, J. W. (1964). *J. Bact.*, **88**, 313–318.
Keynan, A., Issahary-Brand, G., and Evenchik, Z. (1965). *In* "Spores III", pp. 180–187.
King, W. L., and Gould, G. W. (1969). *J. appl. Bact.*, **32**, *In press*.
Knaysi, G. (1961). *J. Bact.*, **82**, 556–563.
Knaysi, G. (1964). *J. Bact.*, **87**, 619–622.
Knaysi, G. (1965). *J. Bact.*, **90**, 453–455.
Knaysi, G., and Curran, H. R. (1961). *J. Bact.*, **82**, 691–694.
Kobayashi, Y., Steinberg, W., and Higa, A., Halvorson, H. O., and Levinthal, C. (1965). *In* "Spores III", pp. 200–212.
Kondo, M., and Foster, J. W. (1967). *J. gen. Microbiol.*, **47**, 257–271.
Kornberg, A., Spudich, J. A., Nelson, D. L., and Deutscher, M. P. (1968). *A. Rev. Biochem.*, **37**, 51.

Krask, B. J., and Fulk, G. E. (1959). *Archs Biochem. Biophys.*, **79**, 86–90.
Krywienczyk, J., and Angus, T. A. (1960). *J. Insect Path.*, **2**, 411–417.
Lawrence, N. L. (1955). *J. Bact.*, **70**, 583–587.
Lawrence, N. L., and Halvorson, H. O. (1954). *J. Bact.*, **78**, 334–337.
Lawrence, N. L., and Tsan, Y-C. (1962). *J. Bact.*, **83**, 228–233.
Layne, J. S., and Johnson, E. J. (1964). *J. Bact.*, **87**, 684–689.
Lechowich, R. V., and Ordal, Z. J. (1962). *Con. J. Microbiol.*, **8**, 287–295.
Lee, W. H., and Ordal, Z. J. (1963). *J. Bact.*, **85**, 207–217.
Leitzmann, C., and Bernlohr, R. W. (1965). *J. Bact.*, **89**, 1506–1510.
Levinson, H. S. (1961). *In* "Spores II", pp. 14–23.
Levinson, H. S., and Hyatt, M. T. (1955). *J. Bact.*, **70**, 368–374.
Levinson, H. S., and Hyatt, M. T. (1962). *J. Bact.*, **83**, 1224–1230.
Levinson, H. S., and Hyatt, M. T. (1964). *J. Bact.*, **87**, 876–886.
Levinson, H. S., and Hyatt, M. T. (1965). *In* "Spores III", pp. 198–199.
Levinson, H. S., and Hyatt, M. T. (1966). *J. Bact.*, **91**, 1811–1818.
Levinson, H. S., and Sevag, M. G. (1954). *Archs Biochem. Biophys.*, **50**, 507–510.
Levinson, H. S., Sloan, J. D., and Hyatt, M. T. (1958). *J. Bact.*, **75**, 291–299.
Levisohn, S., and Aronson, A. I. (1967). *J. Bact.*, **93**, 1023–1030.
Lewis, J. C. (1967). *Analyt. Biochem.*, **19**, 327–337.
Lewis, J. C., Snell, N. S., and Alderton, G. (1965). *In* "Spores III", pp. 47–54.
Lewis, J. C., Snell, N. S., and Burr, H. K. (1960). *Science, N.Y.*, **132**, 544–545.
Long, S. K., and Williams, O. B. (1958). *J. Bact.*, **76**, 332.
Lund, A. J., Janssen, F. W., and Anderson, I. E. (1957). *J. Bact.*, **74**, 577–583.
Lundgren, D. G., and Beskid, G. (1960). *Can. J. Microbiol.*, **6**, 135–151.
Lundgren, D. G., and Cooney, J. J. (1962). *J. Bact.*, **83**, 1287–1293.
MacDonald, R. E., and MacDonald, S. W. (1962). *Can. J. Microbiol.*, **8**, 795–808.
Mandelstam, J. (1969). *Symp. Soc. Gen. Microbiol.*, **19**, 377–404.
Martin, H. H., and Foster, J. W. (1958). *J. Bact.*, **76**, 167–178.
Mastroeni, P., Nacci, A., and Rocca, A. (1967). *J. Bact.*, **94**, 2073–2074.
Matz, L., and Gerhardt, P. (1964). *Bact. Proc.*, 14.
McCormick, N. G. (1965). *J. Bact.*, **89**, 1180–1185.
McCormick, N. G., and Halvorson, H. O. (1964). *J. Bact.*, **87**, 68–74.
Mendelson, N. H., and Gross, J. D. (1967). *J. Bact.*, **94**, 1603–1608.
Michel, J. F. (1966). *Annls Inst. Pasteur, Paris*, **11**, 14–24.
Michel, J. F., Cami, B., and Schaeffer, P. (1968). *Annls Inst. Pasteur, Paris*, **114**, 11–27.
Millet, J. (1969). *Bull. Soc. Chim. Biol.*, **51**, 457–469.
Millet, J., and Aubert, J-P. (1960). *Annls Inst. Pasteur, Paris*, **98**, 282–290.
Millet, J., and Aubert, J. P. (1964). *C. r. hebd. Séance. Acad. Sci., Paris*, **259**, 2555–2560.
Moberly, B. J., Shafa, F., and Gerhardt, P. (1966). *J. Bact.*, **92**, 220–228.
Mol, J. H. H. (1957). *J. appl. Bact.*, **20**, 454–459.
Monro, R. E. (1961). *J. biophys. biochem. Cytol.*, **11**, 321–331.
Murrell, W. G. (1961). *In* 11th Symp. Soc. Gen. Microbiol. (Ed. G. G. Meynell and H. Gooder), pp. 100–150. The University Press, Cambridge, England.
Murrell, W. G. (1967). *Adv. Microbiol Physiol.*, **1**, 133–251.
Murrell, W. G., and Warth, A. D. (1965). *In* "Spores III", pp. 1–24.
Murty, G. G. K., and Halvorson, H. O. (1957). *J. Bact.*, **73**, 230–234.
Nakata, H. M. (1963). *J. Bact.*, **86**, 577–581.
Nakata, H. M. (1964). *J. Bact.*, **88**, 1522–1524.

Nakata, H. M., and Halvorson, H. O. (1960). *J. Bact.*, **80**, 801–810.

Neihof, R., Thompson, J. K., and Deitz, V. R. (1967). *Nature, Lond.*, **216**, 1304–1306.

Norris, J. R. (1962). *J. gen. Microbiol.*, **28**, 393–408.

Norris, J. R., and Baillie, A. (1964). *J. Bact.*, **88**, 264–265.

Norris, J. R., and Watson, D. H. (1960). *J. gen. Microbiol.*, **22**, 744–749.

Norris, J. R., and Wolf, J. (1961). *J. appl. Bact.*, **24**, 42–56.

Northrop, J., and Slepecky, R. A. (1967). *Science*, **155**, 838–839.

O'Brien, R. T., and Campbell, L. L. (1957). *J. Bact.*, **73**, 522–525.

O'Connor, R. J., and Halvorson, H. O. (1960). *Archs Biochem. Biophys.*, **91**, 290–299.

O'Connor, R. J., and Halvorson, H. O. (1961a). *J. Bact.*, **82**, 706–713.

O'Connor, R. J., and Halvorson, H. O. (1961b). *Biochem. biophys. Acta*, **48**, 47–55.

Ohye, D. F., and Murrell, W. G. (1962). *J. Cell Biol.*, **14**, 111–123.

Parker, M. S., and Barnes, M. (1967). *J. appl. Bact.*, **30**, 299–303.

Parker, M. S., and Bradley, T. G. (1968). *Can. J. Microbiol.*, **14**, 745–746.

Pelcher, E. A., Fleming, H. P., and Ordal, Z. J. (1963). *Can. J. Microbiol.*, **9**, 251–258.

Pendleton, I. R., and Morrison, R. B. (1966). *Nature, Lond.*, **212**, 728–729.

Perkins, W. E. (1965). *J. appl. Bact.*, **28**, 1–16.

Perkins, W. E., and Tsuji, K. (1962). *J. Bact.*, **84**, 86–94.

Powell, J. F. (1950). *J. gen. Microbiol.*, **4**, 330–338.

Powell, J. F. (1951). *J. gen. Microbiol.*, **5**, 993–1000.

Powell, J. F., and Hunter, J. R. (1956). *Biochem. J.*, **62**, 381–387.

Pulvertaft, R. J. V., and Haynes, J. A. (1951). *J. gen. Microbiol.*, **5**, 657–663.

Ramaley, R. F., and Bernlohr, R. W. (1966). *Arch Biochem. Biophys.*, **117**, 34–43.

Remsen, C. C., Lundgren, D. G., and Slepecky, R. A. (1966). *J. Bact.*, **91**, 324–331.

Ribi, E., Perrine, T., List, R., Brown, W., and Goode, G. (1959). *Proc. Soc. exp. Biol. Med.*, **100**, 647–649.

Riemann, H. (1963). Thesis, University of Copenhagen.

Riemann, H. (1961). *In* "Spores II", pp. 24–48.

Riemann, H., and Ordal, Z. J. (1961). *Science*, **133**, 1703–1704.

Roberts, T. A. (1965). *J. appl. Bact.*, **28**, 142–146.

Roberts, T. A. (1967). *J. appl. Bact.*, **30**, 430–443.

Roberts, T. A., Gilbert, R. J., and Ingram, M. (1966). *J. Fd. Technol.*, **1**, 227–235.

Roberts, T. A., and Hitchins, A. D. (1969). *In* "The Bacterial Spore", pp. 611–670.

Roberts, T. A., and Ingram, M. (1966). *In* "Botulism" (Eds. M. Ingram and T. A. Roberts), pp. 169–175. Chapman and Hall Ltd., London.

Roberts, T. L., and Rosenkrantz, H. (1966). *Can. J. Biochem.*, **44**, 671–675 and 677–685.

Rode, L. J., and Foster, J. W. (1960a). *Proc. natn. Acad. Sci. U.S.A.*, **46**, 118–128.

Rode, L. J., and Foster, J. W. (1960b). *Arch. Mikrobiol.*, **36**, 67–94.

Rode, L. J., and Foster, J. W. (1961). *J. Bact.*, **81**, 768–779.

Rode, L. J., and Foster, J. W. (1962). *Arch. Mikrobiol.*, **43**, 183–200.

Rode, L. J., and Foster, J. W. (1966). *J. Bact.*, **91**, 1589–1593.

Rode, L. J., Lewis, C. W., and Foster, J. W. (1962). *J. Cell Biol.*, **13**, 423–435.

Rode, L. J., and Williams, M. G. (1966). *J. Bact.*, **92**, 1772–1778.

Rogoff, M. H. (1966). *Adv. appl. Microbiol.*, **8**, 291–313.

Ross, K. F. A., and Billing, E. (1957). *J. gen. Microbiol.*, **16**, 418–425.

Roth, N. G., and Halvorson, H. O. (1952). *J. Bact.*, **63**, 429–435.

Rowley, D. B., and Levinson, H. S. (1967). *J. Bact.*, **93**, 1017–1022.
Rowley, D. B., and Newcomb, H. R. (1964). *J. Bact.*, **87**, 701–709.
Rousseau, M., Flechon, J., and Hermier, J. (1966). *Annls Inst. Pasteur, Paris*, **111**, 140–160.
Rouyard, J-F., Ionesco, H. R., and Schaeffer, P. (1967). *Annls Inst. Pasteur, Paris*, **113**, 675–683.
Rubbo, S. D., and Gardner, J. S. (1955). "A Review of Sterilization and Disinfection". Lloyde-Luke Ltd., London.
Ryter, A., and Szulmajster, J. (1965). *Annls Inst. Pasteur, Paris*, **108**, 640–651.
Sacks, L. E. (1967). *J. Bact.*, **94**, 1789–1790.
Sacks, L. E., and Alderton, G. (1961). *J. Bact.*, **82**, 331–341.
Sacks, L. E., and Bailey, G. F. (1963). *J. Bact.*, **85**, 720–721.
Sacks, L. E., Percell, P. B., Thomas, R. S., and Bailey, G. F. (1964). *J. Bact.*, **87**, 952–960.
Sadoff, H. L. (1961). *In* "Spores II", pp. 180–194.
Sadoff, H. L., Bach, J. A., and Kools, J. W. (1965). *In* "Spores III", pp. 97–110.
Sadoff, H. L., Hitchins, A. D., and Celikkol, E. (1969). *J. Bact.*, **98**, 1208–1218.
Sale, A. J., Gould, G. W., and Hamilton, W. A. (1970). *J. gen. Microbiol.*, *In press*.
Salton, M. R. J., and Marshall, B. (1959). *J. gen. Microbiol.*, **21**, 415–420.
Schaeffer, P. (1967). *Folia microbiol.*, *Praha*, **12**, 291–296.
Schaeffer, P., and Ionesco, H. (1960). *C. r. hebd Séance. Acad. Sci.*, *Paris*, **251**, 3125–3132.
Schaeffer, P., Ionesco, H., Ryter, A., and Balassa, G. (1963). *Colloques int. Cen. natn. Rech. scient.*, *Marseille*, **124**, 553–563.
Schaeffer, P., Millet, J., and Aubert, J. P. (1965). *Proc. natn. Acad. Sci. U.S.A.*, **54**, 704–711.
Schmidt, C. F. (1950). *J. Bact.*, **59**, 433–437.
Schmidt, C. F., and Nank, W. K. (1960). *Fd. Res.*, **25**, 321–327.
Schmidt, C. F., Nank, W. K., and Lechowich, R. V. (1962). *J. Fd Sci.*, **27**, 77–84.
Schneider, M. D., Grecz, N., and Anellis, A. (1963). *J. Bact.*, **85**, 126–133.
Sebald, M., and Schaeffer, P. (1965). *C. r. hebd. Séance. Acad. Sci.*, *Paris*, **260**, 5398–5404.
Shoesmith, J. G., and Holland, K. T. (1968). *Biochem. J.*, **106**, 38P.
Sierra, G. (1963). *Can. J. Microbiol.*, **9**, 643–645.
Sierra, G. (1967a). *Can. J. Microbiol.*, **13**, 489–501.
Sierra, G. (1967b). *Can. J. Microbiol.*, **13**, 673–678.
Simmons, R. J., and Costilow, R. N. (1962). *J. Bact.*, **84**, 1274–1281.
Singer, S., Goodman, N. S., and Rogoff, M. H. (1966). *Ann. N.Y. Acad. Sci.*, **139**, 16–23.
Slepecky, R. A. (1963). *Biochem. Biophys. Res. Commun.*, **12**, 369–373.
Slepecky, R. A., and Celkis, Z. (1964). *Bact. Proc.*, 14.
Slepecky, R. A., and Foster, J. W. (1959). *J. Bact.*, **78**, 117–123.
Slepecky, R. A., and Law, J. H. (1961). *J. Bact.*, **82**, 37–42.
Snudden, B. H., and Lechowich, R. V. (1966). *In* "Botulism" (Eds. M. Ingram and T. A. Roberts), pp. 144–149. Chapman and Hall Ltd., London.
Socolofsky, M. D., and Wyss, O. (1961). *J. Bact.*, **81**, 946–954.
Spencer, R. E. J., and Powell, J. F. (1952). *Biochem. J.*, **51**, 239–245.
Spizizen, J. (1958). *Proc. natn. Acad. Sci. U.S.A.*, **44**, 1072–1078.
Splittstoerser, C. M., and McEwen, F. L. (1961). *J. Insect Path.*, **3**, 391–398.

"Spores" (1957). (Ed. H. O. Halvorson), Publication No. 5. Amer. Inst. Biol. Sci., Washington, U.S.A.

"Spores II" (1961). (Ed. H. O. Halvorson), Burgess Publishing Co., Minneapolis, Minn., U.S.A.

"Spores III" (1965). (Ed. L. L. Campbell and H. O. Halvorson). Amer. Soc. Microbiol., Ann Arbor, Mich., U.S.A.

"Spores IV" (1969). (Ed. L. L. Campbell), Am. Soc. Microbiol., Ann Arbor, Mich., U.S.A.

Spudich, J. A., and Kornberg, A. (1969). *J. Bact.*, **98**, 69–74.

Stahly, D. P., Srinivasan, V. R., and Halvorson, H. O. (1966). *J. Bact.*, 1875–1882.

Steinberg, W., and Halvorson, H. O. (1968). *J. Bact.*, **95**, 469–478.

Stent, G. J., and Fuerst, C. (1955). *J. gen. Physiol.*, **38**, 441–458.

Stern, J. A., and Proctor, B. E. (1954). *Fd Technol.*, **8**, 139–143.

Stewart, B. T., and Halvorson, H. O. (1953). *J. Bact.*, **65**, 160–166.

St. Julian, G., Pridham. T. G., and Hall, H. H. (1967). *Can. J. Microbiol.*, **13**, 279–285.

Strange, R. E., and Dark, F. A. (1956). *Biochem. J.*, **62**, 459–465.

Strange, R. E., and Dark, F. A. (1957a). *J. gen. Microbiol.*, **16**, 236–249.

Strange, R. E., and Dark, F. A. (1957b). *J. gen. Microbiol.*, **17**, 525–537.

Strange, R. E., and Hunter, J. R. (1968). *In* "The Bacterial Spore", pp. 445–483.

Strange, R. E., and Powell, J. F. (1954). *Biochem. J.*, **58**, 80–85.

Strasdine, G. A. (1966). *J. Fish. Res. Bd Can.*, **24**, 595–606.

Stumbo, C. R. (1948). *Fd Technol.*, **2**, 228–234.

Stumbo, C. R. (1965). *In* "Thermobacteriology in Food Processing". Academic Press, London.

Sussman, A. S., and Halvorson, H. O. (1966). "Spores: Their Dormancy and Germination". Harper and Row, New York.

Suzuki, Y., and Rode, L. J. (1967). *Bact. Proc.*, 22.

Sykes, G. (1965). *In* "Disinfection and Sterilization", 2nd Edition. E. and F. N. Spon, London.

Szulmajster, J. (1964). *Bull. Soc. Chim. biol.*, **46**, 443–481.

Tabatabai, L., and Walker, H. W. (1967). *J. Bact.*, **94**, 1805–1806.

Tallentire, A., and Davies, D. J. G. (1961). *Expl Cell Res.*, **24**, 148–150.

Tamir, H., and Gilvarg, C. (1966). *J. biol. Chem.*, **241**, 1085–1090.

Tansoka, H., and Sakakibara, Y. (1968). *Biochim. biophys. Acta*, **155**, 130–142.

"The Bacterial Spore" (1969). (Ed. G. W. Gould and A. Hurst). Academic Press, London.

Thomas, R. S. (1964). *J. Cell Biol.*, **23**, 113–133.

Thorley, C. M., and Wolf, J. (1961). *In* "Spores II", pp. 1–13.

Tono, H., and Kornberg, A. (1967). *J. biol. Chem.*, **242**, 2375–2382.

Tsuji, K., and Perkins, W. E. (1962). *J. Bact.*, **84**, 81–85.

Uehara, M., and Frank, H. A. (1965). *In* "Spores III", pp. 38–46.

Uehara, M., Fujioka, R. S., and Frank, H. A. (1965). *J. Bact.*, **89**, 929–930.

Vary, J. C., and Halvorson, H. O. (1965). *J. Bact.*, **89**, 1340–1347.

Vary, J. C., and McCormick, N. G. (1965). *In* "Spores III", pp. 188–198.

Vinter, V. (1960). *Folia microbiol., Praha*, **5**, 217–230.

Vinter, V. (1962a). *Folia microbiol., Praha*, **7**, 115–120.

Vinter. V. (1962b). *Folia microbiol., Praha*, **7**, 275–287.

Vinter, V. (1963). *Folia microbiol., Praha*, **8**, 147–155.

Vinter, V. (1964). *Folia microbiol., Praha*, **9**, 58–72.
Vinter, V. (1965a). *Folia microbiol., Praha*, **10**, 280–287.
Vinter, V. (1965b). *Folia microbiol., Praha*, **10**, 288–297.
Vinter, V. (1966). *Folia microbiol., Praha*, **11**, 392–398.
Vinter, V., and Slepecky, R. A. (1965). *J. Bact.*, **90**, 803–807.
Wagenaar, R. O., and Dack, G. M. (1958). *J. Dairy Sci.*, **41**, 1182–1200.
Waites, W. M. (1968). *Biochem. J.*, **109**, 803–810.
Walker, P. D., and Betty, I. (1965). *J. appl. Bact.*, **28**, 194–196.
Walker, P. D., Thompson, R. O., and Baillie, A. (1967). *J. appl. Bact.*, **30**, 444–449.
Wang, D. I-C, Scharen, J., and Humphrey, A. E. (1964). *Appl. Microbiol.*, **12**, 451–454.
Warth, A. D. (1965). *Biochim. biophys. Acta*, **101**, 315–326.
Warth, A. D., Ohye, D. F., and Murrell, W. G. (1963a). *J. Cell. Biol.*, **16**, 579–592.
Warth, A. D., Ohye, D. F., and Murrell, W. G. (1963b). *J. Cell Biol.*, **16**, 593–609.
Widdowson, J. P. (1967). *Nature, Lond.*, **214**, 812–814.
Windle, J. J., and Sacks, L. E. (1963). *Biochem. biophys. Acta.*, **66**, 173–179.
Wilson, P. W., and Knight, S. G. (1952). "Experiments in Bacterial Physiology". Burgess Publishing Co., Minneapolis, Minn., U.S.A.
Woese, C. R. (1958). *J. Bact.*, **75**, 5–8.
Woese, C. R. (1959). *J. Bact.*, **77**, 38–42.
Woese, C. R., Morowitz, H. J., and Hutchinson, C. A. (1958). *J. Bact.*, **76**, 578–588.
Wolf, J., and Mahmoud, S. A. Z. (1957). *J. appl. Bact.*, **20**, 373–383.
Wolf, J., and Thorley, C. M. (1957). *J. appl. Bact.*, **20**, 384–389.
Wynne, E. S., Mehl, D. A., and Schmeiding, W. R. (1954). *J. Bact.*, **67**, 435–437.
Yolton, D. P., Pope, L., Williams, M. G., and Rode, L. J. (1968). *J. Bact.*, **95**, 231–238.
Young, I. E. (1964). *J. Bact.*, **88**, 242–254.
Young, I. E., and Fitz-James, P. C. (1959a). *J. biophys. biochem. Cytol.*, **6**, 467–482.
Young, I. E., and Fitz-James, P. C. (1959b). *J. biophys. biochem. Cytol.* **6**, 483–498.
Young, I. E., and Fitz-James, P. C. (1962). *J. Cell Biol.*, **12**, 115–133.

CHAPTER VII

Inhibitors of Electron Transport and Oxidative Phosphorylation

W. Heinen

Department of Exobiology, Microbiology Branch, University of Nijmegen,
Nijmegen, Netherlands

I. INHIBITORY AGENTS AND THEIR SITE OF ACTION

For the investigation of the function and properties of the respiratory chain in mammalian systems, i.e. in mitochondria, inhibitory agents continue to play a major role. These substances can act either on electron transport, energy transfer, or the coupling between phosphorylation and electron transfer. Since an overlapping of the effects of certain inhibitors is frequently observed, the classification of the various substances as uncoupling agents, energy transfer-inhibitors, etc. is somewhat superficial, but still useful.

In general, the same inhibitory agents that have been powerful tools for the study of mammalian systems can also be applied to reveal the functioning of electron transport and oxidative phosphorylation in micro-organisms. The inhibitors most frequently used in microbial systems are listed in Table I. These can be classified either by their site of action, or by their chemical nature. Azide and cyanide both block the transfer of electrons to oxygen by reacting with cytochrome oxidase. The same is true for carbon monoxide, although its inhibition is light reversible. The reversible CO inhibition is one of the most feasible methods to determine the characteristics of terminal oxidases, as was for instance shown with the two pigments of *Bacillus megaterium*, which were defined as cytochrome a_3 and cytochrome o by Broberg and Smith (1967).

The action of Actinomycin D on cytochrome c is more indirect. The

TABLE I

Site of action, and concentration range, of inhibitors of electron transport and oxidative phosphorylation

Inhibitor	Site of action	Concentration range*
Azide		10^{-3}–10^{-2}M
Cyanide Carbon monoxide	Cytochrome oxidase $\xrightarrow{\;\;\;}$ O_2	10^{-3}–10^{-2}M
B.A.L.† Urethane	Cytochrome b	10^{-4}–5×10^{-3}M
HOQNO NHQNO	Cytochrome $b \xrightarrow{\;\;\;}$ cyt. c or F.P. $\longrightarrow$ cyt. b	10^{-5}–5×10^{-4}M 5×10^{-5}–5×10^{-4}M
Antimycin A	Cytochrome $b \longrightarrow$ cyt. c_1‡	5×10^{-7}–10^{-5}M
o-Phenanthroline Salicylaldoxim 8-Hydroxyquinoline EDTA	F.P. $\xrightarrow{\;\;\;}$ cytochrome b	10^{-3}–10^{-2}M
Amytal Rotenone Acriflavin	NADH $\xrightarrow{\;\;\;}$ F.P. Flavoproteins	10^{-6}–2×10^{-3}M 10^{-5}–5×10^{-4}M 10^{-5}–10^{-3}M
Pentachlorophenol CCCP FCCP	Energy-transfer inhibitors	5×10^{-4}–5×10^{-3}M 10^{-6}–10^{-5}M 10^{-6}–2×10^{-5}M
2,4-DNP	Uncoupling agent	10^{-4}–10^{-3}M
Oligomycin	Blocks final ATP formation	10^{-5}–10^{-4}M

* Upper and lower limits, according to various publications.
† Abbreviations used are explained in the text.
‡ In mitochondria; in some bacteria presumably at the F.P.-cyt. b link.

substance has been shown to inhibit the synthesis of cytochrome c in Zn-depleted cells of the fungus *Ustilago* (Brown *et al.*, 1966).

Acting on cytochrome b are BAL (British Anti-Lewisite) and urethane while HOQNO (2-N-heptyl-4-hydroxyquinoline-N-oxide) and NHQNO (2-N-nonylhydroxyquinoline-N-oxide) have been reported to inhibit electron transport either between cytochromes b and c, or between the flavoproteins and cytochrome *b* (Asano and Brodie, 1965; Imai *et al.*, 1965; Lanyi, 1969). At the latter site, between flavoprotein and cytochrome *b*, several metal chelating agents such as *o*-phenanthroline, salicylaldoxim, 8-hydroxyquinoline, and EDTA also act as inhibitors (Asano and Brodie, 1965; Kurup and Brodie, 1967). This segment is also sensitive to Hg-compounds which can furthermore act on the segment NADH-flavoprotein (Schatz *et al.*, 1966). Amytal, acriflavin, and rotenone all act on the flavoproteins (Benziman and Perez, 1965; Asano and Brodie, 1965; Imai *et al.*, 1967). Antimycin A, a powerful inhibitor of this part of the chain in mammalian systems, has been reported not to act in intact micro-organisms (see L. Smith, 1961). However, in cell-free systems of both yeasts (Itoh and Nosoh, 1967), and bacteria (Asano and Brodie, 1965; Bernofsky and Mills, 1966; Heinen, 1967), this inhibitor has been used successfully. The substances most commonly used as energy transfer inhibitors are pentachlorophenol, *CCCP* (carbonyl-cyanide-*m*-chlorophenylhydrazine) and *FCCP* (carbonyl-cyanide trifluoromethoxyphenylhydrazine) (Imai *et al.*, 1964).

2,4-Dinitrophenol (DNP), which acts as an uncoupling agent allowing electron flow but not phosphorylation, and oligomycin, which inhibits the last step of the ATP-formation (Ernster and Lee, 1964), show similar effects in both mammalian and microbial systems, though higher concentrations are necessary in the latter. The necessity of using higher concentrations of inhibitors holds for most of the compounds listed in that table.

II. CONDITIONS AFFECTING THE USE OF INHIBITORS IN MICROBIAL SYSTEMS

We may conclude from the foregoing that the use of inhibitors is a useful means of elucidating pathways of electron transport and oxidative phosphorylation in micro-organisms. There are, however, a number of limitations and restrictions that complicate the applications, and especially the evaluation of these kinds of studies in the case of micro-organisms: (a) There are "microbial systems" such as yeasts and molds which are anatomically complex, and contain true mitochondria. Other "microbial systems"—bacteria—have no mitochondria, although some of them contain intra-cellular membranous organelles which may feature at least some of the mitochondrial functions (see 2b). Mitochondria are, on the other hand, not present in yeast cells under anaerobic conditions. Instead, sub-units exist—of the order of magnitude of the ribosomes—with which at least some of the typical mitochondrial enzymes are associated (Klein and Jahnke, 1968; Watson, Haslam, and Linnane, 1970). (b) The efficiency of oxidative phosphorylation seems to be lower in micro-organisms than in

14

mammalian mitochondria, discounting other means of trapping the energy derived from electron transport. One example in this context is the fact that yeast mitochondria have only two phosphorylating sites (Schatz and Racker, 1966; Onishi *et al.*, 1967) rather than the three which are observed in mammalian mitochondria, such as beef heart (Green, 1966). (c) Variations on the "classical" components of the respiratory chain are frequent in micro-organisms. Furthermore, the composition of not only the respiratory chain but also other constituents of the membrane is much more flexible, for instance, with regard to the lipid components. (d) A variety of factors, such as mutation and growth conditions, can affect the composition and effectiveness of the respiratory chain. Before discussing this problem, we should briefly look into these points with some more detail.

A. Modifications of the respiratory chain in several micro-organisms

The properties found for mammalian mitochondria can in a general way also be attributed to the mitochondria of molds and yeasts. But even in these organisms, we find some modifications with respect to the composition of the chain.

Several yeast strains, for instance, contain a pigment with an absorption maximum at 503 nm, which intensifies on prolonged aerobic growth; simultaneously, a second peak at 475 nm appears (Itoh and Nosoh, 1967). Other differences are given with respect to oxidative phosphorylation. Stable phosphorylating submitochondrial particles from yeast have one phosphorylating site less than beef heart mitochondria (Schatz and Racker, 1966; Onishi *et al.*, 1967) because the first segment (NADH-cytochrome *b*) is not involved in phosphorylation. Beef heart mitochondria have two functional groups which are sensitive for Hg-compounds: the segment flavoprotein—cytochrome *b*, and the segment NADH—flavoprotein. Yeast submitochondrial fragments, however, contain just one group where the Hg-inhibitor acts, the flavoprotein—cytochrome *b* segment (Schatz *et al.*, 1966). Only one phosphorylating site is present in *Micrococcus lysodeikticus* (Fujita *et al.*, 1966).

More frequently than in higher organisms we find mutants of micro-organisms with alterations of the electron transport chain. In contrast to normal strains of bakers yeast, which contain cytochromes $a + a_3$, $c + c_1$, and *b*, "petite-colony" mutants of *Saccharomyces cerevisiae* were found to be unable to catalyze the reduction of cytochrome *c* by NADH, or the oxidation of reduced cytochrome *c* by oxygen, because they contain no cytochrome *b*, and are also missing cytochromes $a + a_3$ (Mahler *et al.*, 1964). Phosphorylation and electron transport of a cytochrome *c*-deficient mutant of *S. cerevisiae* can, on the other hand, be reconstituted by the addition of yeast or equine cytochrome *c*. The cytochrome is then tightly bound and is retained during reisolation of mitochondria from this mutant (Mattoon and Sherman, 1966). In the fungus *Ustilago shaerogena*, the formation of large amounts of cytochrome *c* can be induced by the addition of zinc to the sporidia of the smut fungus (Brown *et al.*, 1966). In general, however, the components of mitochondria from higher organisms and micro-organisms are quite similar as can be seen from the fact that the succinate-cytochrome *c* reductase activity of acetone-extracted beef heart mitochondria can be restored by the addition of lipids from *Claviceps purpurea* mitochondria (Anderson *et al.*, 1964).

In this context it should be mentioned that both cytological and bio-chemical evidence point to the probability that the mitochondrion in its present function within the cell represents the final stage of an evolutionary process which started with a symbiosis between bacteria and a primitive cell. In the course of cell-differentiation, the outer membrane, with its special properties for fatty acid oxidation and substrate level phosphory-lation (Allman *et al.*, 1967), was supplied by the "host" cell, while the "cell-adapted bacteria" kept their own membrane, now representing the inner mitochondrial membrane, and their ability for oxidative phosphory-lation. Even the submicroscopical surface structure of the inner membrane of mitochondria, as revealed by freeze-etching, and the cytoplasmic membrane of bacteria representing a relatively early evolutionary stage, show a striking similarity (Wrigglesworth, Packer and Branton, 1970; Heinen and Heinen, 1971).

B. Electron transport in bacterial membrane systems

If we study the composition and function of bacterial cytoplasmic membrane systems, we find that their properties are in general similar to those of mitochondria. However, we should notice at the same time that these systems are much more flexible with respect to their cytochrome composition, the number of pathways that can be followed by the electrons, and the variety of donors and acceptors operating at various levels of the respiratory chain.

In most bacteria these membrane systems form the circumference of the cytoplasm, with more or less pronounced invaginations extending into the interior. Some bacteria, such as *Bacillus subtilis*, possess a second membranous structure located within the cytoplasm. So far, we do not know yet whether this membrane system has at one or more positions conjunctures with the main membrane, or whether it should be con-sidered as a cell organelle. Concerning its function, van Iterson and Leene (1964a) have demonstrated that after the reductive accumulation of tellurite, metallic tellurium is accumulated at this membranous structure in greater

amounts than in the enveloping membrane, while in organisms such as
Proteus mirabilis, which have no interplasmatic membrane system, the
metal is bound to the cytoplasmic membrane (van Iterson and Leene,
1964b). From this electron microscopic evidence, we can conclude that the
organelle-like membrane system of *B. subtilis* has the capacity to reduce
anions, such as tellurite, to their metallic form, and for this process, seg-
ments of the electron transport chain are necessary.

Studies of the bacterial membrane system were initially restricted to
intact cells, but more recently have focused on isolated membrane fragments. In these studies the use of various inhibitors has provided a valuable
tool to reveal the composition of bacterial respiratory systems and the basic
processes which depend on the structural and functional properties of the
membrane. If we compare these results with those from mammalian mitochondria, we find always at least one of the two enzymes which mediate
electron flow via NAD or succinate, NADH-oxidase or succinic dehydrogenase (F_D and F_S, according to Green, 1966), aerobic conditions provided.
We also find a lipid-soluble link like CoQ or vitamin K, followed by a set
of cytochromes and one or more terminal oxidases. With respect to these
latter enzymes, the apparent difference with the mitochondrial electron
transport chain is obvious: While the mitochondrion has only one terminal
link to oxygen, many bacteria provide more than one exit for the electrons,
often including at least one terminal oxidase which is insensitive to cyanide
and azide.

A soluble cytochrome *o* type terminal oxidase has lately been reported
to exist in *Nitrosomonas europaea* (Rees and Nason, 1965). Other soluble
cytochromes are, for instance, the cytochromes b_{562} and c_{550} found in
Enterobacteriaceae (Fujita, 1966). Soluble cytochromes are unknown in
mitochondria. Another striking difference is the fact that some bacteria are
cytochrome *c* deficient.

Furthermore, we find quite a number of pigments in bacteria with absorption peaks that deviate from the "standard" cytochromes of mitochondria.

Another property which highlights the flexibility of the bacterial respiratory chain is the fact that at least all anaerobes and facultative anaerobes
provide various exits to acceptors other than oxygen, i.e. to electron
acceptors such as sulphite and sulphate, or nitrate and nitrite, or even such
"poisonous" substances as AsO_4^{2-}, SeO_3^{2-}, and PbO_2 (Woolfolk and
Whiteley, 1962). Apart from these variations within the cytochrome set, the
lipid-soluble CoQ-link of the mitochondria can be replaced by many other
compounds such as vitamin K or menadione (Asano *et al.*, 1965; Benziman
and Perez, 1965; Klubes and Brodie, 1966; Knowles and Redfearn, 1966;
Krogstad and Howland, 1966; Repaske and Lizotte, 1965; Scholes and
King, 1965; White and Frerman, 1967).

Further variations on the respiratory chain are exemplified by the existence of diaphorases and by-pass enzymes: several diaphorases which provide a link to oxygen and other acceptors from various sites of the electron transport chain have been demonstrated in *Mycobacterium tuberculosis* (Heinen *et al.*, 1964). The 105,000 g fraction of *Aerobacter aerogenes* was shown to contain five different diaphorases which behave differently with either dichlorophenol-indophenol, ferricyanide, menadione or cytochrome *c* as acceptors. One of these enzymes, which all depend on the presence of FMN, is linked to cytochrome b_1 (Bernofsky and Mills, 1966). By-pass enzymes, which mediate the oxidation of NADH and NADPH independently of the electron transfer chain, or re-enter the chain at the level of cytochrome *c*, have been purified from the supernatant of the 144,000 g fraction. This fraction contains the particulate electron transport chain of *Mycobacterium phlei* (Asano and Brodie, 1965). Variations of this kind are illustrated in Table II.

TABLE II

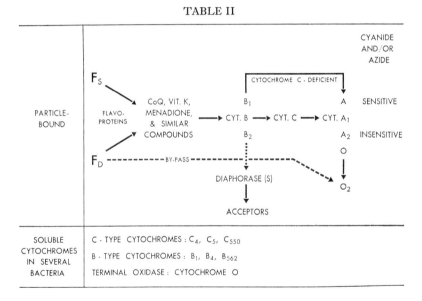

	C - TYPE CYTOCHROMES : C_4, C_5, C_{550}
SOLUBLE CYTOCHROMES IN SEVERAL BACTERIA	B - TYPE CYTOCHROMES : B_1, B_4, B_{562}
	TERMINAL OXIDASE : CYTOCHROME O

III. FACTORS AFFECTING THE COMPOSITION OF THE MICROBIAL RESPIRATORY CHAIN

Mutations which may affect the constitution of the cytoplasmic membrane are more frequent in microbes than in higher organisms. This is one factor which then can also affect the composition of the electron transfer chain in bacteria and other microbes. In a pleiotropic mutation of two species of the Enterobacteriaceae (*Escherichia coli* and *Proteus vulgaris*) produced by $KClO_4$, the nitrate- and chlorate-reductase activities are lost simultaneously with hydrogen-lyase activity. The sedimentation profiles on sucrose density gradients of particle preparations from one of these mutant strains (*E. coli*) change: the peak containing the nitrate-reductase activity disappears. Since the particles containing the reductase represent a part of the cytoplasmic membrane, drastic alterations of the membrane and its respiratory chain are obviously caused by the mutagenic agent (Azoulay *et al.*, 1967). From a mutant of *Saccharomyces cerevisiae*, respiratory subparticles have been isolated and compared to those of the wild type by Mahler *et al.* (1964). The particle fraction of the mutant was found to be devoid of the terminal oxidases ($a + a_3$), as well as cytochrome *b*. Certain single gene mutants of *S. cerevisiae* contain only the *iso*-2-cytochrome *c*, while the wild type contains this in small amounts together with the *iso*-1-cytochrome *c*. The mutant strains still have the capacity of some respiration and contain approximately normal amounts of the other particle-bound respiratory enzymes, but cannot utilize DL-lactate for growth (Mattoon and Sherman, 1966).

Variations of the chain composition can also be induced by irradiation: inactivation of electron transfer, due to an alteration in the flavoprotein-cytochrome *b* region, was found to occur with electron transport particles from *Mycobacterium phlei* after irradiation with 360 nm light. While the succinate oxidation could not be restored, oxidation of substrates which enter via NAD could be reactivated by the addition of vitamin K or naphthoquinone (Kurup and Brodie, 1966).

Furthermore, the conditions of growth and cultivation have a marked influence on the composition of the electron transport chain. Recently, Frerman and White (1967) have shown that the addition of oxygen to anaerobically growing cultures of *Staphylococcus aureus* results in the formation of a membrane-bound electron transfer system. A 15-fold increase of cytochrome *a*, and a 55-fold increase in cytochrome *o* were found with the shift to aerobic growth, so that after completion of the adaptation, the cytochrome levels were equal to those of entirely aerobically grown cells. The cytochromes b_1 and *o* were found to be formed first, their synthesis slowing down when cytochrome *a* became detectable. Protoheme, which is also synthesized in anaerobically growing cells that are unable to form a functional cytochrome system, increased nine-fold during the shift to aerobiosis, while heme *a* appears only after a period of aerobic growth. Simultaneously, the vitamin K_2 content increases, with an alteration in the ratios of the 35 and 45 carbon side chain isoprene analogue. The amount of phosphatidyl glycerol and cardiolipin also increases, while lysyl-phosphatidyl glycerol remains essentially constant during the shift.

Similar results were obtained by the addition of heme to anaerobically growing cells of *Staphylococcus epidermis* (Jacobs *et al.*, 1967). These cells showed a marked increase of cytochromes o and b_1, as compared to heme-deficient cells.

A cyanide- and azide-resistant terminal oxidase can be induced in *Achromobacter*, which normally contains just one cytochrome oxidase (cytochrome a), by aerobic cultivation of the cells in presence of cyanide (Arima and Oka, 1965a, b). The cytochrome formed under these conditions is the cyanide-insensitive terminal oxidase, a_2.

In context with the above-mentioned laboratory culture conditions, the influence of the natural environment from which the organisms originate has also to be taken into account as a factor that can affect the membrane composition. This is more evident the more extreme the environmental conditions are. The membranes of extremely halophilic bacteria, for instance, dissolve rapidly in distilled water (Larsen, 1967), which means that the properties of these membranes are quite different from those of normal bacteria. One of these organisms (*Halobacterium cutirubrum*) contains flavoprotein, two b-type cytochromes, two c-type cytochromes and one terminal oxidase, cytochrome a_{592} (Lanyi, 1968). The activity of the NADH-oxidase from this organism depends on high salt concentrations (Lanyi, 1969). Bacteria that live in another kind of an extreme environment, the thermophilic bacteria from hot springs as those described by Brock (1967), contain no unsaturated fatty acids in their membranes, but 60–80% of branched-chain fatty acids (Heinen, 1970). Whether or not the carotenoid-like pigment, which is present in the membrane of these organisms in relatively great amounts, partakes in electron transport is not yet clear (Heinen, 1969), although peak-shifts upon reduction have been observed. The variations in lipid-components in bacterial membranes are another factor that adds up to membrane modifications (Salton, 1967), but as yet we do not know how much alterations of these "secondary" components of the membrane influence its function. It is clear, however, that these constituents play a vital role within the basic functions of membranes, i.e. electron transport, oxidative phosphorylation, and ion transfer (Fleischer and Klauwen, 1961; Richardson *et al.*, 1964; Fleischer *et al.*, 1966).

In summarizing, one should say that inhibitor studies can provide very definite insights into the properties of microbial membrane functions if the flexibility and variability of micro-organisms is fully considered.

REFERENCES

Allmann, D. W., Harris, R. A., and Green, D. E. (1967). *Arch. Biochem. Biophys.*, **120**, 623–702.
Anderson, J. A., Kang Sun, F., McDonald, J. K., and Cheldelin, V. H. (1964). *Arch. Biochem. Biophys.*, **107**, 37–50.

Arima, K., and Oka, T. (1965a). *J. Bacteriol.*, **90**, 734–743.
Arima, K., and Oka, T. (1965b). *J. Bacteriol.*, **90**, 744–747.
Asano, A., and Brodie, A. F. (1965). *Biochem. Biophys. Res. Commun.*, **19**, 121–126.
Asano, A., Kaneshiro, F., and Brodie, A. F. (1965). *J. biol. Chem.*, **240**, 895–905.
Azoulay, E., Puig, J., and Pichinoty, F. (1967). *Biochem. Biophys. Res. Commun.*, **27**, 270–274.
Bernofsky, C., and Mills, R. C. (1966). *J. Bacteriol.*, **92**, 1404–1413.
Broberg, P. L., and Smith, L. (1967). *Biochim. biophys. Acta*, **131**, 479–483.
Brock, T. D. (1967). *Science*, **158**, 1012–1018.
Brown, D. H., Capellini, and Price, C. A. (1966). *Plant Physiol.*, **41**, 1543–1546.
Ernster, L., and Lee, C. P. (1964). *Ann. Rev. Biochem.*, **33**, 729–788.
Fleischer, B., Casu, A., and Fleischer, S. (1966). *Biochem. Biophys. Res. Commun.*, **24**, 189–194.
Fleischer, S., and Klauwen, H. (1961). *Biochem. Biophys. Res. Commun.*, **5**, 78–3 383.
Frerman, F. E., and White, D. C. (1967). *J. Bacteriol.*, **94**, 1868–1874.
Fujita, M., Ishikawa, S., and Shimazons, N. (1966). *J. Biochem.*, **59**, 104–114.
Fujita, T. (1966). *J. Biochem.*, **60**, 323–334.
Green, D. E. (1966). *In* "Comprehensive Biochemistry" (Eds M. Florkin and E. H. Stoltz), pp. 303–326. Elsevier Publishing Co., Amsterdam, London, New York.
Heinen, W., Kusunose, M., Kusunose, E., Goldman, D. S., and Wagner, M. J. (1964). *Arch. Biochem. Biophys.*, **104**, 452.
Heinen, W. (1967). *Arch. Biochem. Biophys.*, **120**, 101–107.
Heinen, W. (1969). *Bacteriol. Proc.*, p. 122.
Heinen, W. (1970). *Arch. Mikrobiol.*, **72**, 199–202.
Heinen, U. J., and Heinen, W. (1971). *J. Bacteriol.*, **105**, in press.
Imai, K., Asano, A., and Sato, R. (1967). *Biochim. biophys. Acta*, **143**, 462–476.
Iterson, W. van, and Leene, W. (1964). *J. Cell Biol.*, **20**, 361–375.
Iterson, W. van, and Leene, W. (1964). *J. Cell Biol.*, **20**, 377–387.
Itoh, M., and Nosoh, Y. (1967). *Arch. Biochem. Biophys.*, **118**, 525–530.
Jacobs, N. J., Maclosky, E. R., and Conti, S. F. (1967). *J. Bacteriol.*, **93**, 278–285.
Klein, H. P., and Jahnke, L. (1968). *J. Bacteriol.*, **95**, 1632–1639.
Klubes, P., and Brodie, A. F. (1966). *Biochemistry*, **5**, 4171–4178.
Knowles, C. J., and Redfearn, E. R. (1966). *Biochem. J.*, **99**, 33–34.
Krogstad, D. J., and Howland, J. L. (1966). *Biochim. biophys. Acta*, **118**, 189–191.
Kurup, C. K. R., and Brodie, A. F. (1967). *J. biol. Chem.*, **242**, 197–203.
Lanyi, J. K. (1968). *Arch. Biochem. Biophys.*, **128**, 716–724.
Lanyi, J. K. (1969). *J. biol. Chem.*, **244**, 2864–2869 and 4168–4173.
Larsen, H. (1967). *Advances Microbiol. Physiol.*, **1**, 97–132.
Mahler, H. R., Mackler, B., Grandchamp, S., and Slonimsky, P. P. (1964). *Biochemistry*, **3**, 668–677.
Mattoon, J. R., and Sherman, F. (1966). *J. biol. Chem.*, **241**, 4330–4338.
Onishi, T., Kroger, A., Heldt, H. W., Pfaff, E., and Klingenberg, M. (1967). *Europ. J. Biochem.*, **1**, 301–311.
Rees, M., and Nason, A. (1965). *Biochem. Biophys. Res. Commun.*, **21**, 248–256.
Repaske, R., and Lizotte, C. L. (1965). *J. biol. Chem.*, **240**, 4774–4779.
Richardson, S. H., Hultin, H. O., and Fleischer, S. (1964). *Arch. Biochem. Biophys.*, **105**, 254–260.
Salton, M. R. J. (1967). *Ann. Rev. Microbiol.*, **21**, 417–442.

Schatz, G., and Racker, E. (1966). *Biochem. Biophys. Res. Commun.*, **22**, 579–584.
Schatz, G., Racker, E., Tyler, D. D., Gonze, J., and Estabrook, R. W. (1966). *Biochem. Biophys. Res. Commun.*, **22**, 585–590.
Scholes, P. B., and King, H. K. (1965). *Biochem. J.*, **37**, 766–768.
Smith, L. (1961). *In* "The Bacteria" (Eds I. C. Gunsalus and R. Y. Stanier), Vol. II, pp. 365–396. Academic Press, New York and London.
White, D. C., and Frerman, F. E. (1967). *J. Bacteriol.*, **94**, 1854–1867.
Watson, K., Haslam, J. M., and Linnane, A. W. (1970). *J. Cell Biol.*, **46**, 88–96.
Woolfolk, C. A., and Whiteley, H. R. (1962). *J. Bacteriol.*, **84**, 647–658.
Wrigglesworth, J. M., Packer, L., and Branton, D. (1970). *Biochim. Biophys. Acta*, **205**, 125–135.

CHAPTER VIII

Some Applications and Uses of Metabolite Analogues in Microbiology

ELIZABETH WORK

Department of Biochemistry, Imperial College of Science and Technology, London, S.W.7

I. INTRODUCTION

Descriptions of metabolite analogues and their mode of action are available in several reviews and books; discussion of these aspects is not relevant here (Davis and Feingold, 1962; Baker, 1967; Richmond, 1962, 1965, 1966; Fowden *et al.*, 1967; Webb, 1966). The purpose of this chapter is to draw attention to the numerous ways in which metabolite analogues may be used in microbiology, and to discuss in detail the only group of analogues which is not dealt with as a whole in review articles—namely the analogues of cell wall constituents or precursors.

The high hopes of planned chemotherapy through the use of tailored drugs (Work and Work, 1948) which were raised by the elucidation of the mode of action of sulphonamides have, unfortunately, not been fulfilled, even though many antimetabolites acting at various points in the cell have been synthesized or isolated from natural sources. The failure of such substances as drugs to combat infection is due largely to the general similarity of fundamental biochemical processes throughout the living world, and also to the ingenuity of cellular control mechanisms in overcoming the effects of antimetabolites, thus producing temporary or permanent states of resistance to the antimetabolite (Richmond, 1966).

The great success of the penicillin-type drugs can be attributed to the specific nature of their target which occurs only in the cell walls of bacteria and related organisms. The enzymes inhibited by penicillins are outside the cytoplasmic membrane and possibly are not subjected to the same types of control as the normal intra-cellular biosynthetic enzymes.

II. SOME GENERAL APPLICATIONS OF METABOLITE ANALOGUES IN MICROBIOLOGY

(a) Analogues which resemble end-product metabolites can act as false feed-back inhibitors of the first enzymes of biosynthetic pathways, or they may repress all the enzymes of these pathways. Either of these activities by amino acid analogues causes inhibition of the synthesis of certain amino acids and consequently of proteins.

(b) Mutants resistant to analogues may have developed enzymes so altered as to be no longer sensitive to false feed-back inhibition by the analogue. In some, but not all cases, sensitivity to control by the normal metabolite may also have been lost by the enzymes, and the resistant mutants then accumulate and excrete the metabolite. This property can be used industrially to obtain mutants which produce large amounts of a desired end-product. Another type of analogue-resistant mutant is de-repressed, and over-produces all the enzymes of the particular biosynthetic pathway because the enzymes cannot be repressed by the excess of the natural metabolite so produced. These mutants less frequently accumulate large amounts of end-product as this metabolite is still usually capable of exercising feed-back inhibition on the first enzyme of the pathway.

(c) Analogue-resistant mutants may be of help in recognizing the regulatory genes for a given pathway. Thus, de-repressed mutants usually map in either the operator region or the regulator gene governing expression of the operon. Most analogue-resistant mutations which lead to excretion of an amino acid usually map in the gene specifying the first enzyme specific to that pathway.

(d) Investigations of mechanisms of resistance to various analogues may help in the elucidation of problems of resistance to other drugs.

(e) Analogues may be incorporated to various extents into intracellular macromolecules, and so produce altered RNA, DNA or proteins whose physical and biological properties may be compared with those of the normal molecule. Various examples are known where progressive incorporation of amino acid analogues into enzymes may cause progressive loss of activity (enzymic and/or immunological), while other enzymes in the same cells may be unaffected by the presence of the same analogue in their molecules. Incorporation into RNA can also lead to production of altered enzymes, presumably due to errors in translation of DNA information into protein.

(f) A particular application of incorporation into macromolecules is the use of "tagged" DNA labelled with 5-bromouracil; it is heavier than natural DNA and can be separated from it by density-gradient centrifugation.

(g) Certain analogues which are mutagenic can be used to produce chemically predictable types of errors in DNA, and so provide tools for the study of fine-structure genetics.

(h) Amino acid analogues may be incorporated into the protein product of a regulator gene and so alter the product as to impair the repression mechanism and thus produce de-repression.

(i) Studies on permeability may be helped by analogues which are usually bound, and therefore taken into the cell, by the permeases specific for the natural metabolite. Permeases usually have low affinities for analogues so that natural metabolites in the growth medium compete very effectively against the analogue and can prevent its access to the cell. One type of analogue resistance is due to the development of a permease which does not transport the analogue; sometimes the permease has also lost the ability to take up the natural metabolite.

III. CHARACTERISTIC EFFECTS OF METABOLITE ANALOGUES ON CULTURES

A general characteristic of all toxic analogues is that their action is reversed by the natural metabolite. The main observable response of a microbial culture to a toxic analogue is a change in growth rate, but since this may only occur in the absence of the natural metabolite, the effect can only be observed in the relatively few bacterial species which will grow in defined media. Therefore, growth tests on analogues are not always indicative of toxic activities. A growth-inhibitory analogue added to an exponentially-growing susceptible culture causes the growth (e.g. increase in mass measured turbidimetrically) to change to a linear rate of increase; the change may occur either immediately, or within one generation.

Although the action of each analogue is reversed by its natural metabolite, antagonism is not always confined to this single metabolite. Examples are known where growth inhibition may also be reversed non-specifically by another metabolite; this could be due to the exclusion of the analogue from the cell through competition by the substrate of a permease other than that concerned with the uptake of the true metabolite. Therefore, reversal of toxic effects *in vivo* should be interpreted cautiously, bearing in mind that not all antagonists may be the true natural metabolite.

IV. ANALOGUES OF CELL-WALL CONSTITUENTS

Analogues concerned with cell wall constituents or precursors fall into two groups.

(a) Those which inhibit enzymes concerned with the biosynthesis of cell wall constituents.

(b) Those which are incorporated into cell wall macromolecules.

A. Effects of inhibition of wall biosynthesis

These inhibitors, like other metabolite analogues, act only on growing cells and can be growth inhibitors under suitable conditions. The consequences of their action are:

1. Intracellular accumulation of nucleotide-sugar precursors of wall polymers; the control mechanism of the accumulation is unknown.

2. Cell-wall fragility, leading to cell lysis unless osmotic protection is provided, in which case morphological variants such as spheroplasts, protoplasts or L-forms may be produced.

Practical use can be made of either of these consequences.

1. *Accumulation of nucleotide precursors*

(a) *D-alanine analogues.* Certain antibiotics such as penicillin or D-cycloserine lead to accumulation of uridine diphosphate N-acetyl muramic acid (UDP-NAM) peptides which are precursors of mucopeptides, and which are used in the laboratory for biosynthetic studies on mucopeptides. In the organism, the peptides are built up by sequential reactions involving ATP, the nucleotide sugar, an amino acid and a specific intracellular adding enzyme (ligase). The following reactions illustrate in *Staphylococcus aureus* (Strominger, 1962) the sequence leading to the mucopeptide precursor.

1. UDP-NAM[1] + L-Ala $\xrightarrow[\text{Ligase}]{\text{ATP} + \text{Mn}^{++}}$ UDP-NAM·L-Ala + ADP + Pi[1]

2. UDP-NAM·L-Ala + D-Glu $\xrightarrow[\text{Ligase}]{\text{ATP} + \text{Mn}^{++}}$ UDP-NAM·L-Ala·D-Glu + + ADP + Pi

3. UDP-NAM·L-Ala·D-Glu + L-Lys $\xrightarrow[\text{Ligase}]{\text{ATP} + \text{Mn}^{++}}$ UDP-NAM·L-Ala·D-Glu·L-Lys + ADP + Pi

4. L-Ala $\xrightleftharpoons[\text{Racemase}]{}$ D-Ala

5. 2 D-Ala $\xrightarrow[\text{Synthetase}]{\text{ATP} + \text{Mn}^{++}}$ D-Ala·D-Ala + ADP + Pi

6. UDP-NAM·L-Ala·D-Glu·L-Lys + D-Ala·D-Ala $\xrightarrow[\text{Ligase}]{\text{ATP} + \text{Mn}^{++}}$ UDP-NAM·L-Ala·D-Glu·L-Lys·D-Ala·D-Ala + ADP + Pi

The mucopeptide precursor is a nucleotide pentapeptide, whose composition determines the ultimate mucopeptide structure, which is species dependent (Work, 1970). The pentapeptide always contains D-glutamic acid, and terminates at the carboxyl end in 2 D-alanine residues; it usually, but not invariably, contains a diamino acid and has an L-alanine

[1] NAM = N-acetylmuramic acid; Pi = inorganic phosphate.

residue at the amino terminal linked to the carboxyl group of muramic acid. This type of pentapeptide is the main nucleotide accumulating in cells grown in the presence of penicillins, vancomycin, bacitracin or ristocetin (see also p. 402).

D-Cycloserine, the antibiotic shown in formula I, leads to accumulation of a UDP-NAM-tripeptide (product of reaction 3).

I. D-Cycloserine   II. D-Alanine

The antibiotic acts as an analogue of D-alanine (formula II) and is a strong competitive inhibitor of both alanine racemase and D-Ala·D-Ala synthetase (reactions 4 and 5), and thus limits the supply of D-Ala·D-Ala for reaction 6 (Strominger et al., 1959, 1960). The K_i for D-cycloserine with either enzyme is about 100 times less than the Michaelis constants (K_m), indicating that the antibiotic is bound more effectively than the substrate. All the effects of this analogue are reversed, in vitro and in vivo, by D-alanine.

Another antibiotic, O-carbamyl-D-serine NH_2-CO-O-CH_2-CH(NH_2)-COOH, also acts as an analogue of D-alanine (Tanaka, 1963), but in this case only alanine racemase is inhibited (Lynch and Neuhaus, 1966). In vitro some of the antibiotic is incorporated instead of D-alanine by the appropriate enzyme systems (reactions 5 and 6), into D-Ala·O-carbamyl-D-serine and UDP-NAM·L-Ala·D-Glu·L-Lys·D-Ala·O-carbamyl-D-Ser respectively. In vivo, the only product accumulating is nucleotide tripeptide (UDP-NAM·L-Ala·D-Glu·L-Lys) suggesting that the racemase (4) is the primary site of action of this antibiotic.

Acquisition of resistance to D-cycloserine by mutants of Streptococcus, strain Challis, resulted either in increased levels of activity of both racemase and dipeptide synthetase (reactions 4 and 5) or in an inability to concentrate both alanine and D-cycloserine; resistance to O-carbamyl-D-serine only resulted in a raised level of alanine racemase (Reitz et al., 1967).

A series of specificity experiments in Strep. faecalis R on the two enzymes in the biosynthetic sequence involving D-Ala. D-Ala (reactions 5 and 6) has shown some lack of specificity (Neuhaus, 1962; Neuhaus and Struve, 1965). Both enzymes show slight activities towards certain other D-amino acid substrates, but they have complementary specificity profiles so that the result of the two enzymes acting in sequence is a greater specificity towards substrate analogues than each individual enzyme acting alone. Of all the possible peptide analogues of D-ala·D-Ala, only D-α-amino-n-butyryl-D-α-amino-n-butyric acid is formed by the synthetase (5) and utilized by the adding enzyme (6) to form the nucleotide penta-peptide analogue containing D-α-aminobutyric acid. This accords with growth experiments with *Strep. faecalis* R which, when grown on vitamin B_6 deficient media, requires D-alanine as a growth factor in addition to L-amino acids but can utilize and incorporate D-α-amino-n-butyric acid instead (Snell *et al.*, 1955).

Other antibiotics, probably connected structurally with D-analyl·D-alanine, act by interfering with reactions 7–11, in which UDP-NAM-pentapeptide is converted into completed, cross-linked, mucopeptide polymer.

7.   Lipid-P + UDP-NAM-pentapeptide $\rightleftharpoons$
      Translocase

      NAM-(pentapeptide)-P-P-lipid + UMP

8.   NAM-(pentapeptide)-P-P-lipid + UDP-NAG[2] $\longrightarrow$
      NAG-NAM-(pentapeptide)-P-P-lipid + UDP

9.   NAG-NAM-(pentapeptide)-P-P-lipid + acceptor $\longrightarrow$
      NAG-NAM-(pentapeptide)-acceptor + lipid-P-P

      acceptor
      /
10.   NAG-NAM-L-Ala. D-Glu. *meso*-Dap. D-Ala. D-Ala
      /   +
      acceptor
      /
      NAG-NAM. L-Ala. D-Glu. *meso*-Dap. D-Ala. D-Ala.
      /   acceptor   │ transpeptidase
      /   ↓
      NAG-NAM. L-Ala. D-Glu. *meso*-Dap. D-Ala
      /   acceptor   /
      /
      NAG-NAM. L-Ala. D-Glu. *meso*-Dap. D-Ala. D-Ala + D-Ala
      /   acceptor   │ carboxypeptidase
      /   ↓
11.   NAG-NAM. L-Ala. D-Glu. *meso*-Dap. D-Ala
      /   acceptor   /
      /
      NAG-NAM. L-Ala. D-Glu. *meso*-Dap. D-Ala + D-Ala
      /

[2] NAG = N-acetyl-glucosamine.

In this series of reactions, investigated in *Escherichia coli*, 7–10 take place in a particulate (membrane-bound?) enzyme system (Strominger *et al.*, 1967) as opposed to reactions 1–6 and 11 which are carried out by soluble enzymes. The first step (7) is the transfer of the NAM-pentapeptide residue from the UDP-derivative to a high-energy pyrophosphate complex with a C_{55} isoprenoid alcohol (Anderson *et al.*, 1967, Higashi *et al.*, 1967). This complex then accepts N-acetylglucosamine (NAG)[2] from UDP-NAG to form the disaccharide pentapeptide (reaction 8) and, where appropriate, accepts additional amino-acids or amide residues, added by steps not discussed here. The complete mucopeptide monomer unit is thus built up while complexed to the lipid. The monomer is then transferred from the lipid to an acceptor, thought to be the growing mucopeptide chain (reaction 9). The final step is thought to be a transpeptidation reaction (10) whereby a terminal D-alanine from one chain is discarded and exchanged for an amino-acid residue (-*meso*-Dap in *E. coli*, reaction 10) of an adjacent peptide chain; the result is cross-linking between peptide chains which conveys rigidity to the polymer. A further reaction (11) may remove the remaining terminal D-alanine residues from the pentapeptide chain by D-alanine carboxypeptidase.

Penicillin is thought to prevent the transpeptidation cross-linking step (10) and so produce a non-rigid mucopeptide and fragile cell walls (Tipper and Strominger, 1965, 1968; Strominger *et al.*, 1967; Izaki *et al.*, 1968; Wise and Park, 1965). The suggested mechanism of action is that penicillins act as analogues of acyl·D-Ala·D-Ala, and by irreversibly acylating the transpeptidase through their β-lactam ring, prevent access of the natural pentapeptide substrate terminating in D-Ala·D-Ala. Further work is needed to prove this hypothesis.

Penicillins also inhibit competitively the D-alanine carboxypeptidase of *E. coli* which is not involved in cross-linking (reaction 11) (Izaki and Strominger, 1968). The partially purified enzyme is extremely sensitive to the antibiotics, showing K_i values for penicillin G and ampicillin of $1·6 \times 10^{-8}$ and $6·4 \times 10^{-9}$ M respectively (K_m for UDP-NAM-pentapeptide was 6×10^{-4}M). Concentrations of $0·002$ μg/ml caused 50% inhibition of carboxypeptidase, while 3 μg/ml was needed for inhibition of transpeptidation (10) by a crude particulate fraction.

Vancomycin and ristocetin are known also to interfere with mucopeptide synthesis; their effects are reversed by addition of cell walls. The structures of these antibiotics are not known; they are thought to act similarly and both form compounds with UDP-NAM-pentapeptides and other peptides ending in D-Ala·D-Ala (Perkins, 1969). It appears that this modification of the substrate stimulates the formation of a NAM-pentapeptide phospholipid intermediate (reaction 7), but that final transfer of the completed modified monomer to the acceptor (reaction 9) does not take place (Matsuhashi et al., 1967; Izaki et al., 1968; Chaterjee et al., 1967; Sinha and Newhaus, 1968).

(b) 5-*Fluorouracil*. Incorporation into nucleic acids is not the only reaction of 5-fluorouracil; it also affects cell wall synthesis and produces spheroplasts in *E. coli* (Tomasz and Borek, 1960, 1962). The 5-fluorouracil analogue of UDP-NAM-pentapeptide accumulates in *Staph. aureus* grown in the presence of the analogue (Rogers and Perkins, 1960). The accumulation is due to the fact that this analogue acts as a competitive inhibitor of NAM-pentapeptide translocase (reaction 7) which introduces the lipid moiety to NAM-pentapeptide (Stickgold and Neuhaus, 1967). 5-Fluorosubstitution has no effect on an earlier step (3), the addition of L-lysine to nucleotide dipeptide.

(c) *Preparation of uridine nucleotide-N-acetylmuramic acid peptides.* These nucleotide peptides are useful both as precursors in cell wall biosynthetic studies and for sequence and structural work in studies on mucopeptide composition. They are prepared from cells grown in the presence of certain antibiotics (see above). The usual method is either to use an exponentially growing culture or to harvest cells in the mid-exponential growth phase and rapidly re-suspend them (1–2 mg, dry wt/ml) either in the growth medium (without Mg^{++} or Mn^{++} if vancomycin is to be used, Best and Durham, 1964) or in a solution containing glucose (5×10^{-2}M), phosphate buffer pH 7 (0.05M) and 1.0–2.0 mM concentrations of appropriate "cell wall" amino acids or their precursors (e.g. aspartic acid can be used as a Dap precursor). The antibiotic is present in the resuspension medium: the following concentration ranges may be suitable; penicillin G, 250 μg/ml; vancomycin 20–50 μg/ml, D-cycloserine 100 μg/ml (Strominger et al., 1960; Strominger, 1957; Ito and Saito, 1963; Plapp and Kandler, 1965; Nakatani et al., 1968). Optimum conditions must be worked out for each species and antimetabolite; some workers advocate the use of an osmotic stabilizer (e.g. 20% sucrose) to increase yields in certain species (Mandelstam et al., 1962), others use chloramphenicol in addition to the antimetabolite, presumably to prevent protein synthesis (Chaterjee and Perkins, 1966). Cells are shaken in the antibiotic-containing medium at 37° for 0.5–1.5 h, centrifuged and extracted twice at 0° with four times their packed volume of cold 10–25% (w/v) trichloroacetic acid (the higher concentrations are recommended by Chaterjee and Perkins (1966) for cases in which the nucleotides are not fully extracted by the more usual concentration of 10%). The extracts are clarified by centrifugation, and freed from trichloroacetic acid by four extractions with ether; the ether is evaporated *in vacuo* at room temperature from the aqueous phase, which is then adjusted to pH 7·0 with Na_2CO_3. Alternatively, the cold packed cells may be extracted with four volumes of ice-cold 0·6N percholoric acid (L. Fellows and E. Work, unpub.). After centrifugation the acidic extract is immediately neutralized with KOH. Potassium perchlorate is insoluble in cold water and may be removed from the extract by centrifugation or filtration. Avoidance of the use of ether is advantageous for large scale work. The nucleotide peptides in the extract are separated from the other nucleotides present by Sephadex chromatography (Rosenthal and Sharon, 1964). The solution (6 ml containing about 22 μ moles of N-acetylhexosamine) is applied to a column of Sephadex G-25 (2·6 × 80 cm); either 0·01N acetic acid or water may be used to equilibrate the column and elute the nucleotides. The nucleotide peptides emerge soon after the void volume, well separated from most other nucleotides which are retarded. Chromatography on Dowex-1-formate columns (200–400 mesh) using a formic acid-ammonium formate gradient is an alternative separation method (Park and Chaterjee, 1966). The eluates from either type of column are analysed for absorbancy at 260 nm and for N-acetyl amino sugars (Work, this series, Volume 5A, p. 361); generally, a correspondence of UV-absorbing and hexosamine-reacting material is indicative of the presence of nucleotide peptides.

These preparations of nucleotide peptides are seldom homogeneous, as the anti-metabolite often causes accumulation of small amounts of the shorter nucleotide peptides as well as the one which is being prepared. Final purification may be effected after concentration *in vacuo*, by chromatography on washed Whatman No. 3 MM paper as shown in Table I,

TABLE I

Behaviour of uridine nucleotide peptides on paper chromatograms

Nucleotide	Solvent I	Solvent II
UDP-NAM-penta-peptide	0·17	0·25
UDP-NAM-tri-peptide	0·14	0·22
UDP-NAM-di-peptide		0·37
UDP-NAM		0·30
UDP-NAG		0·38
Vancomycin-UDP-NAM-pentapeptide	0*	

Solvent I, *iso*-butyric acid—0·5M ammonia (5 : 3, by vol) Strominger *et al.*, 1966.

Solvent II, ethanol—M-ammonium acetate pH (7·5 (7·5 : 3, by vol) (Ito and Saito, 1963; Saito *et al.*, 1963).

* Complex is described by Chaterjee and Perkins, 1966.

combined with paper electrophoresis in 0·05M ammonium acetate buffer pH 4·6. The compounds, visualized as fluorescent spots in ultraviolet light, are eluted from the paper and lyophilized. New purification methods involving perhaps column chromatography would be more convenient, and will doubtless be developed soon.

The compounds in the eluates are identified as uridine nucleotides by their absorption spectra in 0·01N HCl and 0·01N NaOH, both showing a characteristic maximum at 261·0 nm. The amino acids are estimated after hydrolysis in 6N HCl for 12–18 h at 100° as described by Work (this series, Vol. 5A, p. 361). As mentioned earlier, vancomycin forms a compound with part of the nucleotide pentapeptide, this is immobile on paper chromatograms. This reduces the final yield of nucleotide pentapeptide, necessitating careful selection of drug concentration and incubation conditions to ensure maximum yields.

Isotopically-labelled nucleotide peptides can be prepared for use as enzyme substrates in biosynthetic studies (Neuhaus and Struve, 1965; Park and Chaterjee, 1966; Anderson et al., 1966; Strominger et al., 1966; Izaki et al., 1968). Nucleotide pentapeptides labelled with ^{14}C-D-Ala · C^{14}-D-Ala are made from appropriate tripeptides and C^{14}-D-Ala by reactions 4, 5 and 6 (p. 398), using D-Ala·D-Ala ligase prepared from E. coli (Comb, 1962).

2. Production of morphological variants of bacteria (Guze, 1968)

(a) Spheroplasts. Growth of Gram-negative bacteria in the presence of penicillins and an osmotic stabilizer leads to the development of osmotically-sensitive spherical bodies which are able to increase in mass but are usually unable to divide and form colonies on solid media. This type of organism lacks the rigid cross-linked mucopeptide, but retains the outer lipopolysaccharide-lipoprotein layers of the wall; it is referred to as "spheroplast" rather than "protoplast" (a term used to describe the osmotically-sensitive spherical form of an organism, such as a Gram-positive bacterial species, which is completely devoid of cell wall). Vancomycin does not readily induce spheroplast formation. Since spheroplasts may also be produced by other means (e.g. glycine, p. 406) those produced by penicillin are usually referred to as "penicillin spheroplasts".

This type of spheroplast may be produced as follows: cells in the expontial phase, growing in for example Difco Penassay Broth, are innoculated (3 ml into 10 ml) into fresh broth containing in addition 60 μg penicillin G per ml, 20% (w/v) sucrose and 0·2% (w/v) MgSO$_4$.7H$_2$O. The culture is shaken at 37° for 2–3 h until the cells have all been converted to spheres, as observed under phase-contrast; during this time there is no rise in number of organisms. The concentrations of penicillin, sucrose and MgSO$_4$

can be varied without adverse effects on conversion to spheroplasts, but do have an effect on the subsequent stability of the spheroplasts. Therefore, optimal conditions may have to be worked out for each species.

(b) L-*forms*. Conversion of cultures of Gram-negative and Gram-positive bacteria to L-forms can be brought about by various types of penicillins and other antibiotics which inhibit mucopeptide biosynthesis, although vanco-mycin does not work with all species (e.g. Staphylococcus). L-Forms can be defined as morphological variants which are capable of growth and which form colonies on agar having the so-called "fried egg" appearance. (Dienes and Weinberger, 1951; Dienes, in Guze, 1968). They can be produced or maintained on soft agar plates containing antibiotic, a rich broth, serum and on osmotic stabilizer such as NaCl. A useful formula contains Bacto Brain Heart Infusion (Difco Laboratories), Ionagar (Oxoid, 0·75%, w/v), NaCl (3·0%, w/v), PPLO serum fraction (0·5%), penicillin G 60 μg/ml. Antibiotic may be present throughout the agar, or a gradient plate may be used where antibiotic is added (10–5000 μg/ml) to a ditch at one side of the plate. A washed cell suspension is spread over the plate which is dried and incubated 4–5 days at 37° (in a polythene bag as precaution against loss of water). During this time, L-form colonies may appear, at random if antibiotic is dispersed in the agar, or near the margin of bacterial growth inhibition on the gradient plate. Transfer of L-form growth is effected by transferring small blocks of agar with colonies on their surface, either inverted on to another plate or into liquid media in which they are then disintegrated. Growth in liquid media can only be established after several transfers on agar; the components of liquid media are similar to those of solid media except for omission of agar. Relatively large inocula are required for the initial transfers of these liquid cultures, but the organisms appear to adapt to the conditions during long cultivation, and well-established broth cultures will usually develop simpler nutritional requirements and will grow relatively fast and abundantly from small inocula. Omission of antibiotic from media of well-established cultures does not usually cause reversion to bacillary forms.

Accumulation of nucleotide peptides has been reported in L-forms grown in the absence of antibiotic (Edwards and Panos, 1962; Fodor and Tóth, 1965).

3. *Inhibition of synthesis of yeast cell walls*

The analogue, 2-deoxyglucose causes lysis of growing yeast cells by acting at the site of synthesis of the wall glucan polymer (Johnson, 1968). It is known to inhibit synthesis of new glucan by yeast protoplasts, but the mechanism of action is not known (Farkas *et al.*, 1969).

B. Incorporation of analogues into cell-wall polymers

Evidence for incorporation of analogues into cell-wall polymers is only available for analogues of the amino acids in the peptide moiety of mucopeptides. In some cases substitution of an amino acid leads to cell-wall fragility with consequences similar to those caused by antibiotics; in other cases there is no noticeable effect on wall stability.

1. Glycine

(a) *Mode of action.* High concentrations of glycine in growth media have been known for some time to inhibit growth and cause cellular lysis or morphological variants such as protoplasts, spheroplasts or L-forms (Gordon *et al.*, 1949; Dienes and Zamecnik, 1952; Welsch and Osterrieth, 1958; Rubio-Huertos and Gonzalez-Vazquez, 1960; Diena *et al.*, 1964). Nucleotides were found to accumulate in *Staph. aureus* cells grown in the presence of 3·75% (w/v) glycine (Strominger and Birge, 1965); these were mainly UDP-NAM, UDP-NAM.Gly·D,LGlu·L-ys and UDP-NAM-Gly·D-Glu·L-Lys·D-Ala·D-Ala with a small amount of UDP-NAM-L-Ala·D-Glu·L-Lys. This shows that glycine can substitute for L-alanine as the first amino-acid of the peptide chain and that the altered pentapeptide can be completed after the substitution. Since the amount of UDP-NAM far exceeded that of the other nucleotides, the L-alanine-adding enzyme (step 1 p. 398) probably has a lower affinity for glycine than for L-alanine in this species. In some *Lactobacillus* species grown in high levels of glycine, L-alanine is partly replaced by glycine in the mucopeptide (O. Kandler, private communication), it is therefore evident that the altered penta-peptide can be further utilized for mucopeptide synthesis. The suscepti-bility to glycine and extent of incorporation into mucopeptide varied with species; *L. cellobiosus* could grow slowly in the presence of as much as 12% (w/v) glycine and then replaced 80% of L-alanine by glycine to form irregular-shaped organisms; *L. coryniformis* would not grow in only 2% glycine, and could only replace 40% of L-alanine.

It is worth noting (Work, 1970) that in nucleotide peptides and muco-peptides of certain organisms, such as *Corynebacterium poinsettiae* or *Microbacterium lacticum*, glycine is normally attached to the muramic acid residue (Perkins, 1967; Schliefer *et al.*, 1967, 1968).

(b) *Preparation of "glycine" spheroplasts and L-forms.* The usual methods of preparation of these forms can be used, except that glycine (usually 1·5–5% w/v) replaces the antibiotic. The concentration of glycine which will produce variants varies with species, and is usually limited to a rather narrow effective range for each species.

2. Hydroxylysine

The analogue of lysine, 2,6-diamino-5-hydroxyhexanoic acid or hydro-xylysine, inhibits growth of bacteria which do not require lysine as a growth factor (Smith et al., 1965). The inhibition is competitively reversed by lysine and so does not occur in exacting organisms where lysine has to be present in the growth medium. Hydroxylysine is incorporated into both protein and mucopeptide fractions of growing cells, incorporation into protein is inhibited by chloramphenicol but that into mucopeptide is not. The analogue is also incorporated into UDP-NAM-pentapeptide of *Staph. aureus*. In lysine-exacting *Strep. faecalis*, hydroxylysine replaces lysine in the mucopeptide of growing cells or of cell suspensions in a "wall amino-acid" medium, but only after exhaustion of lysine from the media (Shockman et al., 1965). The walls of cells containing hydroxylysine exhibited mechanical and autolytic properties similar to those of control cells of comparable physiological state; it is thus probable that the growth-inhibitory effects of the analogue arise from its incorporation into proteins rather than into mucopeptides. Since cells do not take up hydroxylysine from the medium until lysine is exhausted, one site of competition is probably at the permeability barrier.

3. Analogues of diaminopimelic acid (Dap)

Of many analogues of Dap tried for biological activity only a few have observable effects. The mutant of *E. coli* 173–25 which requires Dap and lysine for growth can use 3-methyldiaminopimelic acid as a substitute growth factor if lysine is supplied (Rhuland and Hamilton, 1961); the analogue was shown to be incorporated into unfractionated cell walls, but mucopeptide was not isolated. No information is available about the fragility of the cells.

The *meso* forms of 2,7-diaminosuberic acid (the higher homologue of Dap), lanthionine (the analogue with S replacing the γ-CH_2 group) and 3-dehydrodiaminosuberic acid were all found to be incorporated into mucopeptide when mutant *Escherichia coli* 173–25 was grown in the presnce of Dap (Pelzer, 1969), although the first two analogues were not found to substitute for Dap as growth factors (Meadow et al., 1957). Lanthionine was said to produce some weakness in the cell envelopes (Pelzer, 1969), although it prevented lysis of cultures grown in suboptimal amounts of Dap (Meadow et al., 1957). The other two analogues had no visible effect on wall rigidity. The results suggest that incorporation of the analogues only occurred after exhaustion of Dap from the medium, as in the case of hydroxylysine and lysine.

4. D-amino acids

Mucopeptides invariably contain D-glutamic acid and D-alanine so it might be expected that other D-amino acids would have some activity in the enzyme systems concerned with cell-wall biosynthesis. D-Serine has been found to be incorporated from the medium by cells of *Micrococcus lysodeikticus* into mucopeptide at the expense of glycine (Whitney and Grula 1964); it inhibits growth by about 60% but does not cause cell fragility. Both inhibition of growth and incorporation into mucopeptide are reversed by L-serine or glycine. In the normal mucopeptide of this organism, glycine is attached to the α-COOH group of D-glutamic acid (Tipper *et al.*, 1967) and about 75% of the incorporated D-serine was identified at this location (Whitney and Grula, 1968); the position of the rest of the D-serine is uncertain.

In *Alcaligenes fecalis* the presence of D-amino acids, particularly D-methionine, in the growth medium is known to induce cell fragility and spheroplast formation by inhibiting synthesis of mucopeptide (Lark and Lark, 1959, 1961). The mechanism of inhibition is not known, but isotopic work showed that a very small amount of D-methionine is incorporated into the phenol-insoluble mucopeptide-containing fraction. The incorporation, which is insensitive to chloramphenicol, is proportional to the amount of D-methionine in the medium, reaching a maximum at the concentration (600 μg/ml) which is also the minimum concentration required to induce spheroplast formation. Incorporation is not prevented by high concentrations of L-methionine.

REFERENCES

Anderson, J. S., Meadow, P. M., Haskin, M. A., and Strominger, J. L. (1966). *Arch. Biochem. Biophys.*, **116**, 487–515.

Anderson, J. S., Matsuhashi, M., Haskin, M. A., and Strominger, J. L. (1967). *J. biol. Chem.*, **242**, 3180–3190.

Baker, B. R. (1967). "Design of Active-site-directed Irreversible Enzyme Inhibitors. The Organic Chemistry of the Enzymic Active-site". Wiley and Sons Inc., New London, Sydney.

Best, G. K., and Durham, N. N. (1964). *Arch. Biochem. Biophys.*, **105**, 120–125.

Chaterjee, A., and Perkins, H. R. (1966). *Biochim. biophys. Acta.*, **24**, 489–494.

Chaterjee, A., Ward, J. B., and Perkins, H. R. (1967). *Nature, Lond.*, **214**, 1311–1314.

Comb, D. G. (1962). *J. biol. Chem.*, **237**, 1601–1604.

Davis, B. D., and Feingold, D. S. (1962). *In* "The Bacteria" (Eds I. C. Gunsalus and R. Y. Stanier), Vol. IV, pp. 343–397. Academic Press, New York and London.

Diena, B. B., Wallace, R., and Greenberg, L. (1964). *Canad. J. Microbiol.*, **10**, 543–549.

Dienes, L., and Weinberger, H. J. (1951). *Bact. Rev.*, **15**, 245–288.

Dienes, L., and Zamecnik, P. C. (1952). *J. Bact.*, **64**, 770–771.

Edwards, J., and Panos, C. (1962). *J. Bact.*, **84**, 1202–1208.
Farkas, V., Svoboda, A., and Bauer, S. (1969). *J. Bact.*, **98**, 744–748.
Fodor, M., and Tóth, B. (1965). *Acta Microbiol. Acad. Sci. Hung.*, **12**, 173–179.
Fowden, L., Lewis, D., and Tristram, H. (1967). *Adv. in Enzymol.*, **29**, 89–163.
Gordon, J., Hall, R. A., and Stickland, L. H. (1949). *J. Path. Bact.*, **61**, 581–585.
Guze, L. B. (1968). Editor of "Microbial Protoplasts, Spheroplasts and L-forms". Williams and Wilkins, Baltimore.
Higashi, Y., Strominger, J. L., and Sweeley, C. C. (1967). *Proc. Natl. Acad. Sci U.S.*, **57**, 1878–1884.
Ito, E., and Saito, M. (1963). *Biochim. biophys. Acta*, **78**, 237–247.
Izaki, K., and Strominger, J. L. (1968). *J. biol. Chem.*, **243**, 3193–3201.
Izaki, K., Matsuhashi, M., and Strominger, J. L. (1968). *J. biol. Chem.*, **243**, 3180–3192.
Johnson, B. F. (1968). *J. Bact.*, **95**, 1169–1172.
Lark, C., and Lark, K. G. (1959). *Canad. J. Microbiol.*, **5**, 369–379.
Lark, C., and Lark, K. G. (1961). *Biochim. biophys. Acta*, **49**, 308–322.
Lynch, J. L., and Neuhaus, F. C. (1966). *J. Bact.*, **91**, 449–460.
Mandelstam, P., Loercher, R., and Strominger, J. L. (1962). *J. biol. Chem.*, **237**, 2683–2688.
Matsuhashi, M., Dietrich, C. P., and Strominger, J. L. (1967). *J. biol. Chem.*, **242**, 3191–3206.
Meadow, P. M., Hoare, D. S., and Work, E. (1957). *Biochem. J.*, **66**, 270–282.
Nakatani, T., Araki, Y., and Ito, E. (1968). *Biochim. biophys. Acta*, **156**, 210–212.
Neuhaus, F. C. (1962). *J. biol. Chem.*, **237**, 778–786, 3128–3135.
Neuhaus, F. C., and Struve, W. G. (1965). *Biochemistry*, **4**, 120–131.
Park, J. T., and Chaterjee, A. N. (1966). *In* "Methods in Enzymology" (Eds E. F. Neufield and V. Ginsburg), Vol. VIII, pp. 466–472. Academic Press, New York and London.
Pelzer, H. (1969). VIth Meeting F.E.B.S., Abstracts, 143.
Perkins, H. R. (1967). *Biochem. J.*, **102**, 29C.
Perkins, H. R. (1969). *Biochem. J.*, **111**, 195–205.
Plapp, R., and Kandler, O. (1965). *Arch. Mikrobiol.* **50**, 282–297.
Reitz, R. H., Slade, H. D., and Neuhaus, F. C. (1967). *Biochemistry*, **6**, 2561–2570.
Rhuland, L. E., and Hamilton, R. D. (1961). *Biochim. biophys. Acta*, **51**, 525–528.
Richmond, M. R. (1962). *Bact. Rev.*, **26**, 398–420.
Richmond, M. R. (1965). *Biol. Rev.*, **40**, 93–128.
Richmond, M. R. (1966). *In* "Biochemical Studies of Antimicrobial Drugs" (Eds B. A. Newton and P. E. Reynold), pp. 301–335. XVIth Symposium of Soc. Gen. Microbiol., Cambridge University Press.
Rogers, H. J., and Perkins, H. R. (1960). *Biochem. J.*, **77**, 448–459.
Rosenthal, S., and Sharon, N. (1964). *Biochim. biophys. Acta*, **83**, 376–378.
Rubio-Huertos, M., and Gonzalez-Vazquez, C. (1960). *Ann. N.Y. Acad. Sci.*, **79**, 626–631.
Saito, M., Ishimoto, N., and Ito, E. (1963). *J. Biochem. (Japan)*, **54**, 273–278.
Schleifer, K. H., Plapp, R., and Kandler, O. (1967). *Biochem. Biophys. Res. Comm.*, **26**, 492–496.
Schleifer, K. H., Plapp, R., and Kandler, O. (1968). *Biochim. biophys. Acta*, **154** 573–582.
Shockman, G. D., Thompson, J. S., and Conover, M. J. (1965). *J. Bact.*, **90**, 575–588.

Sinha, R. K., and Neuhaus, F. C. (1968). *J. Bact.*, **96**, 374–382.

Smith, W. G., Gilboe, D. P., and Henderson, L. M. (1965). *J. Bact.*, **89**, 136–140.

Snell, E. E., Radin, N. S., and Ikawa, M. (1955). *J. biol. Chem.*, **217**, 803–818.

Stickgold, R. A., and Neuhaus, F. C. (1967). *J. biol. Chem.*, **242**, 1331–1337.

Strominger, J. L. (1957). *J. biol. Chem.*, **224**, 509–523.

Strominger, J. L. (1962). *Fed. Proc.*, **21**, 134–143.

Strominger, J. L., and Birge, C. H. (1965). *J. Bact.*, **89**, 1124–1127.

Strominger, J. L., Threnn, R. H., and Scott, S. S. (1959). *J. Amer. Chem. Soc.*, **81**, 3803.

Strominger, J. L., Ito, E., and Threnn, R. H. (1960). *J. Amer. Chem. Soc.*, **82**, 998–999.

Strominger, J. L., Matsuhashi, M., Anderson, J. S., Dietrich, C. P., Meadow, P. M., Katz, W., Siewert, G., and Gilbert, J. M. (1966). *In* "Methods in Enzymology" (Eds E. F. Neufield, and V. Ginsburg), Vol. VIII, pp. 475–476. Academic Press, New York.

Strominger, J. L., Izaki, K., Matsuhashi, M., and Tipper, D. J., (1967). *Fed. Proc.*, **26**, 9–22.

Tanaka, N. (1963). *Biochem. Biophys. Res. Comm.*, **12**, 68–71.

Tipper, D. J., and Strominger, J. L. (1965). *Proc. Natl. Acad. Sci.*, R.S., **54**, 1133–1141.

Tipper, D. J., and Strominger, J. L. (1968). *J. biol. Chem.*, **243**, 3169–3179.

Tipper, D. J., Katz, W., Strominger, J. L., and Ghuysen, J. M. (1967). *Biochemistry*, **6**, 921–929.

Tomasz, A., and Borek, E. (1960). *Proc. Natl. Acad. Sci. U.S..*, **46**, 324–327.

Tomasz, A., and Borek, E. (1962). *Biochemistry*, **1**, 543–552.

Webb, J. L. (1966). *In* "Enzyme and Metabolic Inhibitors", Vol. II, pp. 245–633. Academic Press, New York.

Welsch, M., and Osterrieth, P. (1958). *Antonie van Leeuwenhoek J. Microbiol. Serol.*, **24**, 257–273.

Whitney, J. G., and Grula, E. A. (1964). *Biochem. Biophys. Res. Comm.*, **14**, 375–381.

Whitney, J. G., and Grula, E. A. (1968). *Biochim. biophys. Acta.*, **158**, 124–219.

Wise, E. M., and Park, J. T. (1965). *Proc. Natl. Acad. Sci. U.S.*, **54**, 75–81.

Work, E. (1970). *Internat. J. Systematic Bacteriol.*, **20**, 425–433.

Work, T. S., and Work, E. (1948). "The Basis of Chemotherapy". Oliver and Boyd, Edinburgh.

CHAPTER IX

Assay of Enzymes Representative of Metabolic Pathways

W. A. WOOD

Department of Biochemistry, Michigan State University, East Lansing, Michigan, U.S.A.

There has been continued interest in assessing the kind and relative contribution of the various pathways of carbohydrate metabolism in micro-organisms. In an approximate way, many genera or species may be characterized by the predominant pathways displayed. Thus, anaerobic forms such as homofermentative streptococci and lactobacilli, as well as clostridia and others are characterized by a simple Embden–Meyerhof type of glycolysis. Many other organisms display a mixture of glycolysis and hexose monophosphate pathways in which transaldolase and transketolase are responsible for the carbon chain rearrangements. Heterolactic species and *Acetobacter xylinum*, on the other hand, exclusively utilize a version of the hexose monophosphate pathway involving phosphoketolase. Examples of the cycling hexose monophosphate system serving as the sole glucose catabolic pathway are rare, but evidence for its existence has been presented for *Acetobacter suboxydans*. In contrast. *Pseudomonas* and *Gluconobacter* or *Acetobacter* species carry out oxidations without phosphorylation to yield 2- or sometimes 5-ketogluconate. Phosphorylation of the onic acid then yields intermediates which follow the Entner–Doudoroff pathway via 2-keto-3-deoxy-6-phosphogluconate.

These metabolic pathways were established mainly during the 1950's and few changes have been made since that time except for embellishments, such as the steps in the modification of a variety of carbohydrates and polyols for entry into the central pathways. Thus, the reviews published during that period (Wood *et al.*, 1961; Gunsalus *et al.*, 1955) still accurately describe the details of these sequences. Unfortunately, the current situation is no longer as simple as in the past because further investigations have served to compromise our concepts that a particular pathway is characteristic of a genus or species. Under appropriate conditions, enzymes of supposedly atypical pathways may be induced; for instance, a major role of the hexose monophosphate and Entner–Doudoroff pathway has been indicated for *Streptococcus faecalis* grown on gluconate (Sokatch and Gunsalus, 1957). Table I lists the major pathways and enzymes which, within limits, might be considered as diagnostic of the existence of a pathway.

Although considerable reliance has been placed upon the demonstration of unique enzymes, a large number of assumptions and pitfalls accompany this approach. Thus, awareness of the problems and appropriate experimental design are needed before demonstration of unique enzymes can have maximum value.

The inability to demonstrate the presence of a particular enzyme is the most difficult to interpret and is generally of little value in eliminating a pathway (De Moss, 1968; Sapico and Anderson, 1967). The necessity of preserving enzyme activity during preparation of the extract is a major problem. Another is the fact that such extracts are very crude and present the maximum possibility of side reactions which can obscure the enzyme activity under test. This is particularly evident in assays involving the utilization or formation of NADH or ATP or both. Devices have been developed which minimize but do not eliminate this problem. A third difficulty, until recently seldom encountered, is the use of an improper assay system stemming from a misconception of the reaction in the first place (Wood, 1966). A clear-cut example of this involves an inability to

TABLE I

Pathway	Hexo-kinase	Gluconate Dehydro-genase	FDP Aldolase	G-6-P Dehydro-genase	Trans-aldolase Trans-ketolase	Phospho-ketolase	KDPG Aldolase	Type species
I. Involving initial phosphorylation								
A. Glycolysis	+	-	+	-	-	-	-	*Lactobacillus plantarum*
B. Hexose monophosphate pathways								
1. via transketolase-transaldolase	±†	±‡	-	±†	+	-	-	*Escherichia coli*
2. via phosphoketolase	±†	-	-	±†	-	+	-	*Acetobacter xylinum* *Leuconostoc mesenteroides*
3. via 2-keto-3-deoxy-6-phosphogluconate	±†	±†	-	±	-	-	+	*Pseudomonas lindneri*
II. Involving initial oxidation	-	±§	-	±	±‖	-	±‖	*Pseudomonas putida* *Gluconobacter suboxydans*

† Not required starting with gluconate.
‡ In *Pseudomonas putida*, multiple pathways for 2-ketogluconate are possible (Frampton and Wood (1961)).
§ Phosphorylation may follow oxidation to gluconate.
‖ Alternate possibilities.

demonstrate a fructokinase in fructose-grown *Aerobacter aerogenes* which cast doubt on the existence of a pathway of fructose metabolism involving fructose phosphate intermediates. It has recently been shown (Hanson and Anderson, 1968), however, that fructose phosphorylation can be accomplished, not by utilizing ATP as a donor, but by utilizing phosphoenolpyruvate in a 3-protein component system first described by Kundig and Roseman (Kundig *et al.*, 1964). Mannose phosphorylation in the same organism appears to involve an even more complicated pattern (Kamel and Anderson, 1968). In making something useful out of negative data, it is therefore necessary to go to great lengths to eliminate the above sources of a negative result. Even then, a satisfactory conclusion can only be approached and never reached, primarily because numerous other unappreciated factors may prevent demonstration of enzyme activity. It is recommended, when enzyme activity cannot be detected, that a positive control be run, preferably by adding a known bacterial source of the enzyme directly to the negative test to demonstrate that the reaction components and the extract under test allow the enzyme to function.

The demonstration of activity in extracts is a step in the direction of establishing a major possibility. However, the demonstration of activity by itself is insufficient. It is also necessary to show that the amount of enzyme is great enough to be compatible with the overall rate of the pathway. Also, other factors must be favourable such as a low K_m for the substrate and a pH optimum of the enzyme near that of the culture medium or of the cell interior. Further, it is essential that proper controls be run to correct for side reactions.

Finally, the probability of a major role of an enzyme is strengthened when its presence is influenced by physiological conditions. The most convincing evidence involves showing the induction of an enzyme in response to the relevant growth substrate, or better, the predicted change in physiological behaviour of a culture due to loss of an enzyme by mutation (Sapico *et al.*, 1968; Fraenkel and Horecker, 1964).

I. KINASES

Although phosphorylation of substrates occurs in all catabolic sequences, the specific circumstances and position in the sequence varies from (a) initiation, as in glycolysis or the hexose monophosphate pathways, or (b) continuation, as an intermediate step such as the phosphorylation of a hexonic acid, to (c) modification of other substrates preliminary to entry into the standard pathways. Thus, a general assay for kinases is detailed below. This method is applicable to the assay of a wide variety of substrates including gluconic and 2-ketogluconic acids, pentoses, and polyols, as well as to hexoses.

A. General assay for kinases

1. *Principle*

The spectrophotometric assay described depends on measurement of the ADP produced and has been utilized to assay crude extracts and purified fractions. The method suffers from the fact that both ATPase and NADH oxidase give rates which must be subtracted.

The assay is based upon a coupling of the ADP generated in the kinase reaction to the phosphoenolpyruvate kinase-lactic dehydrogenase system:

$$ROH + ATP \xrightarrow{kinase} ROP + ADP$$

$$ADP + PEP \xrightarrow[kinase]{PEP} ATP + pyruvate$$

$$Pyruvate + NADH \rightarrow lactate + NAD$$

The resynthesis of ATP is of distinct advantage in that low levels may be used (thereby diminishing side reactions and inhibitions by ATP) and the concentration remains essentially constant. The velocity can be obtained from continuous measurement of the absorbance change at 340 nm with time. This approach gives more reliable data than do single point velocity methods. Recording spectrophotometers have been devised which allow rate measurements on several reaction mixtures simultaneously (Wood and Gilford, 1961). The method is applicable to measurement of nearly all kinases with modifications which fit the characteristics of the kinase involved; i.e., pH optimum, metal concentration, etc.

The procedure described was developed for the assay of L-xylulokinase (Anderson and Wood, 1962) and subsequently has been applied to measurement of a number of kinases in crude extracts (Mortlock and Wood, 1964).

2. *Reagents*

Tris-HCl buffer, 0·7M, pH 7·5; MgCl$_2$, 0·1M; Na$_2$ATP, 0·05M trisodium or tricyclohexylammonium phosphoenolpyruvate, 0·05M; sodium glutathione (reduced), 0·15M; Na$_2$NADH, 0·005M; lactic dehydrogenase-pyruvate kinase (commercial crystalline suspension of rabbit muscle lactic dehydrogenase in ammonium sulphate); substrate 0·015M.

3. *Procedure*

The quantities given below are for microcuvettes of 1 cm light path and 2·5 mm width and give a final reaction volume of 0·15 ml. These cuvettes are routinely used in spectrophotometers equipped with a pin-hole diaphragm. The quantities may be increased by any factor necessary to fill larger cuvettes. The following volumes are transferred by micropipette or gas chromatography syringe:

Tris buffer,	0·05 ml
MgCl₂	0·01 ml
ATP	0·01 ml
Phosphoenolpyruvate	0·01 ml
Gluthathione	0·01 ml
NADH	0·01 ml
LDH	0·5 µl
Water, kinase fraction, and substrate to	0·15 ml

The reaction is initiated by addition of substrate. Controls measure the combined NADH oxidase-ATPase rate (substrate omitted) and combined NADH oxidase, NADH-linked substrate reduction (ATP omitted). For routine measurement of a large number of samples, reagents may be combined to reduce the number of additions.

A useful variant of this procedure greatly diminishes the rate of reduced pyridine nucleotide oxidation by substituting NADPH for NADH. Lactic dehydrogenase utilizes NADPH at approximately 10% the rate with NADH. Therefore, since NADPH oxidase activity in bacterial extracts is generally very low, a compensatory increase in lactic dehydrogenase is all that is needed to circumvent a bothersome high rate of NADH oxidation.

In this and subsequent spectrophotometric methods based upon oxidation or reduction of pyridine nucleotide, the slope of absorbancy changes at 340 nm, an extinction coefficient of $6·22 \times 10^6/cm^2/mole$, and the reaction volume are used to determine the velocity in µmoles per time unit.

B. Specific assay for hexoses

For assay of hexokinase, glucokinase, mannokinase, fructokinase, and any other substrates yielding ultimately glucose-6-phosphate upon addition of appropriate enzymes, advantage is taken of a coupling with glucose-6-phosphate dehydrogenase.

$$\text{Glucose} + \text{ATP} \xrightarrow{\text{kinase}} \text{glucose-6-P} + \text{ADP}$$

$$\text{Glucose-6-P} + \text{NADP} \xrightarrow{\text{dehydrogenase}} \text{6-phosphogluconate} + \text{NADPH}$$

This method is somewhat more specific, and usually has much lower blank rates since ATPase is not measured and NADPH oxidation is rare in bacterial extracts. The procedure described is that of Anderson and Kamel (Anderson and Kamel, 1966).

1. Reagents

Na₂ATP, 0·5M; MgCl₂, 0·1M; NADP, 0·01M; glycylglycine, pH 6·9, 0·08M; D-glucose 0·2M; glucose-6-phosphate dehydrogenase. Other enzymes such as phosphoglucoisomerase or phosphomannoisomerase may be added in excess to adapt the assay to other substrates (Kamel and Anderson, 1966).

2. *Procedure*

A microcuvette of 1 cm light path and 2·5 mm width is filled with:

Glycylglycine	0·01 ml
ATP	0·01 ml
MgCl₂	0·01 ml
NADP	0·01 ml

excess of coupling enzymes, G-6-P dehydrogenase, and isomerase, 1·0 μmole of substrate, kinase preparation, and water to 0·15 ml total volume. The reaction is initiated by adding substrate and appropriate controls are run to account for NADP oxidation.

II. FRUCTOSE DIPHOSPHATE ALDOLASE

Bacterial FDP aldolases thus far reported belong to the group called Class II aldolases in that a metal ion, either tightly bound or dissociable and sulphydryl compounds are needed for activity (Rutter, 1964). Further, the mechanism does not involve azomethine formation between a lysine ε-amino group of the enzyme and the substrate. Thus, assays of crude extracts may encounter difficulties owing to a lack of knowledge of the metal requirement or to failure to control the inactivation by oxygen during preparation of the extract. A lack of awareness of these problems led to an inability for several years to demonstrate FDP aldolase in blue-green algae (Fewson *et al.*, 1962; Willard and Gibbs, 1968). The assay system given below is that of Rajkumar, Woodfin, and Rutter (1966) for the FDP aldolase of *Clostridium perfringens* and involves the spectrophotometric measurement of triose phosphates by reduction with added α-glycerol phosphate dehydrogenase and NADH.

A. Reagents

A solution containing tris hydroxymethylaminomethane, 0·01M, pH 7·5 (adjusted with acetic acid); potassium acetate, 0·2M; CoCl₂, 1·4 × 10⁻³M; L-cysteine·HCl, 2 × 10⁻⁴M; NaFDP, 0·02M, pH 7·5; NaNADH, 0·002M, in 0·001M NaOH; α-Glycerol phosphate dehydrogenase-triose phosphate isomerase-mixed crystals (Boehringer), diluted to 2 mg/ml in distilled water at 0°.

B. Procedure

0·5 ml of buffer-cobalt-potassium-cysteine mixture, 0·1 ml of FDP, 0·1 ml of NADH, and 10 μl of glycerophosphate dehydrogenase-triose phosphate isomerase solution and water to 1 ml total volume are added to a

15

1-ml cuvette with a light path of 1·0 cm. 0·003 to 0·03 unit of adolase is added in up to 10 μl volume. Absorbancies are read at 340 nm and 28° until a linear rate is obtained for 3 to 5 min. It is assumed that two equivalents of NADH are produced per equivalent of FDP cleaved. Appropriate controls are needed to measure the spontaneous utilization of NADH.

III. GLUCOSE-6-PHOSPHATE DEHYDROGENASE

The procedure given was described in Volume I of *Methods of Enzymology* 13 years ago by DeMoss (1955). It is included here because G-6-P dehydrogenase is the point of departure for two or three versions of the hexose monophosphate pathway. There is little new information which would warrant alteration of this procedure.

A. Reagents

G-6-P solution, 0·2M. Either the sodium or barium salts may be used. The barium is removed by acidification and treatment with Dowex 50 (H$^+$) or by adding a 10% molar excess of sodium sulphate followed by centrifugation. The solution is then neutralized to pH 7·8; tris buffer, 0·1M, pH 7·8; NAD or NADP, 0·0027M, depending upon the specificity of the dehydrogenase under test; MgCl$_2$, 0·1M; the dehydrogenase is appropriately diluted in tris buffer or water.

B. Procedure

1·5 ml of tris buffer, 0·2 ml of NAD, 0·1 ml of MgCl$_2$, 0·1 ml of enzyme, and 1·05 ml of water are mixed and 0·05 ml of G-6-P are added to start the reaction.

The presence of a NAD-specific or a pyridine nucleotide nonspecific dehydrogenase can be completely obscured by a strong NADH oxidase alone or acting with transhydrogenase (Schwert and Wood, 1954). A control without substrate should be run and the amount of enzyme preparation reduced by dilution until the rate of NADH oxidation is in a reasonable range. This will allow observation of a differential rate when substrate is added. Alternatively, with more enzyme, sufficient time is allowed in the spectrophotometer for consumption of the dissolved oxygen in the cuvette, after which NADH will accumulate. Stirring the cuvette contents should be avoided and sufficient G-6-P must be added to allow for the period of cycling of NADP during which measurements cannot be made (ibid). The length of lag due to NADH oxidation is dependent upon the dehydrogenase rate with a longer lag resulting from a slow dehydrogenase rate.

6-Phosphogluconate dehydrogenase potentially could contribute to the observed rate. However, when NADH oxidase is low or absent, error in initial velocity from 6-phosphogluconate dehydrogenase is negligible. Further, the activity of this dehydrogenase is weak in extracts of most bacteria.

IV. TRANSALDOLASE-TRANSKETOLASE

Although this pair of enzymes may be considered as diagnostic of the combined hexose-monophosphate-glycolytic pathway and of the hexose monophosphate cycle, no simple assay for their presence is available. As the equations show, it should be possible to monitor the appearance of sedoheptulose-7-phosphate, glyceraldehyde-3-phosphate, fructose-6-phosphate, and other possibilities exist also.

$$\text{Xu-5-P} + \text{R-5-P} \xrightarrow{\text{transketolase}} \text{S-7-P} + \text{G-3-P}$$
$$\text{S-7-P} + \text{G-3-P} \xrightarrow{\text{transaldolase}} \text{F-6-P} + \text{E-4-P}$$
$$\text{Xu-5-P} + \text{E-4-P} \xrightarrow{\text{transketolase}} \text{F-6-P} + \text{G-3-P}$$

Unfortunately, spectrophotometric assays on crude extracts are unreliable because of side reactions and the complicated nature of the sequence. It is possible, however, to follow the disappearance of ribose and the appearance of heptulose colorimetrically by the orcinol procedure for pentoses (Vandemark and Wood, 1956), and to confirm the presence of heptulose using the orcinol-TCA spray of Bevenue and Williams (1951), but these are rather indirect and only qualitative. Alternatively, the accumulation of hexose can be measured by the anthrone method (Brin, 1966) or by enzymatic determination of glucose-6-phosphate with yeast glucose-6-phosphate dehydrogenase (Krichevsky and Wood, 1961).

Under some conditions, G-3-P production from R-5-P can be measured spectrophotometrically at 340 nm as follows:

$$\text{R-5-P} \xrightarrow{\text{isomerase}} \text{Ru-5-P} \xrightarrow{\text{3-epimerase}} \text{Xu-5-P}$$
$$\text{Xu-5-P} + \text{R-5-P} \rightarrow \text{S-7-P} + \text{G-3-P}$$
$$\text{G-3-P} \rightarrow \text{DHAP}$$
$$\text{DHAP} + \text{NADH} \rightarrow \alpha\text{-glycerol P} + \text{NAD}$$

The method requires that the NADH oxidase level be low, that phosphoriboisomerase and 3-epimerase be present in the extract under test or, alternatively, that an isomerase-epimerase product be prepared in advance for use as substrate (de la Haba and Racker, 1955).

None of these methods has been perfected for use with bacteria. For this reason, reference is made to procedures used with yeast (ibid.), serum (Brin, 1966), and spinach (Horecker et al., 1953), instead of describing one of these in detail here.

V. PHOSPHOKETOLASE

Assays are based on a direct or indirect spectrophotometric measurement of G-3-P or on the colorimetric determination of acetyl phosphate as the ferric chelate of its hydroxamate. Goldberg, Fessenden, and Racker (1966) describe the conversion of the G-3-P formed to FDP in the presence of triose phosphate isomerase, FDP aldolase, and α-glycerol phosphate dehydrogenase (NADH not present). The FDP content of heated aliquots is determined using aldolase, α-glycerol phosphate dehydrogenase, and triose phosphate epimerase as the oxidation of NADH. For purified fractions, these authors determine the rate of acetyl phosphate formation.

The procedure described below is a modification of that published for 3-epimerase assays (Williamson and Wood, 1966) and depends upon continuous measurement of the rate of G-3-P formation. It gives semi-quantitative (lower) values with crude extracts and is highly satisfactory on partially purified fractions. The reaction requires as substrate either xylulose-5-P (Simpson, 1966), an isomerase-epimerase product (de la Haba and Racker, 1955) or R-5-P plus an excess of phosphoketolase-phosphoriboisomerase (Axelrod, 1955) and Ru-5-P 3-epimerase (Williamson and Wood, 1966) added or present in the fraction under test.

R-5-P $\xrightarrow{\text{isomerase}}$ Ru-5-P $\xrightarrow{\text{3-epimerase}}$ Xu-5-P

Xu-5-P $\rightarrow$ G-3-P + acetyl P

G-3-P $\rightarrow$ DHAP

DHAP + NADH $\rightarrow$ α-glycerol P + NAD

A. Reagents

Reagent I. A mixture of buffer, magnesium ions, sodium arsenate, thiamine diphosphate, and glutathione is prepared from stock solutions as follows:

MgCl$_2$ (0·05M)	1 ml
Na arsenate (0·01M)	1 ml
Thiamine pyrophosphate (5 mg/ml)	1 ml
Succinate buffer (0·5M, pH 6·2)	2 ml
Na glutathione (38 mg/ml)	1 ml

are combined and diluted to 10 ml. Triose phosphate isomerase-α-glycerol phosphate dehydrogenase-suspension of crystals, Boehringer (0·33 mg/ml); D-xylulose-5-phosphate, 0·05M; NADH, 0·01M.

B. Procedure

0·1 ml of Reagent I, 0·01 ml of α-glycerol phosphate dehydrogenase-triose phosphate isomerase, 0·02 ml of D-xylulose-5-phosphate, 0·01 ml of NADH and water to 0·20 ml are added to a microcuvette 1·0 × 2·5 mm inside dimensions. The reaction is started by adding the phosphoketolase preparation, and the rate of NADH oxidation is followed by 340 nm for 5 to 10 min. A control without Xu-5-P is included to correct for NADH oxidase.

VI. 2-KETO-3-DEOXY-6-PHOSPHOGLUCONIC ALDOLASE

2-Keto-3-deoxy-6-phosphogluconic adolase and 6-phosphogluconic dehydrase are unique to the Entner–Doudoroff pathway for glucose, gluconic, and 2-keto-gluconic acids. The aldolase is very stable and easily assayed spectrophotometrically by measuring the rate of pyruvate formation in the presence of lactic dehydrogenase and NADH (Simpson, 1966). Unfortunately, the substrate, 2-keto-3-deoxy-6-phosphogluconate is not readily available, but it can be prepared enzymatically (Axelrod, 1955; Meloche and Wood, 1966). An alternative would be to measure the combined function of the dehydrase and adolase in the same manner using commercially available 6-phosphogluconate. However, in some extracts, the dehydrase is labile and often difficult to detect. The conversion of 6-phosphogluconate to pyruvate in extracts of *Pseudomonas putida* presents no problems except for the presence of NADH oxidase.

A. Reagents

1. Stock assay solution consists of:

Na$_2$NADH	4 mg
1·0M imidazole, pH 8	0·25 ml
Commercial suspension of crystalline muscle lactic dehydrogenase	0·05 ml
and water to a final volume of	5 ml

2. Dithiothreitol (0·15M)

3. Na or K salt of 2-keto-3-deoxy-6-phosphogluconate (0·05M) pH 6; or Na 6-phosphogluconate (0·2M)

4. MnCl$_2$ (0·003M)

B. Procedure

For assays with 2-keto-3-deoxy-6-phosphogluconate, 0·05 ml of Reagent I, 0·015 ml of 2-keto-3-deoxy-6-phosphogluconate, and 0·085 ml of water and enzyme sample are mixed in a microcuvette of 1 cm light path and 2·5 mm width. For assays using 6-phosphogluconate, 0·05 ml of Reagent I, 0·01 ml of 6-phosphogluconate, 0·01 ml of dithiothreitol, and 0·01 ml of MnCl$_2$ and 0·07 ml of water and enzyme fraction comprise the reaction mixture. The reaction is started by adding the adolase fraction and a control for NADH oxidase is needed.

VII. GLUCOSE AND GLUCONATE DEHYDROGENASES

Indications of a pathway of direct oxidation of glucose may be obtained from a demonstration of glucose or gluconate dehydrogenases. However, due to the variety of glucose dehydrogenases, no single assay can be recommended. Further, unknown cofactors have been detected in some instances. Both particulate and soluble dehydrogenases have been reported, and assays have involved (a) spectrophotometric measurement of dye, ferricyanide, or NAD reduction, and (b) manometric measurements of oxygen uptake (Kovachevich and Wood, 1955; Meloche and Wood, 1966; Hauge, 1966). It is likely for some organisms that a glucose-oxidizing system may be present but that this route does not represent a major or characteristic pathway for the organism. For *Pseudomonas* and *Acetobacter* species, at least, a direct oxidative pathway assumes major importance.

Assays for the particulate, cytochrome-linked gluconate dehydrogenases are more reliable and are characteristic of *Pseudomonas* and *Acetobacter* or *Gluconobacter* species. In *Pseudomonas*, the product is 2-ketogluconate identified by its reactivity with semicarbazide and characteristic R_f value. The NADP-linked soluble 2-ketogluconate reductase is too widely distributed to be useful as an indicator of pathways.

VIII. GLUCONIC DEHYDROGENASE†

The oxidation velocity is determined either (a) manometrically in crude extract or particulate preparations, (b) colorimetrically as the rate of ferricyanide reduction to Prussian blue, or (c) spectrophotometrically as the rate of ferricyanide disappearance. The method described measures Prussian blue formation in a fixed time period.

A. Reagents

0·2M potassium gluconate; 0·1M potassium ferricyanide; 0·5M Na acetate buffer, pH 5·5; ferric sulphate-Dupenol (sodium lauryl sulphate), 95 ml of 85% phosphoric acid, and distilled water to 1000 ml.

B. Procedure

0·1 ml of ferricyanide solution, 0·2 ml of acetate buffer, a suitable dilution of extract, and water to 0·9 ml are mixed in a colorimeter tube. The reaction is started by adding 0·1 ml of potassium gluconate. After 10 min at 37°, 0·5 ml of ferric sulphate-Dupenol reagent is added, and the mixture allowed to stand for 1 min. The blue colour is read at 660 nm and compared to standards prepared from fresh ferrous sulphate or from ferricyanide chemically reduced. Protein precipitates have not interfered with the assay because of the small amount of extract needed to give activity.

† King, 1966.

A modification of this procedure for observation of ferricyanide disappearance spectrophotometrically would involve only a decrease in the amount of ferricyanide so as to fall within the linear absorbance range of the instrument. The molar extinction coefficient of ferricyanide at 420 nm is approximately 1040.

REFERENCES

Anderson, R. L., and Kamel, M. Y. (1966). *In* "Methods in Enzymology" (Ed. W. A. Wood), Vol. IX, p. 388. Academic Press, New York.

Anderson, R. L., and Wood, W. A. (1962). *J. biol. Chem.*, **237**, 296.

Axelrod, B. (1955). *In* "Methods in Enzymology" (Eds S. P. Colowick and N.O. Kaplan), Vol. I, p. 363. Academic Press, New York.

Bevenue, A., and Williams, K. T. (1951). *Arch. Biochem. Biophys.*, **34**, 225.

Brin, M. (1966). *In* "Methods in Enzymology" (Ed. W. A. Wood), Vol. IX, p. 506. Academic Press, New York.

de la Haba, G., and Racker, E. (1955). *In* "Methods in Enzymology" (Eds S. P. Colowick and N. O. Kaplan). Vol. I, p. 375. Academic Press, New York.

DeMoss, R. D. (1955). *In* "Methods in Enzymology" (Eds S. P. Colowick and N. O. Kaplan), Vol. I, p. 328. Academic Press, New York.

DeMoss, R. D. (1968). *J. Bacteriol.*, **95**, 1692.

Fewson, C. A., Al-Hafidh, M., and Gibbs, M. (1962). *Plant Physiol.*, **37**, 402.

Fraenkel, D. G., and Horecker, B. L. (1964). *J. biol. Chem.*, **239**, 2765.

Frampton, E. W., and Wood, W. A. (1961). *J. biol. Chem.*, **236**, 2571.

Goldberg, M., Fessenden, J. M., and Racker, E. (1966). *In* "Methods in Enzymology" (Ed. W. A. Wood), Vol. IX, p. 515. Academic Press, New York.

Gunsalus, I. C., Horecker, B. L., and Wood, W. A. (1955). *Bact. Revs.*, **19**, 79.

Hanson, T. E., and Anderson, R. L. (1968). *Proc. Natl. Acad. Sc., U.S.*, **61**, 269.

Hauge, J. G. (1966). *In* "Methods in Enzymology" (Ed. W. A. Wood), Vol. IX, p. 92. Academic Press, New York.

Horecker, B. L., Smyrniotis, P. S., and Klenow, H. (1953). *J. biol. Chem.*, **205**, 661.

Kamel, M. Y., and Anderson, R. L. (1966). *J. Bacteriol.*, **92**, 1689.

King Tsoo E. (1966). *In* "Methods in Enzymology" (Ed. W. A. Wood), Vol. IX, p. 98. Academic Press, New York.

Kovachevich, R., and Wood, W. A. (1955). *J. biol. Chem.*, **213**, 745.

Krichevsky, M. I., and Wood, W. A. (1961). *J. Bacteriol.*, **81**, 246.

Kundig, W., Ghosh, S., and Roseman, S. (1964). *Proc. Natl. Acad Sc., U.S.*, **52**, 1067.

Meloche, H. P., Ingram, J. M., and Wood, W. A. *In* "Methods in Enzymology" (Ed. W. A. Wood), Vol. IX, p. 520. Academic Press, New York.

Meloche, H. P., and Wood, W. A. (1966). *In* "Methods in Enzymology" (Ed. W. A. Wood), Vol. IX, p. 51. Academic Press, New York.

Mortlock, R. P., and Wood, W. A. (1964). *J. Bacteriol.*, **88**, 838.

Rajkumar, T. V., Woodfin, B. M., and Rutter, W. J. (1966). *In* "Methods in Enzymology" (Ed. W. A. Wood), Vol. IX, p. 491. Academic Press, New York.

Rutter, W. J. (1964). *Federation Proc.*, **23**, 1248.

Sapico, V., and Anderson, R. L. (1967). *J. biol. Chem.*, **242**, 5086.

Sapico, V., Hanson, T. E., Walter, R. W., and Anderson, R. L. (1968). *J. Bacteriol.*, **96**, 51.

Schwert, R. W., and Wood, W. A. (1954). *J. biol. Chem.*, **206**, 625.

Simpson, F. J. (1966). *In* "Methods in Enzymology" (Ed. W. A. Wood), Vol. IX, p. 41. Academic Press, New York.

Sokatch, J. T., and Gunsalus, I. C. (1957). *J. Bacteriol.*, **73**, 452.

Vandemark, P. J., and Wood, W. A. (1956). *J. Bacteriol.*, **71**, 385.

Willard, J. M., and Gibbs, M. (1968). *Plant Physiol.*, **43**, 793.

Williamson, W. T., and Wood, W. A. (1966). *In* "Methods in Enzymology" (Ed. W. A. Wood), Vol. IX, p. 605. Academic Press, New York.

Wood, W. A. (1966). *Ann. Revs. Biochem.*, **35**, 534.

Wood, W. A., and Gilford, S. R. (1961). *Anal. Biochem.*, **2**, 589.

Wood, W. A. (1961). *In* "The Bacteria" (Eds I. C. Gunsalus and R. Y. Stanier), Vol. II, p. 59. Academic Press, New York.

CHAPTER X

Assays of Enzymes of the Tricarboxylic Acid and Glyoxylate Cycles

H. C. REEVES,[1] R. RABIN,[2] W. S. WEGENER[3] AND S. J. AJL[4]

Present addresses:

[1] Dept. of Microbiology, Arizona State Univ., Tempe, Arizona, U.S.A.
[2] Office of Interdisciplinary Research, N.S.F., Washington, D.C., U.S.A.
[3] Dept. of Microbiology, Univ. Indiana Med. Sch., Indianapolis, Ind., U.S.A.
[4] Res. Laboratories, Albert Einstein Med. Center, Philadelphia, Pa., U.S.A.

I. INTRODUCTION

Even a cursory literature search reflects the dominance of the spectrophotometer in the development of assays of enzymes of the tricarboxylic acid and glyoxylate cycles. The methods selected for inclusion in this Chapter are, wherever possible, photometric or spectrophotometric because they combine the most desirable advantages: simplicity, rapidity, sensitivity, specificity and the fact that they can be used to assay relatively crude preparations of each enzyme. In the Comments section of each method, we have tried to indicate significant advantages or short-comings of the selected assay and, where applicable, to provide an alternative method.

The novice must be cautioned that a compilation of enzyme assay methods cannot be treated as dogma. Each method was originally developed for specific conditions, although some methods are more generally applicable than others. To attempt to apply these methods to all situations without appreciation of the subtleties involved, will surely provide opportunities for drawing erroneous conclusions. With the heterogeneity of structure and function displayed in microbial forms of life, factors such as permeability of mitochondrial preparations, rate limitations imposed by reactions competing for the same substrate or cofactor, differential pH optima for the same reactions in different organisms, or differences between organisms in equilibria states of a reaction, must be carefully considered in the interpretation of results. Culture conditions via catabolite repression, or the unwitting exposure of the enzyme being assayed to an inhibitor present in a crude extract, may also have pronounced effects.

It should be noted that no method is given for succinate dehydrogenase. The properties of this enzyme vary so greatly between micro-organisms (as, for example, between strict and facultative anaerobes, and between yeast and bacteria) than no single method is applicable. As a further complication, *Escherichia coli* contains two succinate dehydrogenases, the activities of which vary independently with the conditions of growth (Hirsch *et al.*, 1963). The dehydrogenases of *Micrococcus lactilyticus* and *Pseudomonas pentosaceum* possess the unusual property of dual pH optima in the direction of fumarate reduction, but only one in succinate oxidation. The eventual choice of an assay among the several available must be made with great care and with full cognizance of the technical difficulties inherent in each. Reference should be made to the following papers for background information: Singer and Kearney (1957); Singer (1963); Singer (1966).

II. CITRATE SYNTHASE

[Citrate Oxaloacetate Lyase (CoA acetylating) E.C. 4.1.3.7]
(Condensing Enzyme)

A. Introduction

The aerobic oxidation of acetate to carbon dioxide is catalysed by a series of discrete enzymatic reactions collectively referred to as the tricarboxylic acid cycle. The reaction initiating this cyclic sequence is the condensation of acetyl-S-CoA with oxaloacetate to form citrate [eqn. (1)]. This aldol condensation, catalysed by citrate synthase, is reversible, but its equilibrium greatly favours citrate synthesis.

$$\text{Acetyl-S-CoA} + \text{oxaloacetate} + H_2O \rightleftarrows \text{citrate} + \text{CoA.SH} + H^+ \quad (1)$$

Earlier studies on the reaction mechanism of citrate synthase have been reviewed by Jaenicke and Lynen (1960) and by Stern (1961). More recently, evidence has been presented for the formation of an enzyme-oxaloacetate binary complex (Srere, 1966), and for the enzyme-induced enolization of acetyl-S-CoA (Eggerer, 1965). The acetyl-S-CoA carbanion is considered to react with the carbonyl group of the enzyme-oxaloacetate complex to form an enzyme-citryl-CoA intermediate which is hydrolysed to form the free acid (Eggerer and Klette, 1967). Evidence in support of the intermediary formation of an enzyme-citryl-CoA complex is the fact that citrate synthase catalyses the hydrolysis of citryl-CoA (Eggerer and Remberger, 1964), and further, that citryl-CoA competitively inhibits the binding of oxaloacetate and acetyl-S-CoA to the enzyme (Srere, 1963). The inhibition of citrate synthase by palmityl-S-CoA (Wieland and Weiss, 1963) has been shown to involve competition for the oxaloacetate binding site (Srere, 1965).

B. Method of assay

1. *Principle*

Several methods are available for assaying citrate synthase. The purified enzyme is conveniently assayed by determining the formation of citrate from oxaloacetate and acetyl-S-CoA either colorimetrically (Natelson *et al.*, 1948) or enzymatically (Moellering and Gruber, 1966). The enzyme also may be assayed spectrophotometrically in a coupled system (Ochoa, 1955) with malate dehydrogenase. In this procedure, the NAD-dependent oxidation of malate to oxaloacetate is coupled with the condensation of acetyl-S-CoA and oxaloacetate to form citrate [eqn (1 and 2)]. The acetyl-S-CoA dependent rate of NAD reduction is proportional to citrate synthase activity. These methods are not applicable using crude enzyme preparations which further metabolize citrate or which exhibit NADH oxidase activity.

$$\text{Oxaloacetate} + \text{acetyl-S-CoA} + H_2O \rightleftarrows \text{citrate} + \text{CoA.SH} + H^+ \quad (1)$$

$$\text{Malate} + NAD^+ \rightleftarrows \text{oxaloacetate} + NADH + H^+ \quad (2)$$

$$\text{SUM: Malate} + \text{acetyl-S-CoA} + NAD^+ \rightleftarrows \text{citrate} + \text{CoA.SH} +$$
$$NADH + 2H^+$$

In crude extracts, citrate synthase activity may be determined in a phosphotransacetylase coupled system (Ochoa, 1955). In this procedure the CoA.SH-dependent conversion of acetyl-phosphate to acetyl-S-CoA is coupled to CoA.SH formation via citrate synthase [eqn. (1 and 3)]. The oxaloacetate-dependent utilization of acetyl-phosphate is determined as the ferric acetohydroxamate complex (Lipmann and Tuttle, 1945) and is proportional to citrate synthase activity.

$$\text{Oxaloacetate} + \text{acetyl-S-CoA} + H_2O \rightleftharpoons \text{citrate} + \text{CoA.SH} + H^+ \quad (1)$$

$$\text{Acetyl-phosphate} + \text{CoA.SH} \rightleftharpoons \text{acetyl-CoA} + \text{orthophosphate} \quad (3)$$

SUM:

$$\text{Acetyl-phosphate} + \text{oxaloacetate} + H_2O \underset{}{\overset{\text{CoA.SH}}{\rightleftharpoons}} \text{citrate} + \text{orthophosphate} + H^+$$

Crude preparations also may be assayed using a non-coupled system by measuring the oxaloacetate dependent cleavage of acetyl-S-CoA to CoA.SH. CoA.SH formation is determined spectrophotometrically by measuring the decrease in absorbance at 232 nm (Stadtman, 1957) or by a polarographic method (Weitzman, 1966). The direct spectrophotometric procedure suffers from the disadvantage that several components of the reaction mixture exhibit strong absorbance at this wavelength. The polaro-graphic assay requires specialized equipment. Alternatively the formation of CoA.SH may be assayed spectrophotometrically at 412 nm (Srere et al., 1963) by measuring the appearance of thiol groups using Ellman's reagent (Ellman, 1959). The latter procedure is described below.

2. Reagents

2M Tris-HCl buffer, pH 8·1

2 mM 5,5′-bisthiol (2-nitrobenzoic acid) DTNB; prepared fresh in 0·5M potassium phosphate buffer, pH 7·0

1 mM Acetyl-S-CoA (prepared according to the method of Simon and Shemin, 1953)

5 mM Potassium oxaloacetate; enzyme solution to be assayed.

3. Procedure

The complete reaction mixture contains in a total volume of 1·0 ml: enzyme extract, water and 0·1 ml each of Tris.HCl buffer, DTNB, acetyl-S-CoA and oxaloacetate. The blank cuvette lacks acetyl-S-CoA.

All the components except acetyl-S-CoA and oxaloacetate are mixed and preincubated for 1–2 min. Acetyl-S-CoA is then added to the complete system and any increase in absorbance at 412 nm (due to acetyl-S-CoA deacylase activity) is measured. After the change in absorbance has become linear, oxaloacetate is added to both cuvettes, and the subsequent initial rate of increase in absorbance is recorded. The initial, rate of increase in absorbance at 412 nm, is proportional to citrate synthase concentration.

4. *Enzyme unit and specific activity*

One unit is the amount of enzyme catalysing the formation of 1 μmole of the *p*-nitrobenzoate anion per min. At 412 nm the molar absorbancy index of this mercaptide ion is 13,600. Calculation of mercaptide ion concentration is made using the equation $C = A/\epsilon \times D$ where: C = molar concentration; A = absorbance ($\triangle A_{412}$/min); ϵ = extinction coefficient (13,600 M^{-1} cm^{-1}); and D = dilution factor. Specific activity is expressed as units per milligram of protein.

C. Comments

The chromogen-linked spectrophotometric assay procedure is suitable using both crude and purified enzyme preparations. The assay is rapid, sensitive, and is measured at a wavelength where the other components of the reaction mixture do not exhibit strong absorbance. In preliminary investigations it is recommended that the method be used in conjunction with a second assay procedure in order to rule out the possibility of chromogen inhibition of enzyme activity. The colorimetric determination of acetyl phosphate utilization, rather than the direct measurement of CoA.SH formation at 232 nm, is recommended for preparations containing low enzyme activity.

In addition, one should be aware, when using oxaloacetic acid as a substrate in any enzymatic reaction, that this acid is relatively unstable and that aqueous solutions of the acid exist as a mixture of the *keto* and *enol* isomers. Total oxaloacetate concentration may be determined by the method of Greenwood and Greenbaum (1953).

III. CITRATE OXALOACETATE-LYASE

[Citrate lyase, EC 4.1.3.6] (Citritase; Citrase; Citrate aldolase; Citridesmolase)

A. Introduction

Citrate lyase, an inducible microbial enzyme, catalyses the cleavage of citrate to *keto*-oxaloacetate (eqn. 1). It requires a divalent metal ion such as Mg^{2+} or Mn^{2+}, but not CoA.SH.

$$\text{Citrate} \rightleftharpoons \text{oxaloacetate} + \text{acetate} \qquad (1)$$

The enzyme has been studied by numerous investigators (Dagley and Dawes, 1953, 1955; Grunberg-Manago and Gunsalus, 1953; Gillespie and Gunsalus, 1953; Dagley, 1954; Wheat and Ajl, 1955; Smith *et al.*, 1956; Harvey and Collins, 1961). It has been isolated and purified from

Streptococcus faecalis (Smith *et al.*, 1956), *E. coli* (Bowen and Raman, 1960), *Aerobacter aerogenes* (Raman, 1961; Tate and Datta, 1965) and *Streptococcus diacetilactis* (Harvey and Collins, 1963). A discussion of recent studies on physicochemical properties of the enzyme (Bowen and Rogers, 1963, 1965; Ward and Srere, 1965), binary complex formation [metal-citrate, metal-enzyme] (Harvey and Collins, 1963; Ward and Srere, 1965; Eisenthal, *et al.*, 1966), equilibrium of the reaction (Harvey and Collins, 1963; Tate and Datta, 1965), and enzyme inhibition and inactivation (Harvey and Collins, 1963; Bowen and Rogers, 1963; Tate and Datta, 1964; Eisenthal *et al.*, 1966) is beyond the scope of this chapter. But their citation serves to conveniently collate the pertinent references until work on the enzyme is comprehensively reviewed.

B. Method of assay

1. *Principle*

The method depends upon measurement of the *keto* form of oxaloacetate (Harvey and Collins, 1963; Tate and Datta, 1964) which, at pH 7 in the presence of Mg^{2+}, shows an absorption maximum at 285 to 287 nm.

2. *Reagents*

1M Potassium phosphate buffer, pH 7·0; 100 mM potassium citrate; 15 mM $MgCl_2$. Enzyme solution to be assayed.

It is recommended (Harvey and Collins, 1963) that bacterial cell-free extracts be treated with Dowex-1 anion exchange resin to free them of oxaloacetate decarboxylase activity. This is easily done as follows (Chantrenne and Lipmann, 1950); treat the 70-mesh resin several times with 1N HCl and then carefully wash the resin acid-free with water. Centrifuge the neutral resin and draw off the last drops of adhering water with a little filter paper. Mix about one-half the volume of this semi-dry resin with a volume of bacterial extract and place in an ice bath for 20–30 min. Centrifuge the mixture and filter the supernatant fluid through a small cotton plug. The pH of the treated extract is about 6. If the same extract is also to be used for assaying enzymes other than citrate lysae, which are acid-sensitive, addition of base to the original extract to pH 8 will prevent the pH from falling below 7 during Dowex treatment.

3. *Procedure*

In a total volume of 1·0 ml, add 0·2 ml phosphate buffer, 0·2 ml $MgCl_2$, enzyme and 0·1 ml citrate. In the spectrophotometer, the base line is obtained with reference and sample cuvettes containing all components except substrate; citrate is then added to the sample cuvette and the ΔA_{285} (initial velocity) is measured.

4. *Enzyme unit and specific activity*

One unit is the amount of enzyme catalysing a ΔA_{285} of 0·100 per min which is equivalent to 0·2 μmole of oxaloacetate formed per min. Specific activity is expressed as units per milligram of protein.

C. Comments

The assay is rapid, convenient and suitable for routine use. It is not recommended for accurate kinetic studies since it is difficult to relate the change in absorbance to the stoicheiometry of the reaction (Ward and Srere, 1965; Kosicki and Lipovac, 1964). A coupled assay system (Ward and Srere, 1965), in which excess malate dehydrogenase and NADH convert the oxaloacetate formed, makes it possible to relate ΔA_{285} to an activity in stoicheiometric units. This assay is briefly described since it is highly accurate and more useful for purified enzyme in the presence of which *keto*-oxaloacetate is much less stable (Harvey and Collins, 1963). The assay requires considerably less enzyme, is linear for most of its course and may be adapted for use as a rapid, specific assay for citrate (Ward and Srere, 1965). The reaction mixture contains in 1·0 ml, 50 μmoles Tris.HCl (pH 7·3), 10 μmoles potassium citrate, 10 μmoles $MgCl_2$, malate dehydrogenase and 0·15 μmoles NADH. The decrease in absorbance at 340 nm due to converson of NADH to NAD is measured. With this method as well as the one described above (II.A.), a ΔA_{285} of 0·100/ min is equivalent to a rate of 0·2 μmole of oxaloacetate/min.

Other coupled assays have been described by Dagley (1965) and by Moellering and Gruber (1966). In the former, the oxaloacetate formed by the citrate lyase of *A. aerogenes* is converted to pyruvate by the very active oxaloacetate decarboxylase present in extracts of this organism; pyruvate is determined with lactate dehydrogenase and NADH. In the latter method (essentially similar to that of Ward and Srere (1965), the oxaloacetate is converted to malate by malate dehydrogenase and NADH; any pyruvate formed from oxaloacetate non-enzymatically is determined with lactate dehydrogenase and NADH. By coupling the dehydrogenase, citrate cleavage is virtually complete. These methods also form the bases for sensitive assays of citrate.

The method of Friedemann and Haugen (1943) has so been used to measure oxaloacetate formation from citrate (Bowen and Rogers, 1963), but no precautions were taken to exclude enzymatic breakdown of the product in crude extracts. This method could be made more useful for crude extracts by coupling citrate lyase to purified oxaloacetate decarboxylase and measuring all the keto acid as pyruvate. In view of the simpler assays available, in which it is also possible to get a recorded rate of reaction, the chemical determination of keto acid offers no competitive advantage.

IV. ACONITATE HYDRATASE

[Citrate (Isocitrate) Hydro-Lyase EC 4.2.1.3]
(Aconitase)

A. Introduction

The interconversion of citrate, isocitrate and *cis*-aconitate is catalysed by aconitate hydratase. The percentages of the respective tricarboxylic acids present at equilibrium (Krebs, 1953) is shown in eqn. (1).

$$\text{Citrate} \rightleftharpoons \textit{cis}\text{-aconitate} \rightleftharpoons \text{isocitrate} \qquad (1)$$
$$90\cdot9\% \qquad 2\cdot9\% \qquad 6\cdot2\%$$

The pig heart enzyme has been most throughly studied and appears to be a single protein (Buchanan and Anfinson, 1949; Morrison, 1954). A separate enzyme, citrate dehydratase, (citrate hydrolyase [EC 4.2.1.4]) catalyses the interconversion of *cis*-aconitate with citrate but not with isocitrate (Neilson, 1962), and has been demonstrated in several fungi.

Studies concerning the reaction mechanism (Dickman, 1961; Hanson and Rose, 1963; Rose, 1966; Rose and O'Connell, 1967) suggest that *cis*-aconitate is not an obligatory intermediate in the reaction sequence, but rather, the formation of a common enzyme-bound intermediate which can undergo rearrangement to form either citrate, isocitrate, or *cis*-aconitate is proposed.

B. Method of assay

1. *Principle*

The purified enzyme may be assayed either by determining the formation of citrate or isocitrate from *cis*-aconitate or by measuring the utilization or formation of *cis*-aconitate. The quantitation of citrate formation (for references, see citrate synthase) is unsuitable using preparations which catalyse the cleavage of this substrate to oxaloacetate plus acetate. In addition, the interconversion of citrate and *cis*-aconitate is common for both the aconitate hydratase and to citrate dehydratase. The spectrophotometric determination of isocitrate formation, assayed by coupling aconitate hydratase with purified isocitrate dehydrogenase plus NADP (Ochoa, 1955), is specific for aconitate hydratase, but is not applicable to preparations possessing NADPH oxidase activity.

The procedure most frequently employed to assay enzyme activity in crude extracts is the spectrophotometric determination of the formation of aconitate from isocitrate (Racker, 1950; Anfinson, 1955). This assay is based on the principle that ethylenic acids exhibit strong ultraviolet absorbance. At the wavelength usually employed (240 nm), proteins also exhibit absorbance and consequently only small amounts of enzyme extract can be employed.

2. Reagents

1M Tris.HCl, pH 7·5
200 mM dl-Sodium isocitrate.
Enzyme solution to be assayed.

3. Procedure

The complete reaction mixture contains in 1·0 ml: enzyme, water and 0·10 ml each of Tris.HCl and isocitrate. The blank cuvette lacks substrate. The reaction is initiated with isocitrate and the initial rate of increase in absorbance at 240 nm is recorded.

4. Enzyme units and specific activity

One unit is the amount of enzyme which catalyses an increase in absorbance of 0·001 per min at initial rates. Each 0·001 change in optical density is equivalent to $2·82 \times 10^{-4}$ μmoles of cis-aconitate per ml. Specific activity is expressed as units per milligram of protein.

C. Comments

Aconitate hydratase is relatively unstable (for review see Dickman, 1960). Partial loss of activity results during storage at $-20°$; inactivation is accelerated at an acidic pH and in the presence of phosphate. Dialysis also results in loss of activity but the enzyme is reactivated by addition of Fe^{2+} and a reducing agent. In the presence of citrate the enzyme can be precipitated without loss of activity using $(NH_4)_2SO_4$ or ethanol.

Since some micro-organisms may possess both aconitate hydratase and citrate dehydratase activity, it is recommended that crude enzyme preparations be assayed by measuring the dehydration of isocitrate rather than the hydration of aconitate or the dehydration of citrate. The assay procedure described here is specific for aconitate hydratase but is complicated by the fact that the cis-aconitate formed from isocitrate may undergo subsequent rehydration to yield citrate; therefore, enzyme activity must be calculated from the initial rate of increase in absorbance at 240 nm.

To further verify the presence of aconitate hydratase activity, this assay may be augmented by an independent determination of isocitrate formation from *cis*-aconitate. This may be done using the reaction mixture described above except that *cis*-aconitate is substituted for isocitrate. After incubation for varying time intervals, 0·20 ml aliquots of the mixture are removed, the reaction terminated by heating at 100°, and isocitrate concentration determined as described by Stern (1957). This determination should be performed using extracts free of endogenous NADP. It is not applicable to preparations possessing isocitrate lyase activity.

V. ISOCITRATE DEHYDROGENASE
[L_s-Isocitrate: NADP Oxidoreductase (decarboxylating) EC 1.1.1.42]

A. Introduction

The literature up until 1951 describing the properties of isocitrate dehydrogenases has been summarized (Ochoa, 1951). The assay methods and the purification of these enzymes from a variety of sources have also been reviewed (Ochoa, 1955; Kornberg, 1955; Plaut and Sung, 1955; Plaut 1962). Although both NAD- and NADP-linked isocitrate dehydrogenases have been described, it is the latter that is found in most bacterial cells. Both enzymes are present in yeast (Bernofsky and Utter, 1966).

Since this volume is concerned primarily with microbial methodology, only the assay of the NADP-linked isocitrate dehydrogenase will be described. The reader is referred to the review by Plaut (1963) for a comprehensive discussion of the enzymes.

B. Method of assay

1. *Principle*

The overall reaction catalysed by isocitrate dehydrogenase is shown in eqn. (1):

$$L_s\text{-Isocitrate} + NADP^+ \rightarrow \alpha\text{-Ketoglutarate} + CO_2 + NADPH + H^+ \quad (1)$$

The reaction is followed spectrophotometrically by measuring the rate of NADP reduction at 340 nm in the presence of enzyme and isocitrate. The assay method is essentially that reported by Daron *et al.* (1966).

2. *Reagents*

> 200 mM Tris.HCl buffer, pH 7·5
> 40 mM $MnCl_2$
> 10 mM NADP
> 10 mM *dl*-Sodium isocitrate.
> Enzyme solution to be assayed.

3. *Procedure*

To the experimental cuvette are added 0·10 ml of Tris buffer and 0·05 ml each of $MnCl_2$, NADP and enzyme. Water is added to make the volume 0·95 ml. The reference cuvette is prepared in the same manner except that water is added to give a total volume of 1·0 ml. The absorbance is adjusted to zero, and the reaction is started by the addition of 0·05 ml of isocitrate to the experimental cuvette. The increase in absorbance at 340 nm is linear for several minutes, and the initial slope is used to calculate the enzyme activity. Under these conditions, the ΔA_{340} divided by 6·22 is equal to the total number of μmoles of NADP reduced.

4. *Enzyme unit and specific activity*

One unit is the amount of enzyme catalysing the formation of 1·0 μmole of reduced nicotinamide-adenine dinucleotide phosphate per min. Specific activity is expressed as units per milligram of protein.

C. Comments

As with other enzymes, when the determination of activity is based upon the spectrophotometric determination of reduced NAD or NADP, it may be necessary to correct for oxidase activity. In most cases, however, the activity of NADPH oxidase activity in crude bacterial extracts is rather low.

VI. OXALOSUCCINATE DECARBOXYLASE
(Oxalosuccinate Carboxy-lyase)

A. Introduction

Both the NAD- and the NADP-specific isocitrate dehydrogenase systems catalyse the reversible oxidative decarboxylation of L_s-isocitrate to α-ketoglutarate plus CO_2. However, only the latter system catalyses the NADPH-dependent reduction and the divalent metal-dependent decarboxylation of exogenous oxalosuccinate (eqn. 1, 2) [for review see Krebs and Lowenstein, 1960].

$$\text{Isocitrate} + NADP^+ \rightarrow \text{oxalosuccinate} + NADPH + H^+ \qquad (1)$$

$$\text{Oxalosuccinate} \xrightleftharpoons[\hphantom{Mn^{++}}]{Mn^{++} \text{ or } Mg^{++}} \alpha\text{-ketoglutarate} + CO_2 \qquad (2)$$

Using the NADP-specific enzyme, the formation of oxalosuccinate from isocitrate can be demonstrated in the absence of a divalent metal. Attempts to differentially purify two separate enzymes, catalysing isocitrate dehydrogenation and oxalosuccinate decarboxylation, respectively, have been unsuccessful (Moyle and Dixon, 1956; Silbert *et al.*, 1957). Thus, the reactions shown in eqn. 1 and 2 are assumed to be catalysed by a single "isocitrate enzyme"; further, it is probable that enzyme-bound oxalo-succinate rather than the free acid is the physiological intermediate (Kornberg and Pricer, 1951; Ramakrishnan and Martin, 1955).

B. Method of assay

Unless the investigator is specifically concerned with assaying the reactions of a purified isocitrate dehydrogenase system, it is more convenient to measure the oxidative decarboxylation of isocitrate rather than to assay for oxalo succinate decarboxylation activity. Accordingly, procedures by which the latter activity may be assayed are cited but are not described in detail. Using crude enzyme preparations, the decarboxylation of oxalo-succinate may be determined manometrically under carefully controlled conditions (Barban and Ajl, 1953). Purified enzyme preparations are best assayed spectrophotometrically (Kornberg et al., 1948) by measuring the rate of increase in absorbance at 240 nm due to the formation of an oxalosuccinate-Mn complex; this increase in absorbance is followed by a rapid decrease indicating decarboxylation.

VII. α-KETOGLUTARATE DEHYDROGENASE SYSTEM
(Overall Reaction)

A. Introduction

The α-ketoglutarate dehydrogenase system in *E. coli* and in animal tissues exists in the form of a complex (Sanadi, 1963; Reed and Cox, 1966) which catalyses the overall reaction shown in eqn. (1).

$$\alpha\text{-Ketoglutarate} + CoA.SH + NAD^+ \rightarrow \text{succinyl-S-CoA} + CO_2 + \\ + NADH + H^+ (1)$$

The components of the purified complex (mol. wt. $2\cdot4 \times 10^6$) include three enzymes, Mg^{2+}, thiamine pyrophosphate (TPP), a lipoyl moiety, flavine adenine dinucleotide (FAD) and a disulphide group. Although the complex may be isolated as an intact moiety by appropriate methods, it is often desirable to measure the overall reaction using crude enzyme preparations. The individual components of the complex may become disaggregated when extracts are subjected to such routine purification processes as $(NH_4)_2SO_4$ fractionation. Methods by which the component enzymes of the complex may be assayed individually using crude preparations are described in a subsequent section.

The overall oxidation of α-ketoglutarate eqn. (1) is considered to proceed via the reaction sequence shown in eqn. (2–6) where: $R = HOOC -(CH_2)_2-$; $LipS_2$ = an enzyme-bound lipoyl moiety and the brackets represent enzyme bound intermediates. E_1 = α-ketoglutarate decarboxylase; E_2 = lipoyl reductase transsuccinylase and E_3 = dihydrolipoyl dehydrogenase.

$$R\text{–}CO\text{–}COOH + TPP\text{–}E_1 \rightarrow [R\text{–}CH(OH)\text{–}TPP]\text{–}E_1 + CO_2 \quad (2)$$

$$[R\text{–}CH(OH)\text{–}TPP]\text{–}E_1 + [LipS_2]\text{–}E_2 \rightarrow [R\text{–}CO\text{–}S\text{–}LipSH]\text{–}E_2 + TPP\text{–}E_1 \quad (3)$$

$$[R\text{–}CO\text{–}S\text{–}LipSH]\text{–}E_2 + CoA.SH \rightarrow [Lip(SH)_2]\text{–}E_2 + R\text{–}CO\text{–}SCoA \quad (4)$$

$$[Lip(SH)_2]\text{–}E_2 + E_3\text{–}FAD \rightarrow [LipS_2]\text{–}E_2 + \text{Reduced } E_3\text{–}FAD \quad (5)$$

$$\text{Reduced } E_3\text{–}FAD + NAD^+ \rightarrow E_3\text{–}FAD + NADH + H^+ \quad (6)$$

B. Method of assay: Spectrophotometric assay

1. *Principle*

The overall conversion of α-ketoglutarate to succinyl-CoA plus CO_2 [eqn. (1)] is most easily assayed by measuring the reduction of NAD spectrophotometrically. The procedure employed by Amarasingham and Davis (1965), for assaying the α-ketoglutarate dehydrogenase system in sonic extracts of *E. coli*, is described below. It is based on the principle that in crude extracts of *E. coli*, 3-acetyl-NAD (APNAD) will substitute for NAD in the α-ketoglutarate dehydrogenase reaction, but is less susceptible to reoxidation than is the natural cofactor.

2. *Reagents*

    500 mM Tris.HCl, pH 8·5
    78 mM L-cysteine;
    250 mM Potassium α-ketoglutarate
    2·6 mM CoA.SH
    60 mM APNAD
    Enzyme solution to be assayed.

3. *Procedure*

The reaction mixture contains in 3·0 ml: enzyme, 1·0 ml Tris.HCl buffer, and 0·1 ml each of cysteine, α-ketoglutarate, CoA.SH, APNAD. All components except APNAD are preincubated for 3 min; then the reaction is initiated by addition of APNAD to the experimental cuvette and the increase in absorbance at 365 nm is recorded. An amount of enzyme extract should be employed which gives a linear rate of APNAD reduction over a period of 1 min. The rate of APNAD reduction observed in the absence of α-ketoglutarate is subtracted from that obtained with the complete system.

4. Enzyme unit and specific activity

One unit is the amount of enzyme causing the formation of 1 μmole of reduced APNAD per min. The ΔA_{356} divided by 3·01 is equal to the total number of μmoles of APNAD reduced. Specific activity is expressed as units per milligram of protein.

5. Comments

The spectrophotometric assay is satisfactory when the purified complex is employed; however, the data must be interpreted with caution when assaying crude preparations possessing NADH oxidase activity. It cannot be assumed a priori that APNAD will substitute for NAD in the α-ketoglutarate dehydrogenase system of other organisms. In addition, extracts of various micro-organisms may differ in their ability to reoxidize APNADH.

Using the procedure described above, the α-ketoglutarate dehydrogenase system in extracts of E. coli exhibit maximal activity in a pH range of 8·5–9·0, and do not show a requirement for exogenous Mg^{2+} or TPP. Since these co-factors are essential components of the purified complex, it is advisable, particularly if dialysed enzyme preparations are employed, to include as a control a complete system containing TTP and Mg^{2+}. For other modifications of the spectrophotometric procedure see Hager and Kornberg (1961), Holzer et al. (1963) and Mukherjee et al. (1965).

C. Method of assay: Manometric assay

1. Principle

This method (Kaufman, 1955), may be employed to assay the overall reaction at all stages of purity of the α-ketoglutarate dehydrogenase complex. The assay is based on measuring the CoA.SH and NAD-dependent evolution of CO_2 from α-ketoglutarate in the presence of excess glutamate dehydrogenase and excess succinyl-CoA deacylase [eqn. (1) and (7–8)]. Under these conditions, eqn. (1) represents the rate limiting step:

$$\alpha\text{-Ketoglutarate} + CoA.SH + NAD^+ \rightarrow \text{succinyl-S-CoA} + CO_2 + \quad\quad\quad\quad\quad\quad\quad\quad\quad\quad\quad\quad NADH + H^+ \quad (1)$$

$$\alpha\text{-Ketoglutarate} + NH_3 + NADH \rightarrow \text{L-glutamate} + NAD^+ \quad (7)$$

$$\text{Succinyl-S-CoA} \rightarrow \text{succinate} + CoA.SH \quad (8)$$

SUM:

$$2\ \alpha\text{-Ketoglutarate} + NH_3 \rightarrow \text{succinate} + CO_2 + \text{L-glutamate}$$

2. *Reagents*

100 mM Potassium phosphate buffer, pH 7·4;
100 mM NH$_4$Cl;
1·5 mM NAD;
1·3 mM CoA.SH
500 mM Potassium α-ketoglutarate
Glutamate dehydrogenase (obtained commercially).
Succinyl-CoA deacylase (purified from pig heart; Gergely, 1955).
Enzyme solution to be assayed.

3. *Procedure*

The assay system contains in 2·0 ml: 1·0 ml phosphate buffer, and 0·1 ml each of NH$_4$Cl, NAD, CoA.SH and α-ketoglutarate. An excess of glutamate dehydrogenase and succinyl-CoA deacylase (10 units each) is added to regenerate NAD and CoA.SH respectively. The reaction is initiated by tipping in α-ketoglutarate from the sidearm of the Warburg vessels after equilibration under N$_2$ at 37° and CO$_2$ evolution is measured as described by Umbreit *et al.* (1964). Appropriate controls should include complete systems individually lacking α-ketoglutarate and enzyme extract.

4. *Enzyme unit and specific activity*

One unit is the amount of enzyme catalysing the evolution of 1 μmole of CO$_2$ per min. Specific activity is expressed as units per milligram of protein.

5. *Comments*

Although the manometric assay is more laborious than the spectrophotometric assay, it is not complicated by the presence of NADH oxidase in crude extracts. Unless the manometric assay is to be employed on a routine basis, it is desirable to avoid the purification of succinyl-CoA deacylase. Theoretically, this enzyme can be replaced by providing excess CoA.SH.Titration of the effect of increasing concentrations of CoA.SH on CO$_2$ evolution can be determined. The lowest CoA.SH concentration which is not rate-limiting should be selected for future assays.

VIII. OXOGLUTARATE DEHYDROGENASE

[2-Oxoglutarate: Lipoate Oxidoreductase (acceptor-acylating)
EC 1.2.4.2] (α-Ketoglutarate Decarboxylase)

A. Introduction

The first enzyme of the α-ketoglutarate dehydrogenase system, α-ketoglutarate decarboxylase (for review see Sanadi 1963), catalyses a reaction between α-ketoglutarate and TPP in which a succinic semialdehyde-TPP-enzyme complex is formed and CO_2 is liberated [eqn. (2)]. The decarboxylation reaction can be assayed using ferricyanide as an electron acceptor (eqn. 9).

$$\alpha\text{-Ketoglutarate} + 2Fe(CN)_6^{-3} + H_2O \rightarrow \text{succinate} + CO_2 +$$
$$2Fe(CN)_6^{-4} + 2H^+ \quad (9)$$

Under the assay conditions, the "active aldehyde"-enzyme complex is further oxidized by ferricyanide to succinyl-TPP which undergoes hydrolysis in aqueous media. In the intact complex, in the absence of ferricyanide, the "active aldehyde" is further oxidized by a protein bound lipoyl moiety in a reductase transsuccinylase reaction.

B. Method of assay

1. Principle

The decarboxylation of α-ketoglutarate using ferricyanide as an electron acceptor may be assayed in crude enzyme extracts either colorimetrically by measuring ferricyanide reduction, or manometrically, by measuring CO_2 evolution. The colorimetric procedure has been described in detail for pyruvate decarboxylase (Reed and Willms, 1966) and may be modified for estimation of α-ketoglutarate decarboxylase activity by substituting α-ketoglutarate for pyruvate. The manometric procedure employed by Hager and Kornberg (1961) is described below:

2. Reagents

200 mM Potassium phosphate buffer, pH 6.0
200 mM Potassium α-ketoglutarate
250 mM $K_3Fe(CN)_6$
40 mM TPP
Enzyme solution to be assayed.

3. Procedure

The complete assay system contains in 2.0 ml: enzyme, 0.5 ml phosphate buffer, and 0.1 ml each of α-ketoglutarate, $K_3Fe(CN)_6$, and TPP. After equilibration under N_2 at 37°, the reaction is initiated by tipping in α-ketoglutarate from the sidearm and CO_2 evolution is measured in a Warburg respirometer.

4. Enzyme units and specific activity

In the manometric assay, a unit is the amount of enzyme catalysing the evolution of 1 μmole of CO_2 in 30 min. Specific activity is expressed as units per milligram of protein.

C. Comments

Both assay methods are applicable using either purified or crude enzyme preparations, but crude extracts should be dialysed to remove endogenous substrates, pyridine nucleotides and CoA.SH. In each assay method, incubation mixtures individually lacking substrate and enzyme extract should be employed as controls. A $^{14}CO_2$-α-ketoglutarate exchange assay for the decarboxylase enzyme has also been described (Hager and Kornberg, 1961).

IX. LIPOYL REDUCTASE TRANSSUCCINYLASE
[Succinyl-CoA: Dihydrolipoate S-Succinyl Transferase EC 2.3.1.12]
(Lipoate Succinyl Transferase)

A. Introduction

The second enzyme of the α-ketoglutarate dehydrogenase system, lipoyl reductase transsuccinylase (for review see Sanadi, 1963), catalyses the reactions shown in eqn. (3–4). The enzyme contains, as a prosthetic group, a lipoyl moiety bound in amide linkage to the ϵ-amino group of a lysine residue. It is proposed that the "active aldehyde" resulting from the decarboxylase reaction [eqn. (2)] is oxidized by enzyme-bound lipoate to form an S-succinyl-dihydrolipoyl-enzyme intermediate [eqn. (3)] which then transfers the acyl group to CoA.SH with liberation of the dihydrolipoyl-enzyme [eqn. (4)]. Thus, the enzyme is considered to catalyse a reductive transacylation reaction. In an alternate mechanism for this reaction [eqn. (10, 11)], it is proposed that the reduction and acylation of the enzyme bound lipoyl moiety occur as distinct steps.

$$[R\text{–}CH(OH)\text{–}TPP]\text{–}E_1 + [LipS_2]\text{–}E_2 \rightarrow [R\text{–}CO\text{–}TPP]\text{–}E_1 + [Lip(SH)_2]\text{–}E_2 \quad (10)$$

$$R\text{–}CO\text{–}TPP\text{–}E_1 + [Lip(SH)_2]\text{–}E_2 \rightarrow [R\text{–}CO\text{–}S\text{–}LipSH]\text{–}E_2 + TPP\text{–}E_1 \quad (11)$$

B. Method of assay

1. *Principle*

The enzyme is most conveniently assayed (Reed and Willms, 1966) in crude extracts by measuring the transfer of the succinyl group from succinyl-CoA to dihydrolipoic acid or dihydrolipoamide [eqn. (12)]. This reaction does not involve participation of the enzyme bound lipoyl prosthetic group:

$$Succinyl\text{–}S\text{–}CoA + Lip(SH)_2 \rightarrow succinyl\text{–}S\text{–}LipSH + CoA.SH \quad (12)$$

In the assay, catalytic amounts of succinyl-CoA are generated by the addition of succinate, CoA.SH, ATP and purified succinyl-CoA synthetase. The formation of S–succinyl-dihydrolipoic acid or S–succinyl–dihydrolipoamide from succinyl–CoA is determined colorimetrically as the ferric succinohydroxamate complex.

2. Reagents

1M Tris-HCl, pH 7·3;

100 mM MgCl$_2$;

1M Potassium succinate;

200 mM ATP;

2 mM CoA.SH;

100 mM (−) Dihydrolipoic acid [prepared by reduction of (−) lipoic acid with NaBH$_4$ (Gunsalus and Razzell 1957)]

Succinyl-CoA synthetase [purified from pig heart (Kaufman (1955)] enzyme solution to be assayed.

2M NH$_2$OH solution, pH 6·4 (freshly prepared by adjusting 4M NH$_2$OH.HCl to pH 6·4 with 3·5M NaOH and diluting to a final concentration of 2M).

100 mM Potassium citrate buffer, pH 6·4

Ferric chloride reagent (prepared by mixing equal volumes of 3·0N HCl, 12% trichloroacetic acid and 5% FeCl$_3$ in 0·1N HCl).

To prepare the reference standard, dissolve 1·0 g of succinic anhydride in 40 ml of the neutralized hydroxylamine solution, and dilute to 100 ml with water. When 0·5 ml of this solution is diluted to 40 ml with water, 1·0 ml of the final solution contains 1 μmole of succinohydroxamic acid giving a Klett reading of 61 (Klett photoelectric colorimeter, filter No. 54) Alternatively, readings may be taken spectrophotometrically at 540 nm.

3. Procedure

To a 13 × 100 mm test tube are added 0·1 ml each of Tris.HCl buffer, MgCl$_2$, succinate, ATP and dihydrolipoic acid. Succinyl-CoA synthetase (5 units), enzyme extract and water are added to a volume of 0·9 ml and the reaction is initiated by the addition of 0·1 ml CoA.SH. After incubation at 30° for 30 min, the reaction is terminated by the addition of 1·0 ml of neutralized NH$_2$OH and 1·0 ml of citrate buffer. The mixture is incubated at room temperature for an additional 10 min, then the coloured complex is developed by adding (with shaking) 3·0 ml of ferric chloride reagent. Precipitated protein is removed by centrifugation and the absorbance of the supernant fluid is determined at 540 nm against a reagent blank (all components except enzyme extract and succinyl-CoA synthetase) using a suitable spectrophotometer.

To determine the colour due to the formation of succinyl-CoA, a control tube containing all the components of the complete system except dihydro-lipoic acid is employed. The absorbance of this control is substracted from that obtained with the complete system; the difference represents ferric succinohydroxamate absorbance due to formation of S-succinyl-dihydro-lipoic acid.

To calculate μmoles of S-succinyl-dihydrolipoic acid formed during incubation, a standard curve is prepared using synthetic succino-hydroxamic acid (as described below for succinyl-CoA synthetase). An amount of enzyme extract should be employed such that 0·5–2·0 μmoles of S-succinyl-dihydrolipoate are formed during the incubation period.

4. Enzyme unit and specific activity

One unit is the amount of enzyme catalysing the formation of 1·0 μmole of S–succinyl–dihydrolipoic acid in 60 min. Specific activity is expressed as units per milligram of protein.

C. Comments

This procedure is suitable at all stages of enzyme purification. Assay of lipoyl reductase transsuccinylase requires that the catalytic formation of succinyl-CoA be non-rate-limiting. Since crude extracts of many micro-organisms contain succinyl-CoA synthetase of relatively high activity, it may be unnecessary to add the purified enzyme to the reaction mixture.

The initial velocity of the reaction may be assayed by determining S-suc-cinyl dihydrolipoate formation at time intervals less than 30 min and the specific activity defined accordingly.

X. DIHYDROLIPOYL DEHYDROGENASE
[NADH$_2$: Lipoamide Oxidoreductase EC 1.6.4.3]

A. Introduction

The third enzyme of the α-ketoglutarate dehydrogenase system, dihydro-lipoyl dehydrogenase, contains two functional prosthetic groups, FAD and a disulphide moiety (for review see Massey, 1963). It catalyses the NAD-dependent reoxidation of the enzyme-bound dihydrolipoyl moiety [eqn. (5, 6)] formed in the preceding reductive transacylation reaction. It is proposed that reoxidation of the enzyme-bound dihydrolipoate is accompanied by reduction of the disulphide group of the flavoprotein to a dithiol (presumably by a disulphide exchange reaction). The dithiol is then reoxidized with concomitant reduction of FAD through an intermediate which has an absorption maximum at 530 nm. FADH$_2$, in turn, is reoxidized by NAD, thus completing the oxidation reduction cycle. For the sake of simplicity, the participation of the dithiol group in eqn. (5) has not been shown.

B. Method of assay

1. *Principle*

When a purified preparation is employed, dihydrolipoyl dehydrogenase is most easily assayed by measuring the rate of NADH oxidation in the presence of soluble lipoamide (Reed and Willms, 1966). In extracts possessing NADH oxidase activity, this procedure is not suitable and enzyme activity is best assayed by measuring the disappearance of thiol groups in the presence of catalytic amounts of NAD (Hager and Gunsalus, 1953). NAD regeneration is accomplished by coupling the lipoyl dehydrogenase of the extract to crystalline lactate dehydrogenase plus pyruvate (eqn. (12–13)]. Thiol concentration is conveniently assayed by the method of Ellman (1959).

$$Lip(SH)_2 + NAD^+ \rightarrow LipS_2 + NADH + H^+ \qquad (12)$$

$$Pyruvate + NADH \rightarrow lactate + NAD^+ \qquad (13)$$

2. *Reagents*

  500 mM Potassium phosphate buffer, pH 7·0
  500 mM Potassium phosphate buffer, pH 8·0
  30 mM (−) Dihydrolipoic acid [prepared by reduction of (−) lipoic acid with NaBH⁴ (Gunsalus and Razzell, 1957)]
  200 mM Sodium pyruvate
  5 mM NAD;
  Lactate dehydrogenase (obtained commercially);
  DTNB reagent [freshly prepared by dissolving 19·8 mg of 5,5'*bis*-dithiol(2-nitrobenzoic acid) in 5 ml of 100 mM potassium phosphate buffer pH 7·0]
  Enzyme solution to be assayed.

3. *Procedure*

To a 13×100 mm test tube are added 0·2 ml phosphate buffer, pH 7·0 and 0·1 ml each of pyruvate and NAD. Crystalline lactate dehydrogenase (2000 units), enzyme extract and water are added to a volume of 0·9 ml and the reaction is initiated by the addition of 0·1 ml of dihydrolipoic acid. After incubation at 30° for 30 min, the reaction is terminated by the addition of 2·0 ml of 95% ethanol. Precipitated protein is removed by centrifugation and aliquots of the supernatant solution are analysed for residual thiol.

The determination of thiol concentration is performed in photometric cuvettes, which contain in 3·0 ml: 0·10–0·40 ml aliquots of the solution to be analysed, 0·50 ml of phosphate buffer, pH 8·0 and 0·02 ml of DTNB. The reaction is initiated by addition of DTNB. After a 5-min incubation period, the absorbance of the solution is determined at 412 nm against a reagent blank containing all components except test solution.

Thiol concentration is calculated using a standard curve prepared with varying concentrations of dihydrolipoic acid (0·02–0·20 μmoles). To compensate for colour formation due to the enzyme extract, a control tube containing all the components of the complete system except dihydrolipoic acid is employed. The absorbance of this control is subtracted from that obtained using an equal aliquot of the complete reaction mixture.

Initial thiol concentration is determined by analysing a 0·20 ml aliquot of the complete system immediately deproteinized by addition of alcohol.

4. Enzyme units and specific activity

One unit is the amount of enzyme catalysing the oxidation of 1·0 μmole of dihydrolipoic acid in 60 min. Specific activity is expressed as units per milligram of protein.

C. Comments

This procedure is suitable for assaying dihydrolipoyl dehydrogenase at all stages of enzyme purification, but purified preparations are more easily assayed by measuring the lipoic acid-dependent oxidation of NADH. The initial velocity of the reaction may be determined by measuring residual thiol concentration at time intervals less than 30 min and specific activity defined accordingly.

XI. SUCCINYL–CoA SYNTHETASE [SUCCINATE: CoA LIGASE (ADP); EC 6.2.1.5]
(Succinate Thiokinase; P Enzyme)

A. Introduction

The oxidation of α-ketoglutarate is accompanied by a substrate level phosphorylation reaction involving a nucleoside diphosphate (NDP)-dependent conversion of succinyl-CoA to succinic acid (eqn. 1).

$$\text{Succinyl–S–CoA} + \text{NDP} + \text{Pi} \rightarrow \text{Succinic acid} + \text{NTP} + \text{CoA–SH} \quad (1)$$

With succinyl-CoA synthetase of E. coli, NDP and NTP are adenosine di- and triphosphates; mammalian preparations of the enzyme require either guanosine or inosine nucleotides.

For background, the reader is referred to the comprehensive review of this enzyme by Hager (1962). More recently, studies with the E. coli enzyme (Nishimura and Meister, 1965; Nishimura, 1967) have clarified the mechanism of the overall reaction. The presently postulated reaction sequence catalysed by this enzyme is shown below [eqn. 2, 3 and 4].

$$\text{Enzyme} + \text{Succinyl--S--CoA} + \text{Pi} \rightleftharpoons \text{Enzyme-succinyl phosphate} + \text{CoA--SH} \quad (2)$$

$$\text{Enzyme-succinyl phosphate} \rightleftharpoons \text{P--Enzyme} + \text{Succinate} \quad (3)$$

$$\text{P--Enzyme} + \text{ADP} \rightleftharpoons \text{ATP} + \text{Enzyme} \quad (4)$$

B. Method of assay

1. *Principle*

The procedure of Kaufman *et al.* (1953; 1955) is simple and sensitive and is the only completely described method. It is based on the formation of succinyl--S--CoA from succinate, ATP, CoA and enzyme. In the presence of excess hydroxylamine, succinyl-CoA reacts to form succinohydroxamic acid with continual regeneration of CoA. Succinohydroxamic acid, in the presence of ferric salts at acid pH, produces complexes that may be quantitated by colorimetric assay (Lipmann and Tuttle, 1945).

2. *Reagents*

$1M$ Tris . HCl, pH 7·4
$1M$ Potassium succinate
100 mM ATP
1·3 mM CoA
200 mM GSH (prepare and neutralize just before use)
100 mM $MgCl_2$
$2M$ NH_2OH neutralized (see page 443)
$FeCl_3$ solution (see page 443)
Enzyme solution to be assayed.

Just before use, prepare 2·0M NH_2OH by neutralizing stock 28% solution of NH_2OH.HCl (4·0M) with an equal volume of 14% NaOH (3·5N). The ferric chloride reagent is prepared by mixing equal volumes of 5% $FeCl_3$ (in 0·1N HCl), 12% trichloroacetic acid and 3·0N HCl.

3. *Procedure*

To 0·5 ml of the NH₂OH reagent, add 0·1 ml of each of the other reagents. Allowing for the volume of enzyme solution, which is used to start the reaction, add water to a final volume of 2·0 ml. Incubate the reaction mixture at 37° for 30 min. Add 2·0 ml of FeCl₃ reagent to stop the reaction remove the protein precipitate by centrifugation and immediately read the absorbance. The rate of reaction is proportional to enzyme concentration in the range of 0 to 1·5 μmoles of succinohydroxamic acid. Replicate reactions with varying concentrations of enzyme should be incubated. With crude enzyme solutions, a blank should be run containing the complete system to which the FeCl₃ reagent is added at zero time. It is essential that another blank, containing the complete system except for succinate, be incubated especially when using crude enzyme preparations.

4. *Enzyme unit and specific activity*

One unit is the amount of enzyme catalysing the formation of 1·0 μmole of succinohydroxamic acid in 30 min at 37°. Specific activity is expressed as units per milligram of protein.

C. Comments

The assay can be used with crude extracts as well as with more purified preparations of the enzyme. When initial velocities are measured in which the reaction is complete within 30 min, the enzyme activity defined must reflect the change in conditions. It should be noted that phosphate and fluoride (often used to inhibit phosphatases present in the assays) inhibit colour development in the reaction of hydroxamic acids with FeCl₃ (Stadtman, 1957). Therefore, proper precautions must be taken in washing cells harvested from media containing these compounds, in the use of these compounds in solutions in which cells are suspended prior to breakage and in solutions used for dialysis. Since NH₂OH can markedly inhibit the enzyme (Kaufman, 1955), the concentration of this reagent recommended above should not normally be exceeded.

XII. SUCCINYL-CoA HYDROLASE
[EC 3.1.2.3] (Succinyl-CoA Deacylase)

A. Introduction

Succinyl-CoA synthetase catalyses the formation of succinic acid, a key intermediate in the Krebs tricarboxylic acid cycle. The functioning of succinyl-CoA deacylase affords an alternative route for the formation of succinate from succinyl-CoA [eqn. 1] (Gergely *et al.*, 1952; Kaufman *et al.*, 1953; Hift *et al.*, 1953; Gergely, 1955), although the importance of the deacylase relative to the synthetase in providing succinate *in vivo* is questionable (Hager, 1962).

$$\text{Succinyl–S–CoA} + \text{H}_2\text{O} \rightarrow \text{Succinate} + \text{HS–CoA} \qquad (1)$$

The discovery of the deacylase was important in the initial studies elucidating the oxidation of α-ketoglutarate. However, it does not appear to be a component of the α-ketoglutarate dehydrogenase complex in *E. coli* or mammalian cells (Reed and Cox, 1966). Surprisingly, the deacylase has been relatively ignored judging from the paucity of reports in the literature. It has been purified only from animal tissue (Gergely *et al.*, 1952; Kaufman, *et al.*, 1953; Gergely, 1955), although there is evidence for its occurrence in *Propionibacterium pentosaceum* and *Veilonella gazogenes* (Delwiche *et al.*, 1956).

B. Method of assay

Since no definitive, optimal procedure has been reported for this enzyme in crude microbial extracts, a specific method of assay cannot be recommended. Delwiche *et al.* (1956) measured the disappearance of succinyl-CoA catalysed by crude extracts using the hydroxamate assay (Lipmann and Tuttle, 1945; Stadtman, 1957) [see Succinyl-CoA Synthetase]. Two blank reactions must be run concurrently as described in the method for succinyl-CoA synthetase.

Polakis and Bartley (1965) could not detect succinyl-CoA deacylase in crude extracts of *Saccharomyces cerevisiae*. The assay was carried out in potassium phosphate buffer (50 nM), pH 6·45 using succinyl-CoA (about 0·2 mM) as substrate in the sample cuvette, but not in the reference cuvette. The reaction was started with extract and measured at 232 nm using a molar extinction coefficient $\epsilon(\text{M}^{-1}\,\text{cm}^{-1})$ of $4·5 \times 10^3$ (Stadtman, 1957). This method also suffers from the fact that a ΔA_{232} accompanies the hydrolysis of acetyl-CoA in the presence of acetyl-CoA deacylase.

A complication of any devised assay is the instability of succinyl-CoA at netural pH values (although at pH 1 it is quite stable(Simon and Shemin, 1953). Polakis and Bartley (1965) reported a spontaneous breakdown of the thiol ester at 35° and pH 6·45 of about 20 nmoles/min; Delwiche *et al.* (1945) noted that the half-life of succinyl-CoA at 30° in the absence of extract was 160 min, and in the presence of extract was about 18 min.

16

XIII. FUMARATE HYDRATASE
[L-Malate Hydro-Lyase EC 4.2.1.2] (Fumarase)

A. Introduction

Fumarate hydratase catalyses the *trans* addition of water to fumarate to form L-malate [eqn. (1)]. The reaction is reversible, has a high turnover number, and is specific for fumarate and malate.

$$\text{Fumarate} + H_2O \rightleftharpoons \text{L-malate} \qquad (1)$$

The kinetics and mechanism of fumarate hydratase have been studied extensively, particularly with the pig heart enzyme, and are reviewed by Alberty (1961). The rate and equilibrium constant of the reaction are markedly influenced by several assay parameters including, pH, temperature, and nature and concentration of anions present. At 25°, pH 6·5, and 0·01 ionic strength, the equilibrium ratio of malate to fumarate is 4·4.

B. Method of assay

1. *Principle*

Fumarate hydratase may be assayed in several different ways. The reaction has been followed by determining malate formation fluorometrically, (Hummel, 1949), by measuring the optical rotation of L-malic acid, (Clutterbuck, 1927), and by titrating fumaric acid with permanganate (Straub, 1935). The most convenient method is to measure the formation or utilization of fumaric acid spectrophotometrically (Racker, 1950).

The assay is similar to that described for aconitate hydratase and is based on the principle that ethylenic acids exhibit strong ultraviolet absorbance. The formation of fumarate from malate is satisfactorily assayed at 240 nm; however, due to the high extinction coefficient of fumarate, the assay of fumarate utilization must be measured either using low substrate concentrations or at a higher wavelength (300 nm). The method outlined below is that described by Massey (1955).

2. *Reagents*

    25 mM Sodium fumarate
    100 mM Potassium phosphate buffer, pH 7·3
    Enzyme solution to be assayed.

3. *Procedure*

The complete reaction mixture contains, 3·0 ml: water, enzyme extract and 1·0 ml each of fumarate and potassium phosphate. The blank cuvette lacks substrate. The reaction is initiated by addition of enzyme and the initial rate of decrease at 300 nm is recorded.

4. *Enzyme unit and specific activity*

One unit is the amount of enzyme which catalyses an initial decrease in absorbance of 0·003 per min. Each 0·003 change in optical density is equivalent to $8·46 \times 10^{-4}$ μmoles of fumarate. Specific activity is expressed as units per milligram of protein.

C. Comments

This procedure, using either fumarate or malate as the substrate, is suitable at all stages of enzyme purification. For accurate determinations, temperature must be controlled. While the assay is considerably more sensitive at a wavelength of 240 nm, only small amounts of enzyme can be used due to strong protein absorbance. At 300 nm, the sensitivity of the assay is decreased, but greater amounts of extract can be employed.

XIV. MALATE DEHYDROGENASE
[L-Malate: NAD Oxidoreductase EC 1.1.1.37]

A. Introduction

Malate dehydrogenase catalyses the reversible, pyridine nucleotide-dependent dehydrogenation of L-malate to oxaloacetate:

$$\text{L-Malate} + \text{NAD}^+ \rightleftarrows \text{Oxaloacetate} + \text{NADH} + \text{H}^+$$

The discovery and earlier literature concerning malate dehydrogenase have been reviewed by Schlenk (1951) and more recently by Kun (1963). Although both NAD and NADP, and their reduced forms, serve as co-factors in the reaction, the former (NAD) is much more active (Mehler *et al.*, 1948). It should also be noted that the purified enzyme has a rather wide substrate specificity (Davis and Kun, 1957).

B. Method of assay

1. *Principle*

The reaction is followed spectrophotometrically by measuring the rate of NADH oxidation at 340 nm in the presence of enzyme and oxaloacetate. The method below is essentially that previously described by Ochoa (1955) for assaying the enzyme from pig heart.

2. *Reagents*

        250 mM Phosphate buffer, pH 7·4
        1·5 mM NADH
        7·5 mM Oxaloacetate, pH 7·4
        Enzyme solution to be assayed.

3. Procedure

The reaction mixture contains 0·1 ml of buffer, 0·05 ml each of NADH, oxaloacetate, enzyme and water to a final volume of 1·0 ml. The reaction is started by the addition of oxaloacetate and readings at 340 nm are made against a blank containing all components except NADH. The decrease in optical density between 30 and 34 sec after the start of the reaction is linear and is used to calculate the enzyme activity.

4. Enzyme unit and specific activity

One unit is the amount of enzyme catalysing the oxidation of 1·0 μmole of NADH per min. Specific activity is expressed as units per milligram of protein. The ΔA_{340} divided by 6·22 equals the number of μmoles of NADH oxidized under these conditions.

C. Comments

The equilibrium of the reaction lies far to the left (malate formation) and the experimental values of the overall equilibrium constant are $K_{eq} = 1 \cdot 04 - 1 \cdot 17 \times 10^{-12}$ (Raval and Wolfe, 1962; Burton and Wilson, 1953). For this reason, the reaction is usually studied by measuring the oxidation of NADH in the presence of oxaloacetate. However, since the latter is unstable and should be prepared fresh, two other methods of assay are described. The first is that described by Hohorst (1965). When protons are bound by the use of an alkaline reaction medium and oxaloacetate is trapped as the hydrazone, the reaction proceeds to the right:

$$\text{L-Malate} + \text{NAD}^+ + \text{hydrazine} \rightarrow \text{oxaloacetate hydrazone} + \text{NADH} + \text{H}^+$$

The second method, using the 3-acetylpyridine analogue of NAD (AP–NAD) without the use of a trapping agent for oxaloacetate, is made possible by the favourable redox potential of AP–NAD/AP–NADH in contrast to that of NAD/NADH (Holzer and Soling, 1965).

Both of these methods depend upon measuring the rate of NAD or AP–NAD reduction spectrophotometrically. With this enzyme assay as well, the activity of NADH oxidase must be considered.

XV. ISOCITRATE LYASE

[L_s-Isocitrate Glyoxylate-Lyase EC 4.1.3.1] Isocitritase, Isocitratase

A. Introduction

Isocitrate lyase catalyses the aldol cleavage of L_s-isocitrate to glyoxylate and succinate

$$L_s\text{-Isocitrate} \rightleftarrows \text{glyoxylate} + \text{succinate} \tag{1}$$

Although the enzyme is widely distributed in bacteria, fungi, plants and protozoa (Kornberg, 1959; Wegener et al., 1968), it has never been reported to occur in higher animals.

B. Method of assay

Isocitrate lyase catalyses a reversible reaction which can be assayed in either the forward (L_s-isocitrate→glyoxylate + succinate) or the back (glyoxylate + succinate→$L_s$isocitrate) direction. Assay methods for measuring the forward reaction usually depend, in principle, upon determining the glyoxylate formed (Olson, 1959; McFadden and Howes, 1960; Daron and Gunsalus, 1962) whereas the back reaction is measured employing a coupled assay system to measure the isocitrate formed (Daron et al., 1966).

C. Assay of the forward reaction

1. *Principle*

The spectrophotometric assay originally described by Dixon and Kornberg (1959) is recommended because of its relative simplicity and reproducibility. The method depends upon measuring glyoxylate formation in the presence of isocitrate and enzyme, as the phenylhydrazone derivative at 324 nm.

2. *Reagents*

     500 mM Tris.HCl buffer, pH 7·5
     100 mM Phenylhydrazine.HCl (freshly prepared, analytical grade)
     1 mM Cysteine.HCl
     100 mM MgCl$_2$
     20 mM Potassium isocitrate (*allo* free)
     Enzyme solution to be assayed.

3. *Procedure*

To the experimental cuvette are added 0·10 ml each of Tris buffer, and phenylhydrazine hydrochloride and 0·05 ml each of cysteine, MgCl$_2$ and enzyme. Water is added to make the volume 1·45 ml. The reference cuvette is prepared in the same way except that water is added to give a total volume of 1·50 ml. The optical density is adjusted to zero, and the reaction started by the addition of 0·05 ml of isocitrate to the experimental cuvette. There is a short lag period after which the optical density change remains linear for several minutes. The linear portion of the curve is used to calculate enzyme activity.

4. Enzyme unit and specific activity

One unit is the amount of enzyme catalysing the formation of 1.0 μmole of glyoxylic acid phenylhydrazone in 1 min. Since the ΔA_{324} of 1 μmole/ ml of glyoxylic acid phenylhydrozone is 1.7×10^4 (Dixon and Kornberg, 1959), 1 unit of enzyme in the assay system described above catalyses a ΔA_{324} of 11.55 per min. Therefore, a ΔA_{324} of 0.100 per min is equivalent to 0.0087 unit.

5. Comments

The enzyme exhibits a requirement for $-SH$ and is particularly sensitive to heavy metal inactivation during purification. These properties have been discussed by McFadden and co-workers (1964). It should also be noted that Tris.HCl buffer should be employed since phosphate, imidazole or histidine buffers have been observed to markedly affect substrate K_m values and enzyme inhibitors (Reeves, H. C. and Ajl, S., unpublished data).

D. Assay of the back reaction

1. Principle

The back reaction is most conveniently measured using a coupled spectrophotometric assay:

$$\text{Glyoxylate} + \text{succinate} \rightarrow L_s\text{-isocitrate} \qquad (2)$$

$$L_s\text{-Isocitrate} + NADP^+ \rightarrow \alpha\text{-ketoglutarate} + NADPH + H^+ + CO_2 \qquad (3)$$

The coupled assay is very satisfactory because of the low K_m for isocitrate (Ochoa, 1945) and the equilibrium favouring α-ketoglutarate formation (Ochoa, 1945). Isocitrate dehydrogenase is always used in excess in the assay so that either isocitrate lyase or its substrates, succinate or glyoxylate, is limiting. The method described is a modification of that reported by Daron et al. (1966).

2. Reagents

200 mM Tris.HCl buffer, pH 8.0
60 mM $MgCl_2$
20 mM Cysteine.HCl
10 mM NADP
20 mM Sodium succinate
20 mM Sodium glyoxylate
Isocitrate dehydrogenase (available commercially)
Enzyme solution to be assayed.

3. Procedure

In a total volume of 1·5 ml, add 1·0 ml buffer, 0·5 ml each of MgCl$_2$ NADP, sodium glyoxylate, isocitric dehydrogenase and 0·10 ml each of cysteine. HCl and the enzyme solution to be assayed. The absorbance at 340 nm is recorded for several minutes and 0·05 ml of sodium succinate is added. The resultant increase in optical density is linear for several minutes and the initial slope is used to calculate the enzyme activity. Under these conditions, a ΔA_{340} of 0·242 is equal to the formation of 1 μmole of NADP.

4. Enzyme unit and specific activity

One unit is the amount of enzyme catalysing the formation of 1·0 μmole of NADPH per min. Specific activity is expressed as units per milligram of protein.

5. Comments

Although the activity of isocitrate lyase can be easily measured in both crude and purified preparations using the phenylhydrazine assay, the coupled system described here is usually restricted to purified preparations. The use of the coupled assay with crude preparations is often precluded because of the presence of NADPH oxidase. In addition, in many cases employing crude extracts, a reduction of NADP is often observed with glyoxylate in the absence of succinate (Reeves, H. C. and Ajl, S. J., unpublished data).

XVI. MALATE SYNTHASE
[L-Malate glyoxylate-lyase (CoA-acetylating) EC 4.1.3.2]
(Malate synthetase)

A. Introduction

Malate synthase catalyses the condensation of acetyl-S-CoA with glyoxylate to form malate. The overall reaction may be written as follows:

$$Ac–S–CoA + glyoxylate + H_2O \rightarrow L\text{-malate} + CoA.SH \quad (1)$$

The recent studies by Eggerer and Klette (1967) have provided an insight into the mechanism of the enzymatic reaction. In the presence of Mg^{++} and the carboxylate-anion of glyoxylate, enolic acetyl-CoA is formed. The latter then reacts with the aldehyde-carbonyl of glyoxylate to form (S)–malyl–CoA which is hydrolysed by the enzyme to yield malate.

Although the enzyme is widely distributed in nature (Kornberg, 1959; Wegener et al., 1968), there have been no corroborated reports that it occurs in any mammalian or other higher animal systems. Multiple forms of the enzyme (isoenzymes) have been reported to exist in bacteria (Vanderwinkel and Wiame, 1965).

B. Method of assay

Although several methods of assay are available (Hummel, 1949; Dixon and Kornberg, 1959; Wegener et al., 1965; Weitzman, 1966), the spectrophotometric assay is recommended for its relative sensitivity and simplicity.

1. Principle

The spectrophotometric assay is based upon the change in absorbance at 232 nm which occurs concomitant with the cleavage of the thiol ester bond of acetyl-$_\text{s}$-CoA in the presence of glyoxylate and enzyme. The method described is essentially that described by Eggerer and Klette (1967).

2. Reagents

20 mM Pyrophosphate buffer, pH 8·0
2 mM Acetyl-S-CoA
50 mM MgCl$_2$
10 mM K$_2$Mg-EDTA
10 mM Sodium glyoxylate
20 mM Trisodium ATP
Enzyme solution to be assayed.

The acetyl-S-CoA is most conveniently prepared according to the method described by Simon and Shemin (1953) and assayed as described by Lipmann and Tuttle (1945) [see also this chapter, section of Succinate: CoA Ligase]. Acetyl-S-CoA can also be conveniently assayed using the coupled assay system described by Buckel and Eggerer (1965). This latter method is particularly advantageous since it provides a method for determining the enzymatically active thiol ester.

3. Procedure

To each of two cuvettes, add the following : 1·0 ml pyrophosphate buffer, 0·1 ml MgCl$_2$, 0·1 ml K$_2$Mg–EDTA and 0·05 ml of enzyme. 0·1 ml of acetyl–S–CoA is then added to the experimental cuvette, and 0·1 ml each of trisodium ATP and water to the reference cuvette. The decrease in absorbance at 232 nm is measured for several minutes to determine whether any acetyl–S–CoA deacylase is present, and then the reaction is started by the addition of 0·05 ml of sodium glyoxylate to the experimental cuvette. The initial velocity, which is linear for several minutes, is recorded and used to calculate the enzyme activity.

4. Enzyme unit and specific activity

One unit is the amount of enzyme catalysing the glyoxylate-dependent cleavage of $1\cdot0\ \mu$mole of acetyl-S-CoA in 1 min. The difference in molecular extinction coefficients of acetyl-CoA and its hydrolysis products (ΔA_{232}) is $4\cdot5 \times 10^3$ cm^2/mole. Therefore, under the above conditions, 1 unit of enzyme catalyses a ΔA_{232} of $3\cdot22$ per min and a ΔA_{232} of $0\cdot100$ per min is equal to $0\cdot031$ unit. Specific activity is expressed as units of enzyme per milligram of protein.

C. Comments

The assay can be used with crude extracts as well as with more purified preparations of the enzyme. It should be noted, however, that crude extracts often contain acetyl-S-CoA deacylase activity which must be taken into consideration when calculating the activity of malate synthase. The use of Tris buffer in the assay is precluded since it reacts with glyoxylate (Eggerer and Klette, 1967).

XVII. PYRUVATE DEHYDROGENASE SYSTEM

A. Introduction

An enzyme system which catalyses the lipoic acid mediated oxidative decarboxylation of pryuvate has been isolated from *Escherichia coli* (Koike, Reed and Carrol, 1960) and studied in great detail. The overall reaction is shown in eqn. (1).

$$\text{Pyruvate} + \text{CoA–SH} + \text{NAD}^+ \rightarrow \text{acetyl–S–CoA} + \text{CO}_2 +$$
$$\text{NADP}^+ + \text{H}^+ (1)$$

The *E. coli* pyruvate dehydrogenase complex has a molecular weight of ca. $4\cdot8$ million and has been separated into three enzymes:

(a) Pyruvate decarboxylase [Pyruvate: lipoate oxidoreductase (acceptor-acetylating), E.C. 1.2.4.1].

(b) Lipoyl reductase-transacetylase [Acetyl-CoA: dihydrolipoate S–acetyl–transferase, E.C. 2.3.1.12] (Lipoate acetyl-transferase).

(c) Dihydrolipoyl dehydrogenase [NADH$_2$: lipoamide oxidoreductase, E.C. 1.6.4.3] (Lipoamide dehydrogenase).

The complex from *E. coli* has been found to contain 12 molecules of pyruvate decarboxylase (mol. wt. 183,000), 6 molecules of flavoprotein (mol. wt. 112,000) and 24 subunits (mol. wt. 70,000) or 48 subunits (mol. wt. 35,000) comprising the lipoyl reductase-transacetylase aggregate (Reed and Cox, 1966).

The pyruvate dehydrogenase complex from *E. coli* is very similar to the α-ketoglutarate dehydrogenase complex (mol. wt. ca. 2·4 million) and the component enzymes catalyse the same types of reactions. The reader can find a more complete description of the pyruvate dehydrogenase complex elsewhere (Koike *et al.*, 1963 and Reed and Cox, 1966).

B. Method of assay

The assay of the individual enzymes comprising the pyruvate dehydrogenase are analogous to those described in the section of the α-ketoglutarate dehydrogenase complex (pp. 440–448). For the details of the most recent, complete and reliable assays for the individual enzymes of the pyruvate dehydrogenase complex, the reader is referred to the excellent chapter by Reed and Willms (1966).

The overall reaction, eqn. (1), may be measured by the dismutation assay which is given in detail by Reed and Willms (1966). The reaction in eqn. (1) is coupled with phosphotransacetylase (eqn. 2) and lactate dehydrogenase (eqn. 3):

$$\text{Acetyl–S–CoA} + \text{Pi} \rightarrow \text{acetyl–P} + \text{CoA–SH} \tag{2}$$

$$\text{Pyruvate} + \text{NADH} + \text{H}^+ \rightarrow \text{lactate} + \text{NAD}^+ \tag{3}$$

The assay is useful even with crude preparations of the pyruvate dehydrogenase complex.

Reed and Mukherjee (1969) have recently described in detail a simple spectrophotometric assay for the overall reaction based on reduction of NAD. Since NADH oxidase and lactate dehydrogenase interfere, the method is recommended only for relatively pure preparations of the complex.

REFERENCES

Alberty, R. A. (1961). *In* "The Enzymes" (Eds. P. D. Boyer, H. Lardy and K. Myrback), Vol. 5, p. 531. Academic Press, New York.
Amarasingham, C. R., and Davis, B. D. (1965). *J. biol. Chem.*, **240**, 3664.
Anfinson, C. B. (1955). *In* "Methods in Enzymology" (Eds. S. P. Colowick and N. O. Kaplan), Vol. I, p. 695. Academic Press, New York.
Barban, S., and Ajl, S. J. (1953). *J. Bacteriol.*, **66**, 68.
Bernofsky, C., and Utter, M. F. (1966). *J. biol. Chem.*, **241**, 5461.
Bowen, T. J., and Siva Raman, C. (1960). *Biochem. J.*, **75**, 9 P.
Bowen, T. J., and Rogers, L. J. (1963). *Biochim. biophys. Acta*, **67**, 633.
Bowen, T. J., and Rogers, L. J. (1965). *Nature, Lond.*, **205**, 1316.
Buchanan, J. M., and Anfinson, C. B. (1949). *J. biol. Chem.*, **180**, 47.
Buckel, W., and Eggerer, H. (1965). *Biochem. Z.*, **343**, 29.
Burton, K., and Wilson, T. H. (1953). *Biochem. J.*, **54**, 86.
Chantrenne, H., and Lipmann, F. (1950). *J. biol. Chem.*, **187**, 757.
Clutterbuck, P. W. (1927). *Biochem. J.*, **21**, 512.

Dagley, S. (1965). *In* "Methods of Enzymatic Analysis" (Ed. H. J. Bergmeyer), p. 313. Academic Press, New York.

Dagley, S. (1954). *J. gen. Microbiol.*, **11**, 218.

Dagley, S., and Dawes, E. A. (1955). *Biochim. biophys. Acta*, **17**, 177.

Dagley, S., and Dawes, E. A. (1953). *Nature, Lond.*, **172**, 345.

Dagley, S., and Dawes, E. A. (1955). *Biochim. biophys. Acta*, **17**, 177.

Daron, H. H., and Gunsalus, I. C. (1962) *In* "Methods in Enzymology" (Eds. S. P. Colowick and N. O. Kaplan), Vol. V, p. 628. Academic Press, New York.

Daron, H. H., Rutter, W. J., and Gunsalus, I. C. (1966). *Biochemistry*, **5**, 895.

Davies, D. D., and Kun, E. (1957). *Biochem. J.*, **66**, 307.

Dickman, S. R. (1961). *In* "The Enzymes" (Eds. P. D. Boyer, H. Lardy and K. Myrback), Vol. 5, p. 495. Academic Press, New York.

Delwiche, E. A., Phares, E. F., and Carson, S. F. (1956). *J. Bacteriol.*, **71**, 598.

Dixon, G. H., and Kornberg, H. L. (1959). *Biochem. J.*, **72**, 3.

Eggerer, H. (1965). *Biochem. Z.*, **343**, 111.

Eggerer, H., and Klette, A. (1967). *European J. Biochem.*, **1**, 447.

Eggerer, H., and Remberger, U. (1964). *Biochem. Z.*, **337**, 202.

Eisenthal, R., Tate, S. S., and Datta, S. P. (1966). *Biochim. biophys. Acta*, **128**, 155.

Ellman, G. (1959). *Arch. Biochem. Biophys.*, **82**, 70.

Friedemann, T. E., and Haugen, G. E. (1943). *J. biol. Chem.*, **147**, 415.

Gergely, J. (1955). *In* "Methods in Enzymology" (Eds. S. P. Colowick and N. O. Kaplan), Vol. I, p. 602. Academic Press, New York.

Gergely, J., Hele, P., and Ramakrishnan, C. V. (1952). *J. Biol. Chem.*, **198**, 323.

Gillespie, D. C., and Gunsalus, I. C. (1953). *Bacteriol. Proc.*, p. 80.

Greenwood, F. C., and Greenbaum, A. L. (1953). *Biochim. biophys. Acta*, **10**, 623.

Grunberg-Manago, M., and Gunsalus, I. C. (1953). *Bacteriol. Proc.*, p. 73.

Gunsalus, I. C., and Razzell, W. S. (1957). *In* "Methods in Enzymology" (Eds. S. P. Colowick and N. O. Kaplan), Vol. III, p. 941. Academic Press, New York.

Hager, L. P. (1962). *In* "The Enzymes" (Eds. P. D. Boyer, H. Lardy and K. Myrback), Vol. 6, pp. 387–8. Academic Press, New York.

Hager, L. P., and Gunsalus, I. C. (1953). *J. Am. Chem. Soc.*, **75**, 5767.

Hager, L. P., and Kornberg, H. L. (1961). *Biochem. J.*, **78**, 194.

Hanson, K. R., and Rose, I. A. (1963). *Proc. natl. Acad. Sci. U.S.*, **50**, 981.

Harvey, R. J., and Collins, E. B. (1961). *J. Bacteriol.*, **82**, 954.

Harvey, R. J., and Collins, E. B. (1963). *J. biol. Chem.*, **238**, 2648.

Hift, H., Quillet, L., Littlefield, J. W., and Sanadi, D. R. (1953). *J. biol. Chem.*, **204**, 565.

Hirsch, D., Raminsky, M., Davis, B. D., and Lin, E. C. C. (1963). *J. biol. Chem.*, **238**, 3370.

Hohorst, H. J. (1965). *In* "Methods of Enzymatic Analysis" (Ed. H. O. Bergmeyer), p. 328. Academic Press, New York.

Holzer, M., Hierholzer, G., and Witt, I. (1963). *Biochem. Z.*, **337**, 115.

Holzer, H., and Soling, H. D. (1965). *In* "Methods of Enzymatic Analysis" (Ed. H. O. Bergmeyer), p. 332. Academic Press, New York.

Hummel, J. P. (1949). *J. biol. Chem.*, **180**, 1225.

Jaenicke, L., and Lynen, F. (1960). *In* "The Enzymes" (Eds. P. D. Boyer, H. L. Lardy and K. Myrback), Vol. 3, pp. 61–64. Academic Press, New York.

Kaufman, S. (1955). *In* "Methods in Enzymology" (Eds. S. P. Colowick and N. O. Kaplan), Vol. I, p. 714. Academic Press, New York.

Kaufman, S. (1955). *In* "Methods in Enzymology" (Eds. S. P. Colowick and N. O. Kaplan), Vol. I, p. 718. Academic Press, New York.

Kaufman, S., Gilvarg, C., Cori, O., and Ochoa, S. (1953). *J. biol. Chem.*, **203**, 869.

Koike, M., Reed, L. J., and Carrol, W. R. (1960). *J. biol. Chem.*, **235**, 1924.

Koike, M., Reed, L. J., and Carrol, W. R. (1963). *J. biol. Chem.*, **288**, 30.

Kornberg, A. (1955). *In* "Methods in Enzymology" (Eds. S. P. Colowick and N. O. Kaplan), Vol. I, pp. 705, 707. Academic Press, New York.

Kornberg, A., Ochoa, S., and Mehler, A. H. (1948). *J. biol. Chem.*, **174**, 159.

Kornberg, A., and Pricer, W. E. (1951). *J. biol. Chem.*, **189**, 123.

Kornberg, H. L. (1959). *An. Rev. Microbiol.*, **13**, 49.

Kosicki, G. W., and Lipovac, S. N. (1964). *Can. J. Chem.*, **42**, 403.

Krebs, H. A. (1953). *Biochem. J.*, **54**, 78.

Krebs, H. A., and Lowenstein, J. M. (1960). *In* "Metabolic Pathways" (Ed. D. M. Greenberg), Vol. 1, p. 145. Academic Press, New York.

Kun, E. (1963). *In* "The Enzymes" (Eds. P. D. Boyer, H. Lardy and K. Myrback), 2nd ed., Vol. VII, p. 149. Academic Press, New York.

Lipmann, F., and Tuttle, L. C. (1945). *J. biol. Chem.*, **159**, 21.

Massey, V. (1955). *In* "Methods in Enzymology" (Eds. S. P. Colowick and N. O. Kaplan), Vol. I, p. 729. Academic Press, New York.

Massey, V. (1963). *In* "The Enzymes" (Eds. P. D. Boyer, H. Lardy and K. Myrback), Vol. 7, p. 275. Academic Press, New York.

Mayle, J. (1956). *Biochem. J.*, **63**, 552.

McFadden, B. A., and Howes, W. V. (1960). *Anal. Biochem.*, **1**, 240.

Moellering, H., and Gruber, W. (1966). *Anal. Biochem.*, **17**, 369.

Morrison, J. F. (1954). *Biochem. J.*, **56**, 99.

Moyle, J., and Dixon, M. (1956). *Biochem. J.*, **63**, 548.

Mukherjee, B. B., Matthews, J., Horney, D. L., and L. J. Reed (1965). *J. biol. Chem.*, **240**, PC 2268.

Natelson, S., Pincus, J. B., and Lugovoy, J. K. (1948). *J. biol. Chem.*, **175**, 745.

Neilson, N. E. (1962). *In* "Methods in Enzymology" (Eds. S. P. Colowick and N. O. Kaplan), Vol. V, p. 614. Academic Press, New York.

Nishimura, J. S., and Meister, A. (1965). *Biochemistry*, **4**, 1457.

Nishimura, J. S. (1967). Abstracts, 7th International Congress of Biochem., Tokyo, p. 812.

Ochoa, S. (1945). *J. Biol. Chem.*, **159**, 243.

Ochoa, S. (1951). *In* "The Enzymes", 1st ed., Vol. II, Part 2, p. 929. Academic Press, New York.

Ochoa, S. (1955). *In* "Methods in Enzymology" (Eds. S. P. Colowick and N. O. Kaplan), Vol. I, p. 685. Academic Press, New York.

Ochoa, S. (1955). *In* "Methods in Enzymology" (Eds. S. P. Colowick and N. O. Kaplan), Vol. I, p. 699. Academic Press, New York.

Ochoa, S. (1955). *In* "Methods in Enzymology" (Eds. S. P. Colowick and N. O. Kaplan), Vol. I, p. 735. Academic Press, New York.

Olson, J. A. (1959). *J. biol. Chem.*, **234**, 5.

Plaut, G. W. E., and Sung, S. C. (1955) *In* "Methods in Enzymology" (Eds. S. P. Colowick, and N. O. Kaplan), Vol. I, p. 710. Academic Press, New York.

Plaut, G. W. E. (1962). *In* "Methods in Enzymology" (Eds. S. P. Colowick and N. O. Kaplan), Vol. V, p. 645. Academic Press, New York.

Plaut, G. W. E. (1963). *In* "The Enzymes" (Eds. P. D. Boyer, H. Lardy and K. Myrback), 2nd ed., Vol. VII, Chapter 5, p. 105. Academic Press, New York.

Polakis, E. S., and Bartley. W. (1965). *Biochem. J.*, **97**, 284.
Racker, E. (1950). *Biochim. biophys. Acta*, **4**, 211.
Ramakrishnan, C. V., and Martin, S. M. (1955). *Arch. Biochem. Biophys.*, **55**, 403.
Ravel, D. N., and Wolfe, R. G. (1962). *Biochemistry*, **1**, 263, 1113, 1118.
Reed, L. J., and Cox, D. J. (1966). *Ann. Rev. Biochem.*, **35**, 57.
Reed, L. J., and Mukherjee, B. B. (1969). *In* "Methods in Enzymology" (Eds. S. P. Colowick, N. O. Kaplan and J. M. Lowenstein), Vol. XIII, p. 55. Academic Press, New York.
Reed, L. J., and Mukherjee, B. B. (1969). *In* "Methods in Enzymology" (Eds. S. P. Colowick, N. O. Kaplan and W. A. Wood), Vol. IX, pp. 247, 253, 258, 262. Academic Press, New York.
Rose, I. A. (1966). *Ann. Rev. Biochem.*, **35**, 23.
Rose, I. W., and O'Connell, E. L. (1967). *J. biol. Chem.*, **242**, 1870.
Sanadi, D. R. (1963). *In* "The Enzymes" (Eds. P. D. Boyer, H. Lardy and K. Myrback), 2nd ed., Vol. VII, p. 307. Academic Press, New York.
Schlenk, F. (1951). *In* "The Enzymes" (Eds. P. D. Boyer, H. Lardy and K. Myrback), 1st ed., Vol. II, Part 1, p. 279. Academic Press, New York.
Shiio, I., Shiio, T., and McFadden, B. A. (1964). *Biochim. biophys. Acta*, **96**, 123.
Silbert, G., Dubric, J., Warner, R. C., and Plaut, G. W. E. (1957). *J. biol. Chem.*, **226**, 965.
Simon, E. J., and Shemin, D. (1953). *J. Am. Chem. Soc.*, **75**, 2520.
Singer, T. P. (1963). *In* "The Enzymes" (Eds. P. D. Boyer, H. Lardy and K. Myrback), Vol. VII, p. 345. Academic Press, New York.
Singer, T. P. (1966). *In* "Comprehensive Biochemistry" (Eds. M. Florkin and E. H. Stotz), Vol. XIV, p. 127. Elsevier Publishing Co., Amsterdam.
Singer, T. P., and Kearney, E. B. (1957). *In* "Methods of Biochemical Analysis" (Ed. D. Glick), Vol. IV, p. 307. Academic Press, New York.
Siva Raman, C. (1961). *Biochim. biophys. Acta*, **52**, 212.
Simon, E. J., and Shemin, D. J. (1953). *J. Am. Chem. Soc.*, **75**, 2520.
Smith, R. A., Stamer, J. R., and Gunsalus, I. C. (1956). *Biochim. biophys. Acta*, **19**, 563.
Srere, P. A. (1963). *Biochim. biophys. Acta*, **77**, 693.
Srere, P. A. (1965). *Biochim. biophys. Acta*, **106**, 445.
Srere, P. A. (1966). *J. biol. Chem.*, **241**, 2157.
Srere, P. A., Brazil, H., and Gonen, L. (1963). *Acta Chem. Scand.*, **17**, S129.
Stadtman, E. R. (1957). *In* "Methods in Enzymology" (Eds. S. P. Colowick and N. O. Kaplan), Vol. III, pp. 228, 935. Academic Press, New York.
Stern, J. R. (1957). *In* "Methods in Enzymology" (Eds. S. P. Colowick and N. O. Kaplan), Vol. III, p. 428. Academic Press, New York.
Stern, J. R. (1961). *In* "The Enzymes" (Eds. P. D. Boyer, H. L. Lardy and K. Myrback), Vol. V, p. 367. Academic Press, New York.
Straub, F. B. (1935). *Z. physiol. Chem.*, **236**, 43.
Tate, S. S., and Datta, S. P. (1964). *Biochem. J.*, **91**, 18 C.
Tate, S. S., and Datta, S. P. (1965). *Biochem. J.*, **94**, 470.
Umbreit, W. W., Burris, R. H., and Stauffer, J. F. (1964). *In* "Manometric Techniques". Burgess Publishing Co., Minneapolis, Minnesota.
Vanderwinkel, E., and Wiame, J. M. (1965). *Biochim. biophys. Acta*, **99**, 246.
Ward, R. L., and Srere, P. A. (1965). *Biochim. biophys. Acta*, **99**, 270.
Wegener, W. S., Reeves, H. C., and Ajl, S. J. (1965). *Anal. Biochem.*, **11**, 111.

Wegener, W. S., Reeves, H. C., Rabin, R., and Ajl, S. J. (1968). *Bacteriol. Rev.*, **23**, 1.
Weitzman, P. D. J. (1966). *Biochem. J.*, **99**, 18P.
Wheat, R. W., and Ajl, S. J. (1955). *J. biol. Chem.*, **217**, 897.
Wheat, R. W., and Ajl, S. J. (1955). *J. biol. Chem.*, **217**, 909.
Wieland, O., and Weiss, L. (1963). *Biochem. biophys. Res. Commun.*, **13**, 26.

CHAPTER XI

Assay of Enzymes of Aromatic Metabolism

D. T. GIBSON

Department of Microbiology, The University of Texas at Austin, Texas 78712

I. INTRODUCTION

The ubiquity of soil micro-organisms capable of metabolizing aromatic compounds was first demonstrated by Gray and Thornton (1928). Examination of 245 soil samples revealed that 146 yielded bacteria capable of oxidizing naphthalene, cresol or phenol.

The last four decades have produced a wealth of information concerning the metabolic pathways utilized by micro-organisms to degrade aromatic compounds (Ornston *et al.*, 1966; Dagley *et al.*, 1964; Ribbons, 1965; Gibson, 1968). In addition, studies on individual enzymes led to the concept of "oxygen fixation", a phenomenon no less important, but nevertheless overshadowed by detailed studies of carbon dioxide and nitrogen fixation. Excellent reviews are available (Hayaishi, 1964; Hayaishi, 1966) which describe the enzymes responsible for the incorporation of atmospheric oxygen into organic compounds.

Although organisms from many different groups are capable of degrading the benzene ring, it is notably species from the genus *Pseudomonas* that have yielded much of our present information. Catechol and protocatechuic acid are central intermediates in the degradation of many different aromatic substrates. The further metabolism of these two compounds may proceed either by fission between the hydroxyl groups ("ortho-fission") or between the bond adjacent to one of the hydroxyl groups ("meta-fission"). Since these reactions initiate completely different metabolic pathways, the mode of cleavage of protocatechuic acid has been used as a taxonomic character of the aerobic pseudomonads (Stanier *et al.*, 1966). Fluorescent pseudomonads cleave protocatechuic acid between the hydroxyl groups, while the two species of the acidivorans group, *P. acidivorans* and *P. testosteroni*, attack the bond in the 4,5-position. Thus the demonstration of the presence of either "ortho-" or "meta-cleavage" enzymes in a pseudomonas species indicates which metabolic pathway is utilized and also aids in classifying the organism. Catechol is not such a reliable substrate for classification since the presence of "ortho-" or "meta-cleavage" enzymes appears to depend on the nature of the aromatic growth substrate.

The metabolism of tryptophan is also characteristic of the two groups of aerobic pseudomonads (Fig. 1). Both groups metabolize this amino acid to kynurenine. At this point the fluorescent group takes the pathway through anthranilic acid (aromatic pathway) while the acidivorans group metabolizes kynurenine through kynurenic acid (quinoline pathway).

By demonstrating the presence of key enzymes in the degradation of an aromatic substrate it is possible to gain much information as to which pathway is employed. However care must be taken when interpreting the results obtained. Not all aromatic compounds are metabolized through catechol or protocatechuic acid. Substituted mononuclear aromatic sub-

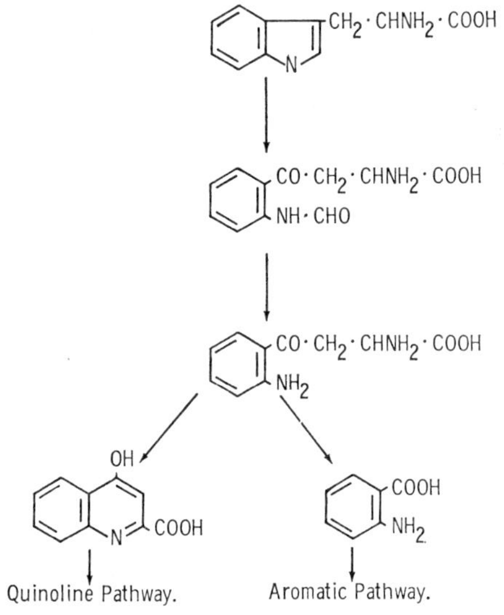

FIG. 1. Divergent pathways of tryptophan metabolism.

strates i.e., 3-methylcatechol (Bayly *et al.*, 1966), 2,3-dihydroxy-β-phenyl-propionic acid (Dagley *et al.*, 1965), may undergo "meta-cleavage" with the side-chain intact. To account for these observations Dagley *et al.* (1964) have proposed a general pathway for the degradation of aromatic compounds. In addition not all enzymes are specific and care should be taken when drawing conclusions based on the presence of enzyme activity. The true metabolic intermediate compounds in an aromatic pathway may act as inducers for enzymes unrelated to those used for the degradation of growth substrate. Thus the degradation of catechol by *Pseudomonas putida* proceeds through β-oxoadipic acid. The latter compound is also a metabolic intermediate in the degradation of protocatechuic acid by this organism. Since β-oxoadipic acid or its coenzyme A derivative induces the synthesis of two enzymes in the protocatechuic acid pathway, cells of *P. putida* which metabolize benzoic acid through catechol also contain enzymes which are used in the metabolism of protocatechuic acid (Ornston, 1966).

One of the most useful techniques in the study of aromatic metabolism is the method of simultaneous adaptation (Stanier, 1947). The majority of enzymes concerned in the degradation of the benzene nucleus are synthesized in response to the presence of an aromatic substrate. The basic assumption is that the metabolism of a given substrate A, proceeds through a series of intermediate compounds B, C, D, E... Cells grown on A contain the enzymes responsible for the degradation of B, C, D, E... Cells grown on C contain the enzymes which degrade D, E..., but not the enzymes which metabolize A and B. Thus by using conventional manometry it is possible to obtain a large amount of information concerning the enzymes involved in the dissimilation of an aromatic substrate. The use of this technique led to the discovery and eventual isolation of the majority of the enzymes described below. The basic limitations depend on the user being aware of the fact that not all enzymes are specific. Also the permeability properties of the cell must be taken into account. For a detailed discussion of the use of simultaneous adaptation studies (see Dagley and Chapman, this Volume, p. 217).

It is generally accepted that dihydroxylation of the aromatic nucleus is a prerequisite for ring fission. The hydroxyl groups may be *ortho* to each other as in catechol or *para* to each other as in gentisic acid. Enzymes diagnostic of aromatic pathways are those which prepare the substrate for ring fission (mono-oxygenases or hydroxylases) and those which actually cleave the benzene ring (dioxygenases) (Hayaishi, 1966).

II. MONO-OXYGENASES

In the past the majority of these enzymes have proved difficult to isolate. They catalyse the incorporation of one atom of oxygen into the substrate molecule. In the presence of a suitable electron donor the other atom of the oxygen molecule is reduced to water. A useful technique is to produce a continuous supply of electron-donating potential by enzymatic means (Ichihara *et al.*, 1962). Thus a continuous supply of NADH may be provided by NAD^+, alcohol and alcohol dehydrogenase. Similarly NADPH may be supplied by $NADP^+$, glucose 6-phosphate and glucose 6-phosphate dehydrogenase. The use of a generating system often proves valuable in the early stages of enzyme purification when high levels of NADH and NADPH oxidase can mask hydroxylase activity.

A. p-Hydroxybenzoate hydroxylase

p-Hydroxybenzoic acid can serve as a source of carbon and energy for many bacteria. This compound is also a common intermediate in the dissimilation of a variety of aromatic substrates. Its further metabolism involves hydroxylation to form protocatechuic acid.

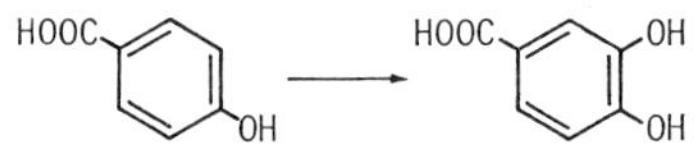

p - Hydroxybenzoic
acid

Protocatechuic
acid

The enzyme may be assayed spectrophotometrically by measuring NADPH oxidation in the presence of p-hydroxybenzoate, oxygen and enzyme (Hosokawa and Stanier, 1966). For satisfactory results the particulate fraction should be removed by high speed centrifugation, e.g., 100,000 g for 1 h. Preparations treated in this manner show negligible NADPH oxidation in the absence of p-hydroxybenzoic acid. The following procedure is that of Hosokawa and Stanier (1966).

1. Reagents

0·100M Tris-HCl buffer, pH 8·0
0·015M NADPH
0·001M FAD
0·100M Sodium p-hydroxybenzoic acid.

2. Procedure 1

To a cuvette having a 1 cm light path add 1·0 ml of Tris buffer, 0·025 ml of NADPH, 0·010 ml of FAD, enzyme and distilled water to make a final volume of 3·0 ml. The reaction is started by the addition of 0·020 ml of sodium p-hydroxybenzoic acid. A control cuvette contains all components except p-hydroxybenzoic acid. Readings are taken at 340 nm after the addition of substrate. Since the reaction rate declines rapidly, accurate results can only be obtained by conducting measurements during the first 10–20 sec of the reaction. Although FAD has been identified as a component of this reaction, it is tightly bound by the enzyme and may be omitted from the standard assay system. One unit of enzyme is defined as that amount which oxidizes 1 μmole of NADPH per minute.

The activity of the enzyme may also be measured manometrically. A NADPH-generating system (glucose 6-phosphate, glucose 6-phosphate dehydrogenase (yeast) and NADP$^+$) must be present.

3. *Procedure 2*

To the main compartment of a Warburg flask add, Tris-HCl buffer, pH 8·0, 100 μmoles; FAD, 0·01 μmole; glucose 6-phosphate, 10 μmoles; glucose 6-phosphate dehydrogenase, 1·4 units; MgCl$_2$, 10 μmoles; NADP$^+$, 0·15 μmole; reduced glutathione, 1 μmole; enzyme and water to a final volume of 2·30 ml. The centre well contains 0·20 ml of 5N KOH. The reaction is initiated by the addition of 0·50 ml of sodium p-hydroxybenzoic acid (0·01M) from the side arm of the flask. A control flask contains all components except that water replaces p-hydroxybenzoate in the side arm. The reaction is conducted at 30°C. One unit of enzyme catalyses the uptake of 1 μmole of oxygen per min. This calculation is based on the linear portion of the oxygen uptake curve.

4. *Properties of* p-*hydroxybenzoate hydroxylase*†

A crystalline enzyme has been prepared from cells of *P. putida*. The enzyme was induced by growth on p-hydroxybenzoate as sole source of carbon and energy. The purified enzyme (m.w. 83,600) contains one mole of FAD per mole of protein and requires specifically NADPH as electron donor. It is of interest to note that this enzyme, which is specific for p-hydroxybenzoic acid, appears similar to the p-hydroxybenzoate hydroxylase from *Pseudomonas desmolytica*. The latter organism metabolizes protocatechuic acid by "meta-fission" while *P. putida* employs "ortho-cleavage".

Other hydroxylases which contain flavin and require a reduced pyridine nucleotide are; salicylate hydroxylase (Katagiri *et al.*, 1966), melilotate hydroxylase (Levy, 1967), and kynurenate hydroxylase (Mori *et al.*, 1966). The latter enzyme also requires ferrous ions and appears to catalyse a double hydroxylation.

B. Phenylalanine hydroxylase

Phenylalanine may be used as a sole source of carbon by several micro-

† Hosokawa and Stanier, 1966.

organisms. *Pseudomonas fluorescens* K1 metabolizes phenylalanine through homoprotocatechuic acid (Kunita, 1955). *Moraxella lwoffii* (*Vibrio* 01) oxidizes phenylalanine to homogentisic acid. Tyrosine or phenylacetic acid may be intermediates in this conversion (Dagley *et al.*, 1953).

The hydroxylation of phenylalanine to form tryosine is of considerable interest as it illustrates a reaction known as the "NIH shift". When a purified preparation of bacterial phenylalanine hydroxylase was incubated with L-phenylalanine tritiated in the *para* position, the tyrosine produced contained a considerable amount of tritium. It was shown that the isotope had migrated to the *meta* position (Guroff *et al.*, 1966). It has been suggested (Renson *et al.*, 1966) that this mechanism explains the migration of the pyruvic acid side chain during the hydroxylation of *p*-hydroxyphenylpyruvic acid to homogentisic acid (Schepartz and Gurin, 1949).

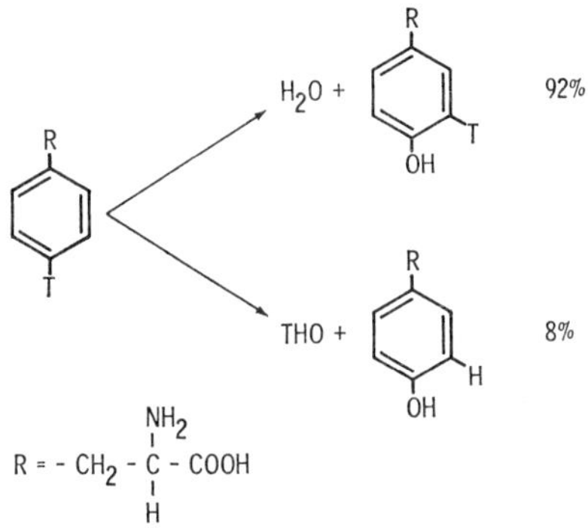

FIG. 2. Phenylalanine hydroxylation, an example of the "NIH shift".

1. *Principle of enzyme assay*

p-Tritio-L-phenylalanine is incubated with enzyme to produce a mixture of tyrosine, *meta*-tritio-tyrosine and tritiated water (THO) (Fig. 2). The whole reaction mixture is treated with N-iodosuccinimide which produces *m,m*-diiodotyrosine and releases all the bound tritium as THO. The THO is counted and used as a measure of enzyme activity. The method described is that of Guroff and Abramowitz, 1967.

2. *Reagents*

p-Tritio-L-phenylalanine ($1 \cdot 3 – 1 \cdot 6 \times 10^5$ cpm/10 μl)
0·01M L-Phenylalanine
0·25M Tris-HCl buffer, pH 7·3
0·02M NADH
0·005M 2-Amino-4-hydroxy-6,7-dimethyltetrahydropteridine
in 0·1M mercaptoethanol.

Enzyme
Distilled water
0·02M Sodium acetate buffer, pH 5·5
1% N-Iodosuccinimide
30% Trichloroacetic acid
Dowex 50 (H+)
Activated charcoal
Bray's counting solution†

3. *Procedure*

The enzyme should first of all be preactivated by incubating with ferrous ammonium sulphate (1 μmole/mg protein) for 10 min at 30°C. To a conical centrifuge tube add 0·01 ml *p*-tritio-L-phenylalanine; 0·01 ml, L-phenyl-alanine; 0·10 ml, Tris-HCl buffer; 0·05 ml, NADH; 0·03 ml, 2-amino-4-hydroxy-6,7-dimethyltetrahydropteridine; activated enzyme and distilled water to make a final volume of 0·25 ml. The reaction is carried out for 10 min at 30°C in air. At this time heat the reaction mixture of 1 min at 100°C and then cool on ice. Keep the reaction mixtures cool for the remainder of the procedure. Add 0·50 ml of sodium acetate buffer. If a substantial precipitate occurs, centrifuge in a refrigerated centrifuge and use the clear supernatant solution for subsequent procedures. To the cold supernatant solution add 0·2 ml of freshly prepared N-iodosuccinimide solution and allow the mixture to remain at 0°C for 5 min. Add 0·05 ml of trichloroacetic acid to each tube. The coloured supernatant solution is then placed on a Dowex 50/charcoal column. To prepare a column pipette 1·0 ml of an 80% slurry of acid-washed Dowex (50 (H+) into a cotton-plugged, disposable Pasteur pipette. Allow the resin to settle and add 0·10 ml of a 10% slurry of activated charcoal. Wash the column with 2·0 ml of distilled water. Transfer the reaction supernatant solution to the column. Rinse the tube with 1·0 ml of water and transfer the washings to the column. The combined effluent and washings are collected in a counting vial; 10 ml of counting solution is added and the vial is counted in a scintillation counter.

The authors claim that in the enzymatic hydroxylation 92% of the tritium is retained in the tyrosine. Under the conditions of assay 81% of this tritium is released. Thus the following equation may be used to calculate them μ mole of phenylalanine hydroxylated by the enzyme.

$$\text{nmoles} = \frac{\text{cpm of H}_2\text{O observed}}{\text{sp.act. phenylalanine added}} \times \frac{1}{0·82}$$

Another method of assaying tyrosine production is the fluorometric

† Bray, 1960.

method of Waalkes and Udenfriend (1957). This assay will not be described here, since the isotopic method is more sensitive and is especially suitable for small amounts of crude enzyme preparation where endogenous tyrosine limits the sensitivity of the fluorometric procedure.

Recently the natural pteridine cofactor, for Pseudomonas phenylalanine hydroxylase, has been identified as reduced 2-amino-4-hydroxy-6-(L-threotrihydroxypropyl) pteridine (L-threoneopterin) (Guroff and Rhoads, 1969). However, the pteridine requirement may be satisfied by a number of different reduced pteridines. Thus phenylalanine hydroxylase (Guroff and Ito, 1965) has been used to determine the amounts of tetrahydrobiopterin in crude extracts of various animal tissues (Guroff et al., 1967).

III. DIOXYGENASES

These enzymes are principally concerned with the fission of the aromatic nucleus. They catalyse the incorporation of two oxygen atoms into an organic substrate. However, it should be noted that the hydroxylation of anthranilic acid (Kobayashi et al., 1964) and 2-fluorobenzoic acid (Milne et al., 1968) to form catechol and 3-fluorocatechol respectively are catalysed by dioxygenases.

A. Homogentisic acid oxygenase

This enzyme was first isolated from cells of a Pseudomonas sp. The enzyme was induced by growth on tryosine (Suda and Takeda, 1950). Chapman and Dagley 1962) also reported the presence of homogentisate oxygenase in cell extracts of a Vibrio (Moraxella lwoffii) which had been grown on phenylacetic acid. The enzyme catalyses the ring fission of homogentisic acid to form maleylacetoacetic acid.

Homogentisic acid   Maleylacetoacetic acid

Crude enzyme preparations may be assayed manometrically. According to Adachi et al., 1966) the enzyme should be preincubated with ferrous ions for 13 min prior to the addition of substrate.

1. *Reagents*

   0·01M Homogentisic acid, pH 6·0
   0·01M $FeSO_4$ is distilled water
   0·20M Tris-maleate buffer, pH 6·0
   Enzyme
   5N NaOH

2. *Procedure*

To the main compartment of a Warburg flask add 1·5 ml of Tris-maleate buffer; 0·2 ml of ferrous sulphate and 0·6 ml of enzyme (20–30 mg of protein/ml). After preincubation at 30°C for 13 min the reaction is started by the addition of 0·5 ml of homogentisic acid from the side arm. Carbon dioxide is absorbed by 0·2 ml of 5N NaOH in the centre well. Oxygen consumption is corrected by reference to an endogenous control flask which contains all components except that homogentisic acid in the side arm is replaced by 0·5 ml of Tris-maleate buffer. One unit of enzyme catalyses the uptake of 1 μmole of oxygen per min. This should be based on the linear portion of the oxygen uptake curve. Specific activity is defined as the number of units per mg of protein.

For purified preparations it is possible to devise a spectrophotometric assay (Knox and Edwards, 1955). To a cuvette of 1-cm light path add the following (in μmoles): $FeSO_4$, 0·2; reduced glutathione, 6; ascorbic acid, 3; Tris-maleate buffer, 400, and enzyme in a total volume of 2·90 ml. After preincubation for 13 min at 30°C, the reaction is initiated by the addition of 15 μmoles of homogentisate in 0·1 ml. The amount of maleylacetoacetate formed is calculated from the increase in absorbance at 330 nm, using a molar extinction coefficient of 14,000. One unit of enzyme activity catalyses the formation of 1 μmole of maleylacetoacetate per min.

B. Catechol-2,3-oxygenase (Metapyrocatechase)

Dagley and Stopher (1959) first demonstrated the presence of this enzyme in cell extracts of a *Pseudomonas* sp. which was grown with *o*-cresol as sole source of carbon. The enzyme catalyses the oxidation of catechol to 2-hydroxymuconic semialdehyde.

Catechol   2 - Hydroxymuconic semialdehyde

In alkaline solutions the ring-fission product produces an intense yellow colour which is abolished upon acidification. Table I records the molar

TABLE I

Molar extinction coefficients of 2-hydroxymuconic semialdehyde at different pH values

pH	λ_{max} (nm)	ε
11·0	375	37,100
7·6	375	33,400
2·5	320	16,200

extinction coefficients which have been reported for 2-hydroxymuconic semialdehyde (Bayly et al., 1966). The high extinction at pH 7·6 provides a convenient method for enzyme assay. The following procedure is based on that of Nozaki et al. (1963).

1. *Reagents*

> 0·05M Potassium dihydrogen phosphate, pH 7·5
> 0·01M Catechol (resublimed) in distilled water
> Enzyme, suitably diluted with buffer

Although the catechol solution may be stored at 4°C for several days, it is preferable to prepare a fresh solution every day. This will eliminate any errors produced by auto-oxidation of the substrate.

2. *Procedure*

Place 2·8 ml of phosphate buffer and 0·1 ml of suitably diluted enzyme in a cuvette having a 1 cm light path. Readings are taken at 375 nm every 30 sec after the addition of 0·1 ml of catechol solution. A reference cuvette contains 2·9 ml of phosphate buffer and 0·1 ml of enzyme. The time required to give an increase in optical density of 0·10 is measured at room temperature. One unit of enzyme is defined as that amount which oxidizes 1 μmole of catechol per min. A molar extinction coefficient of 33,000 is used for these calculations. Protein concentration is measured by the phenol method of Lowry et al. (1951) using crystalline bovine serum albumin as the reference protein. Specific activity is defined as the number of enzyme units per mg of protein.

3. *Properties of catechol-2,3-oxygenase*

The enzyme, which has been crystallized by Nozaki et al. (1963) is extremely sensitive to oxygen and is easily inactivated in the presence of air. These authors found that the presence of 10% acetone in the enzyme solution protected the enzyme almost completely from inactivation by air. Although no easily dissociable cofactors are required for activity the enzyme (M.W. approximately 140,000) contains 1 atom of iron per molecule. The only other substrate attached at the same initial rate as catechol is 3-methylcatechol (2,3-dihydroxy-1-methylbenzene). However, the substrate specificity may vary with the source of the enzyme.

The enzyme, first demonstrated by Dagley and Stopher (1959) in cells of a *Pseudomonas* sp. grown with *o*-cresol as sole source of carbon, has not been purified to any great extent. It is stable to heat treatment which inactivates the enzyme catalysing the further metabolism of 2-hydroxymuconic semialdehyde. The following procedure may be used. Crude cell extract (20–30 mg protein/ml) is maintained at 55°C for 10 min. After cooling in ice the denatured protein is removed by centrifugation. The resulting cell extract catalyses the stoicheiometric formation of 2-hydroxy-muconic semialdehyde from catechol.

It should be noted that the demonstration of catechol-2,3-oxygenase activity in cells of a micro-organism after growth on an aromatic substrate, is not proof that catechol is an intermediate in the degradation of that substrate. The enzyme is constitutive in *Pseudomonas arvilla* (Stanier *et al.*, 1966). Also *P. putida*, when grown with toluene as sole source of carbon, oxidizes 3-methylcatechol and catechol at equal rates (Gibson *et al.*, 1968). The former substrate and not catechol is the true intermediate in the degradation of toluene by this organism.

C. Protocatechuic acid-4,5-oxygenase

This enzyme catalyses the "meta-cleavage" of protocatechuic acid with the formation of γ-carboxy-α-hydroxy-*cis*, *cis*-muconic semialdehyde (CHMS).

Protocatechuic acid   CHMS

Like the analogous catechol-2,3-oxygenase the protocatechuate enzyme is extremely unstable. Although the ring-fission product (CHMS) absorbs strongly at 410 nm a satisfactory spectrophotometric assay has not been developed. This is due to the rapid loss of activity which the enzyme suffers on dilution. Dagley *et al.* (1968) developed a satisfactory manometric assay which is described below.

1. *Reagents.*

  0·015M L-Cysteine
  0·025M KH_2PO_4, pH 7·2
  0·033M $FeSO_4$ in distilled water
  0·010M Protocatechuic acid in phosphate buffer
  20% (w/v) KOH

2. *Procedure*

To the main compartment of a Warburg flask add 0·20 ml of L-cysteine; 1·50 ml of phosphate buffer; 0·50 ml of enzyme and 0·10 ml of $FeSO_4$ (added last). Carbon dioxide is absorbed by 0·20 ml of KOH solution which is placed in the centre well. After equilibration at 30°C the reaction is started by the addition of 0·50 ml of protocatechuic acid solution from the side arm. Results are corrected for endogenous oxygen consumption in the absence of substrate by use of a control flask which contains all components except that the side arm contains 0·50 ml of phosphate buffer in place of protocatechuic acid. For each determination it is necessary to use sufficient enzyme to catalyse a linear uptake of about 50 μl of oxygen in a reaction time of 5 min. This rate is just below the maximum rate imposed by the diffusion of oxygen to the enzyme. Shaking speeds in excess of 160 oscillations per min may be required. Under these conditions a stoicheiometric relationship of 1 μmole of oxygen per μmole of protocatechuic acid is obtained. One unit of activity oxidizes 1 μmole of protocatechuic acid per min. Specific activity is defined as units per mg of protein. The protein contents of extracts containing 10–20 mg/ml are determined by the method of Sols (1947), and those with 2–10 mg/ml by a modified biuret method (Layne, 1957) (see also Strange, Herbert and Phipps, Volume 5B, this Series).

3. *Properties of protocatechuic acid-4,5-oxygenase*

Dagley *et al.* (1968) purified the enzyme from cells of *P. testosteroni* which was grown on *p*-hydroxybenzoic acid as sole source of carbon. The enzyme has a molecular weight of approximately 140,000 which is the same as that reported for catechol-2,3-oxygenase. Unlike the latter enzyme protocatechuic acid-4,5-oxygenase readily looses its ferrous ions and is less sensitive to inactivation by oxygen. The instability on dilution is disconcerting as it appears that one molecule of enzyme can catalyse only a limited number of ring-fissions before it becomes inactive.

D. Catechol-1,2-oxygenase (Pyrochatechase)

This enzyme was first isolated from Pseudomonas by Hayaishi and Hashimoto (1950). It incorporates two atoms of oxygen into catechol with the formation of *cis*, *cis*-muconic acid (MA).

| Catechol | *cis*, *cis* - muconic acid |

1. *Principle*

The reaction product (MA) absorbs strongly at 260 nm ($\epsilon = 16,900$). Sistrom and Stanier (1954) showed that the further metabolism of MA was inhibited by disodium ethylenediaminetetraacetate (EDTA). This observation was used by Hegeman (1966) to develop the assay described below.

2. *Reagents*

0·01M EDTA
0·10M KH_2PO_4, pH 7·0
0·001M Catechol in distilled water

3. *Procedure*

In a cuvette having a 1 cm light path place 2·0 ml of phosphate buffer, 0·4 ml of EDTA solution and enzyme. Dilute to 2·7 ml with distilled water. The reaction is initiated by the addition of 0·3 ml of catechol solution. Readings are taken every 30 sec at 260 nm. A reference cuvette contains all components except that 0·3 ml of water replaces the catechol solution. One unit of enzyme activity oxidizes 1 μmole of catechol to MA per min. Specific activity is defined as the number of units per mg of protein.

E. Protocatechuic acid-3,4-oxygenase

This enzyme initiates the pathway described by Ornston and Stanier (1966). The reaction involves "ortho-fission" of protocatechuic acid (PCA) to form β-carboxy-*cis*, *cis*-muconic acid (CMA).

HOOC \quad OH $\longrightarrow$ HOOC \quad COOH \quad COOH

Protocatechuic acid \qquad β - Carboxy - *cis, cis* - muconic acid

1. *Principle*

The enzyme may be assayed either manometrically by determination of oxygen uptake (Stanier, 1950), or spectrophotometrically (Stanier and Ingraham, 1954). The spectrophotometric method is preferable. In very crude cell extracts CMA may be metabolized to β-oxoadipic acid. In such circumstances, measurements are taken at 290 nm and 270 nm and the amount of CMA formed and the amount converted to β-oxoadipate calculated from the following extinction coefficients: ϵPCA (290) = 3890, ϵPCA (270) = 2730, ϵCMA (290) = 1590, and ϵCMA (270) = 6400. Usually it is seldom necessary to take measurements at two wave-lengths since low concentrations of the oxygenase are required for accurate measurement of enzyme activity and at these dilutions the enzyme removing CMA is inactive. In such cases the rate of PCA oxidation is measured at 290 nm.

2. *Reagents*

0·1M KH_2PO_4 buffer, pH 7·0
0·001M Sodium protocatechuate

3. *Procedure*

Cuvettes (1 cm light path) contain 2·0 ml of phosphate buffer, enzyme and distilled water to bring the volume of 2·5 ml. The reaction is initiated by the addition of 0·5 ml of sodium protocatechuate solution. Readings are taken at 290 nm every 30 sec. A blank cuvette contains in the same final volume all components except substrate. The temperature should be maintained at 30°C ± 1°C. One unit of enzyme oxidizes PCA at an initial rate of 0·075 μmole per min. If the reaction product is CMA this is equivalent to a decrement of 0·057 in optical density per min at 290 nm.

4. *Properties of protocatechuic acid-3,4-oxygenase*

The enzyme has been prepared in crystalline form from cells of a *Pseudomonas* sp. (Hayaishi, 1966). Highly purified preparations have a deep wine red colour. Reducing agents readily inactivate the enzyme. The presence of ferrous iron chelating agents such as *o*-phenanthroline and α, α'-dipyridyl do not affect enzymic acivity. However, Tiron, a chelating agent for trivalent iron inactivates the enzyme under anaerobic conditions.

F. Kynurenic acid hydroxylase

Micro-organisms grown on tryptophan may metabolize this amino acid through anthranilic acid and catechol (aromatic pathway) or through kynurenic acid (quinoline pathway). Thus the presence of catechol-2,3-oxygenase or catechol-1,2-oxygenase in cell extracts of an organism grown on tryptophan is indicative of the aromatic pathway. Alternatively the presence of an enzyme which catalyses the double hydroxylation of kynurenic acid demonstrates the presence of the quinoline pathway.

Kynurenic acid   Kynurenic acid - 7, 8 - dihydrodiol

1. *Principle*

A spectrophotometric assay is used. The estimation of the various components is based on the following molar extinction coefficients in 0·1M Tris-HCl buffer: kynurenic acid, $\epsilon_{333\,nm}$ 11,100; NADH, $\epsilon_{333\,nm}$ 6050. The procedure described below is essentially that of Mori *et al.* (1966).

2. *Reagents*

0·15M Tris-HCl buffer, pH 7·5
0·001M NADH
0·001M $FeSO_4 \cdot 7H_2O$
0·01M Kynurenic acid

3. *Procedure*

To a cuvette having a 1 cm light path add 2·0 ml Tris-HCl buffer, 0·30 ml NADH, 0·30 ml $FeSO_4$ and 0·24 ml kynurenic acid. The reaction is started by the addition of enzyme solution to make a final volume of 3·0 ml. The initial rate of disappearance of kynurenic acid and NADH are measured spectrophotometrically at 333 nm at 30-sec intervals against a control cell which contains all of the above components except the sub-strate. One unit of enzyme activity is defined as that amount which causes the decrease of 1 μmole of substrate per min under the above conditions. The specific activity is expressed as activity units per mg of protein.

4. *Enzyme preparation*

The enzyme may be purified from cells of *P. fluorescens* (ATCC 11299 B) (Mori *et al.*, 1966). It is interesting to note that according to Stanier *et al.* (1966) the fluorescent pseudomonads use the aromatic pathway. The organism is grown in the presence of DL-tryptophan and the cell extracts are prepared by sonic disintegration. Such extracts rapidly oxidize NADH and accurate measurements of enzyme activity are difficult to obtain. For this reason the crude cell extract is made 0·01M with L-cysteine and treated with 0·8 volumes of neutral 2% protamine sulphate solution. The resulting precipitate is centrifuged and the supernatant solution discarded. The precipitate is washed with 0·05M Tris-HCl buffer (pH 8·0) containing 0·01M cysteine and the mixture centrifuged. The resulting precipitate is taken up in 0·4M Tris-HCl buffer (pH 8·0) containing 0·01M cysteine. After centrifuging the straw-coloured solution is taken as a source of the enzyme. Such preparations contain little NADH-oxidizing activity and the amount of enzyme in this fraction may be arbitrarily defined as 100%.

REFERENCES

Adachi, K., Iwayama, Y., Tanioka, H., and Takeda, Y. (1966). *Biochem. biophys. Acta*, **118**, 88–97.
Bayly, R. C., Dagley, S., and Gibson, D. T. (1966). *Biochem. J.*, **101**, 293–301.
Bray, G. A. (1960). *Anal. Biochem.*, **1**, 279–285.
Chapman, P. J., and Dagley, S. (1962). *J. gen. Microbiol.*, **28**, 251–256.
Dagley, S., and Chapman, P. J. This Volume, p. 217.
Dagley, S., Chapman, P. J., Gibson, D. T., and Wood, J. M. (1964). *Nature, Lond.*, **202**, 775–778.
Dagley, S., Chapman, P. J., and Gibson, D. T. (1965). *Biochem. J.*, **97**, 643–650.
Dagley, S., Fewster, M. E., and Happold, F. C. (1953). *J. gen. Microbiol.*, **8**, 1–7.
Dagley, S., Geary, P. J., and Wood, J. M. (1968). *Biochem. J.*, **109**, 559–568.
Dagley, S., and Stopher, D. A. (1959). *Biochem. J.*, **73**, 16P.
Gibson, D. T. (1968). *Science*, **161**, 1093–1097.
Gibson, D. T., Koch, J. R., and Kallio, R. E. (1968). *Biochemistry*, **7**, 2653–2661.
Gray, P. H. H., and Thornton, H. G. (1928). *Zbl. Bakt. II*, **73**, 74–83.
Guroff, G., and Abramowitz, A. (1967). *Anal. Biochem.*, **19**, 548–555.
Guroff, G., and Ito, T. (1965). *J. Biol. Chem.*, **240**, 1175–1184.
Guroff, G., Levitt, M., Daly, J., and Udenfriend, S. (1966). *Biochem. Biophys. Res. Commun*, **25**, 253–262.
Guroff, G., Rhoads, C. A., and Abramowitz, A. (1967). *Anal. Biochem*, **21**, 273–278.
Guroff, G., and Rhoads, C. A. (1969). *J. biol. Chem.*, **244**, 142–146.

Hayaishi, O. (1964). *Proc. 6th Int. Congr. Biochem.*, New York, I.U.B. Vol. 33, 31–38.

Hayaishi, O. (1966). *Bacteriol. Rev.*, 30, 720–731.

Hayaishi, O., and Hashimoto, K. (1950). *J. Biochem. Tokyo*, 37, 371–374.

Hegeman, G. D. (1966). *J. Bacteriol.* 91, 1140–1154.

Hosokawa, K., and Stanier, R. Y. (1966). *J. biol. Chem.*, 241, 2453–2460.

Ichihara, A., Adachi, K., Hosokawa, K., and Takeda, Y. (1952). *J. biol. Chem.*, 237, 2296–2302.

Katagiri, M., Takemori, S., Suzuki, K., and Yasuda, H. (1966). *J. biol. Chem.*, 241, 5675–5677.

Knox, W. E., and Edwards, S. W. (1955). *J. biol. Chem.*, 216, 479–487.

Kobayashi, S., Kuno, S., Itada, N., and Hayaishi, O. (1964). *Biochem. Biophys. Res. Commun.*, 16, 556–561.

Kunita, N. (1955). *Med. J. Osaka Univ.*, 6, 703–801.

Layne, E. (1957). *In* "Methods in Enzymology" (Eds. S. P. Colowick and N. O. Kaplan), Vol. 3, pp. 447–454. Academic Press, New York.

Levy, C. C. (1967). *J. biol. Chem.*, 242, 747–753.

Lowry, D. H., Rosebrough, N. J., Farr, A. L., and Randall, R. J. (1951). *J. biol. Chem.*, 193, 265–275.

Milne, G. W. A., Goldman, P., and Holtzman, J. L. (1968). *J. biol. Chem.*, 243, 5374–5376.

Mori, M., Taniuchi, H., Kojima, Y., and Hayaishi, O. (1966). *Biochem. biophys, Acta*, 128, 535–546.

Nozaki, M., Kagamiyama, H., and Hayaishi, O. (1963). *Biochem. Z.*, 338, 582–590.

Ornston, L. N. (1966). *J. biol. Chem.*, 241, 3800–3810.

Ornston, L. N., and Stanier, R. Y. (1966). *J. biol. Chem.*, 241, 3776–3786.

Renson, J., Daly, J., Wiessbach, H., Witkop, B., and Udenfriend, S. (1966). *Biochem. Biophys. Res. Commun.*, 25, 504–513.

Ribbons, D. W. (1965). *Annu. Rep. Progr. Chem.*, 62, 445–468.

Schepartz, B., and Gurin, S. (1949). *J. biol. Chem.*, 180, 663–673.

Sistrom, W. R., and Stanier, R. Y. (1954). *J. biol. Chem.*, 210, 821–836.

Sols, A. (1947). *Nature, Lond.*, 160, 89–89.

Stanier, R. Y. (1947). *J. Bacteriol.*, 54, 339–348.

Stanier, R. Y. (1950). *J. Bacteriol.*, 59, 527–532.

Stanier, R. Y., and Ingraham, J. L. (1954). *J. biol. Chem.*, 210, 799–808.

Stanier, R. Y., Palleroni, N. J., and Doudoroff, M. (1966). *J. gen. Microbiol.*, 43, 159–271.

Suda, M., and Takeda, Y. (1950). *J. Biochem. Tokyo*, 37, 375–378.

Waalkes, T. P., and Udenfriend, S. (1957). *J. Lab. Clin. Med.*, 50, 733–736.

CHAPTER XII

Assay of Enzymes of CO$_2$ Metabolism

MICHAEL C. SCRUTTON

Department of Biochemistry, Rutgers Medical School,
New Brunswick, N.J. 08903, U.S.A.

I. INTRODUCTION

A. General considerations

This article describes procedures used for the assay of enzymes of CO_2 metabolism in micro-organisms. The description of the assay method(s) for each enzyme is preceded by a brief summary which includes the species distribution of the enzyme, the probable physiological role of the enzyme (where appropriate), and some relevant properties. The species distribution given is not the product of a comprehensive survey of the literature and is only intended to indicate some types of micro-organism in which the enzyme has been found as a possible guide to further studies. The summary of the properties of the enzyme is in most instances confined to a description of the requirement for bound or dissociable cofactors and of the effect (if any) of metabolites which are neither substrates nor products of the reaction ("metabolic effectors") on the rate of catalysis.

The only enzymes of CO_2 metabolism which have been omitted are (i) those enzymes which catalyse reactions in which decarboxylation accompanies oxygenation or hydroxylation, e.g., salicylate hydroxylase: (ii) α-ketoglutarate oxidase which is discussed in the article by Reeves et al. (this Volume); and (iii) 6-phosphogluconate dehydrogenase which is discussed in the article by Wood (this Volume).

B. Use of assay procedures

The assay procedures described have been devised in most cases for the enzyme in a given micro-organism. It cannot be stressed too strongly that conditions which are necessary to obtain maximal activity for the enzyme in one species are not necessarily optimal for the same enzyme in a different species, cf. for example, the properties of the NAD-dependent L-malate enzyme in *Lactobacillus arabinosus* as compared with the properties of this enzyme in *Escherichia coli* (see IX.A). The indicated procedure should therefore be used only as a guideline when examining a different species. In all cases such parameters as the pH optimum, K_m's, and linearity with time and enzyme concentration should be examined before attempting any quantitative evaluation of the data.

The procedures have been modified from the original description when necessary, such that standard total volumes of 1 ml and 3 ml are used for spectrophotometric and manometric procedures respectively. These standard volumes are adopted for convenience and have no especial significance. In all cases "units of enzyme activity" refer to a unit defined as 1 μmole substrate utilized (or product produced) per minute as recommended by the Commission on Enzymes of the I.U.B. Units of enzymic activity are often expressed on a different basis in the original publications.

C. Scintillation fluids

The system most commonly used for estimation of ^{14}C in aqueous samples by liquid scintillation counting is the dioxan-based system described by Werbin *et al.* (1959). This system contains, in 1 litre dioxan; 100 g naphthalene; 10 g 2,5-diphenyloxazole (PPO); and 0·25 g 2,2'-*p*-phenylene-*bis*-(5'phenyloxazole) (POPOP). Other secondary scintillators such as dimethyl-POPOP, or *p*-*bis*-(*o*-methylstyryl)-benzene (*bis*-MSB) may be used in place of POPOP.

D. Abbreviations

The abbreviations used are: XTP, a nucleoside triphosphate; XDP, a nucleoside diphosphate; CoA, coenzyme A; PEP, phosphoenolpyruvate; TPP, thiamine pyrophosphate; NAD(NADH), the oxidized (reduced) forms of nicotinamide adenine dinucleotide; NADP (NADPH), the oxidized (reduced) forms of nicotinamide adenine dinucleotide phosphate; Me^{2+}, divalent metal ion, HEPES, N-2-hydroxyethyl piperazine-N'-2-ethane sulphonate; TCA, tricholoroacetic acid.

E. Microbial taxonomy

The classification of the micro-organisms, to which reference is made in this article, is in most cases taken from the original publications. However, it should be noted that the taxonomic basis for these classifications is often inadequate, especially in the case of the Pseudomonads. A comprehensive taxonomic study of this latter genus has recently been published by Stanier *et al.* (1966).

17

II. ANAPLEROTIC ENZYMES

All micro-organisms which possess a functional tricarboxylic acid cycle have a requirement for replenishment of the intermediates of this cycle when these latter are utilized in anabolic pathways. The reactions or sequences which fulfil this requirement have been termed "anaplerotic" by Kornberg (1966) to emphasize their unique metabolic status. The presence of these anaplerotic sequences permits the micro-organism to synthesize all its cell constituents *de novo* when supplied with two or three carbon compounds or their precursors, e.g., glucose, as growth substrates. Certain enzymes of CO_2 metabolism are involved in the anaplerotic sequences which permit growth on three carbon compounds. These sequences, all of which involve a net conversion of pyruvate to oxalo-acetate, are of two types:

(i) A direct carboxylation of pyruvate by the enzyme, pyruvate carboxylase, as in yeasts (Losada *et al.*, 1964; Gailiusis *et al.*, 1964) *Arthrobacter globiformis* (Bridgeland and Jones, 1967), *Pseudomonas citronellolis* (Seubert and Remberger, 1961) and *Aspergillus niger* (Bloom and Johnson, 1962).

(ii) Conversion of pyruvate to PEP by pyruvate synthetase (Cooper and Kornberg, 1965) or pyruvate phosphate dikinase (Evans and Wood, 1968) and subsequent carboxylation of PEP to yield oxaloacetate. This latter reaction is catalysed by PEP carboxylase in the Enterobacteriaceae (Ashworth and Kornberg, 1963; Theodore and Englesberg, 1964) and by PEP carboxytransphosphorylase in the Propionibacteria (Siu and Wood, 1962).

The enzymes of CO_2 metabolism which catalyse anaplerotic reactions are discussed in a separate section to emphasize both their unique physiological role, and also the similarities in the effects of such metabolites as acetyl-CoA and L-aspartate which may regulate the activity of pyruvate carboxylase (in yeast) and PEP carboxylase (in the Enterobacteriaceae).

A. Pyruvate carboxylase (EC 6.4.1.1.)

$$\text{Pyruvate} + \text{MeATP}^{2-} + \text{HCO}_3^- \xrightleftharpoons[]{\text{Me}^{2+}, \text{Me}^+} \text{Oxaloacetate} + \text{MeADP}^- + \text{P}_i$$

1. *Distribution*

Three types of pyruvate carboxylase are recognized which differ in their requirement for activation by an acyl-CoA, e.g., acetyl-CoA:

(i) Active in the absence of an acyl-CoA. *P. citronellolis*, *Asp. niger*, *Clostridium kluyveri* (Seubert and Remberger, 1961; Bloom and Johnson, 1962; Stern, 1965).

(ii) Activated by addition of an acyl-CoA but partially active in the absence of this co-factor. Yeasts (Losada *et al.*, 1964; Gailuisis *et al.*, 1964; Cazzulo and Stoppani, 1965).

(iii) Inactive in the absence of an acyl-CoA. *A. globiformis* (Bridgeland and Jones, 1967).

Cell-free extracts of other organisms, e.g., *Chromatium* (Fuller *et al.*, 1961) also possess pyruvate carboxylase activity which is activated by acetyl-CoA.

In addition to its anaplerotic role, pyruvate carboxylase may also be involved in hexose synthesis from three-carbon precursors in some micro-organisms, e.g., yeasts (Ruiz-Amil *et al.*, 1965).

2. *Properties*

All pyruvate carboxylases which have been examined are (i) inactivated by incubation with avidin (Seubert and Remberger, 1961; Bloom and Johnson, 1962; Losada *et al.*, 1964; Gailuisis *et al.*, 1954): (ii) inactivated by incubation with low (0·01–0·1 mM) concentrations of reagents which react specifically with sulphydryl groups (Gailuisis *et al.*, 1964; Seubert and Weicker, 1968); and (iii) inhibited by oxalate at concentrations lower than 0·1 mM (Losada *et al.*, 1964; Seubert and Weicker, 1968). These findings indicate the presence of functional biotin residues and suggest the presence of sulphydryl groups and a protein-bound metal ion at or near the active site of these enzymes. In contrast to pyruvate carboxylase purified from chicken liver which possesses a tightly bound manganese atom as a constituent of the active site (Scrutton *et al.*, 1966; Mildvan *et al.*, 1966; Mildvan and Scrutton, 1967), the identity of the bound metal ion has not been established for pyruvate carboxylases purified from many microbial sources. However, tightly bound manganese is not present in pyruvate caroboxylase purified from baker's yeast (Young *et al.*, 1968), and recent studies (Scrutton *et al.*, 1970) demonstrate that this enzyme contains bound zinc in equimolar ratio with the biotin residues. In addition, this enzyme is inhibited by L-aspartate (Ruiz-Amil *et al.*, 1965) and the acyl-CoA activation is much less specific than that observed for the avian liver enzyme (Scrutton and Utter, 1967). For example, acetyl-CoA, methylmalonyl-CoA, benzoyl-CoA and palmityl-CoA are all potent activators of pyruvate carboxylase purified from yeast (Utter *et al.*, 1967). This lack of specificity may indicate that activation by an acyl-CoA is not an important physiological mechanism for regulation of pyruvate carboxylase in yeast. All pyruvate carboxylases examined thus far also require activation by Me^+.

3. *Assay methods*

Pyruvate carboxylase may be assayed either spectrophotometrically by measurement of oxaloacetate production with malate dehydrogenase (Seubert and Weicker, 1968; Young *et al.*, 1969) or using a radiochemical assay in which the incorporation of $^{14}CO_2$ into citrate is measured (Ruiz-Amil *et al.*, 1965).

(a) *Spectrophotometric.* This procedure is applicable to all three types of pyruvate carboxylase with the modifications noted below for the acetyl-CoA-independent enzyme.

Reagents:

0·5M K+HEPES pH 7·8—The procedure described by Seubert and Weicker (1968) for the enzyme from *P. citronellolis* utilizes Tris-Cl pH 7·2. However, equal or better activity is obtained at pH 7·8 (M. R. Young and M. C. Scrutton, unpublished data).

> 0·1M Potassium pyruvate, pH 6·8
> 0·0165M ATP, pH 7·0
> 0·2M KHCO₃
> 0·134M MgCl₂
> 3·2mM NADH
> 1·7mM Acetyl-CoA—not required for assay of the acetyl CoA-independent pyruvate carboxylase.
> Malate dehydrogenase diluted in 0·05M K+HEPES pH 7·8 to give a solution containing 100 units/ml.

The assay system contains, in 1·0 ml, 100 μmoles K+HEPES pH 7·8, 10 μmoles potassium pyruvate, 3·3 μmoles ATP, 6·7 μmoles MgCl₂, 20 μmoles KHCO₃, 0·085 μmole acetyl-CoA (omitted for acetyl CoA-independent enzyme), 5 units malate dehydrogenase and 0·16 μmole NADH. After equilibration to 25°C the reaction is initiated by the addition of 0·02–0·05 units pyruvate carboxylase and the initial rate of NADH oxidation is measured at 340 nm. Both lactate dehydrogenase and NADH oxidase interfere with this assay procedure. The contribution of these latter enzymes can be assessed by preincubation of the enzyme preparation with an equal amount (w/w) of avidin for 10 min before assay. However, in crude extracts the greater part of the overall rate of NADH oxidation may be due to contaminating activities (cf. Young *et al.*, 1969). Additionally, if the pyruvate carboxylase under investigation requires activation by acetyl CoA and the crude extract contains citrate synthetase, further interference will occur since citrate synthetase competes with malate dehydrogenase for the oxaloacetate produced by pyruvate carboxylase. A reliable estimate of pyruvate carboxylase activity cannot therefore be obtained in crude extracts by the spectrophotometric procedure and the radiochemical assay should be used. Recently Martin and Denton (1970) have described a spectro-photometric assay procedure for pyruvate carboxylase which appears applicable to crude extracts of micro-organisms.

(b) *Radiochemical.* The procedure described is modified from that of Henning and Seubert (1964).

Reagents:

K$^+$HEPES pH 7·8, pyruvate, ATP ,and MgCl$_2$—as described for spectro-photometric assay.

> 0·2M KH^{14}CO$_3$ (10^6 cpm/μmole)
> 0·01M CoASH, pH 6·0
> 0·05M Acetyl-phosphate
> Phosphotransacetylase diluted in 0·05M K$^+$HEPES pH 7·8 to give a solution containing 100 units/ml.
> Citrate synthetase diluted in 0·05M K$^+$HEPES pH 7·8 to give a solution containing 10 units/ml.

The assay system contains, in 1·0 ml, 100 μmoles K$^+$HEPES pH 7·8, 10 μmoles potassium pyruvate, 3·3 μmoles ATP, 6·7 μmoles MgCl$_2$, 10 μmoles KH^{14}CO$_3$, 0·5 μmoles CoASH, 2·5 μmoles acetyl-phosphate, 5 units phosphotransacetylase and 1 unit citrate synthetase. After equilibration to 25°C the reaction is initiated by addition of 0·01–0·02 units pyruvate carboxylase and the system is incubated for 10–15 min. The reaction is stopped by addition of 0·5 ml 4N HCl and the precipitated protein removed by centrifugation. An aliquot (0·5 ml) of the supernatant fraction is dried in a scintillation vial for 30 min at 85°C to remove residual H^{14}CO$_3^-$ and 1 ml H$_2$O plus 10 ml liquid scintillator (see I.C.) are added. Acid-stable radioactivity which is present as citrate is estimated in a liquid scintillation spectrometer. Incorporation of H^{14}CO$_3^-$ which is not dependent on pyruvate carboxylase may be estimated by preincubation of the enzyme preparation with avidin as described above.

Although this assay procedure was designed for estimation of pyruvate carboxylases which require activation by acetyl-CoA, it may be used for any pyruvate carboxylase and has the advantages that addition of NADH is not required and that accumulation of oxaloacetate does not occur during the period of incubation. However, a correction must be applied for the dilution of the added H^{14}CO$_3^-$ by endogenous HCO$_3^-$. In an alternative procedure (Henning and Seubert, 1964) the radioactivity is added as 2-^{14}C-pyruvate. Although dilution problems are eliminated in this case the ^{14}C-citrate formed must be separated from the residual ^{14}C-pyruvate by electrophoresis.

B. PEP carboxylase (EC 4.1.1.31.)

$$PEP + HCO_3^- \xrightleftharpoons{Me^{2+}} Oxaloacetate + P_i$$

1. Distribution

Enterobacteriaceae (Ashworth and Kornberg, 1966; Maeba and Sanwal, 1965); *Pseudomonas AM1* (grown on methanol) (Large *et al.*, 1962); *Thiobacillus thio-oxidans* (Suzuki and Werkman, 1957); *Ferrobacillus ferroxidans* (Din *et al.*, 1967); *Chlorobium thiosulfatophilum* (Evans *et al.*, 1966); *Streptomyces aureofaciens* (Vorisek *et al.*, 1970).

2. Properties

The enzyme purified from Enterobacteriaceae is activated by acetyl-CoA (Nishikido *et al.*, 1965; Canovas and Kornberg, 1966), fructose-1,6-diphosphate (Sanwal and Maeba, 1966a) and CDP, CTP and GTP (Sanwal and Maeba, 1966b); and is inhibited by L-aspartate, fumarate and L-malate (Maeba and Sanwal, 1965; Nishikido *et al.*, 1965). Addition of organic solvents, e.g., dioxan, ethanol, or certain polycations, e.g., poly-L-lysine, spermidine, also activate the enzyme and cause a partial or complete desensitization to the effects of the various metabolites described above (Sanwal *et al.*, 1966). The enzymes from *F. ferroxidans* and *S. aureofaciens* are also activated by acetyl-CoA and inhibited by L-aspartate (Din *et al.*, 1967; Vorisek *et al.*, 1970). No bound co-factors, e.g., biotin, have been detected in purified PEP carboxylase.

3. Assay method

PEP carboxylase may be assayed spectrophotometrically by measurement of oxaloacetate production with malate dehydrogenase (Ashworth and Kornberg, 1966).

Reagents:

> 0·5M Tris-Cl, pH 8·8
> 0·1M Trisodium PEP
> 0·1M NaHCO$_3$
> 0·5M MgCl$_2$
> 0·002M Acetyl-CoA
> 0·002M NADH
> Malate dehydrogenase diluted to a final concentration of 100 units/ ml in 0·1% bovine serum albumin.

The assay system contains, in 1·0 ml, 100 μmoles Tris-Cl pH 8·8 5 μmoles trisodium PEP, 5 μmoles MgCl$_2$, 10 μmoles NaHCO$_3$, 0·5 μmole acetyl-CoA, 0·1 μmole NADH and 5 units malate dehydrogenase. After equilibration to 25°C 0·02–0·05 units PEP carboxylase are added and the initial rate of NADH oxidation is measured at 340 nm.

In crude preparations NADH oxidase may interfere with this assay procedure. The contribution of NADH oxidase to the overall rate of NADH oxidation may be estimated by omitting PEP from the system described above. This spectrophotometric assay has been used for estimation of PEP carboxylase in cell-free extracts of *E. coli* after correction for the contribution of NADH oxidase (Ashworth and Kornberg, 1966). The presence of citrate synthetase in the crude preparations would also interfere with this assay procedure for reasons similar to those detailed above for the assay of pyruvate carboxylase. If citrate synthetase is present PEP carboxylase may either be assayed in the absence of activator, i.e., as described by Maeba and Sanwal (1968) or in the presence of 10 mM CDP.

Similar assay conditions are used for this enzyme in other species except that the enzyme from *F. ferroxidans* exhibits optimal activity at or below pH 7·0 (Din *et al.*, 1967).

C. PEP carboxytransphosphorylase (EC 4.1.1.3)

$$PEP + P_i + CO_2 \overset{Me^{2+}}{\rightleftharpoons} Oxaloacetate + PP_i$$

The enzyme also catalyses a reaction:

$$PEP + P_i \overset{Me^{2+}}{\longleftarrow} Pyruvate + PP_i$$

This latter reaction is inhibited by increasing the concentration of CO$_2$ or by addition of thiol reagents which activate the fixation of CO$_2$ on PEP (Wood *et al.*, 1969b).

1. *Distribution*

Propionibacteria (Siu and Wood, 1962).

2. *Properties*

PEP carboxytransphosphorylase contains no bound co-factors and, in contrast to PEP carboxylase and pyruvate carboxylase, has no known metabolic effectors. However, marked inhibition of this enzyme by both substrates and products of the reaction is observed. Most common buffers are also inhibitory (Lochmuller *et al.*, 1966).

3. *Assay Method*

PEP carboxytransphosphorylase is routinely assayed in the direction of

CO_2 fixation by measurement of oxaloacetate production with malate dehydrogenase (Lochmuller *et al.*, 1966; Wood *et al.*, 1969b).

Reagents:

>   0·125M K_2HPO_4
>   0·05M Trisodium PEP
>   0·75M $KHCO_3$
>   0·30M $MgCl_2$
>   3·0 mM NADH
>   3·0 mM $CoCl_2$
>   Malate dehydrogenase diluted in 1% bovine serum to give a solution containing 40 units/ml.

A mix is prepared of all the above reagents except malate dehydrogenase and $CoCl_2$ at the following concentrations (in μmoles/ml): K_2HPO_4, 12·5; PEP, 2·5; $KHCO_3$, 37·5; $MgCl_2$, 15; NADH, 0·15.

The pH is adjusted by 6·5 by bubbling CO_2 through this mix at 25°C for approximately 15 min and is maintained below 7·0 by bubbling with CO_2 as required. The assay system contains, in 1·0 ml, 0·82 ml of the mix at pH 6·5 to 7·0 as above, 0·1 μmole $CoCl_2$ and 2 units malate dehydrogenase. The reaction is initiated by addion of 0·01–0·02 units PEP carboxytransphosphorylase and the maximal rate of NADH oxidation is measured at 340 nm. The reaction rate may show an initial lag period before attaining its maximal value. The contribution of other enzymes to the rate of NADH oxidation may be estimated by omitting PEP from the assay system. If this control rate of NADH oxidation is greater than 50% of the rate observed in the presence of PEP a more accurate assay of carboxytransphosphorylase activity is obtained if a stepwise procedure is used (Lochmuller *et al.*, 1966; Wood *et al.*, 1969b). The mix and assay system are prepared as described above except that NADH and malate dehydrogenase are omitted. After addition of PEP carboxytransphosphorylase (0·05–0·1 units) the system is incubated for 4 min at 25°C. The reaction is stopped by addition of 0·2 ml 10% trichloroacetic acid and precipitated protein removed by centrifugation at 0°C. The oxaloacetate content of the supernatant fraction is measured in a system which contains, in 1·0 ml, 200 μmoles potassium phosphate pH 7·6, 1·2 μmoles NADH, 5 units malate dehydrogenase and an aliquot (0·1–0·2 ml) of the supernatant fraction.

PEP carboxytransphosphorylase cannot readily be assayed in the direction of PEP formation since both oxaloacetate and PP_i are potent inhibitors.

III. ENZYMES OF CO_2 METABOLISM WHICH ARE CHARACTERISTIC OF CERTAIN METABOLIC PATHWAYS

Some enzymes of CO_2 metabolism may be used as "marker" enzymes, i.e., their presence is indicative of the operation of a certain metabolic pathway. These enzymes and the pathways of which they are characteristic in most micro-organisms are summarized in Table I.

A. PEP carboxykinase (EC 4.1.1.32)

$$PEP + CO_2 + GDP(ADP) \overset{Me^{2+}}{\rightleftharpoons} Oxaloacetate + GTP(ATP)$$

1. *Distribution*

Two types of PEP carboxykinase are recognized which differ in nucleotide specificity.

(a) *Specific for adenine nucleotides.* Yeasts (Cannata and Stoppani, 1959), *Propionibacterium shermanii* (Pomerantz, 1958), *Escherichia coli* (Amarasingham, 1959; Ashworth and Kornberg, 1966), *Thiobacillus thio-oxidans*

TABLE I

Characteristic enzymes of certain metabolic pathways

Enzyme	Pathway
PEP Carboxykinase	Hexose synthesis from three and four carbon precursors
Methylmalonyl-CoA-oxalacetate	Propionate fermentation
Transcarboxylase	(Propionibacteria)
Acetyl–CoA carboxylase	Fatty acid synthesis
Ribulose-1,5-diphosphate carboxylase	CO_2 fixation by the Calvin cycle
Pyruvate synthetase	Reductive carboxylation cycle
Carbamyl phosphate synthetase	Pyrimidine biosynthesis, Arginine biosynthesis
β-Methylcrotonyl-CoA carboxylase	Leucine catabolism

(Suzuki and Werkman, 1958), *Tetrahymena pyriformis* (Shrago and Sug, 1966).

(b) *Specific for guanosine or inosine nucleotides. Arthrobacter globiformis* (Bridgeland and Jones, 1967).

Examination of the levels of PEP carboxykinase in yeasts grown on a variety of carbon sources has suggested that this enzyme functions as a decarboxylase *in vivo* and catalyses the first step in hexose synthesis from oxaloacetate (and hence from three and four carbon precursors) (Ruiz-Amil *et al.*, 1965; Claisse *et al.*, 1967). This role is analogous to that suggested for mammalian and avian liver (Utter *et al.*, 1964). Both these studies and those of Ashworth and Kornberg (1966) with mutants of *E. coli* are inconsistent with an anaplerotic role for PEP carboxykinase.

2. Properties

No metabolic effectors have been described for PEP carboxykinase in most species although it is the first enzyme of the pathway by which hexoses are formed via oxaloacetate from three and four carbon precursors. However, recently Wright and Sanwal (1969) have reported that the enzyme purified from *E. coli* is inhibited by NADH and have suggested that the inhibition may be of importance in regulation of this pathway. No bound co-factors have been detected in purified preparations of this enzyme.

3. Assay procedures

Although PEP carboxykinase probably functions *in vivo* as a decarboxy-lase, it is most readily assayed in the direction of CO_2 fixation by either a spectrophotometric (Chang and Lane, 1966) or radiochemical procedure (Cannata and Stoppani, 1959; Chang and Lane, 1966).

(a) *Spectrophotometric.* Oxaloacetate production is measured with malate dehydrogenase and NADH.

Reagents:

0·5M Imidazole-Cl pH 6·5
0·02M Trisodium PEP
0·012M Sodium ADP (or GDP)
0·5M NaHCO$_3$
0·01M MnCl$_2$
0·02M Glutathione
3·2 mM NADH
Malate dehydrogenase diluted in 0·1% bovine serum albumin to give a solution containing 100 units/ml.

The assay system contains, in 1·0 ml, 100 μmoles imidazole-Cl buffer pH 6·5, 2 μmoles PEP, 1·2 μmoles ADP (or GDP), 50 μmoles NaHCO$_3$ 1 μmole MnCl$_2$, 2 μmoles glutathione, 0·16 μmole NADH and 5 units malate dehydrogenase. After equilibration to 25°C, the reaction is initiated by addition of 0·02–0·05 units PEP carboxykinase and the initial rate of NADH oxidation is measured at 340 nm. The contribution of PEP carboxylase to the overall rate may be estimated by a control system in which ADP (GDP) is omitted and that due to NADH oxidase with a system which lacks PEP. In crude systems the control rate of NADH oxidation in the absence of PEP often constitutes a major portion of the overall rate and an accurate determination of the activity of PEP carboxy-kinase is not possible. In this case the radiochemical assay should be used.

(b) *Radiochemical*

Reagents:

Imidazole-Cl, PEP, ADP (or GDP), $MnCl_2$, glutathione and malate dehydrogenase—as described for the spectrophotometric assay.

0·5M $NaH^{14}CO_3$ (10^5 cpm/μmole)
0·05M NADH

The assay system contains, in 1·0 ml, 100 μmoles imidazole-Cl, pH 6·5, 2 μmoles PEP, 1·2 μmoles ADP (or GDP), 50 μmoles $NAH^{14}CO_3$, 1 μmole $MnCl_2$, 1 μmole glutathione, 5 μmoles NADH and 5 units malate dehydrogenase. After equilibration to 25°C the reaction is initiated by addi-tion of 0·002–0·004 units PEP carboxykinase and the system is incubated for 15 min. The reaction is terminated by addition of 1 ml 2N HCl and precipitated protein is removed by centrifugation. Acid-stable ^{14}C (as malate) is determined by incubating an 0·5 ml aliquot of the supernatant fraction for 30 min at 85°C in a scintillation counting vial. After addition of 1 ml water plus 10 ml liquid scintillator (see I.C.) to the dry vial, ^{14}C is determined in a liquid scintillation spectrometer.

Control incubations in which PEP and/or ADP (GDP) are omitted are required to ensure that PEP carboxykinase is responsible for the observed $^{14}CO_2$ fixation. The assay procedures described are also subject to possible interference due to removal of PEP and ADP (or GDP) by pyruvate kinase if this enzyme is present in high concentration. The possibility of such interference is decreased by using sodium salts of the reagents and preparing the cell-free extract in a sodium containing buffer.

(c) *PEP formation.* Although assays (i) and (ii) are most commonly used they do not measure the activity of PEP carboxykinase in the direction of its probable function *in vivo*. Measurement of PEP production from oxaloacetate and ATP (GTP) in crude systems is most readily accom-plished in a two-step assay in which PEP formation is estimated by the difference between alkali- and hypoiodite-labile phosphate. This procedure has been used by Shrago and Shug (1966) to estimate PEP carboxykinase in *Tet. pyriformis*.

Reagents:

1M Glycine-NaOH buffer, pH 9·5.
0·2M Sodium oxaloacetate, pH 6·0.
0·1M ATP (GTP)
0·2M $MnCl_2$

The assay system contains, in 1·5 ml, 100 μmoles glycine-NaOH, pH 9·5, 20 μmoles sodium oxaloacetate, 10 μmoles ATP (GTP), and 20 μmoles MnCl$_2$. After equilibration to 25°C the reaction is initiated by addition of 0·1–0·2 units PEP carboxykinase and the system is incubated for 7 min. The reaction is stopped by addition of 0·4 ml 10% TCA and PEP is determined in the supernatant fraction after centrifugation by the procedure of Lohmann and Meyerhof (1935) as modified by Nordlie and Lardy (1963). This procedure is likely to give low values for PEP carboxykinase activity in crude systems since both enolase and pyruvate kinase will remove PEP.

B. Methylmalonyl-CoA-oxaloacetate transcarboxylase (EC 2.1.3.1.)

Methylmalonyl-CoA + Pyruvate $\rightleftharpoons$ Propionyl CoA + Oxaloacetate

1. Distribution

Propionibacterium shermanii. The enzyme plays a crucial role in the propionate fermentation characteristic of this micro-organism (Stjernholm and Wood, 1963). The reaction catalysed is unique since it involves trans-carboxylation between an acyl-thioester and an α-keto acid.

2. Properties

The enzyme contains bound biotin which is involved in the carboxyl transfer reaction (Wood et al., 1963a; Wood et al., 1963b). Bound cobalt and zinc have been detected in this enzyme. The role of these metal ions may be similar to that suggested for the bound manganese of pyruvate carboxylase (Northrop and Wood, 1969).

3. Assay procedures

Methylmalonyl-CoA-oxaloacetate transcarboxylase is assayed spectro-photometrically (Wood et al., 1969a).

Reagents:
> 1·0M Potassium phosphate buffer pH 6·8.
> 0·1M sodium pyruvate
> 4 mM Methylmalonyl-CoA (prepared as described by Beck et al., 1957)
> Malate dehydrogenase diluted in 0·1% bovine serum albumin to give a solution containing 100 units/ml
> 3·2 mM NADH.

The assay system contains, in 1·0 ml, 350 μmoles potassium phosphate, pH 6·8, 10 μmoles sodium pyruvate, 0·4 μmoles methylmalonyl-CoA, 0·16 μmoles NADH and 5 units malate dehydrogenase. After equilibration to 25°C the reaction is initiated by addition of 0·01–0·02 units methylmalonyl-CoA-oxaloacetate transcarboxylase and the rate of NADH oxidation is measured at 340 nm. If dilutions of the enzyme are required they are prepared in 0·25M potassium phosphate, pH 6·8 containing 0·005M gluthatione.

NADH oxidation which is not dependent on methylmalonyl-CoA-oxaloacetate transcarboxylase may be estimated either by omitting methyl-malonyl-CoA from the assay system or by preincubating the enzyme preparation with an equal amount (w/w) of avidin for 10 min at 25°C before addition to the reaction mixture. In crude systems this control rate of NADH oxidation may constitute a major portion of the total rate. In this case the assay is conducted stepwise. Malate dehydrogenase and NADH are omitted from the assay system as described above and after initiating the reaction with 0·2 unit methylmalonyl-CoA-oxaloacetate transcarboxylase, the system is incubated for 10 min at 25°C. The reaction is stopped by addition of 0·2 ml 20% trichloroacetic acid and precipitated protein is removed by centrifugation. The supernatant fraction is neutralized to pH 5–6 by addition of NaOH and made up to 1·5 ml. The oxaloacetate content of an aliquot (0·5 ml) of this supernatant fraction is determined in a system containing 200 μmoles potassium phosphate pH 7·5, 0·16 μmoles NADH and 5 units malate dehydrogenase.

C. Ribulose-1,5-diphosphate carboxylase (carboxydismutase) (EC 4.1.1.f)

$$\text{Ribulose-1,5-diphosphate} + CO_2 \xrightarrow{Me^{2+}} \text{Two 3-Phosphoglycerate}$$

1. Distribution

Chlorella (Quayle *et al.*, 1954); *Thiobacillus* (Santer and Vishniac, 1955; Trudinger, 1956; Gale and Beck, 1966); *Pseudomonas oxalaticus* (grown on formate) (Quayle and Keech, 1959); Athiorhodaceae (Anderson and Fuller, 1967); *Ferrobacillus ferroxidans* (Din *et al.*, 1967); *Hydrogenomonas* (Kuehn and McFadden, 1969). The enzyme is probably widely distributed and provides a major mechanism for carbon assimilation in many micro-organisms especially during autotrophic growth.

2. Properties

The enzyme contains no detectable bound co-factors.

3. Assay procedure

Ribulose-1,5-diphosphate carboxylase may be assayed either spectro-photometrically by conversion of 3-phosphoglycerate to 1,3-diphosphoglycerate and measurement of this latter compound using glyceraldehyde-3-phosphate and α-glycerophosphate dehydrogenases (Racker, 1962); or radiochemically by measurement of $^{14}CO_2$ fixation into acid-stable product (Quayle and Keech, 1959; Paulsen and Lane, 1966).

(a) *Spectrophotometric*

Reagents:

    1M Tris-Cl, pH 8·0
    0·025M Sodium ribulose-1,5-diphosphate
    0·5M MgCl₂
    0·5M KHCO₃
    0·1M Glutathione
    0·2M Sodium ATP
    3-Phosphoglycerate kinase, 200 units/ml
    Glyceraldehyde-3-phosphate dehydrogenase, 40 units/ml
    3·2 mM NADH
    α-Glycerophosphate dehydrogenase, 40 units/ml
    Triose phosphate isomerase diluted in 0·1% bovine serum albumin
      to give a solution containing 200 units/ml.

The assay system contains, in 1·0 ml, 100 μmoles Tris-Cl pH 8·0, 1 μmole ribulose-1,5-diphosphate, 75 μmoles KHCO₃, 10 μmoles MgCl₂, 5 μmoles glutathione, 12 μmoles ATP, 5 units 3-phosphoglycerate kinase, 2 units glyceraldehyde-3-phosphate dehydrogenase, 0·16 μmoles NADH, 2 units α-glycerophosphate dehydrogenase and 5 units triose phosphate isomerase. After equilibration to 25°C the reaction is initiated by addition of 0·02–0·05 unit ribulose-1,5-diphosphate carboxylase and the maximal rate of NADH oxidation is measured at 340 nm. A lag period is routinely observed in this assay and maximal rates are obtained only after 3–4 min. In this method carboxylation and cleavage of 1 μmole of ribulose-1,5-diphosphate results in the oxidation of 4 μmoles of NADH.

An alternative spectrophotometric procedure would involve the measurement of 3-phosphoglycerate production in a coupled system containing phosphoglycerate mutase, enolase, pyruvate kinase and lactate dehydrogenase plus appropriate co-factors. Although in this system fixation of 1 μmole of CO₂ would lead to oxidation of 2 (rather than 4) μmoles of NADH, the existence of favourable equilibria might overcome some of the problems associated with the procedure described above. The author is not aware of any studies in which this latter assay has been used to measure ribulose-1,5-diphosphate carboxylase.

(b) *Radiochemical*

Reagents:

    0·5M Tris-Cl, pH 8·0
    0·02M Sodium ribulose-1,5-diphosphate
    0·1M $MgCl_2$
    0·1M Glutathione
    0·4M $NaH^{14}CO_3$ (10^6 cpm/μmole)

The assay system contains, in 0·5 ml, 25 μmoles Tris-Cl, pH 8·0, 1 μmole sodium ribulose-1,5-diphosphate, 5 μmoles $MgCl_2$, 5 μmoles glutathione and 20 μmoles $NaH^{14}CO_3$. After equilibration to 25°C the reaction is initiated by addition of 5–15 milliunits ribulose-1,5-diphosphate carboxylase and the system is incubated for 15 min at 25°C. The reaction is stopped by addition of 1 ml 2N HCl, and precipitated protein is removed by centrifugation. An aliquot (0·5 ml) of the supernatant fraction is dried in a scintillation vial at 85°C for 30 min to remove residual $^{14}CO_2$. After addition of 1 ml H_2O followed by 10 ml liquid scintillator (see I.C.) acid-stable ^{14}C is estimated in a liquid scintillation spectrometer. For certain species e.g., *Hydrogenomonas*, glutathione may be omitted from the assay system.

D. Acetyl-CoA carboxylase (EC 6.4.1.2)

$$\text{Acetyl-CoA} + \text{ATP} + \text{HCO}_3^- \overset{Me^{2+}}{\rightleftharpoons} \text{Malonyl-CoA} + \text{ADP} + \text{P}_i$$

1. *Distribution*

Brewer's yeast (Matsuhashi *et al.*, 1964); *Escherichia coli* (Alberts and Vagelos, 1968). This enzyme which catalyses the first step of fatty acid synthesis is probably more widely distributed in micro-organisms than is indicated by the species in which it has been studied.

2. *Properties*

The presence and functional role of biotin has been established for this enzyme (Matsuhashi *et al.*, 1965). The metabolic effector status of acetyl-CoA carboxylases in micro-organisms is uncertain since conflicting reports exist regarding the activation of this enzyme in yeast by citrate and other related metabolites (Matsuhashi *et al.*, 1964; Rasmussen and Klein, 1967). Recent studies on the enzyme purified from *E. coli* have shown that catalytic activity requires the presence of two protein fractions only one of which contains biotin (Alberts and Vagelos, 1968).

3. *Assay procedures*

Four procedures which may be used to assay acetyl-CoA carboxylase are described by Matsuhashi *et al.* (1964). Two of these procedures require availability of the fatty acid synthetase complex, and are not described here since this latter enzyme system is not commercially available.

The other procedures are a spectrophotometric method in which acetyl-CoA-dependent ATPase is estimated using pyruvate kinase and lactate dehydrogenase and a radiochemical method involving measurement of $^{14}CO_2$ fixation into acid-stable product.

(a) *Spectrophotometric*

Reagents:

        0·5M Tris-Cl, pH 8·0
        5 mM Acetyl-CoA
        0·06M Sodium ATP
        0·2M $MgCl_2$
        0·2 MgK_2 EDTA
        0·5M $KHCO_3$
        0·02M PEP
        3·2 mM NADH
        Bovine serum albumin, 10 mg/ml
        Pyruvate kinase, 10 mg/ml
        Lactate dehydrogenase, 10 mg/ml

The assay system contains, in 1·0 ml, 100 μmoles Tris-Cl, pH 8·0, 0·2 μmole acetyl-CoA, 3 μmoles ATP, 10 μmoles $MgCl_2$, 10 μmoles MgK_2 EDTA, 20 μmoles $KHCO_3$, 1 μmole PEP, 0·16 μmole NADH, 0·6 mg bovine serum albumin, 10 μg pyruvate kinase, 25 μg lactate dehydrogenase. After equilibration to 25°C the reaction is initiated by addition of 2–5 milli-units acetyl-CoA carboxylase and the initial rate of NADH oxidation is measured at 340 nm. ATPase activity which is independent of the presence of acttyl-CoA carboxylase is estimated either by omission of acetyl-CoA from the system as above or by pre-incubating the enzyme preparation with an equal quantity (w/w) of avidin for 10 min before addition to the assay system. This control rate is likely to be excessive in crude systems for which the radiochemical procedure should be used.

(b) *Radiochemical*

Reagents:

        0·4M Potassium phosphate, pH 7·0
        0·1M $KHCO_3$
        2 mM $K_2{}^{14}CO_3$ (2×10^6 cpm/μmole)

ATP, $MgCl_2$, MgK_2 EDTA, acetyl-CoA and bovine serum albumin—as for the spectrophotometric procedure. The assay system contains, in 0·5 ml, 40 μmoles potassium phosphate pH 7·0, 0·1 μmole acetyl-CoA,

2 μmoles ATP, 5 μmoles $MgCl_2$, 5 μmoles MgK_2EDTA, 5 μmoles $KHCO_3$, 0·1 μmole $K_2{}^{14}CO_3$ and 0·6 mg bovine serum albumin. After equilibration to 25°C the reaction is initiated by addition of 2–5 milliunits acetyl-CoA carboxylase. The system is incubated for 15 min at 25°C after which the reaction is stopped by addition of 1 ml 2N HCl. An aliquot (0·5 ml) is dried in a scintillation vial at 85°C for 30 min and acid-stable ^{14}C is determined in a liquid scintillation spectrometer after addition of 1 ml H_2O and 10 ml liquid scintillator (see I.C.).

E. Pyruvate synthetase

Acetyl-CoA + HCO_3^- + Reduced Ferredoxin $\rightarrow$ Pyruvate + CoASH + Ferredoxin

1. *Distribution*

Clostridia (Bachofen *et al.*, 1964), *Chromatium* (Buchanan *et al.*, 1964), *Chlorobium thiosulfatophilum* (Evans *et al.*, 1966), *Rhodospirillum rubrum* (Buchanan *et al.*, 1967), *Chloropseudomonas ethylicum* (Evans, 1968). An analogous enzyme system which carboxylates succinyl-CoA to form α-keto-glutarate has been detected in *C. thiosulfatophilum*, *Cps. ethylicum* and *R. rubrum* (Buchanan and Evans, 1965; Buchanan *et al.*, 1967; Evans, 1968).

2. *Assay procedure*

The enzyme is assayed radiochemically by fixation of $^{14}HCO_3^-$ into alanine (Evans *et al.*, 1966; Buchanan and Arnon, 1969).

Reagents:

0·5M Na$^+$HEPES pH 7·5 (*R. rubrum*) or 0·5M K phosphate pH 6·2 (*C. thiosulfatophilum*). The use of HEPES buffer is not essential in the case of the *R. rubrum* enzyme but causes some activation as compared with phosphate buffer pH 7·5

5 mM CoASH

0·2M Acetyl-phosphate

0·1M NaH$^{14}CO_3$ (10^5 cpm/μmole)

0·2M Sodium ascorbate

1 mM Dichlorophenol-indophenol (DCPIP)

1 mM TPP

Phosphotransacetylase diluted in 0·1% bovine serum albumin to give a solution containing 50 units/ml.

0·5M Sodium L-glutamate

Glutamate-pyruvate transaminase diluted in 0·1% bovine serum albumin to give a solution containing 100 units/ml

Ferredoxin—preferably from the species under examination but if this is not available, ferredoxin from *Clostridium pasteurianum* is usually effective.

Ferredoxin reducing system—this is provided by addition of washed spinach chloroplast particles which are prepared as described by Kalberer *et al.* (1967) and may be stored for at least a month at $-20°C$ (Buchanan and Arnon, 1969). Immediately prior to use the chloroplast particle preparation is heated at 55°C for 5 min to destroy its capacity for O_2 evolution since the pyruvate and α-ketoglutarate sybthetase preparations are readily inactivated by O_2.

N.B. Rapid inactivation of pyruvate synthetase has been observed on storage of cell-free extracts of *Cl. pasteurianum* in air at 4°C (Bachofen *et al.*, 1964). The cause of this inactivation is not yet known but until investigated further it is recommended that cell-free extracts should be stored under an inert gas (N_2 or argon) and should be assayed as soon after preparation as possible.

The assay system contains, in 3·0 ml, 300 μmoles HEPES pH 7·5 (or K phosphate pH 6·2), 0·5 μmole CoASH, 0·2 μmole TPP, 50 μmoles acetyl-phosphate, 10 μmoles $NaH^{14}C_3$, 20 μmoles sodium ascorbate, 0·05 μmole DCPIP, 2 units phosphotransacetylase, 100 μmoles sodium-L-glutamate, 10 units glutamate-pyruvate transaminase, 50 μg ferredoxin (*Cl. pasteurianum*), and ferredoxin reducing system (e.g., heated chloroplast fragments containing 0·5 mg chlorophyll). After equilibration to 25°C under argon the reaction is initiated by addition of pyruvate synthetase (0·5–3·0 mg protein from the high speed supernatant fraction) and incubation is continued for 30–60 min under illumination (10,000 lux). If the enzyme preparation contains hydrogenase, carbon monoxide is used as the gas phase in place of argon to prevent H_2 evolution which causes inhibition of CO_2 fixation. The reaction is stopped by addition of 2 ml 4N HCl and precipitated protein is removed by centrifugation. An aliquot (1 ml) of the supernatant fraction is dried in a scintillation vial for 30 min at 85°C and acid stable ^{14}C is then determined in a liquid scintillation spectrometer after addition of 1 ml H_2O plus 10 ml liquid scintillator (see I.C.) Alternatively pyruvate (and α-ketoglutarate) may be isolated as the 2,4-dinitrophenyl-hydrazone as described by Rabinowitz (1960).

An analogous system may be used to determine α-ketoglutarate synthetase except that (i) acetyl-phosphate and phosphotransacetylase are replaced in the assay system by 5 μmoles ATP, 3 μmoles $MnSO_4$ and 10 μmoles potassium succinate and (ii) glutamate-pyruvate transaminase and glutamate are replaced by glutamate-oxaloacetate transaminase and aspartate.

Neither of these enzyme systems have been purified extensively and the procedures described which are adequate for assay in the high speed supernatant fraction from the cell-free extract may require modification for use with more highly purified fractions.

F. Carbamyl phosphate synthetase (EC 2.7.2.a.)

$$\text{L-Glutamine} + 2\,\text{ATP} + \text{HCO}_3^- + \text{H}_2\text{O} \xrightarrow{\text{Me}^+,\ \text{Me}^{2+}}$$
$$\text{Carbamyl phosphate} + \text{L-glutamate} + 2\,\text{ADP} + 2\text{P}_i$$

1. Distribution

Escherichia coli (Pierard and Wiame, 1964). This enzyme differs from carbamate kinase which is found in the Streptococci and related organisms (Jones *et al.*, 1955) in that glutamine rather than NH_4^+ serves as the amino group donor, and an extra mole of ATP is required. The involvement of 2 moles of ATP for the *E. coli* enzyme causes displacement of the equilibrium far towards synthesis of carbamyl phosphate in contrast to carbamate kinase where the equilibrium favours ATP synthesis from carbamyl phosphate (Jones and Lipmann, 1962). Carbamyl phosphate synthetase which supplies a required precursor for pyrimidine and arginine biosynthesis may be widely distributed in micro-organisms which do not require these precursors for growth.

2. Properties

Examination of the mechanism of the enzyme by pulse-labelling techniques and studies of the partial reactions has suggested the involvement of CO_2 and carbamate as enzyme-bound intermediates (Anderson and Meister; 1965, 1966a). Although the presence of biotin has been reported for purified preparations of the enzyme from *E. coli* (Wellner *et al.*, 1968) the significance of this finding has been questioned on the basis of more recent studies (Huston and Cohen, 1969) in which the biotin content of preparations of carbamyl phosphate synthetase was compared to that of pyruvate carboxylase, a known biotin enzyme.

In contrast to carbamyl phosphate synthetase from vertebrate liver which is inactive in the absence of N-acetyl-glutamate (Metzenberg *et al.*, 1957), the enzyme from *E. coli* does not require this co-factor (Anderson and Meister, 1965). Inhibition of the *E. coli* enzyme by UMP and UDP at concentrations in the range 1–10 μM and activation by higher concentrations (0·1–1 mM) of inosine and guanosine nucleotides has been reported (Pierard *et al.*, 1965; Anderson and Meister, 1966b). Synthesis of the enzyme in *E. coli* is subject to cumulative feed-back repression by arginine and uracil (Pierard *et al.*, 1965).

2. *Assay procedures*

Carbamyl phosphate synthetase may be assayed by a variety of procedures. The procedures described here are: (a) $H^{14}CO_3^-$ incorporation into urea (Anderson and Meister, 1965): (b) estimation of citrulline after coupling carbamyl phosphate synthetase with ornithine transcarbamylase (Jones, 1962; Anderson and Meister, 1965); and (c) spectrophotometric estimation of ADP formation by coupling with pyruvate kinase and lactate dehydrogenase (Fahien and Cohen, 1964).

(a) $H^{14}CO^-_3$ incorporation into urea

Reagents:

> 1·0M Potassium phosphate, pH 7·6
> 0·2M ATP pH 7
> 0·2M $MgCl_2$
> 0.1M L-Glutamine
> 0·2M $NaH^{14}CO_3$ ($2 \times 10_4$ cpm/μmole)
> 1·4N NH_4OH
> 5·4N KOH
> 4M NH_4Cl, pH 8·5
> Dowex 1×8, hydroxide form

The assay systems contain, in 1·0 ml, 100 μmoles phosphate pH 7·6, 20 μmoles ATP, 20 μmoles $MgCl_2$, 10 μmoles L-glutamine and 20 μmoles $NaH^{14}CO_3$.

After equilibration to 37°C the reaction is initiated by addition of 2–40 milliunits of carbamyl phosphate synthetase, and the system is incubated for 10 min. The reaction is stopped by addition of 0·1 ml of a freshly prepared solution containing 0·7N NH_4OH and 2·7N KOH and incubation is continued for 10 min at 37°C to ensure quantitative conversion of ^{14}C-carbamyl phosphate to ^{14}C-cyanate. The ^{14}C-cyanate is converted to ^{14}C urea by addition of 0·4 ml 4M NH_4Cl pH 8·5 and incubation at 100°C for 10 min. The ^{14}C-urea is isolated by application of the system to a 6 ml Dowex-1-X8 hydroxide column and elution with 11 ml of H_2O. Aliquots (1 ml) of this eluate are added to 10 ml liquid scintillator (see I.C.) and the ^{14}C content is estimated in a liquid scintillation spectrometer.

The enzymic activities estimated by this procedure must be corrected for dilution of the $H^{14}CO_3^-$ added by endogenous HCO_3^-.

(b) *Citrulline formation.* Citrulline is estimated by the procedure of Gehart and Parde (1962).

Reagents:

Phosphate, pH 7·6, ATP, $MgCl_2$ and L-glutamine—as above

0·2M $NaHCO_3$

0·2M L-Ornithine hydrochloride

Ornithine transcarbamylase, 100 units/ml

10% $HClO_4$

12N H_2SO_4

2,3-Butanedione-2-oxime in H_2O (22·5 mg/ml)

Disodium diphenylamine-*p*-sulphonate (114 mg) in 100 ml 0·1N
HCl containing 0·4 g Atlas BRIJ 35

$K_2S_2O_8$ in H_2O (2·5 mg/ml)

The latter three solutions are kept in the dark and at 0°C.

The assay system contains, in 1·0 ml, 100 μmoles phosphate pH 7·6, 20 μmoles ATP, 20 μmoles $MgCl_2$, 10 μmoles L-glutamine, 20 μmoles $NaHCO_3$, 10 μmoles L-ornithine, and 5 units ornithine transcarbamylase. After equilibration to 37°C the reaction is initiated by addition of 0·01–0·03 units carbamyl phosphate synthetase and the system is incubated for 10 min. The reaction is stopped by addition of 0·5 ml 10% $HClO_4$ and precipitated protein removed by centrifugation. A mixture is prepared (at 0°) of three parts butanedione-2-oxime: 1 part diphenylamine-*p*-sulphonate: 1 part $K_2S_2O_8$ using the solutions as above and 2·5 ml of this 3 : 1 : 1 mixture is added to a 0·5 ml aliquot of the $HClO_4$ supernatant. After shaking, the system is incubated at 60°C for 30 min, cooled to 25°C in ice water, and 0·5 ml $K_2S_2O_8$ is added. Maximal colour development occurs after incubation for approximately 20 min at 25°C and the absorbance at 560 nm is measured against a reagent blank. The citrulline content is estimated by comparison with a standard curve covering the range 0–0·3 μmoles citrulline.

It should be noted that after maximal development the colour then fades at approximately 1% per min. This rate of fading is much decreased by addition of 0·5 ml dioxan and/or storage at 0·C. Increased colour production is obtained if the system is incubated at 25°C for several hours before or after incubation at 60°C and it should be noted that reproducible results can only be obtained in this procedure if the intervals between the times of addition of reagents are standardized (Gerhart and Pardee, 1962).

Alternatively citrulline may be determined by the Archibald procedure as described by Grisolia (1955). The time of heating at 100°C should however be 30 min since colour development is incomplete at earlier times (Spector and Jones, 1963).

(c) *Spectrophotometric estimation of ADP*

Reagents:

Phosphate pH 7·6, ATP, $MgCl_2$, L-glutamine and $NaHCO_3$—as for procedure (ii)

1·0M KCl

0·05M Trisodium PEP

3·2 mM NADH

Pyruvate kinase diluted in 0·1% bovine serum albumin (100 units/ ml)

Lactate dehydrogenase diluted in 0·1% bovine serum albumin (100 units/ml).

The assay system contains, in 1·0 ml, 100 μmoles phosphate pH 7·6, 20 μmoles ATP, 20 μmoles $MgCl_2$, 20 μmoles $NaHCO_3$, 10 μmoles L-glutamine, 50 μmoles KCl, 2·5 μmoles PEP, 0·15 μmole NADH, 2·5 units pyruvate kinase and 5 units lactate dehydrogenase. After equilibration to 25°C the reaction is initiated by addition of 0·01–0·02 units carbamyl phosphate synthetase and the maximal rate of NADH oxidation is measured at 340 nm. The rate of NADH oxidation often shows a brief lag period before the maximal rate is attained.

This procedure is not suitable for estimation of impure enzyme preparations since satisfactory control systems for estimation of contaminating ATPase activity cannot readily be devised. Glutamine synthetase can use NH_4^+ as amino donor and the enzyme exhibits a HCO_3^--dependent ATPase activity (Anderson and Meister; 1965, 1966a).

G. β-Methylcrotonyl CoA carboxylase (EC 6.5.1.5.)

$$\beta\text{-Methylcrotonyl-CoA} + \text{ATP} + \text{HCO}_3^- \xrightarrow{\text{Me}^{2+}} \beta\text{-Methylglutaconyl-CoA} + \text{ADP} + \text{P}_i$$

1. *Distribution*

Pseudomonads (Rilling and Coon, 1960); Mycobacteria, *Achromobacter* (Knappe *et al.*, 1961; Himes *et al.*, 1963). The enzyme is induced in Pseudomonads and Mycobacteria by growth on branched chain compounds such as leucine or isovalerate, and is probably involved in the pathway of degradation of these compounds.

Growth of *Pseudomonas citronellolis* on citronellol induces formation of another biotin carboxylase (geranyl-CoA carboxylase) which catalyses an analogous CO_2 fixation on geranyl-CoA. The assay procedures described below for β-methylcrotonyl-CoA carboxylase may be used for estimation of geranyl-CoA carboxylase if Tris-Cl pH 7·2 and cis-geranyl-CoA are substituted for Tris-Cl pH 8·0 and β-methylcrotonyl-CoA (Seubert *et al.*, 1963).

2. Properties

The enzyme contains bound biotin which participates in the reaction sequence, and in addition possesses the property of carboxylating exogeneous biotin to give the free 1'-N-carboxybiotin derivative (Lynen et al., 1961; Himes et al., 1963).

3. Assay procedures

β-Methylcrotonyl-CoA carboxylase may be assayed spectrophotometrically by measurement of ADP production with pyruvate kinase and lactate dehydrogenase or radiochemically by measurement of $H^{14}CO_3^-$ incorporation into product (Himes et al., 1963).

(a) *Spectrophotometric*

Reagents:

1·0M Tris-Cl, pH 8·0
0·15M $MgCl_2$
0·02M ATP
0·1M $KHCO_3$
2 mM β-methylcrotonyl-CoA [prepared as described by Knappe et al. (1961)]
0·01M trisodium PEP
3·2 mM NADH
Pyruvate kinase and lactate dehydrogenase diluted in 0·1% bovine serum albumin pH 7 to give solution containing 100 units/ml of each enzyme.

The assay system contains, in 1·0 ml, 100 μmoles Tris-Cl pH 8·0, 1 μmole ATP, 15 μmoles $MgCl_2$, 10 μmoles $KHCO_3$, 0·2 μmole β-methylcrotonyl-CoA, 1 μmole PEP, 0·16 μmole NADH, 2 units pyruvate kinase, and 5 units lactate dehydrogenase. After equilibration to 25°C the reaction is initiated by addition of 0·02–0·05 units β-methylcrotonyl-CoA carboxylase and the initial rate of NADH oxidation is determined from the decrease in absorbance at 340 nm. ATPase activity which is not dependent on β-methylcrotonyl-CoA carboxylase may be estimated either by omitting β-methylcrotonyl-CoA from the system described above or preferably by incubating the enzyme preparation with an equal amount (w/w) of avidin for 10 min at 25°C before addition to the assay system. In crude systems the control rate obtained as above may be too great to provide an accurate assay of the carboxylase activity and the radiochemical procedure should be used.

(b) *Radiochemical.* The reagents required are those described for the spectrophotometric assay except that PEP, NADH, pyruvate kinase and lactate dehydrogenase are omitted and $0.1M$ $KHCO_3$ is replaced by $0.1M$ $KH^{14}CO_3$ (10^6 cpm/μmole). The assay system is also similar with the omissions as above and the addition of $KH^{14}CO_3$ (10^6 cpm/μmole) in place of $KHCO_3$. After equilibration to $25°C$ the reaction is initiated by addition of $0.005–0.01$ units β-methylcrotonyl-CoA carboxylase and incubated for 15 min. The reaction is stopped by placing the tubes in a $90°C$ water bath for 1 min and denatured protein is removed by centrifugation. Residual $H^{14}CO_3^-$ is removed from the supernatant fraction by "gassing" with CO_2 for 30 min. After adjustment to pH $9.0–10.0$ a 1 ml aliquot of the supernatant fraction is added to 10 ml liquid scintillator (see I.C.) and fixed ^{14}C estimated in a liquid scintillation spectrometer. It should be noted that the product of this reaction is not acid-stable and hence residual $H^{14}CO_3^-$ cannot be removed by drying an aliquot of the reaction mixture at acid pH.

IV. DECARBOXYLASES—GENERAL

These enzymes, which catalyse a reaction of the type $A \rightarrow B + CO_2$, have been classified according to their dependence on the co-factors biotin (Section V); pyridoxal phosphate (Section VI); thiamin pyrophosphate (Section VII); no defined co-factor requirement (Section VIII). This latter category includes both those enzymes which do not appear either to require addition of a co-factor for catalytic activity or to contain a bound co-factor and also enzymes whose co-factor status has not yet been defined.

Manometric procedures which measure the rate of evolution of CO_2 from the assay system are used for assay of many decarboxylases. For such assays conducted at pH values below 5.0 CO_2 retention in solution is not significant and the observed rate of evolution of CO_2 is equal to the rate of decarboxylation. At pH values above 5.0 retention of CO_2 becomes significant and the rate observed manometrically must be corrected for this factor as described by Umbreit *et al.* (1954). It should be noted that the correction factor for CO_2 retention becomes very large and inaccurate at pH values above 7.0. Hence, when CO_2 evolution is estimated manometrically at pH values above 7.0, a step-wise procedure is therefore more satisfactory. In this procedure a timed incubation of enzyme plus substrate is terminated by addition of excess acid from a second side-arm which lowers the pH below 5.0. In such cases a correction for endogenous CO_2 present in the assay reagents is necessary.

V. DECARBOXYLASES—BIOTIN

A. Oxaloacetate decarboxylase (EC 4.1.1.3.)

Oxaloacetate $\rightarrow$ Pyruvate $+$ CO_2

1. Distribution

Aerobacter (Stern, 1967), *Lactobacillus plantarum* (Flesch and Holbach, 1965). The enzyme is induced during aerobic or anaerobic growth of *Aerobacter* on citrate and is absent from cells grown on glucose or glycerol, suggesting a role in the fermentation of citrate by this and other microorganisms (Stern, 1967).

2. Properties

Several properties distinguish this enzyme from other oxaloacetate decarboxylases (cf. VIII.B). These are (i) the presence of biotin as a bound co-factor, which appears to be implicated in the reaction mechanism since the enzyme is inactivated by incubation with avidin; (ii) the specific activation by Na^+ ions; and (iii) the absence of a requirement for activation by divalent metal cations and of inhibition by 10 mM EDTA. The enzyme appears to be localized on the cytoplasmic membrane (Stern, 1967).

3. Assay methods

Oxaloacetate decarboxylase may be assayed either by measurement of pyruvate production with lactate dehydrogenase or by oxaloacetate disappearance utilizing the absorbance of this substrate at 280 nm (Stern, 1967).

Reagents:

> 0·1M Tris-Cl (or sodium phosphate), pH 8·0
> 0·01M Disodium oxaloacetate pH 6·5

In addition for assay of pyruvate production:

> 0·5M Potassium phosphate, pH 7·6
> 0·024M NADH
> Malate dehydrogenase diluted in 0·1% bovine serum albumin to give a solution containing 100 units/ml
> Lactate dehydrogenase diluted in 0·1% bovine serum albumin to give a solution containing 500 units/ml.

(a) *Pyruvate production.* The assay system contains, in 1·0 ml, 100 μmoles Tris-Cl (or sodium phosphate) pH 8·0, and enzyme (0·1–0·2 units). After equilibration to 30°C the reaction is started by addition of 10 μmoles disodium oxaloacetate and incubation is continued for 5 min. The reaction is terminated by addition of 0·2 ml 10% trichloroacetic acid and the protein precipitate removed by centrifugation at 2°C. Residual oxaloacetate is converted to malate in an aliquot (0·1 ml) of the supernatant fraction by incubation with malate dehydrogenase, and the pyruvate produced is then estimated by addition of lactate dehydrogenase. This procedure is necessary since commercial preparations of lactate dehydrogenase are contaminated with traces of malate dehydrogenase. The system for estimation of pyruvate production contains, in 1·0 ml, 200 μmoles potassium phosphate pH 7·6, 1·2 μmole NADH, 5 units malate dehydrogenase and 0·1 ml of the supernatant fraction (as above). These components are incubated until no further absorbance change is observed at 340 nm (ca 5 min). The absorbance is determined and 10 μl lactate dehydrogenase is then added. The pyruvate produced is estimated from the further decrease in absorbance at 340 nm after addition of lactate dehydrogenase.

Decarboxylation of oxaloacetate by mechanisms not involving biotin is estimated by incubation of 0·2 units oxaloacetate decarboxylase with 0·2 units avidin for 10 min at 25°C prior to addition to the assay system as above. The contribution of avidin to this control rate of oxaloacetate decarboxylation is estimated by incubation of 0·2 units of the avidin-biotin complex in the assay system as above.

(b) *Oxaloacetate disappearance.* The assay system contains, in 1·0 ml 100 μmoles sodium phosphate pH 8·0, 2 μmoles disodium oxaloacetate and enzyme (0·1–0·2 unit). The reaction is initiated by addition of enzyme and the initial rate of the decrease in absorbance at 280 nm is measured. The rate of oxaloacetate decarboxylation is calculated using an extinction coefficient of $0·57 \text{ mM}^{-1}\text{cm}^{-1}$ (Velick and Vavra, 1962). Decarboxylation of oxaloacetate which is not dependent on biotin is estimated by inactivation of oxaloacetate decarboxylase with avidin (as described above) prior to addition to the assay system.

B. Methylmalonyl-CoA decarboxylase

$$\text{Methylmalonyl-CoA} \rightarrow \text{Propionyl-CoA} + CO_2$$

1. Distribution

Micrococcus lactilyticus. The enzyme appears to be involved in the fermentation of lactate to acetate and propionate by this micro-organism and catalyses the final step in the pathway of succinate decarboxylation (Galivan and Allen, 1968).

2. Properties

Methylmalonyl CoA decarboxylase contains biotin as a bound co-factor as indicated by inactivation of this enzyme by avidin and by direct microbiological assay (Galivan and Allen, 1968). The enzyme is isolated from cell-free extracts in the 39 and 48 S ribosomal fractions and is not readily dissociated from these fractions (Galivan and Allen, 1968).

3. *Assay procedures*

Methylmalonyl-CoA decarboxylase may be assayed either spectrophotometrically by measurement of propionyl-CoA formation using methylmalonyl-CoA oxaloacetate transcarboxylase (see III.2) and lactate dehydrogenase, or by a radiochemical procedure based on the loss of $^{14}CO_2$ from methylmalonyl-CoA-3-^{14}C (Galivan and Allen, 1968).

(a) *Spectrophotometric*

Reagents:

> 0·5M Potassium phosphate, pH 6·7
> 0·002M Potassium oxaloacetate
> 0·2 mM Methylmalonyl-CoA (prepared as described by Beck *et al.*, 1957)
> 3·2 mM NADH
> Methylmalonyl-CoA-oxaloacetate transcarboxylase, 500–100 units/ml (purified from *Propionibacterium shermannii* through Step III of the procedure described by Wood *et al.*, 1969a).
> Lactate dehydrogenase, diluted in 0·1% bovine serum albumin to give a solution containing 100 units/ml.

The assay system contains, in 1·0 ml, 200 μmoles potassium phosphate pH 6·7, 0·2 μmole potassium oxaloacetate, 0·2 μmole methylmalonyl-CoA, 0·16 μmole NADH, 1 unit methylmalonyl-CoA-oxaloacetate transcarboxylase and 2 units lactate dehydrogenase. After equilibration to 25°C the reaction is initiated by addition of 0·02–0·05 unit methylmalonyl-CoA decarboxylase and the initial rate of the decrease in absorbance at 340 nm is measured.

(b) *Radiochemical*

Reagents:

> 0·5M Tris-Cl, pH 7·2
> 1 mM Methylmalonyl-CoA-3-^{14}C (10^5 cpm/μmole) (prepared enzymically from propionyl-CoA and $H^{14}CO_3^-$ as described by Allen *et al.*, 1964).

The assay system contains, in 1·0 ml, 100 μmoles Tris-Cl pH 7·2, and 0·1 μmole methylmalonyl-CoA-3-^{14}C. After equilibration to 25°C the reaction is initiated by addition of 0·005–0·02 units methylmalonyl-CoA decarboxylase and incubated for 5 min. The reaction is terminated by addition of 0.2 ml 12% trichloroacetic acid; the precipitated protein is removed by centrifugation; and 0.2 ml 0.5M $NaHCO_3$ is added to the supernatant fraction. The $^{14}CO_2$ liberated during the reaction is removed by bubbling with CO_2 for 10 min at $25°C$. A 1 ml aliquot of the supernatant fraction is added to 10 ml liquid scintillator and residual ^{14}C is estimated in a liquid scintillation spectrometer. A zero time control in which trichloroacetic acid is added to the assay system before addition of methylmalonyl-CoA decarboxylase is necessary for accurate estimation of the loss of radioactivity. The contribution of other mechanisms of decarboxylation may be estimated by pre-incubating the methylmalonyl-CoA decarboxylase preparation with an equal amount (w/w) of avidin for 10 min at $25°C$ before addition to the assay system.

VI. DECARBOXYLASES—PYRIDOXAL PHOSPHATE

A. Amino-acid decarboxylases

The status of this group of related enzymes has been reviewed by Gale (1946) and, more recently by Meister (1965). Only a brief summary of this extensive area will be presented here.

1. *Distribution*

Amino acid decarboxylases have been described in a wide variety of micro-organisms including the Enterobacteriaceae, Clostridia, Pseudomonads, Lactobacilli, etc. In most cases, production of the decarboxylase is induced or much increased by addition of the amino-acid to the growth medium and by growth of the organism in acid media (Gale, 1946). The latter finding supports the suggestion that amine production resulting from the action of these enzymes may provide a mechanism for reducing the acidity of the growth medium (Gale, 1946). However, exceptions are found as, for example, in the case of a *meso-α,ε*-diaminopimelate decarboxylase, which catalyses the production of L-lysine and is present in micro-organisms, e.g., Eubacteria, in which lysine biosynthesis proceeds by the diaminopimelate pathway (Dewey *et al.*, 1954; Vogel, 1959a, b; Peterkofsky and Gilvarg, 1961). Since this enzyme is present at normal levels when growth occurs in the absence of exogenous lysine and is repressed by addition of this amino acid, its role in lysine biosynthesis is clearly indicated (Peterkofsky and Gilvarg, 1961). The pH optimum (7.0) observed for *meso-α,ε*-diminopimelate decarboxylase supports the proposal that this enzyme has a metabolic role differing from that of most amino acid decarboxylases which exhibit maximal activity at more acid pH (cf. Table II). An arginine and an ornithine decarboxylase with pH

TABLE II

Assay systems for some amino acid decarboxylases

Decarboxylase	Main compartment (2·5 ml)	Side arm (0·5 ml)	References
Aspartate-α (E. coli)	300 μmoles Na[+] acetate pH 6·0 0·5–2·0 units decarboxylase	20 μmoles Na[+] L-aspartate pH 6·0	David and Lichstein (1950)
Aspartate-β (Achromobacter)	300 μmoles Na[+] acetate pH 5·0 1 μmole Na pyruvate 0·5–2·0 units decarboxylase	25 μmoles Na[+] L-aspartate	Wilson and Kornberg (1963)
Arginine[e] (E. coli)	500 μmoles Na[+] acetate pH 5·25 75 μmoles L-arginine-HCl 0·2 μmoles pyridoxal phosphate	0·5–1·5 units decarboxylase	Blethen et al. (1968)
Diaminopimelate[a] (E. coli; A. aerogenes)	300 μmoles K[+] phosphate pH 7·0 0·1 μmole pyridoxal phosphate 0·5–2·0 units decarboxylase	12 μmoles Na-meso-α,-ε-diaminopimelate pH 7·0	Dewey et al. (1954)
Glutamate (Cl. welchii; E. coli)	300 μmoles Na acetate pH 4·5 250 μmoles Na-L-glutamate[b]	0·5–2·0 units decarboxylase	Gale (1946); Lawson and Quinn (1967)
Glycine (P. glycinophilus)	This enzyme is routinely assayed by exchange of H[14]CO_3^- into the carboxyl group of glycine		Klein and Sagers (1966)
Histidine (Cl. welchii; Lactobacillus)	300 μmoles Na acetate pH 4·6 0·5–2·0 units decarboxylase	20 μmoles L-histidine	Gale (1964); Rosenthaler et al. (1965)
Leucine (P. vulgaris)	300 μmoles Na[+] phosphate pH 6·0 175 μmoles L-leucine[c] 0·1 μmole pyridoxal phosphate	0·5–2·0 units decarboxylase	Haughton and King (1961)
Lysine (B. cadaveris)	300 μmoles Na[+] acetate pH 6·0 0·5–2·0 units decarboxylase	45 μmoles L-lysine.HCl pH 6·0	Gale (1946)
Ornithine[e] (Cl. septicum)	300 μmoles Na[+] acetate pH 5·2 125 μmoles L-ornithine[d]	0·5–2·0 units decarboxylase	Gale (1946)

TABLE II (continued)

Assay systems for some amino acid decarboxylases

Decarboxylase	Main compartment (2·5 ml)	Side arm (0·5 ml)	References
Tryptophan (B. cereus)	300 μmoles Na phosphate pH 8[a, f], 0·1 μmole pyridoxal phosphate, 50 μmoles L-tryptophan	0·5–2·0 units decarboxylase	Perley and Stowe (1966)
Tyrosine (S. faecalis)	300 μmoles Na+ acetate pH 5·5, 50 μmoles L-tyrosine[g]	0·5–2·0 units decarboxylase	Epps (1944)

(a) This assay should be performed in a manometer vessel with two side arms. The second side arm contains 0·2 ml 4N H_2SO_4. The contents of the side arm containing substrate is tipped into the main compartment to initiate the reaction and the system is incubated for 10 min at 25°. The reaction is stopped by addition of the contents of the side arm containing 4N H_2SO_4 and the increase in pressure is measured after 5 min further incubation. (b) Added as an 0·1M solution of L-glutamic acid in 0·12M Na+ acetate pH 4·6. (c) Added as an 0·7M solution of L-leucine in 0·12 Na+ phosphate pH 6·0. (d) Added as an 0·05M solution of L-ornithine in 0·12M Na+ acetate pH 5·2. (e) Arginine and ornithine decarboxylases which have a pH optima at 7·5–8·0 have been isolated from E. coli by Morris and Pardee (1965). (f) Added as an 0·02M solution of L-tryptophan in 0·12M Na+ phosphate pH 8·0. (g) Added as an 0·02M solution of L-tyrosine in 0·12M Na+ acetate pH 5·5.

optima in the range 7·0–8·0 have been described in *E. coli* and a role for these enzymes in intracellular polyamine biosynthesis has been proposed (Morris and Pardee, 1965; Morris and Pardee, 1966).

2. *Properties*

Most of the amino acid decarboxylases either contain bound pyridoxal phosphate or require addition of this co-factor for activity (Umbreit and Gunsalus, 1945; Dewey *et al.*, 1954; Haughton and King, 1961; Wilson and Kornberg, 1963; Meister, 1965; Lawson and Quinn, 1967; Blethen *et al.*, 1968). Confusion has arisen for many of the enzymes on this point because marked differences exist in the affinity of the various decarboxylases for pyridoxal phosphate. The only well-established exception is a crystalline L-histidine decarboxylase from *Lactobacillus* 30a, which has been shown neither to require not to contain pyridoxal phosphate (Rosenthaler *et al.*, 1965). Recent studies (Riley and Snell, 1968) indicate that an enzyme-bound pyruvate molecule replaces pyridoxal phosphate as the functional group in this enzyme. Certain of the amino acid decarboxylases are also activated by addition of α-keto acids. This finding is best documented for aspartate-β-decarboxylase (Wilson and Kornberg, 1963).

In many cases the amino acid substrates for the decarboxylases contain a third polar group in addition to the α-NH_2 and α-COOH groups (Utter, 1961). The apparent requirement for this group is supported by the finding that substrate analogues in which the third polar group is eliminated, e.g., *o*-methyltyrosine, N^1- or N^3-methylhistidine, ε-N-acetyllysine (Gale and Epps, 1944; Rosenthaler *et al.*, 1965; Meister, 1965) are neither substrates for, nor inducers of the appropriate decarboxylase. Exceptions to this generalization are, however, known, e.g., the L-leucine decarboxylase of *Proteus vulgaris* which is active on neutral amino acids such as L-leucine, L-valine, L-isoleucine, etc. (Haughton and King, 1961) and the glycine decarboxylase of *Peptococcus glycinophilus* (Klein and Sagers, 1966). Additionally, decarboxylation of several neutral amino acids by *Pseudomonas reptilovora* (Seaman, 1960) and of L-methionine by *Streptomyces* (Hagino and Nakayama, 1968) has been reported.

The amino acid decarboxylases described thus far are specific for the L-amino-acids.

3. *Assay procedure*

The amino acid decarboxylases are assayed manometrically. The assay systems used for some of these enzymes are summarized in Table II. In all cases the system is equilibrated at 25°C under an inert gas (N_2, argon) before initiating the reaction by tipping in the contents of the side arm. The absence of oxygen from the gas phase is essential when measurements are conducted on crude systems since amino acid oxidases may be present. In most cases the addition of pyridoxal phosphate is not required but it should be noted that if this co-factor is removed either by design or as a consequence of the procedures used in obtaining the enzyme preparation, maximal activity may not be obtained in its absence (cf. Lawson and Quinn, 1967).

Radiochemical assays for some of these enzymes which are based on the liberation of $^{14}CO_2$ from uniformly or specifically labelled amino acid have also been described (e.g., Wilson and Kornberg, 1963).

VII. DECARBOXYLASES—THIAMINE PYROPHOSPHATE

A. Pyruvate decarboxylase (EC 4.1.1.1.)

$$\text{Pyruvate} \xrightarrow{\text{Me}^{2+}} \text{Acetaldehyde} + CO_2$$

1. Distribution

Yeasts (Neuberg and Rosenthal, 1913; Green et al., 1941); certain Athiorhodaceae (Hussain Qadri and Hoare, 1967); Pseudomonas lindneri, Erwinia amylovora (Dawes et al., 1966); Zymosarcina ventriculi (Arbuthnott et al., 1960); and the acetic acid bacteria (Deley and Schell, 1962). In yeasts the presence of this enzyme is often associated with the capacity to catalyse an ethanol fermentation.

2. Properties

Pyruvate decarboxylase contains bound TPP and divalent metal cation, and shows a requirement for these co-factors only after dialysis for 18 hours at 2°C against 0·01M potassium phosphate pH 6·2 (Hussain Qadri and Hoare, 1967).

3. Assay procedure

The enzyme is assayed manometrically as described by Singer (1955).

Reagents:

0·5M Sodium citrate buffer pH 6·0
1M Potassium pyruvate prepared the same day by neutralization of redistilled pyruvic acid with KOH

The main compartment contains, in 2·5 ml, 300 μmoles sodium citrate pH 6·0 and 0·6–2 units pyruvate decarboxylase; and the side arm, in 0·5 ml, 500 μmoles potassium pyruvate. After equilibration to 25°C the contents of the side arm is tipped into the main compartment and the rate of CO_2 evolution is measured.

If the enzyme has been resolved with respect to TPP and Me^{2+} prior to assay, the holoenzyme is reconstituted by incubation with 0·03 mM TPP and 0·3 mM $MnCl_2$ before addition to the assay system.

B. Oxalyl-CoA decarboxylase (EC 4.1.1.8.)

$$\text{Oxalyl-CoA} \xrightarrow{Me^{2+}} \text{Formyl CoA} + CO_2$$

1. Distribution

Pseudomonas oxalaticus. The enzyme is induced by growth on oxalate as sole carbon source and is absent from cells grown on formate or succinate suggesting its involvement in oxalate utilization (Quayle, 1963b).

2. Properties

The enzyme shows little activity in the absence of TPP and addition of this co-factor as well as a divalent metal ion, e.g., Mg^{2+}, is required for maximal activity. The enzyme is specific for oxalyl-CoA and does not decarboxylate oxalate (Quayle, 1963b).

3. Assay method

Oxalyl-CoA decarboxylase is assayed manometrically by measurement of the rate of CO_2 evolution (Quayle, 1963b).

Reagents:

0·5M Sodium citrate buffer, pH 5·5
0·02M TPP
0·01M $MgCl_2$
0·02M Oxalyl-CoA prepared and assayed as described by Quayle (1963a).

The assay is conducted in micro-manometer cups. The main compartment contains, in 0·8 ml, 50 μmoles citrate buffer pH 5·5, 2 μmoles TPP, 1 μmole $MgCl_2$, and 2 μmoles oxalyl-CoA: and the side arm, in 0·2 ml, 0·05–0·2 units oxalyl-CoA decarboxylase. After flushing with N_2 and equilibration to 25°C the contents of the side arm is tipped into the main compartment and the initial rate of CO_2 evolution is measured. This procedure does not measure the decarboxylase under optimal conditions since (i) the catalytic activity at pH 6·0 is approximately 50% of that observed at the pH optimum for this enzyme (pH 6·6) and (ii) the K_m for oxalyl-CoA is 1 mM (Quayle, 1963b).

18

C. Benzoylformate decarboxylase (EC 4.1.1.7.)

$$\text{Benzoylformate} \rightarrow \text{Benzaldehyde} + CO_2$$

1. Distribution

Pseudomonas putida. The enzyme is present in cells grown on mandelic acid as sole carbon source and catalyses a step in the pathway of degradation of this compound (Gunsalus *et al.*, 1963).

2. Properties

After prolonged dialysis against sodium pyrophosphate at pH 8·5 the enzyme is inactive in the absence of added TPP. No requirement for Me^{2+} is observed (Gunsalus *et al.*, 1953).

3. Assay procedure

Benzoylformate decarboxylase is assayed manometrically by measurement of CO_2 release from benzoylformate (Gunsalus *et al.*, 1953).

Reagents:

> 1M Potassium phosphate, pH 6·0
> 1 mM TPP
> 1·25 mM Sodium benzoylformate

The main compartment contains, in 2·5 ml, 250 μmoles potassium phosphate pH 6·0, 100 μmoles TPP, and 125 μmoles sodium benzoylformate; and the side arm, in 0·5 ml, 0·2–0·5 units benzoylformate decarboxylase. After equilibration to 25°C the enzyme is tipped into the main compartment and the rate of CO_2 evolution is measured. For more purified preparations of the enzyme the gas phase is air but in crude systems, where further oxidation of benzaldehyde by the O_2 present could occur, N_2 is used as the gas phase.

It should be noted that omission of TPP does not provide a suitable control for the estimation of this enzyme unless this co-factor is removed from the preparation as described by Gunsalus *et al.* (1953).

D. Glyoxylate carboligase

$$2 \text{ Glyoxylate} + H^+ \xrightarrow{Me^{2+}} \text{Tartronic semialdehyde} + CO_2$$

1. Distribution

Escherichia coli (Krakow *et al.*, 1961); *Pseudomonas oxalaticus.* (Kornberg and Gotto, 1961); *Streptococcus allantoicus* (Valentine *et al.*, 1964); *Hydrogenomonas* (Kaltwasser, 1968). Synthesis of the enzyme is induced by growth of micro-organisms on two carbon substrates, e.g. glycollate, glycine, which are metabolized by way of glyoxylate, or in *Hydrogenomonas* by growth on uric acid or allantoin.

2. *Properties*

The enzyme requires addition of TPP and a divalent metal cation, e.g., Mg^{2+}, for activity (Krakow *et al.*, 1961). 2-Hydroxymethyl TPP has been identified as an enzyme-bound intermediate (Jaenicke and Koch, 1962). In addition the enzyme from *E. coli* contains bound FAD. Removal of bound flavin or reduction of this co-factor with hydrosulphite causes loss of catalytic activity but the role of the flavin in the catalytic sequences is not established (Gupta and Vennesland, 1964, 1966).

3. *Assay procedure*

Glyoxylate carboligase is assayed manometrically (Gupta and Vennesland, 1966).

Reagents:

      1M Potassium phosphate, pH 7·3
      0·3M Sodium glyoxylate
      6 mM TPP
      4N H_2SO_4
      0·03M $MgCl_2$
      0·05M Cysteine hydrochloride freshly prepared and not neutralized

The assay is conducted in a manometer cup with two side-arms. The main compartment contains, in 2·9 ml, 100 μmoles potassium phosphate pH 7·3, 0·6 moles TPP, 3 μmoles $MgCl_2$, 5 μmoles cysteine hydrochloride and approximately 0·2 units glyoxylate carboligase. If dilutions of the enzyme are required they are prepared in 0·2M potassium phosphate pH 7·3. Side-arm I contains, in 0·1 ml, 30 μmoles sodium glyoxylate and side-arm II 0·3 ml 4NH_2SO_4. After equilibration to 25° and gassing with N_2 or argon sodium glyoxylate is tipped in from side-arm I and the reaction is allowed to proceed for 10 min. The reaction is stopped by addition of H_2SO_4 from side-arm II and the CO_2 released is estimated. Endogenous CO_2 is estimated using a control system which lacks glyoxylate.

A titrimetric procedure for the assay of glyoxylate carboligase has also been described (Krakow *et al.*, 1961).

E. Phenylpyruvate decarboxylase

$$\text{Phenylpyruvate} \xrightarrow{\text{Me}^{2+},\ \text{TPP}} \text{Phenylacetaldehyde} + CO_2$$

1. Distribution

Achromobacter eurydice (Asakawa *et al.*, 1968). The enzyme is induced by growth on phenylalanine or tryptophan as sole carbon source, and is probably present in other micro-organisms, e.g., *Proteus*, which can metabolize aromatic α-keto acids (Seidenberg *et al.*, 1962).

2. Properties

As normally isolated the enzyme preparation contains bound TPP and Mg^{2+}. Requirements for these co-factors can be demonstrated only after preparation of apoenzyme by dialysis against 60% $(NH_4)_2SO_4$ pH 9·8 containing 0·01M EDTA. The enzyme is specific for aromatic α-keto acids, e.g., phenylpyruvate, indolepyruvate, and aliphatic α-keto acids having a straight chain of at least 6 carbon atoms, e.g., α-ketocaproate. No activity is detected with pyruvate as substrate (Asakawa *et al.*, 1968).

3. Assay procedures

The enzyme may be assayed either spectrophotometrically by coupling with phenylacetaldehyde dehydrogenase or manometrically (Asakawa *et al.*, 1968).

(a) *Spectrophotometric*

Reagents:

> 0·5M K phosphate, pH 7·3
> 0·01M Sodium phenylpyruvate
> 0·02M TPP
> 0·01M $MgCl_2$
> 0·01M NAD
> Phenylacetaldehyde dehydrogenase purified from the crude extract to remove decarboxylase activity as described by Asakawa *et al.* (1968).

The assay system contains, in 1·0 ml, 50 μmoles K phosphate pH 7·3, 0·5 μmole Na phenylpyruvate, 2 μmoles TPP, 1 μmole $MgCl_2$, 0·2 μmole NAD, 2–5 units phenylacetaldehyde dehydrogenase. After equilibration to 25°C the reaction is initiated by addition of 0·02–0·05 units phenylpyruvate decarboxylase and the initial rate of the increase in absorbance at 340 nm is recorded.

(b) *Manometric*. The reagents required are as described above with the omission of NAD and phenylacetaldehyde dehydrogenase. The assay is performed in a manometer cup having two side-arms. The main compartment contains, in 2·8 ml, 150 μmoles K phosphate pH 7·3, 5 μmoles TPP, 3 μmoles $MgCl_2$, and approximately 0·5 units phenylpyruvate decarboxylase. Side-arm I contains, in 0·1 ml, 10 μmoles Na phenylpyruvate and side-arm II, 0·1 ml 4N H_2SO_4. After equilibration to 37°C the reaction is initiated by addition of phenylpyruvate from side-arm I and is allowed to proceed for 10 min. The reaction is stopped by addition of H_2SO_4 from side-arm II and the CO_2 released is estimated. A correction for the endogenous CO_2 present is obtained by similar treatment of a control system lacking phenylpyruvate.

Asakawa *et al.* (1968) have also described an assay procedure which depends on the estimation of phenylacetaldehyde as its dinitrophenylhydrazone.

VIII. DECARBOXYLASES—NO APPARENT CO-FACTOR REQUIREMENT

A. Acetoacetate decarboxylase (EC 4.1.1.4.)

$$\text{Acetoacetate} \rightarrow \text{Acetone} + CO_2$$

1. *Distribution*

Clostridium acetobutylicum. The enzyme is produced late in the growth cycle and may be induced by the accumulation of acetoacetate in the medium (cf. Zerner, *et al.*, 1966).

2. *Properties*

Despite earlier reports that this enzyme contains a flavin prosthetic group (Seeley and van Demark, 1960) no evidence for the presence of this co-factor has been obtained with the crystalline enzyme purified from *C. acetobutylicum* (Lederer *et al.*, 1966). The decarboxylation mechanism appears to involve Schiff base formation between the ϵ-NH_2 group of a lysine residue and the carbonyl group of acetoacetate (Warren *et al.*, 1966).

3. *Assay method*

Acetoacetate decarboxylase is assayed spectrophotometrically by measurement of the decrease in absorbance at 270 nm resulting from the disappearance of substrate (Fridovich, 1963).

Reagents:

1·0M Potassium phosphate, pH 5·9
0·3M Potassium acetoacetate, pH 5·9

The assay system contains, in 1·0 ml, 100 μmoles potassium phosphate pH 5·9, and 3·0 μmoles potassium acetoacetate. After equilibration to 25°C the reaction is initiated by addition of 2–3 units acetoacetate decarboxylase and the decrease in absorbance at 270 nm is measured as a function of time against a control system which contains only buffer and acetoacetate. The absorbance of this control system is set in the range 0·8–1·0 absorbance units using the slit control. The extinction coefficients of acetoacetate and acetone at 270 nm in this system are 0·055 $mM^{-1}cm^{-1}$ and 0·028 $mM^{-1}cm^{-1}$, respectively. Greater sensitivity can be achieved by measurement at 210 nm since at this wavelength the extinction coefficient of aceoacetate is increased to 0·42 $mM^{-1}cm^{-1}$ (Fridovich, 1963). An approximate conversion factor has also been estimated by comparison of the spectrophotometric assay method with a manometric procedure. A decrease of 0·1 absorbance units at 270 nm is calculated from this comparison as equivalent to the release of 2·42 μmoles CO_2 (Zerner et al., 1966).

B. Oxaloacetate decarboxylase (EC 4.1.1.3)

$$\text{Oxaloacetate} \xrightarrow{Me^{2+}} \text{Pyruvate} + CO_2$$

1. Distribution

Oxalacetate decarboxylases which require activation by divalent metal cations have been described in *Micrococcus lysodeikticus* (Krampitz and Werkman, 1941; Herbert, 1951), *Azotobacter vinelandii* (Plaut and Lardy, 1949); *Pseudomonas ovalis Chester* (Horton and Kornberg, 1964) and *Acetobacter xylinium* (Benziman and Heller, 1964). An oxaloacetate decarboxylase apparently of this type is induced in *Salmonella typhimurium LT2* by growth on *meso*-tartrate plus glycerol (Rosenberger, 1966). Although low oxaloacetate decarboxylase activity has been detected in other micro-organisms this activity may not be due to a unique decarboxylase, cf. oxaloacetate decarboxylase activity exhibited by the inducible L-malate enzyme of *Lactobacillus arabinosus* (Korkes et al., 1950).

2. Properties

The enzyme requires activation by a divalent metal cation, e.g., Mn^{2+}, Cd^{2+}, Co^{2+}, but other co-factors—either bound or dissociable—do not appear to be involved (Plaut and Lardy, 1949; Herbert, 1951). The properties of this class of oxaloacetate decarboxylase therefore differ markedly from the inducible oxaloacetate decarboxylase of *Aerobacter* (cf. V.A.).

3. Assay methods

Although oxaloacetate decarboxylase has usually been assayed by a manometric procedure (cf. Herbert, 1955), the more convenient spectrophotometric procedures described for the oxaloacetate decarboxylase of *Aerobacter* (Stern, 1967) may be used (cf. V.A.).

Reagents:

> 0·5M Sodium acetate buffer, pH 5·4
> 0·01M $MnSO_4$
> 0·1M Potassium oxaloacetate, pH 5·4

The assay system contains, in 1·0 ml, 100 μmoles sodium acetate pH 5·4, 1 μmole $MnSO_4$ and 0·1–0·2 units oxaloacetate decarboxylase. The reaction is initiated by addition of either 10 μmoles (pyruvate production) or 2 μmoles (oxaloacetate disappearance) potassium oxaloacetate pH 5·4 and subsequent procedures are as described previously (cf. V.A.).

A satisfactory control system is not available for this enzyme. The contribution of the free divalent metal ion to the overall rate of decarboxylation can be estimated by omitting the enzyme.

C. Orotidine-5′-phosphate decarboxylase (EC 4.1.1.23.)

$$\text{Orotidine-5′-phosphate} \xrightarrow{\text{Me}^{2+}} \text{Uridine-5′-phosphate} + CO_2$$

1. *Distribution*

This enzyme has been described in yeasts (Lieberman *et al.*, 1955), *Micrococcus glutamicus* (Nagano *et al.*, 1966) and *Neurospora crassa* (Pynadath and Fink, 1967), but may be widely distributed among micro-organisms which do not require pyrimidines for growth.

2. *Properties*

No bound co-factors appear to be required for the activity of orotidine-5′-phosphate decarboxylase, although the purified enzyme from microbial sources has not been studied extensively.

3. *Assay procedure*

Orotidine-5′-phosphate decarboxylase is assayed spectrophotometrically (Lieberman *et al.*, 1955) using the decrease in absorbance at 285 nm which accompanies decarboxylation. This decrease results from the difference in absorbance maxima of orotidine and uridine nucleotides.

Reagents:

> 1M Tris-Cl, pH 8·0
> 0·2M $MgCl_2$
> 5·0 mM Orotidine-5′-phosphate

The assay system contains, in 1·0 ml, 100 μmoles Tris-Cl pH 8·0, 2 μmoles

$MgCl_2$, and 0·55 μmoles orotidine-5'-phosphate. After equilibration to 25°C the reaction is initiated by addition of 0·1–0·2 units orotidine-5'-phosphate decarboxylase and the initial rate of decrease in absorbance at 285 nm is measured. A decrease of 0·165 absorbance units is equivalent to the conversion of 0·1 μmole orotidine-5'-phosphate to uridine-5'-phosphate. If the enzyme preparation under examination contains material which absorbs strongly at 280–290 nm an equal aliquot should be added to a blank cuvette containing all the reaction components except orotidine-5'-phosphate.

D. Pyridoxine decarboxylase

Pyridoxine $\xrightarrow{Me^{2+}}$ 2-Methyl-3-hydroxypyridine-5-carboxylic acid + CO_2

1. Distribution

Pseudomonas. The enzyme is induced by growth on pyridoxine as sole carbon and nitrogen source and is probably involved in its utilization (Snell *et al.*, 1964).

2. Properties

The enzyme does not appear to contain a bound co-factor. Addition of Mn^{2+} and a reducing agent, e.g. CN^-, cysteine are required for maximal activity (Snell *et al.*, 1964).

3. Assay procedure

Pyridoxine decarboxylase is assayed spectrophotometrically by measurement of the increase in absorbance at 255 nm which accompanies decarboxylation (Snell *et al.*, 1964).

Reagents:

> 0·5M Tris-Cl, pH 8·0
> 5 mM $MnCl_2$
> 2 mM Pyridoxine
> 0·1 mM KCN

The assay system contains, in 1·0 ml, 200 μmoles Tris-Cl pH 8·0, 0·2 μmoles $MnCl_2$, 0·2 μmoles pyridoxine and 0·01 μmole KCN. After equilibration to 25°C the reaction is initiated by addition of 0·05–0·1 units pyridoxine decarboxylase and the initial rate of increase of absorbance at 255 nm is measured.

E. γ-Carboxymuconolactone decarboxylase

| γ-Carboxy- | β-Ketoadipate |
| muconolactone | enol-lactone |

1. Distribution

Pseudomonas putida. (Ornston and Stanier, 1966; Ornston, 1966b); *Moraxella* (Ornston and Stanier, 1966; Canovas and Stanier, 1967); *Hydrogenomonas eutropha* (Ornston, 1966b).

2. Properties

No added co-factors are required. The enzyme has not been examined for bound co-enzymes.

3. Assay procedure

γ-Carboxymuconolactone decarboxylase is assayed spectrophotometrically by measuring the decrease in absorbance at 230 nm which accompanies decarboxylation (Ornston, 1966a). The procedure is complex since (i) the substrate is unstable and must be generated from β-carboxy-*cis, cis*-muconate immediately prior to assay and (ii) the product has residual absorbance at 230 nm and is removed by conversion to β-ketoadipate using purified β-ketoadipate enol-lactone hydrolase.

The substrate is generated in a reaction mixture containing, in 2·0 ml, 100 μmoles Tris-Cl pH 8·0, 10 μmoles β-carboxy-*cis,cis*-muconate (prepared as described by Ornston and Stanier, 1966) and 10 units β-carboxy-*cis,cis*-muconate lactonizing enzyme (specific activity, 280 units 1 mg) (prepared as described by Ornston, 1966a). After incubation for 5 min at 25°C, this reaction mixture (RMI) is cooled rapidly to 0°C and kept at this temperature.

The assay system contains, in 3·0 ml, 1 mmole Tris-Cl pH 8·0, 0·2 ml RMI, and 10 units β-ketoadipate enolhydrolase (specific activity, 350 units/ mg) (prepared as described by Ornston, 1966a). After equilibration to 25°C the reaction is initiated by addition of 0·1–0·2 units γ-carboxymuconolactone decarboxylase and the rate of decrease in absorbance at 230 nm is measured. This rate is corrected for non-enzymic decarboxylation by measuring the decrease in absorbance at 230 nm in a system which lacks the decarboxylase. Conversion of 0·1 μmole γ-carboxymuconolactone to β-ketoadipate in this system results in a decrease of 0·139 absorbance units at 230 nm.

If a less highly purified preparation of lactonizing enzyme is used to generate the substrate, a slow conversion of β-carboxy-*cis,cis*-muconate to

(+) muconolactone may occur in RMI. The latter compound absorbs at 230 nm and interferes with the assay of the decarboxylase. This interference can be abolished by adding 10 units crystalline muconolactone isomerase (prepared as described by Ornston) (1966c) to the assay system.

F. "Malonate" decarboxylase (EC 4.1.1.9.)

$$\text{Malonate} \xrightarrow{\text{ATP, CoASH}} \text{Acetate} + CO_2$$

The ATP requirement can be replaced by addition of acetyl-phosphate and phosphotransacetylase. The preparations of this enzyme obtained thus far appear to contain CoA transferase and malonyl-CoA synthetase in addition to the decarboxylase. The true substrate for the decarboxylase may therefore be malonyl-CoA although this has not been established unequivocally (Hayaishi, 1955).

1. Distribution

Pseudomonas fluorescens. The enzyme system is present in cells grown on malonate (Hayaishi, 1955).

2. Properties

No added co-factors appear to be required for the decarboxylase but more detailed studies are required to clarify this point. If this enzyme is a malonyl-CoA decarboxylase a requirement for thiamine pyrophosphate as a co-factor might be expected by analogy with oxalyl-CoA decarboxylase (cf. VII.B).

3. Assay procedure

"Malonate" decarboxylase is assayed manometrically (Hayaishi, 1955).

Reagents:

       1·0M Potassium phosphate pH 6·0
       0·5M Potassium malonate
       0·01M $MgCl_2$
       0·02M ATP
       2 mM CoASH
       1M KF
       0·1M Glutathione

The main compartment of the manometer cup contains, in 2·5 ml 250 μmoles potassium phosphate pH 6·0, 50 μmoles potassium malonate, 2 μmoles $MgCl_2$, 2 μmoles ATP, 0·2 μmoles CoASH, 100 μmoles KF, and 10 μmoles glutathione; and the side-arm, in 0·5 ml, 0·1–0·2 units "malonate" decarboxylase. After equilibration to 25°C the contents of the side-arm is tipped into the main compartment and the rate of CO_2 evolution is measured.

This procedure can only be used for crude extracts and fractions obtained as described by Hayaishi (1955). Further or different methods of fractionation may result in removal of one or more of the ancillary enzymes, and require modification of this procedure.

G. α-Acetolactate decarboxylase

$$\alpha\text{-Acetolactate} \to \text{Acetoin} + CO_2$$

1. Distribution

Streptococcus faecalis (Dolin, and Gunsalus, 1951); *Aerobacter aerogenes* (Juni, 1962); *Bacillus subtilis* (Milhaud *et al.*, 1952).

2. Properties

No requirement for added or bound co-factors has been described. When the enzyme system from *St. faecalis* which forms acetoin from pyruvate (via α-acetolactate as an intermediate) is resolved for TPP and divalent metal cation, the resolved preparation exhibits no activity with pyruvate as substrate but has unchanged activity on α-acetolacetate (Dolin and Gunsalus, 1951; Juni, 1955).

3. Assay procedure

α-Acetolactate decarboxylase is assayed manometrically (Juni, 1955).

Reagents:

      1M Potassium phosphate pH 5·7
      0·5 Sodium α-acetolacetate

The main compartment contains, in 2·5 ml, 250 μmoles potassium phosphate pH 5·7 and 200 μmoles sodium α-acetolactate; and the side-arm, in 0·5 ml, 0·5–2 units α-acetolactate decarboxylase. After equilibration to 25°C the contents of the side-arm is tipped into the main compartment and the rate of CO_2 evolution is measured.

H. 4-Deoxy-5-ketoglucarate dehydratase (Decarboxylating)

4-Deoxy-5-ketoglucarate $\to$ 2-ketoglutarate semialdehyde + CO_2 + H_2O

1. Distribution

Pseudomonas. (Trudgill and Widdus, 1966). The enzyme is induced by growth on D-glucarate or D-galactarate and catalyses a step in the conversion of these substrates to α-ketoglutarate. Utilization of D-glucarate by conversion to α-ketoglutarate is characteristic of pseudomonads; other micro-organisms, e.g., Enterobacteriaceae, *Aerobacter*, utilize a pathway in which 4-deoxy-5-ketoglucarate is cleaved to yield tartronic semialdehyde and pyruvate (Blumenthal and Fish, 1963; Trudgill and Widdus, 1966).

2. *Properties*

The reaction is catalysed by a single protein which has been purified to homogeneity. Since possible intermediates, e.g., 2-keto-4,5-dihydroxy-valerate, are inactive, both decarboxylation and dehydration of 4-deoxy-5-ketoglucarate may occur in a concerted mechanism (Jeffcoat *et al.*, 1968). No added co-factors are required. The involvement of a lysine residue on the enzyme in the formation of a Schiff base intermediate with the substrate is suggested by the substrate-dependent inactivation of the enzyme by $NaBH_4$ (R. Jeffcoat, H. Hassall and S. Dagley, personal communication).

3. *Assay procedure*

4-Deoxy-5-ketoglucarate dehydratase is assayed manometrically. In crude extracts which also contain 2-ketoglutarate semialdehyde dehydrogenase, a spectrophotometric assay may be used (R. Jeffcoat and S. Dagley, personal communication). Since the substrate for this enzyme, 4-deoxy-5-ketoglucarate is not commercially available, a method of preparation for this compound is also described (R. Jeffcoat and S. Dagley, personal communication).

(a) *Preparation and assay of* 4-*deoxy*-5-*ketoglucarate.* This compound is prepared by incubation of potassium hydrogen glucarate with glucarate dehydratase.

Reagents:

> Potassium hydrogen glucarate (solid)
> $0.05M MgSO_4$
> $0.1M$ Potassium phosphate pH 7·2
> Glucarate dehydratase (specific activity—4–10 units/mg) 0·3 mg/ml.
> A partially purified preparation from cell-free extracts of *Pseudomonas A* is used. The purification procedure involves fractionation with protamine sulphate and $(NH_4)_2SO_4$ followed by chromatography on DEAE-cellulose at pH 8·0 (R. Jeffcoat and S. Dagley, personal communication). Alternatively glucarate dehydratase may be purified from cell-free extracts of *E. coli* as described by Blumenthal (1966).

The incubation mixture contains 1·0 g KH glucarate (4 millimoles),

10 ml $MgSO_4$, 50 ml K phosphate pH 7·2 and 40 ml glucarate dehydratase. After incubation for 60 min at 37°C an aliquot (0·1 ml) is withdrawn for assay of 4-deoxy-5-ketoglucarate by the procedure of Weissbach and Hurwitz (1959) (cf. also Blumenthal, 1966). 4-Deoxy-5-ketoglucarate is purified from the incubation mixture by chromatography on a Dowex-1-formate (8×) column (20×2·5 cm). The column is eluted with a linear formic acid gradient (0–6N in a total volume of 640 ml) and 10 ml fractions are collected. 4-Deoxy-5-ketoglucarate is eluted between 5·5 and 6N formic acid. These fractions are pooled and concentrated by rotary evaporation which causes lactonization of 4-deoxy-5-ketoglucarate. (*N.B.* The lactone is not oxidized by periodic acid and hence the colorimetric assay for 4-deoxy-5-ketoglucarate cannot be used at this stage). The lactone is hydrolysed by dissolving the solid in 0·005M phosphate pH 7·2 and heating at 100°C for 5 min.

(b) *Manometric assay for 4-deoxy-5-ketoglucarate dehydratase*
Reagents:

> 0·5M Potassium phosphate pH 7·2
> 0·1M 4-Deoxy-5-ketoglucarate in 0·05M phosphate pH 7·2

The assay is conducted in manometer cups with two side-arms. The main compartment contains, in 2·8 ml, 50 μmoles phosphate pH 7·2 and 10 μmoles 4-deoxy-5-ketoglucarate; side-arm I, in 0·2 ml, 0·1-0·25 units 4-deoxy-5-ketoglucarate dehydratase; and side-arm II, 0·2 ml 3M metaphosphoric acid. After equilibration to 25°C the enzyme is tipped in from side-arm I and the system is incubated for 10–15 min. The reaction is stopped and CO_2 evolution measured by addition of the metaphosphoric acid from side-arm II. A control incubation system which lacks substrate is required to estimate the endogenous CO_2.

(c) *Spectrophotometric assay for 4-deoxy-5-ketoglucarate dehydratase*

Reagents:

> Phosphate pH 7·2 and 4-deoxy-5-ketoglucarate as described for the manometric procedure
> 0·05M NAD
> 0·1M Na_4 EDTA

The assay system contains, in 1·0 ml, 50 μmoles phosphate pH 7·2, 5 μmoles NAD, 0·5 μmole 4-deoxy-5-ketoglucarate and 10 μmoles EDTA. After equilibration to 25°C the reaction is initiated with 0·01-0·02 units 4-deoxy-5-ketoglucarate dehydratase (1·2 mg cell-free extract from *Pseudomonas A*) and the initial rate of NAD reduction is determined from the increase in absorbance at 340 nm. Before assaying enzyme preparations by this procedure, divalent metal ions must be removed by dialysis against 0·01M EDTA to inactivate glucarate dehydratase. It should also be noted that this procedure is dependent on the presence of excess 2-ketoglutarate semialdehyde dehydrogenase in the preparation assayed. Although this condition is satisfied for cell-free extracts of *Pseudomonas A* it should not be assumed for extracts of other micro-organisms.

J. Other decarboxylases

A number of other decarboxylases of this type have been described in various micro-organisms. Table III summarizes the distribution of some of these enzymes and gives a key reference which describes the assay procedure.

TABLE III

Other decarboxylases described in micro-organisms

All decarboxylases listed are of the type $A \rightarrow B + CO_2$ and have no identified co-factors.

Substrate (A) for decarboxylase	Distribution	Reference
Caffeic acid	*Aerobacter*	Finkle *et al.* (1962)
cis-Aconitic acid	*Aspergillus*	Bentley and Thiessen (1957)
Dihydroxybenzoic acids	*Aspergillus*	Subba Rao *et al.* (1967)
Glutaryl-CoA	*Pseudomonas fluorescens*	Numa *et al.* (1964)
β-Ketolauric acid	*Aspergillus niger* *Neurospora crassa* *Penicillium*	Franke *et al.* (1961)
Orsellinic acid	Certain lichens	Pettersson (1965)
Oxalic acid	Certain fungi, *Aspergillus*	Shimazono and Hayaishi (1957); Emiliani and Ribra (1968).
Stipitatonic acid	*Penicillium stipitatum*	Bentley and Thiessen (1963)
UDP-D-glucuronic acid	*Cryptococcus*, *Tremella mesenterica*	Ankel and Feingold (1966).

IX. PYRIDINE-NUCLEOTIDE-LINKED DECARBOXYLASES

A. NAD-dependent L-malate enzyme (EC 1.1.1.38.)

$$\text{L-Malate} + \text{NAD} \underset{}{\overset{\text{Me}^{2+},\ \text{Me}^+}{\rightleftharpoons}} \text{Pyruvate} + CO_2 + \text{NADH} + H^+$$

1. *Distribution*

Lactobacilli (Korkes *et al.*, 1960; Deal and Lichstein, 1961; Duerre and Lichstein, 1961); *Shizosaccharomyces pombe* (Temperli *et al.*, 1965);

Escherichia coli W (Katsuki *et al.*, 1967). In the Lactobacilli this enzyme is induced by growth on L-malate (Blanchard *et al.*, 1960), but in *E. coli W* growth on C_4 dicarboxylic acids induces synthesis of the NADP-dependent L-malate enzyme (see I. XB) and has little effect on the level of the NAD-dependent enzyme (Katsuki *et al.*, 1967).

2. Properties

The NAD-dependent enzyme from *E. coli* is specifically activated by L-aspartate (Takeo *et al.*, 1967). Comparison of this effect with the inhibition of PEP carboxylase by L-aspartate (see II.B) suggests that in this micro-organism the NAD-dependent L-malate enzyme may be involved in regulation of the size of a C_4 dicarboxylic acid pool. Studies with mutant strains of *E. coli* exclude the possibility that L-malate enzyme might fulfil an anaplerotic function (Ashworth and Kornberg, 1966).

In the Lactobacilli the NAD-dependent malate enzyme may be involved in malate utilization.

3. Assay procedure

The NAD-dependent L-malate enzyme is assayed spectrophotometrically by measurement of the increase in absorbance at 340 nm due to NADH production.

Reagents:

 0·5M Tris-Cl, pH 7·4 (*E. coli* or *S. pombe*): or
 0·5M Sodium acetate pH 6·0 (Lactobacillus)
 0·3M Potassium L-malate
 5 mM NAD
 0·03M $MnCl_2$
 0·5M KCl

The assay system contains, in 1·0 ml, 100 μmoles Tris-Cl pH 7·4 (or sodium acetate pH 6·0), 30 μmoles potassium L-malate, 0·25 μmoles NAD, 3 μmoles $MnCl_2$ and 50 μmoles KCl. After equilibration to 25°C the reaction is initiated by addition of 0·02–0·05 units malate enzyme and the initial rate of increase in absorbance at 340 nm is measured. This procedure is subject to interference by NADH oxidase and lactate dehydrogenase. In the presence of either of these enzymes the NADH generated by malate enzyme is reoxidized and in some cases little, if any, reduction of NAD may be observed. Therefore, in crude systems the manometric procedure (Ochoa, 1955) should be used unless NADH oxidase and lactate dehydrogenase are shown to be absent.

The reagents required for the manometric procedure are as above. For malate enzymes which are optimally active at pH 6·0 the sodium acetate buffer is used and lactate dehydrogenase is added to remove any pyruvate which may accumulate. The main cup of the manometer contains, in 2·5 ml, 300 μmoles sodium acetate pH 6·0, 60 μmoles potassium L-malate, 0·5 μmoles NAD, 9 μmoles $MnCl_2$, 5 units lactate dehydrogenase and 100 μmoles KCl; and the side-arm ,in 0·5 ml, 0·1–0·2 units malate enzyme. After equilibration to 25°C the contents of the side-arm is tipped into the main compartment and the rate of CO_2 evolution is measured. For malate enzymes which are inactive at pH 6·0 a stepwise manometric procedure may be used employing a manometer cup with two side-arms. In this case the contents of the main compartment (with a buffer of suitable pH) and one side-arm are as above, and the second side-arm contains 0·5 ml 4N H_2SO_4. After temperature equilibration the reaction is initiated by tipping in the enzyme as above and is allowed to proceed for 10 min at 25°C. The reaction is then stopped, and the quantity of CO_2 evolved estimated, by tipping in the contents of the second side-arm. In this procedure endogenous CO_2 is estimated in a control system to which no malate enzyme is added.

B. NADP-dependent L-malate enzyme (EC .1.1.40.)

$$\text{L-Malate} + \text{NADP} \underset{}{\overset{Me^{2+},\ Me^+}{\rightleftharpoons}} \text{Pyruvate} + CO_2 + \text{NADPH} + H^+$$

1. Distribution

Pseudomonas putida (Kornberg and Madsen, 1958; Jacobson et al. 1966); Rhodotorula glutinis (Ruiz-Amil et al., 1965); Escherichia coli (Ashworth et al., 1965); Mycobacteria (Parvin et al., 1965); Chromatium (Fuller et al., 1961); Neurospora crassa (Zink, 1967) and Streptomyces aureofaciens (Jechova et al., 1969). In many micro-organisms this enzyme is induced by growth on L-malate or related C_4 dicarboxylic acids and is repressed by addition of either acetate (in E. coli, S. aureofaciens, N. crassa and P. putida) or glucose (in Rh. glutinis) (Ruiz-Amil et al., 1965; Jacobson et al., 1966; Katsuki et al., 1967; Zink, 1967; Jechova et al., 1969). The enzyme may, therefore, be involved in malate utilization and NADPH generation in these organisms.

2. Properties

Many of the NADP-dependent malate enzymes require activation by both Mn^{2+} and K^+ (cf. Parvin et al., 1965). Recently Sanwal et al. (1968) have reported that the NADP-dependent enzyme in E. coli is inhibited by acetyl-CoA in the concentration range 0·1–0·5 mM. Inhibition by L-aspartate has been described for the enzyme from N. crassa (Zink, 1967).

3. *Assay procedure*

The NADP-dependent L-malate enzyme is assayed spectrophotometrically by measurement of the increase in absorbance at 340 nm due to NADPH production.

Reagents:

0·5M Tris-Cl, pH 7·8
0·2M Potassium L-malate
0·03M $MnCl_2$
0·5M KCl
5 mM NADP

The assay system contains, in 1·0 ml, 100 μmoles Tris-Cl pH 7·8, 20 μmoles potassium L-malate, 3 μmoles $MnCl_2$, 50 μmoles KCl, and 0·25 μmoles NADP. After equilibration to 25°C the reaction is initiated by addition of 0·02–0·05 units malate enzyme and the initial rate of increase of absorbance at 340 nm is recorded. This assay procedure is subject to interference by NADPH oxidase; or by lactate dehydrogenase, if present in excess, since this enzyme will react slowly with NADPH. If these enzymes are present the manometric procedures described for NAD-dependent L-malate enzyme may be used except that NAD is replaced by NADP. If Mg^{2+} is used as the divalent cation rather than Mn^{2+} the pH optimum shifts to pH 8·5–9·0 (cf. Zink, 1967).

C. NAD-dependent D-malate enzyme

$$\text{D-Malate} + \text{NAD} \xrightleftharpoons[]{Me^{2+},\ Me^{+}} \text{Pyruvate} + CO_2 + \text{NADH} + H^{+}$$

1. *Distribution*

Serratia marcescens (Hayaishi *et al.*, 1966); *Escherichia coli, Aerobacter aerogenes, Pseudomonas fluorescens, Euglena gracilis, Rhodospirillum rubrum* (Stern and Hegre, 1966); *Pseudomonas P-2* (Magee and Snell, 1966). The enzyme is induced by growth on D-malate (*Ser. marcescens, E. coli, P. fluorescens, E. gracilis, Aer. aerogenes*) or on pantothenic acid (*Pseudonomas P-2*). It is constitutive in *R. rubrum* (Stern and Hegre, 1966). The enzyme appears to be involved in D-malate or pantothenate utilization. In the latter case the enzyme catalyses oxidation of β,β-dimethyl-D-malate to α-ketoisovalerate in a reaction analogous to that shown above (Magee and Snell, 1966).

2 *Properties*

The enzyme requires activation by both Mn^{2+} and a monovalent cation (K^{+} or NH_4^{+}). The enzyme purified from most of the above species has an apparent K_m for D-malate in the range 0·5–1·0 mM (Hayaishi *et al.*, 1966; Stern and Hegre, 1966). However, in the case of the enzyme obtained from *Pseudomonas P-*2 the apparent K_m for D-malate is an order of magnitude higher (11 mM) while the apparent K_m for β,β-dimethyl-DL-malate is 0·15 mM (Magee and Snell, 1966).

3. *Assay procedure*

The enzyme is assayed spectrophotometrically by measurement of the increase in absorbance at 340 nm which results from NADH production.

Reagents:

> 0·5M Tris-Cl, pH 8·2
> 1M Potassium D-malate
> 0·01M MnCl₂
> 0·01M NAD
> 0·5M KCl

The assay system contains, in 1·0 ml, 100 μmoles Tris-Cl pH 8·2, 10 μmoles, potassium D-malate (100 μmoles for the enzyme from *Pseudomonas P-*2), 1 μmole NAD, 1 μmole MnCl₂ and 50 μmoles KCl. After equilibration to 25°C the reaction is initiated by addition of 0·02–0·05 units D-malate enzyme and the initial rate of increase in absorbance at 340 nm is measured.

This procedure is subject to interference by lactate dehydrogenase and NADH oxidase as described for NAD-dependent L-malate enzyme. In the presence of these contaminants the two-step manometric procedure described for the NAD-dependent L-malate enzyme (see IX.A) should be used with the substitution of Tris-Cl pH 8·2 and potassium D-malate. Alternatively, lactate dehydrogenase activity may be minimized by conducting the spectrophotometric assay at pH 9·0 and in this case the direct assay is applicable to crude systems if NADH oxidase is absent (J. R. Stern, personal communication).

D. α-Hydroxy-β-carboxyisocaproate (β-isopropylmalate) dehydrogenase

$$\alpha\text{-Hydroxy-}\beta\text{-carboxyisocaproate} + \text{NAD} \xrightleftharpoons{\text{Me}^{2+},\ \text{Me}^+}$$

$$\alpha\text{-Ketoisocaproate} + CO_2 + \text{NADH} + H^+$$

1. *Distribution*

Neurospora crassa, Enterobacteriaceae (Burns *et al.*, 1963). The enzyme catalyses a reaction in leucine biosynthesis. In the Enterobacteriaceae its synthesis may be derepressed if the cells are grown under conditions of leucine limitation.

2. Properties

Although the reaction catalysed by this enzyme is analagous to that catalysed by the NAD-dependent malate enzymes and similar co-factor requirements are observed, α-hydroxy-β-carboxyisocaproate dehydrogenase does not catalyse the oxidative decarboxylation of DL-malate (Burns et al., 1963).

3. Assay procedure

The enzyme is assayed spectrophotometrically by measurement of the increase in absorbance at 340 nm due to NADH production.

Reagents:

　　0·5M Tris-Cl, pH 8·5
　　0·01M Potassium α-hydroxy-β-carboxyisocaproate
　　0·02M NAD
　　5 mM $MgCl_2$
　　1M KCl

The assay system contains, in 1·0 ml, 100 μmoles Tris-Cl pH 8·5, 1 μmole potassium α-hydroxy-β-carboxyisocaproate, 0·5 μmole $MgCl_2$, 1 μmole NAD, and 100 μmoles KCl. After equilibration to 25°C the reaction is initiated by addition of 0·02–0·05 units of the dehydrogenase and the initial rate of increase in absorbance at 340 nm is measured.

The presence of NADH oxidase will interfere with this procedure and if this activity is present as in crude systems, α-keto acid production may be measured by formation of the 2,4-dinitrophenylhydrazone (Friedemann, 1957).

Reagents:

As described for the spectrophotometric assay and also:

　　0·1% 2,4-Dinitrophenylhydrazine in 2N HCl
　　10% Na_2CO_3
　　1·5M NaOH
　　Redistilled ethylbenzene

The assay system is as described above. After initiation of the reaction at 37°C the system is incubated for 10 min and then stopped by addition of 0·5 ml 0·1% 2,4-dinitrophenylhydrazine. After incubation with this reagent for 5 min 1·5 ml ethylbenzene is added and the dinitrophenylhydrazone formed is extracted into this solvent by rapid and vigorous mixing for 2 min. After separation of the phases the aqueous layer is discarded. The ethylbenzene layer is washed with 0·5 ml water and the 2,4-dinitrophenylhydrazone is then extracted from this solvent into

3·0 ml 10% Na_2CO_3. An aliquot (1·5 ml) of the Na_2CO_3 layer is removed and transferred to a 3·0 ml cuvette. The colour is developed by addition of 1·5 ml NaOH and the absorbance at 435 nm is measured against a reagent blank after incubation for 5 min at 25°C. The keto acid content is determined by comparison with a standard curve obtained by determining the absorbance yield from known amounts of α-ketoisocaproate-2,4-dinitrophenyl-hydrazone formed as described above.

This latter procedure may also be used to assay the various malate enzymes if the standard curve is constructed using pyruvate-2,4-dinitro-phenylhydrazone. Alternatively, the manometric procedure described for the NAD-dependent L-malate enzyme (see IX.A) may be employed for assay of α-hydroxy-β-carboxyisocaproate dehydrogenase but using the assay reagents described above.

E. Formate dehydrogenase (EC 1.2.1.2.)

$$\text{Formate} + \text{NAD (NADP)} + H_2O \rightarrow HCO_3^- + \text{NADH (NADPH)} + H^+$$

1. Distribution

Pseudomonads (Johnson and Quayle, 1964; Johnson et al., 1964); Enterobacteriaceae (Fukuyama and Ordal, 1965); Clostridia (Brill, et al., 1964; Li et al., 1966); Methanobacterium omelianskii (Brill et al., 1964). The enzyme is widely distributed among micro-organisms but differs in properties depending on the source from which it is obtained.

2. Properties

The co-factor requirements for formate dehydrogenase differ in various species and at least three forms of the enzyme are recognized: (i) an NAD-dependent enzyme requiring no other co-factors which is typical of the Pseudomonads; (ii) an NADP-dependent enzyme requiring no other co-factors which is present in Clostridium thermoaceticum (Li et al., 1966); and (ii) an NAD-dependent enzyme which requires ferredoxin as an additional co-factor and has been found in M. omelianskii and Clostridium acidi-urici (Brill et al., 1964). This latter enzyme is a true formate dehydrogenase and does not produce H_2 from formate.

3. Assay procedure

Formate dehydrogenase is assayed either spectrophotometrically utiliz-ing the increase in absorbance at 340 nm which results from NADH (NADPH) production (Quayle, 1966; Li et al., 1966), or manometrically.

(a) *Spectrophotometric*

Reagents:

> 0·2M Sodium phosphate pH 7·6
> 0·2M Sodium formate
> 0·01M NAD (NADP)

The assay mixture contains, in 1·0 ml, 50 μmoles sodium phosphate pH 7·6, 50 μmoles sodium formate and 1 μmole NAD (NADP). After equilibration to 25°C the reaction is initiated by addition of 0·005–0·02 units formate dehydrogenase and the initial rate of increase in absorbance at 340 nm is measured. In crude systems the presence of NADH oxidase will interfere with this procedure by causing reoxidation of the NADH formed, and in an extreme case might totally obscure the presence of formate dehydrogenase. If a linear initial rate of NADH production cannot be observed the manometric procedure should be used.

(b) *Manometric.* The reagents are as described for the spectrophotometric assay with the addition of 4N H_2SO_4. A double side-arm manometer is required. The main compartment of the manometer contains, in 2·5 ml, 150 μmoles sodium phosphate pH 7·6, 150 μmoles sodium formate and 3 μmoles NAD. One side-arm contains, in 0·3 ml, 0·1–0·2 units formate dehydrogenase and the other side-arm, 0·2 ml 4N H_2SO_4. After equilibration to 25° the reaction is initiated by tipping in the enzyme. After incubation for 10 min the reaction is stopped by tipping in 4N H_2SO_4 from the second side-arm and the quantity of CO_2 evolved is measured.

For assay of formate dehydrogenase in species such as *M. omelianskii* the addition of ferredoxin to the above assay systems is also required. In all cases examined thus far ferredoxin obtained from any obligate anaerobe is active in this system (Brill *et al.*, 1964).

F. Other pyridine nucleotide-linked decarboxylases

Several other examples are listed in Table IV which also gives the observed distribution of these enzymes, and a key reference which describes the assay procedure.

TABLE IV

Other pyridine nucleotide-linked decarboxylases

Enzyme	Distribution	Reference
Malonate semialdehyde oxido-decarboxylase	*Pseudomonas fluorescens, Prototheca zopfi*	Yamada and Jakoby (1960)
Oxaloglycolate reductive decarboxylase	Pseudomonads	Kohn and Jakoby (1968)

X. SUMMARY

This article has attempted a survey of the methods of assay, distribution and some properties of enzymes of CO_2 metabolism present in micro-organisms. In conclusion it should be noted that other enzymes of CO_2 metabolism probably exist which either are unknown at present or are not yet purified to a state where a satisfactory assay procedure can be devised. For example, the total synthesis of acetate from CO_2 by some Clostridia, e.g., *Clostridium thermoaceticum*, appears to involve a direct or indirect fixation of CO_2 on methyl-vitamin B_{12} (cf. Wood and Utter, 1965).

The assay procedures described have been primarily of two types: (i) spectrophotometric procedures dependent on an absorbance change which is either an inherent property of the reaction under investigation or which results from coupling product formation with a reaction involving oxidation or reduction of pyridine nucleotide; (ii) manometric procedures involving the evolution of CO_2 and (iii) radiochemical procedures in which fixation of $H^{14}CO_3^-$ into product or evolution of $^{14}CO_2$ from ^{14}C-labelled substrate typically forms the basis of the procedure. The relative merits of these procedures are too well known to require further comment here. However, other techniques are also applicable to the estimation of enzymes of CO_2 metabolism, and in some cases may provide a more sensitive or less cumbersome procedure. Some examples of such techniques are:

(i) The CO_2 electrode. A modified version of this electrode and its application to measurement of carboxylation and decarboxylation reactions in liver mitochondria has recently been described by Nicholls *et al.* (1967). At the present stage of development the sensitivity and response time of the CO_2 electrode do not appear to be markedly better than the Warburg manometer and each procedure has disadvantages. However, further development of the CO_2 electrode may make this the method of choice for measurement of reactions involving fixation or release of CO_2 especially in crude systems, cf. the use of the oxygen electrode as the preferred method for measurement of O_2 uptake. Theoretical and practical aspects of the measurement of pCO_2 are discussed in detail in this series by Nicholls & Garland (Vol. 6B, p. 55).

(ii) Continuous monitoring of $^{14}CO_2$ production from ^{14}C-substrate. In this method $^{14}CO_2$ released from the metabolism of ^{14}C-substrate is removed in a stream of dry air and detected by passage of the air stream through an ionization chamber (Williams, 1965). The only application described thus far is for mitochondrial suspensions and the applicability of the method to assay of decarboxylases cannot be evaluated at present.

(iii) Measurement of H^+ release or uptake. Enzymes of CO_2 metabolism which catalyse reactions involving hydrogen ion as a substrate or product, e.g., the biotin carboxylases, may also be assayed using the change in pH which results from H^+ uptake or release in an unbuffered system. This procedure is advantageous since it permits direct and continuous measurement of the reaction rate and, in contrast to many of the spectrophotometric assays presently used, does not require the addition of accessory enzymes. Two procedures may be used to measure the change in hydrogen ion concentration. An automatic titration system may be employed in which the pH is maintained constant by addition of small aliquots of standard acid or base and the rate of the enzymic reaction is computed from the product of the rate of addition of acid or base and its normality. Alternatively, the change in pH may be measured spectrophotometrically using a pH indicator of appropriate pK and extinction coefficient provided that addition of the indicator does not inhibit the enzyme under study. If a sensitive recording spectrophotometer is used a minimal change in pH will occur during the time required to obtain an initial reaction rate and the method is applicable for all enzymes except those which exhibit an extremely sharp pH optimum. Methods of this latter type for the assay of biotin carboxylases are presently under investigation in the author's laboratory. Table V summarizes the properties of some indicators which may be useful in studies of this type.

TABLE V

Properties of some indicators which are suitable for spectrophotometric assay of H^+ release or uptake

Indicator	pK	λ_{max}[a] nm	$\Delta\varepsilon$[b] $M^{-1}cm^{-1}$
Bromocresol purple	6·4	588	$1·1 \times 10^4$
Bromothymol blue	7·0	615	$2·5 \times 10^4$
Phenol red	7·6	558	$4·8 \times 10^4$
Brilliant yellow	8·2	500	$1·6 \times 10^4$

(a) Defined as the wavelength at which maximal difference in absorbance is observed between the acidic and basic forms of the indicator. (b) Defined as the difference in molar extinction coefficient between the acidic and basic forms of the indicator at λ_{max}.

REFERENCES

Allen, S. H. G., Kellermeyer, R. W., Stjernholm, R., and Wood, H. G. (1964). *J. Bact.*, **87**, 171–187.
Alberts, A. W., and Vagelos, P. R. (1968). *Proc. natl. Acad. Sci., U.S.*, **59**, 561–568.
Amarasingham, C. J. (1959). *Fed. Proc.*, **18**, 181.
Anderson, L., and Fuller, R. C. (1967). *Bact. Proc.*, **67**, 120.
Anderson, P. M., and Meister, A. (1965). *Biochemistry*, **4**, 2803–2809.

Anderson, P. M., and Meister, A. (1966a). *Biochemistry*, **5**, 3157–3163.
Anderson, P. M., and Meister, A. (1966b). *Biochemistry*, **5**, 3164–3169.
Ankel, H., and Feingold, D. S. (1966). *Biochemistry*, **5**, 182–189.
Arbuthnott, J. P., Bauchop. T., and Dawes, E. A. (1960). *Biochem. J.*, **76**, 12P.
Asakawa, T., Wada, H., and Yamano, T. (1968). *Biochim. biophys. Acta*, **170**, 375–391.
Ashworth, J. M., and Kornberg, H. L., (1963). *Biochim. biophys. Acta.*, **73**, 519–522.
Ashworth, J. M., Kornberg, H. L., and Ward, R. L. (1965). *Biochem. J.*, **94**, 28P.
Ashworth, J. M., and Kornberg, H. L. (1966). *Proc. Roy. Soc.* **B165**, 179–188.
Bachofen, R., Buchanan, B. B., and Arnon, D. I. (1964). *Proc. natl. Acad. Sci.*, *U.S.*, **51**, 690–694.
Beck, W. S., Flavin, M., and Ochoa, S. (1957). *J. biol. Chem.*, **229**, 997–1010.
Bentley, R., and Thiessen, C. P. (1963). *J. biol. Chem.*, **238**, 3811–3816.
Benziman, M., and Heller, H. (1964). *J. Bacteriol.*, **88**, 1678–1687.
Blanchard, M. L., Korkes, S., del Campillo, A., and Ochoa, S. (1950). *J. biol. Chem.*, **187**, 875–890.
Blethen, S. L., Boeker, E. A., and Snell, E. E. (1968). *J. biol. Chem.*, **243**, 1671–1677.
Bloom, S. J., and Johnson, M. J. (1962). *J. biol. Chem.*, **237**, 2718–2720.
Blumenthal, H. J. (1966). In "Methods in Enzymology" (Eds S. P. Colowick and N. O. Kaplan), Vol. 9, pp. 660–665. Academic Press Inc., New York.
Blumenthal, H. J., and Fish, D. C. (1963). *Biochem. Biophys. Res. Comm.*, **11**, 239–243.
Bridgeland, E. S., and Jones, K. M. (1967). *Biochem. J.*, **104**, 9P.
Brill, W. J., Wolin, E. A., and Wolfe, R. S. (1964). *Science*, **144**, 297–298.
Buchanan, B. B., and Arnon, D. I. (1969). In "Methods in Enzymology" (Eds S. P. Colowick and N. O. Kaplan), Vol. 13, pp. 170–181. Academic Press Inc., New York.
Buchanan, B. B., Bachofen, R., and Arnon, D. I. (1964). *Proc. natl. Sci.*, *U.S.*, **52**, 839–847.
Buchanan, B. B., Evans, M. C. W., and Arnon, D. I. (1967). *Arch. Mikrobiol.*, **59**, 32–40.
Burns, R. O., Umbarger, H. E., and Gross, S. R. (1963). *Biochemistry*, **2**. 1053–1058.
Cannata, J., and Stoppani, A. O. M. (1959). *Biochim. biophys. Acta*, **32**, 284–285.
Canovas, J. L., and Kornberg, H. L. (1966). *Proc. Roy. Soc.*, **B165**, 189–205.
Canovas, J. L., and Stanier, R. Y. (1967). *Europ. J. Biochem.*, **1**, 289–300.
Cazzulo, J. J., and Stoppani, A. O. M. (1965). *Biochim. biophys. Acta.*, **100**, 276–280.
Chang, H. C., and Lane, M. D. (1966). *J. biol. Chem.*, **241**, 2413–2420.
Claisse, L. M., Cazzulo, J. J., and Stoppani, A. O. M. (1967). *An. Assoc. Quim. Argent.*, **55**, 299–308.
Cooper, R. A., and Kornberg, H. L. (1965). *Biochim. biophys. Acta.*, **104**, 618–620.
Creasey, W. A., and Handschumacher, R. E. (1961). *J. biol. Chem.*, **236**, 2058–2063.
Dagley, S., and Trudgill, P. W. (1965). *Biochem. J.*, **95**, 48–58.
David, W. E., and Lichstein, H. C. (1950). *Proc. Soc. Exptl. Biol. Med.*, **73**, 216–218.
Dawes, E. A., Ribbons, D. W., and Large, P. J. (1966). *Biochem. J.*, **98**, 795–803.

Deal, S. J., and Lichstein, H. C. (1961). *Can. J. Microbiol.*, **7**, 153–161.
DeLey, J., and Schell, J. (1962). *J. gen. Microbiol.*, **29**, 589–601.
Dewey, D. L., Hoare, D. S., and Work, E. (1954). *Biochem. J.*, **58**, 523–531.
Din, G. A., Suzuki, I., and Lees, H. (1967). *Can. J. Microbiol.*, **13**, 1413–1419.
Dolin, M. I., and Gunsalus, I. C. (1951). *J. Bacteriol.*, **62**, 199–214.
Duerre, J. A., and Lichstein, H. C. (1961). *Can. J. Microbiol.*, **7**, 217–226.
Emiliani, E., and Riera, B. (1968). *Biochim. biophys. Acta.*, **167**, 414–421.
Epps, H. M. R. (1944). *Biochem. J.*, **38**, 243–249.
Evans, H. J., and Wood, H. G. (1968). *Proc. natl. Acad. Sci., U.S.*. **61**, 1448–1453.
Evans, M. C. W. (1968). *Biochem. Biophys. Res. Comm.*, **33**, 146–150.
Evans, M. C. W., Buchanan, B. B., and Arnon, D. I. (1966). *Proc. natl. Acad. Sci., U.S.*, **55**, 928–934.
Fahien, L. A., and Cohen, P. P. (1964). *J. biol. Chem.*, **239**, 1925–1934.
Finkle, B. J., Lewis, J. C., Corse, J. W., and Lundin, R. E. (1962). *J. biol. Chem.*, **237**, 2926–2931.
Flesch, P., and Holbach, B. (1965). *Arch. Mikrobiol.*, **51**, 401–413 and **52**, 147–153.
Franke, W., Platzeck, A., and Eichorn, G. (1961). *Arch. Mikrobiol.*, **40**, 73–93.
Fridovich, I. (1963). *J. Biol. Chem.*, **238**, 592–599.
Friedemann, T. E. (1957). *In* "Methods in Enzymology" (Eds S. P. Colowick and N. O. Kaplan), Vol. 3, pp. 414–418. Academic Press, Inc., New York.
Fukuyama, T., and Ordal, E. J. (1965). *J. Bacteriol.*, **90**, 673–680.
Fuller, R. C., Smillie, R. M., Sisler, E. C., and Kornberg, H. L., (1961). *J. biol. Chem.*, **236**, 2140–2149.
Gailuisis, J., Rinne, R. W., and Benedict, C. R. (1964). *Biochim. biophys. Acta*, **92**, 595–601.
Gale, E. F. (1946). *Adv. Enzymol.*, **6**, 1–32.
Gale, E. F., and Epps, H. M. R. (1944). *Biochem. J.*, **38**, 232–242.
Gale, N. L., and Beck, J. V. (1966). *Biochem. Biophys. Res. Comm.*, **24**, 792–796.
Galivan, J. H., and Allen, S. H. G. (1968). *J. biol. Chem.*, **243**, 1253–1261.
Gerhart, J. C. and Pardee, A. B. (1962). *J. biol. Chem.*, **237**, 891–896.
Green, D. E., Herbert, D., and Subrahmanyan, V. (1941). *J. biol. Chem.*, **238**, 327–339.
Grisolia, S. (1955). *In* "Methods in Enzymology" (Eds S. P. Colowick and N. O. Kaplan), Vol. 2, pp. 350–355. Academic Press Inc., New York.
Gunsalus, C. F., Stanier, R. Y., and Gunsalus, I. C. (1953). *J. Bacteriol.*, **66**, 548–553.
Gupta, N. K., and Vennesland, B. (1964). *J. biol. Chem.*, **239**, 3787–3789.
Gupta, N. K., and Vennesland, B. (1966). *In* "Methods in Enzymology" (Eds S. P. Colowick and N. O. Kaplan), Vol. 9, pp. 693–698, Academic Press Inc., New York.
Hagino, H., and Nakayama, K. (1968). *Agr. biol. Chem.* (Tokyo), **32**, 727–733.
Haughton, B. G., and King, H. K. (1961). *Biochem. J.*, **80**, 268–277.
Hayaishi, O. (1955). *J. Biol. Chem.*, **215**, 125–136.
Hayaishi, M., Hayaishi, M., and Unemoto, T. (1966). *Biochim. biophys. Acta*, **122**, 374–376.
Henning, H. V., and Seubert, W. (1964). *Biochem. Z.*, **340**, 160–170.
Herbert, D. (1951). *Symp. Soc. Exp. Biol.*, **5**, 52–71.
Herbert, D. (1955). *In* "Methods in Enzymology" (Eds S. P. Colowick and N. O. Kaplan), Vol. 1, pp. 753–757. Academic Press Inc., New York.

Himes, R. H., Young, D. L., Ringlemann, E., and Lynen, F. (1963). *Biochem. Z.*, 337, 48–61.

Horton, A. A., and Kornberg, H. L. (1964). *Biochim. biophys. Acta*, 89, 381–383.

Hussain Quadri, S. M., and Hoare, D. S. (1967). *Biochim. biophys. Acta*, 148, 304–306.

Huston, R. B., and Cohen, P. p. (1969). *Biochemistry*, 8, 2658–2261.

Jacobson, L. A., Bartholomaus, R. C., and Gunsalus, I. C. (1966). *Biochem. Biophys. Res. Comm.*, 24, 955–960.

Jaenicke, L., and Koch, J. (1962). *Biochem. Z.*, 336, 432–443.

Jechova, V., Hostalek, Z., and Vanek, Z. (1969). *Folia Microbiol.*, 14, 128–134.

Jeffcoat, R., Hassall, H., and Dagley, S. (1968). *Biochem. J.*, 107, 30P.

Johnson, P. A., and Quayle, J. R. (1964). *Biochem. J.*, 93, 281–290.

Johnson, P. A., Jones-Mortimer, M. C., and Quayle, J. R. (1964). *Biochim. Acta*, 89, 351–353.

Jones, M. E., and Lipmann, F. (1960). *Proc. natl. Acad. Sci., U.S.*, 46, 1194–1205.

Jones, M. E., Spector, L., and Lipmann, F. (1960). *J. Am. Chem. Soc.*, 77, 819–820.

Juni, E. (1952). *J. biol. Chem.*, 195, 715–726.

Juni, E. (1955). *In* "Methods in Enzymology" (Eds S. P. Colowick and N. O. Kaplan)., Vol. 1, pp. 471–475. Academic Press, Inc., New York.

Kaltwasser, H. (1969). *Arch. Mikrobiol.*, 64, 71–84.

Katsuki, H., Takeo, K., Kameda, K., and Tanaka, S. (1967). *Biochem. Biophys. Res. Comm.*, 27, 331–336.

Klein, S. M., and Sagers, R. D. (1966). *J. biol. Chem.*, 241, 197–209.

Knappe, J., Schlegel, H., and Lynen, F. (1961). *Biochem. Z.*, 335, 101–122.

Kohn, L. D., and Jakoby, W. B. (1968). *J. biol. Chem.*, 243, 2486–2493.

Korkes, S., del Campillo, A., and Ochoa, S. (1950). *J. biol. Chem.*, 187, 891–905.

Kornberg, H. L. (1966). *In* "Essays in Biochemistry" (Eds P. N. Campbell and G. D. Greville), Vol. 2, pp. 1–31. Academic Press Inc., London.

Kornberg, H. L., and Madsen, N. B. (1958). *Biochem. J.*, 68, 549–557.

Kornberg, H. L., and Gotto, A. M. (1961). *Biochem. J.*, 78, 69–82.

Krakow, G., Barkulis, S. S., and Hayaishi, J. A. (1961). *J. Bact.*, 81, 509–518.

Krampitz, L. O., and Werkman, C. H. (1941). *Biochem. J.*, 35, 595–602.

Kuehn, G. D., and McFadden, B. A. (1969). *Biochemistry*, 8, 2394–2402.

Large, P. J., Peel, D., and Quayle, J. R. (1962). *Biochem. J.*, 85, 243–250.

Lawson, A., and Quinn, A. G. (1967). *Biochem. J.*, 105, 483–490.

Lederer, F., Coutts, S. M., Laursen, R. A., and Westheimer, F. H. (1966). *Biochemistry*, 5, 823–833.

Li, L. F., Ljungdahl, L. J., and Wood, H. G. (1966). *J. Bacteriol.*, 92, 405–412.

Lieberman, I., Kornberg, A., and Simms, E. S. (1955). *J. biol. Chem.*, 215, 403–415.

Lochmuller, H., Wood, H. G., and Davis, J. J. (1966). *J. biol. Chem.*, 241, 5678–5691.

Lohmann, K., and Meyerhof, O. (1934). *Biochem. Z.*, 273, 60–72.

Losada, M., Canovas, J. L., and Ruiz-Amil, M. (1964). *Biochem. Z.*, 340, 60–74.

Lynen, F., Knappe, J., Lorch, E., Jutting, G., Ringlemann, E., and Lachance, J. P. (1961). *Biochem. Z.*, 335, 123–167.

Maeba, P., and Sanwal, B. D. (1965). *Biochem. Biophys. Res. Comm.*, 21, 503–508.

Maeba, P., and Sanwal, B. D. (1969). *In* "Methods in Enzymology" (Eds S. P. Colowick and N. O. Kaplan), Vol. 13, pp. 283–287, Academic Press, Inc., New York.

Magee, P. T., and Snell, E. E. (1966). *Biochemistry*, **5**, 409–416.

Martin, B. R., and Denton, R. M. (1970). *Biochem. J.*, **117**, 861–877.

Matsuhashi, M., Matsuhashi, S., Numa, S., and Lynen, F. (1964). *Biochem. Z.*, **340**, 243–262.

McFadden, B. A., and Tu, C. C. L. (1966). *Bact. Proc.*, **66**, 94.

Meister, A. (1965). "Biochemistry of the Amino Acids", 2nd Edition, Vol. I, pp. 332–338 and 396–401. Academic Press, Inc., New York.

Metzenberg, R. L., Hall, L. M., Marshall, M., and Cohen, P. P. (1957). *J. biol. Chem.*, **229**, 1019–1025.

Mildvan, A. S., and Scrutton, M. C. (1967). *Biochemistry*, **6**, 2978–2994.

Mildvan, A. S., Scrutton, M. C., and Utter, M. F. (1966). *J. biol. Chem.*, **241**, 3488–3498.

Milhaud, G., Aubert, J. P., and Garrard, R. (1952). *Compt. Rend.* **234**, 2026–2028.

Morris, D. R., and Pardee, A. B. (1965). *Biochem. Biophys. Res. Comm.*, **20**, 697–702.

Morris, D. R., and Pardee, A. B. (1966). *J. biol. Chem.*, **241**, 3129–3135.

Neuberg, C., and Rosenthal, P. (1913). *Biochem. Z.*, **51**, 128–142.

Nicholls, D. G., Shepherd, D., and Garland, P. B. (1967). *Biochem. J.*, **103**, 677–691; also Vol. 6B this series.

Nishikido, T., Izui, K., Iwatani, A., Katsuki, H., and Tanaka, S. (1965). *Biochem. Biophys. Res. Comm.*, **21**, 94–99.

Nordlie, R. C., and Lardy, H. A. (1963). *J. biol. Chem.*, **238**, 2259–2263.

Northrop, D. B., and Wood, H. G. (1969). *J. biol. Chem.*, **244**, 5801–5807.

Numa, S., Ishimura, Y., Nakazawa, T., Okazake, T., and Hayaishi, O. (1964) *J. biol. Chem.*, **239**, 3915–3926.

Ornston, L. N. (1966a). *J. biol. Chem.*, **241**, 3787–3794.

Ornston, L. N. (1966b). *J. biol. Chem.*, **241**, 3800–3810.

Ornston, L. N. (1966c). *J. biol. Chem.*, **241**, 3795–3799.

Ornston, L. N., and Stanier, R. Y. (1966). *J. biol. Chem.*, **241**, 3776–3786.

Pal, H. R. S., and Krishnan, P. S. (1961). *Arch. Mikrobiol.*, **39**, 335–342.

Parvin, R., Pande, S. V., and Venditasubramanian, T. A. (1964). *Biochim. biophys. Acta*, **92**, 260–277.

Paulsen, J. M., and Lane, M. D. (1966). *Biochemistry*, **5**, 2350–2357.

Perley, J. E., and Stowe, B. B. (1966). *Biochem. J.*, **100**, 169–174.

Peterkofsky, B., and Gilvarg, C. (1961). *J. biol. Chem.*, **236**, 1432–1438.

Pettersson, G. (1965). *Acta. Chem. Scand.*, **19**, 2013–2021.

Pierard, A., and Wiame, J. M. (1964). *Biochem. Biophys. Res. Comm.*, **15**, 76–81.

Pittard, A. J., Gibson, F., and Doy, C. H. (1962). *Biochim. biophys. Acta*, **57**, 290–298.

Plaut, G. W. E., and Lardy, H. A. (1949). *J. biol. Chem.*, **180**, 13–27.

Pomerantz, S. H. (1958). *Fed. Proc.*, **17**, 290.

Pierard, A., Glansdorff, N., Mergeay, M., and Wiame, J. M. (1965). *J. mol. Biol.*, **14**, 23–36.

Quayle, J. R. (1963a). *Biochem. J.*, **87**, 368–373.

Quayle, J. R. (1963b). *Biochem. J.*, **89**, 492–503.

Quayle, J. R. (1966). *In* "Methods in Enzymology" (Eds S. P. Colowick and N. O. Kaplan), Vol. 9, pp. 360–364. Academic Press, Inc., New York.

Quayle, J. R., and Keech, D. B. (1959). *Biochem. J.*, **72**, 631–637.

Quayle, J. R., Fuller, R. C., Benson, A. A., and Calvin, M. (1954). *J. Am. Chem. Soc.*, **76**, 3610–3611.

Rabinowitz, J. C. (1960). *J. biol. Chem.*, **235**, PC50.

Racker, E. (1963). *In* "Methods in Enzymology (Eds S. P. Colowick and N. O. Kaplan), Vol. 5, pp. 266–270. Academic Press, Inc., New York.

Rasmussen, R. K., and Klein, H. P. (1967). *Biochem. Biophys. Res. Comm.*, **28**, 415–419.

Riley, W. D., and Snell, E. E. (1962). *Biochemistry*, **7**, 3520–3528.

Rilling, H., and Coon, M. J. (1960). *J. biol. Chem.*, **235**, 3087–3092.

Rosenberg, R. F. (1966). *Biochim. biophys. Acta*, **122**, 365–367.

Rosenthaler, J., Guirard, B. M., Chang, G. W., and Snell, E. E. (1965). *Proc. natl. Acad. Sci. U.S.*, **54**, 152–158.

Ruiz-Amil, M., deTorrontegui, G., Palacian, E., Catalina, L., and Losada, M. (1965). *J. biol. Chem.*, **240**, 3485–3492.

Santer, M., and Vishniac, W. (1955). *Biochim. biophys. Acta*, **18**, 157–158.

Sanwal, B. D., and Maeba, P. (1966a). *Biochem. Biophys. Res. Comm.*, **22**, 194–199.

Sanwal, B. D., and Maeba, P. (1966b). *J. biol. Chem.*, **241**, 4557–4562.

Sanwal, B. D., Maeba, P., and Cook, R. A. (1966). *J. biol. Chem.*, **241**, 5177–5182.

Sanwal, B. D., Wright, J. A., and Smando, R. (1968). *Biochem. Biophys. Res. Comm.*, **31**, 623–627.

Scrutton, M. C., and Utter, M. F. (1967). *J. biol. Chem.*, **242**, 1723–1735.

Scrutton, M. C., Utter, M. F., and Mildvan, A. S. (1966). *J. biol. Chem.*, **241**, 3480–3487.

Scrutton, M. C., Young, M. R., and Utter, M. F. (1970). *J. biol. Chem.*, **245**, 6220–6227.

Seaman, G. R. (1960). *J. Bacteriol.*, **80**, 830–836.

Seeley, H. W., and van Demark, P. J. (1950). *J. Bact.*, **59**, 381–386.

Seubert, W., and Remberger, U. (1961). *Biochem. Z.*, **334**, 401–414.

Seubert, W., Fass, E., and Remberger, U. (1963). *Biochem. Z.*, **338**, 265–275.

Seubert, W., and Weicker, H. (1969). *In* "Methods in Enzymology" (Eds S. P. Colowick and N. O. Kaplan), Vol. 13, pp. 258–261. Academic Press, Inc., New York.

Shimazono, H., and Hayaishi, O. (1957). *J. biol. Chem.*, **227**, 151–159.

Shrago, E., and Shug, A. L. (1966). *Biochim. biophys. Acta*, **122**, 376–378.

Siu, P. M. L., and Wood, H. G. (1962). *J. biol. Chem.*, **237**, 3044–3051.

Snell, E. E., Smucker, A. A., Ringlemann, E., and Lynen, F. (1964). *Biochem. Z.*, 109–119.

Spector, L., and Jones, M. E. (1963). *In* "Methods in Enzymology" (Eds S. P. Colowick and N. O. Kaplan), Vol. 6, pp. 557–562. Academic Press, Inc., New York.

Stanier, R. Y., Palleroni, N. Y., and Doudoroff, M. (1966). *J. gen. Microbiol.*, **43**, 159–271.

Stern, J. R. (1965). *In* "Non-Heme Iron Proteins: Role in Energy Conversion" (Ed. A. San Pietro), pp. 199–205. Antioch Press, Yellow Springs, Ohio.

Stern, J. R. (1967). *Biochemistry*, **6**, 3545–3551.

Stern, J. R., and Hegre, C. S. (1966). *Nature, Lond.*, **212**, 1611–1612.

Stjernholm, R., and Wood, H. G. (1963). *Iowa State J. Sci.*, **38**, 123–140.

Subba Rao, P. V., Moore, K., and Towers, G. H. N. (1967). *Arch. Biochem. Biophys.*, **122**, 466–473.

Suzuki, I., and Werkman, C. H. (1958). *Arch. Biochem. Biophys.*, **76**, 103–111.

Takeo, K., Murai, T., Nagai, J., and Katsuki, H. (1967). *Biochem. Biophys. Res. Comm.*, **29**, 717–722.

Temperli, A., Kunsch, U., Mayer, K., and Busch, I. (1965). *Biochim. biophys. Acta*, **110**, 630–632.

Theodore, T. S., and Englesberg, E. (1964). *J. Bacteriol.*, **88**, 946–955.

Trudgill, P. W., and Widdus, R. (1966). *Nature, Lond.*, **211**, 1097–1099.

Trudinger, P. (1965). *Biochem. J.*, **64**, 274–286.

Umbreit, W. W., and Gunsalus, I. C. (1945). *J. biol. Chem.*, **159**, 333–341.

Umbreit, W. W., Burris, R. H., and Stauffer, J. F. (1954). "Manometric Techniques", 4th Edition, pp. 18–27. Burgess Publishing Company, Minneapolis.

Utter, M. F. (1961). *In* "The Enzymes" (Eds P. D. Boyer, H. A. Lardy and K. Myrback), Vol. 5, pp. 319–340. Academic Press, Inc., New York.

Utter, M. F., Keech, D. B., and Scrutton, M. C. (1964). *Advan. Enzyme Regulation*, **2**, 49–68.

Utter, M. F., Scrutton, M. C., Young, M. R., Tolbert, B., Wallace, J. C., Irias, J. J. and Valentine, R. C. (1967). Abstr. 7th Int. Congr. Biochem., Tokyo, Vol. II, p. 247.

Valentine, R. C., Drucker, H., and Wolfe, R. S. (1964). *J. Bact.*, **87**, 241–246.

Velick, S. F., and Vavra, J. (1962). *J. biol. Chem.*, **237**, 2109–2122.

Vogel, H. J. (1959a). *Biochim. biophys. Acta.*, **34**, 282–283.

Vogel, H. J. (1959b). *Fed. Proc.*, **18**, 345.

Vorisek, J., Powell, A. J., and Vanek, Z. (1970). *Folia Microbiologica*, **15**, 153–159.

Warren, S., Zerner, B., and Westheimer, F. H. (1966). *Biochemistry*, **5**, 817–823.

Weissbach, A., and Hurwitz, J. (1959). *J. biol. Chem.*, **234**, 705–709.

Wellner, V. P., Santos, J. I., and Meister, A. (1968). *Biochemistry*, **7**, 2848–2851.

Werbin, H., Chaikoff, I. L., and Imada, M. R. (1959). *Proc. Soc. Exp. Biol. Med.*, **102**, 8–10.

Williams, G. R. (1965). *Can. J. Biochem.*, **43**, 603–615.

Wilson, E. M., and Kornberg, H. L. (1963). *Biochem. J.*, **88**, 578–587.

Wood, H. G., and Utter, M. F. (1965). *In* "Essays in Biochemistry" (Eds G. D. Greville and P. N. Campbell), Vol. 1, pp. 1–27. Academic Press, Inc., London.

Wood, H. G., Allen, S. H. G., Stjernholm, R., and Jacobson, B. (1963a). *J. biol. Chem.*, **238**, 574–556.

Wood, H. G., Lochmuller, H., Riepertinger, C., and Lynen, F. (1963b). *Biochem. Z.*, **337**, 247–266.

Wood, H. G., Jacobson, B., Gerwin, B. I., and Northrop, D. B. (1969a). *In* "Methods in Enzymology" (Eds S. P. Colowick and N. O. Kaplan), Vol. 13, pp. 215–229. Academic Press, Inc., New York.

Wood, H. G., Davis, J. J., and Willard, J. M. (1969b). *In* "Methods in Enzymology" (Eds S. P. Colowick and N. O. Kaplan), Vol. 13, pp. 297–308. Academic Press, Inc., New York.

Wright, J. A., and Sanwal, B. D. (1969). *J. biol. Chem.*, **244**, 1838–1845.

Yamada, E. W., and Jakoby, W. B. (1960). *J. biol. Chem.*, **236**, 589–594.

Young, M. R., Tolbert, B., Valentine, R. C., Wallace, J. C., and Utter, M. F. (1968). *Fed. Proc.*, **27**, 522.

Young, M. R., Tolbert, B., and Utter, M. F. (1969). *In* "Methods in Enzymology" (Eds S. P. Colowick and N. O. Kaplan), Vol. 13, pp. 250–257. Academic Press, Inc., New York.

Zerner, B., Coutts, S. M., Lederer, F., Waters, H. W., and Westheimer, F. H. (1966). *Biochemistry*, **5**, 813–816.

Zink, M. W. (1967). *Can. J. Microbiol.*, **13**, 1211–1221.

Author Index

Numbers in *italics* refer to the page on which references are listed at the end of each chapter

A

Abeles, R. H., 229, *268*
Abelson, P. H., 245, 246, *267*
Abramowitz, A., 468, 470, *477*
Ackermann, W. W., 228, *267*
Adachi, K., 232, *266*, 466, 470, *477, 478*
Adams, E., 260, *267*
Adelberg, E. A., 257, *267*, 280, *325*
Adhya, S., 315, *320*
Ahmed, S. I., 221, *265*
Ajl, S. J., 430, 437, 453, 455, 456, *458, 461, 462*
Alberts, A. W., 495, *535*
Alberty, R. A., 450, *458*
Alderton, G., 338, 346, 350, 355, 360, 369, *373, 377, 379*
Al-Hafidh, M., 417, *423*
Allam, A. M., 253, *268*
Allen, S. H. G., 252, *264, 268*, 492, 506, 507, *535, 537, 541*
Allmann, D. W., 387, *391*
Alper, D. H., 290, *320*
Amaha, M., 371, *373*
Amaral, D., 179, *211*
Amarasingham, C. J., 489, *535*
Amarasingham, C. R., 438, *458*
Ames, B. N., 275, 280, 282, 303, 304, 314, *320, 321, 325, 326*
Anbar, M., 101, 105, *213*
Anderson, B., 312, 313, 317, *323, 326*
Anderson, I. E., *377*
Anderson, J. A., 387, *391*
Anderson, J. S., 401, 403, 404, *408, 410*
Anderson, L., 493, *535*
Anderson, L. E., 350, *376*
Anderson, P. M., 499, 500, 502, *535, 536*
Anderson, R. L., 412, 414, 415, 416, 417, *423*
Anbllis, A., 336, 338, *375, 379*
Anfinson, C. B., 433, 434, *458*
Angelotti, R., 336, *373*
Angus, T. A., 356, *373, 374, 377*

Ankel, H., 526, *536*
Annison, E. F., 65, 70, 71, *211*
Ansensio, C., 179, *211*
Anstiss, C., 193, *212*
Anton, D., 280, 303, 304, *325*
Anton, M. J., 280, 302, 303, 317, 318, *325*
Araki, Y., 402, *409*
Arbuthnott, J. P., 512, *536*
Arima, K., 225, *268*, 391, *392*
Arnon, D. I., 486, 497, 498, *536, 537*
Aronson, A. I., 342, 353, 354, *373, 377*
Arsenault, G. P., 96, 183, *215*
Artsybasheva, Y., 138, *211*
Asakawa, T., 516, 517, *536*
Asano, A., 385, 388, 389, *392*
Ashworth, J. M., 306, *321*, 482, 486, 487, 489, 490, 527, 528, *536*
Aubert, J.-P., 330, 331, 335, 342, 344, *377, 379*, 523, *539*
Avigad, G., 179, *211*
Axelrod, B., 421, *423*
Azoulay, E., 390, *392*

B

Bach, J. A., 335, 353, *373, 379*
Bachofen, R., 497, 498, *536*
Bacon, D. F., 281, *321*
Baer, E., 210, *211*
Baidya, T. K. N., *321*
Bailey, G. F., 349, 351, *373, 379*
Baillie, A., 353, 357, 358, *373, 378, 381*
Baker, B. R., 395, *408*
Baker, R. F., 282, *324*
Balassa, G., 331, 339, 341, 343, 373, *373, 379*
Baldini, I., 109, 155, *214*
Barban, S., 437, *458*
Bard, J., 94, *213*
Bard, R. C., 56, *212*
Barer, Gwendoline, 20, *30*
Barker, H. A., 88, *214*, 235, 251, 252, *264, 266*

19

Subject Index

A

Acetaldehyde, determination, 69, 107–109, 196

Acetate,
determination of, 133–138
fermentation balances, in, 56
GLC analysis of, 131
oxidation-reduction number of, 55
TLC separation of, 123
total synthesis from CO_2, 534

Acetic acid bacteria, *see also under specific names*,
particle-linked dehydrogenases of, 48

Actinomyces sp., spores of, 328

Actinomycin, sporulation inhibitor, 344

Acetoacetate decarboxylase,
assay method for, 517–518
distribution and properties, 517

Acetobacter sp.,
gluconate dehydrogenase, 422
glucose metabolism in, 412

A. liquefaciens, particle-linked dehydrogenases, 48

A. suboxydans, glucose metabolism in, 412

A. xylinum,
hexose monophosphate pathway in, 412, 413
oxaloacetate decarboxylase, 518

Acetoin, fermentation product, 55, 56, 69, 70, 74, 81, 112–113

L-Acetolactate, periodate analysis of, 78, 79, 84–85

L-Acetolactate decarboxylase, assay and properties, 523

Acetomonas suboxydans, glucose oxidation pathway, 226–227

Acetone,
determination of, 109–111
fermentation product, 56, 69, 74

Acetyl-CoA, as allosteric activator, 263, 482, 483

Acetyl-CoA carboxylase, 251
assay procedures, 495–497
distribution and properties, 495
fatty acid biosynthesis and, 489

Acetyl-CoA: dihydrolipoate S-acetyl-transferase,
see under Lipoyl reductase—transacetylase.

Acetylmethylcarbinol, 9

Acetyl phosphate, estimation, 420

Achromobacter
aromatic degradation by, 227
aspartate β-decarboxylase assay, 509
biotin—enzyme, labelling of, 252
β-methylcrotonyl—CoA carboxylase, 502
terminal oxidases in, 391

A. eurydice, phenylpyruvate decarboxylase, 516

Acid phosphatase, test with intact cells, 44

Acid production,
oxidation versus fermentation and, 7–8
tests for, 9–10, 26

Aconitase, *see* Aconitate hydratase.

Aconitate hydratase,
assay of, 433–435
reaction mechanism of, 433
regulation of synthesis of, 306–308
properties of, 434

cis—Aconitic acid, 526
silica gel chromatography, 120, 152

Acriflavin, flavoprotein inhibitor, 384–385

Acrylic acid, alkane oxidation inhibitor, 231

Actinomycin, enzyme synthesis inhibitor, 291, 293, 383–384

Adaptation, enzyme regulation and, 270–272

"Adaptive enzymes", Karlstrom's term, 271

20

8-Azaguanine, sporulation inhibitor, 343

Azotobacter sp., cysts, 328

A. agilis, dicarboxylic acid metabolism, 235

A. vinelandii,
  oxaloacetate decarboxylase, 518
  sporulation medium for, 333

Bacillus anthracis, spore germinants for, 362

B. cadaveris, lysine decarboxylase assay, 509

B. cereus,
  microcycle sporogenesis in, 340
  spores of,
    activation, 359, 360
    cortex fraction, 355
    crystal formation by, 356
    crystal violet staining, 339
    electron microscopy, 357–358
    enzymes from, 352–352, 365
    exosporia from, 349, 351
    germinants, 362
    germination of, 359–361, 366, 370–371
    heat resistance of, 366
    outgrowth in, 372–373
    urea and, 360
  sporulation of,
    cell resistance in, 343
    endotrophic, 346
    inhibition of, 343–344
    media for, 331–332, 329, 334
    metabolic changes in, 342
    synchronous, 340
  tryptophan decarboxylase, 510

B. circulans, spore germinants, 362

B. coagulans, spores,
  activation of, 360
  chloral hydrate effect on, 360
  cleaning of, 338
  crystal violet staining of, 339
  enzymes in, 352
  ethylene glycol and, 360
  germinants for, 362
  germination inhibitors of, 370–371
  outgrowth in, 372

sporulation media for, 330–332

B. licheniformis,
  penicillinase of, 288–289, 316
  spores of, 342, 353, 362, 370–371
  sporulation media for, 330–331, 334

B. macerans, spore germinants, 362

B. megaterium,
  cytochrome system in, 383
  endotrophic sporulation, 340
  microcycle sporogenesis in, 341
  spores of,
    activation, 360
    chlorotetracycline effect on, 344
    crystal violet staining of, 339
    enzymes in, 352–353
    germinants for, 362
    germination of, 364, 366, 370–371
    outgrowth of, 372
    spore coat from 354
  sporulation media for, 330, 332, 334

B. pantothenticus, spore activation, 360

B. popilliae,
  cleaning spores of, 338
  sporulation media for, 333

B. polymyxa, spores,
  electron microscopy of, 357–358
  germinants for, 362

B. sphaericus, spore germinants, 362

B. stearothermophilus,
  spores of,
    activation of, 359, 360
    cleaning of, 338
    deactivation of, 360
    disintegration of, 349–350
    germination for, 366
    heat resistance of, 346, 366
    outgrowth of, 372
    pH effects on, 360
  sporulation medium for, 332

B. subtilis,
  α-acetolactate decarboxylase of, 523
  alkaline phosphatase regulation in, 292
  antibiotic production by, 342–343
  aromatic amino-acid biosynthesis, regulation, 275
  asporogenous mutants of, 344
  fermentation balance for, typical, 56
  histidase induction in, 291
  membrane systems in, 387–388

Lipoate acetyl-transferase, *see* Lipoyl reductase-transacetylase.

Lipoate succinyl transferase, *see* Lipoyl reductase-transsuccinylase.

Lipoic acid,
arsenite inhibition and, 230
auxotrophs in structure studies, 254

Lipoyl reductase-transacetylase, 457, 458

Lipoyl reductase transsuccinylase, assay, 442–444

Litmus milk, preparation and use, 26–27

Lycopene, 229

Lysine, biosynthesis, 222

Lysine decarboxylase, 38
assay system for, 509

Lysozyme, spores and, 345–350, 364

Lysyl-phosphatidyl glycerol, in *Staph. aurous*, 390

Lytic enzymes, in spores, 353

M

M-protein, β-galactoside transport component, 312, 313

MacConkey broth, composition and use, 8–9

Magno-constitutive mutants, 315

Malate dehydrogenase, assay, 451–452

D-Malate enzyme, NAD-dependent, assay, 530
distribution and properties, 529–530

L-Malate enzyme,
NAD-dependent,
assay, 527–528
distribution and properties, 526–527
NADP—dependent,
assay, 529
distribution and properties, 528

L-Malate glyoxylate-lyase, *see* Malate synthase.

L-Malate hydrolyase, *see* Fumarate hydratase.

L-Malate: NAD oxidoreductase, *see* Malate dehydrogenase.

Malate synthase, 249
assay, 456–457
mechanism of, 455
regulation of, 305

Malate synthetase, *see* Malate synthase.

Malic acid,
esterification, for GLC, 154
estimation of, enzymic, 166–168
silica-gel chromatography, 120, 152

Malic dehydrogenase, *see also* Malate dehydrogenase,
regulation of synthesis, 306

"Malic" enzyme, *see also* Malate enzyme, 262, 263

Malonate,
utilization medium, 6
metabolic studies with, 229
silica-gel TLC, 152

Malonate decarboxylase,
assay, 522–523
distribution and properties, 522

Malonate semialdehyde oxido-decarboxylase, 533

Mandelate pathway,
enzymes in constitutive mutants, 315
regulation of aromatic catabolism by, 298–299

Mannitol, periodate procedure for 81

Mannokinase, assay, 416–417

Mannose, metabolism in *A. aerogenes*, 414

Manometry, for enzyme regulation studies, 287–288, 298, 299

"Mechanical germination", of bacterial spores, 365

Melilotate hydroxylase, 467

Membrane systems, in electron transport, 387–391

Menadione, as electron acceptor in respiratory chain, 388, 389

Mercury
compounds inhibiting electron transport, 385
pressure head in fermentation component, 57, 58

"Meta-fission", aromatic ring-cleavage by, 464, 473

Metabolic analogues, *see under* Analogues.

Metabolic pathways, *see also under* Biosynthetic *and* Catabolic,
assessment of function of, 261–264
elucidation of, methods for, 217–268
regulation of, 220–222, 297–308